# The 68000 Microprocessor

I. Scott MacKenzie
University of Guelph
Guelph, Ontario

Prentice Hall

Englewood Cliffs, New Jersey    Columbus, Ohio

**Library of Congress Cataloging-in-Publication Data**

MacKenzie, I. Scott
      The 68000 microprocessor / I. Scott MacKenzie.
           p.      cm.
      Includes bibliographical references and index.
      ISBN 0–02–373654–2
      1. Motorola 68000 (Microprocessor)    I. Title.
  QA76.5.M187549  1995
  004.165—dc20

94–32687
CIP

Editor: Charles E. Stewart, Jr.
Production Editor: Stephen C. Robb
Text Designer: Spectrum Publisher Services, Inc.
Production Buyer: Deidra M. Schwartz
Production Supervision: Spectrum Publisher Services, Inc.

This book was set in Meridien and Novarese by TCSystems, Inc., and was printed and bound by Courier/Westford, Inc. The cover was printed by Phoenix Color Corp.

 © 1995 by Prentice-Hall, Inc.
A Simon & Schuster Company
Englewood Cliffs, New Jersey 07632

PC-VT is a trademark of Athena Systems Development Group and is used with permission.

Enertec software programs A68K (version 3.30 for MS/DOS—68000 cross assembler) and XLINK (version 3.32 for MS/DOS—linker/locator) are used with permission from Enertec Inc.

Printed in the United States of America

10 9 8 7 6 5 4 3 2 1

ISBN: 0-02-373654-2

Prentice-Hall International (UK) Limited, *London*
Prentice-Hall of Australia Pty. Limited, *Sydney*
Prentice-Hall of Canada, Inc., *Toronto*
Prentice-Hall Hispanoamericana, S. A., *Mexico*
Prentice-Hall of India Private Limited, *New Delhi*
Prentice-Hall of Japan, Inc., *Tokyo*
Simon & Schuster Asia Pte. Ltd., *Singapore*
Editora Prentice-Hall do Brasil, Ltda., *Rio de Janeiro*

To Dave German, the teacher who got
me interested in all this neat stuff.

THE MOTOROLA MC68000 MICROPROCESSOR

# Preface

This book examines the hardware and software features of the 68000 microprocessor. The intended audience is students of technology, electronics, computer engineering, and computer science.

In this preface, I present the organization and overall plan of the book. I'll also present arguments as to why the 68000 should be considered for a course on microprocessors or computer architecture. A real advantage of using this textbook is its versatility and completeness as a total package. A complete lecture-plus-lab course on the 68000 microprocessor can be implemented using this text, the enclosed software, a simple 68000-based system (described below), a PC host computer, and the lab manual contained in the Instructor's Manual. I'll say more about the package later.

Chapter 0 is included as a bridge from earlier courses. It covers a variety of foundation topics such as number systems, digital logic, and memory devices. Chapter 1 is also a bridge, but it focuses on the structure of computer systems and the development environment for designing hardware and software for computer systems. Depending on the students' background, portions of chapters 0 and 1 may be omitted.

Our in-depth look at the 68000 begins in Chapter 2 with the programmer's model, memory organization, signal descriptions, read and write timings, and addressing modes.

The 68000's instruction set is presented in Chapter 3. This includes examples of each instruction type, a study of the machine-language format of instructions, and examples of instruction timings. I have adopted a novel presentation of the instruction set that should help students and teachers. Each instruction is categorized either as *introductory*, *intermediate*, or *advanced*. Introductory instructions are those typically found on 8-bit microprocessors. Most programs can be written using only introductory instructions. Students can examine these on a first pass, then learn about intermediate or advanced instructions as necessary as the course progresses.

Chapter 4 examines assembly-language programming. The operation of a two-pass assembler is presented, and the fields in an assembly-language program are defined. Assembler directives and assemble-time expressions are presented in detail with many examples. One aspect of assembly-language programming that is omitted in many textbooks is modular programming—dividing a large program into small, individual files or modules. Because in the "real world," any non-trivial programming task requires a modular approach, the idea is developed in detail here. This is tricky for many courses because of the subtle differences between the assembler and linker that might be discussed in the text and those that students encounter in the lab. I refer to this as the "lecture-lab gap." Because a 68000 cross-assembler and linker/locator are provided on the enclosed disk, this problem is greatly diminished: The examples given in the text are reproducible and expandable by students. Students will use and observe the exact same commands and syntax in the lab as they read about in the text.

Chapter 5 presents detailed examples of small 68000 programs. Problems are defined, and solutions are given and discussed. These programs help ease the student into the challenging task of solving problems in assembly language. The most ambitious problem is solved in just twenty instructions. Some of the more subtle and challenging aspects of the 68000 architecture are deferred to Chapter 6 where exceptions, such as interrupts, bus errors, and traps, are discussed.

Chapter 7 is an in-depth examination of input/ouput. It covers everything from full decoding vs. partial decoding to interrupt-driven I/O and direct memory access. Again, examples help ease the understanding of the trickier aspects of I/O.

Chapter 8 presents the design of a 13-chip 68000-based system called the 68KMB—the 68000 mini-board. It is presented as a case study, but, really, the hope is that schools will adopt and use the complete package: the textbook, the 68KMB, the lab manual found in the Instructor's Manual, and the software on the enclosed disk. At 13 chips, the 68KMB can readily be prototyped by students, or schools can equip a lab with pre-built 68KMBs (available from URDA, Inc.; see Chapter 8). A PC host computer with a COM port is the only additional requirement for a complete system for learning about the 68000 and developing 68000-based application software.

Chapter 9 describes a series of interface case studies using the 68KMB as the target system. These range from simple input and output using switches and LEDs to speech digitizing and playback. The examples are *not* hypothetical; they are complete, fully tested interfaces. Sample programs are given in listing format with complete descriptions. Source code for all the examples is on the enclosed disk. Most of the interfaces require only a handful of components. As with the 68KMB, students can build the interfaces themselves, or schools can purchase pre-built interface boards.

Chapter 10 surveys the advanced processors in the 68000 family and some of the more popular interface ICs used with 68000-family devices.

The text includes nine appendices. Many of these are reference sources adopted from Motorola literature. The most important, perhaps, is Appendix B, which defines each 68000 instruction as per Motorola's literature. Data sheets are also included for the 68000 CPU, as well as for the 68681 and the 6821 peripheral interface ICs discussed in Chapters 8 and 9.

The monitor program for the 68KMB is called MON68K. It is presented in Appendix E in complete detail. This includes a definition of the command set, a technical description of the programmer's interface, and a complete listing. The MON68K listing is an extremely useful addition for several reasons. MON68K is a large, modular program that exemplifies many of the core concepts presented throughout the text on programming the 68000 microprocessor. With the listing close at hand, students can learn how to organize large, modular programs, and they can examine the implementation of a variety of subroutines and traps. Nothing is hidden. For example, interrupt-driven interfaces on all 68000-based systems use vectors near the bottom of memory. MON68K, as typical of monitor programs, defers interrupts through a jump table in the user RAM. All details are revealed in the listings. Since MON68K is provided as a hex file on the enclosed disk, it can be burned into EPROM for those who wish to prototype their own 68KMB.

The accompanying disk contains a variety of MS-DOS and 68000 programs useful in a student laboratory setting. The following MS-DOS programs are included:

- A68K  — A 68000 cross assembler
- XLINK — A linker/locator and conversion utility for 68000 object programs
- PC-VT — A VT100 terminal emulator

More than 30 programming examples from the book and lab portions found in the Instructor's Manual are included. These are provided as both source and hexadecimal (S-records) files. A batch file called INSTALL facilitates setting-up an environment on the host computer.

I'd like now to develop a few ideas underlying the philosophy of this book. To begin, "Why the 68000?" There are two issues here. First, "Why a Motorola processor instead of an Intel processor?", and second, "Why the 68000 16-bit CPU instead of, say, the 68040 32-bit CPU?" As for the ongoing Motorola vs. Intel debate, most coffee-room chat I have encountered agrees that the 68000 is a superb choice for teaching computer architecture. The architecture is *consistent* and *easy to understand*. It is noteworthy that the first device in the family—the 16-bit 68000, introduced in 1979—fully anticipated the inevitable migration to 32-bit devices a decade later. All internal registers on the 68000 are 32 bits wide. The most dramatic benefit in this is the linear address space: Any address is much like any other address. In this respect, the Intel 80X86 architecture is much more complicated.

Make no mistake about it, the 68000 architecture is alive and well. A brochure I received recently from Motorola notes that "chips from the 68000 line are now in over 75 million products worldwide, and new ones are coming on-line at an unprecedented rate of 2 million a month and growing. In fact, 68000-based microprocessors power more 32-bit embedded systems than all the competitors' chips combined." You can't argue with facts like that.

As for "Why the 68000 instead of the 68040?", the answer is pragmatic. Many textbooks similar to this present the 68000 "family" of devices. Although this textbook surveys the advanced devices in the 68000 family, it presents in detail only the 68000. The reasons are simple. First, the 68000 microprocessor is sufficiently complex to challenge any student. By focusing on one "simple" device—the 68000—the chances of success are greater. The question is one of detail. Do we seek to engage students in an in-depth examination of an architecture or to skim over the features in a family of devices? The former is much more important in my view, because it offers more lifelong learning potential. Cost was another issue. A pre-built 68KMB system can be purchased for less than the price of the 68040 IC alone.

The rationale behind "the package" is more subtle. Most courses for which this book is relevant seek to teach computer architecture using a microprocessor as the sample architecture. Although "architecture" is the focus, it is surprising how much effort students expend in "getting past the implementation." Students are often mired in details of the system or the environment in which the target architecture is embedded. Consider the simple programming task of inputting a character from a keyboard. It is a significant challenge for students to distinguish which details are present only because of the "implementation" in the target system vs. which details are present because of the "architecture" of the CPU. When a complex or hidden implementation is used, it often necessitates a "black box" approach to teaching. In my opinion, this is fundamentally wrong since it leads to misconceptions about the relationships between the CPU, memory, I/O, and the levels of software that execute on a target system.

Any course on microprocessors must consider carefully the laboratory environment in which the student's hands-on experience takes place. To avoid swamping or confusing the student in details of an implementation, the laboratory computer must be as simple as possible—ideally a single-board computer—and it must hide nothing. As a start, students should have visual access to the components such as the CPU, RAM, EPROM, configuration jumpers, switches, and I/O connectors. They should also have at their disposal the pin-level schematic of the system hardware and a complete listing of the monitor program that provides their window to the architecture. The more complete the documentation, the more attainable are the educational objectives. The hardware schematic and monitor program listing reveal the critical hardware and software structure of the target machine—the implementation. Armed with these, students will find nothing but their own curiosity to hold them back.

The text contains nearly 200 end-of-chapter questions, with solutions to odd-numbered questions given at the back of the book. An instructors' manual containing solutions to even-numbered questions is available from the publisher. The instructor's manual also contains a lab manual with 15 labs. The manual can be copied and distributed to students for the laboratory component of a course. The labs begin with a simple tutorial of MS-DOS EDIT and proceed through to complex interrupt-driven interfaces using digital-to-analog and analog-to-digital conversion. The lab environment consists of a PC-host computer, a 68KMB, six interface boards (discussed in Chapter 9 of the text), and the software on the accompanying disk. The labs work closely with the text. For example, programs presented in detail in the text frequently surface in the labs. Typically, students study an example program in the text, then load, execute, and demonstrate it on the 68KMB. A programming task that is an extension of the demo program is then defined and students are asked to solve this themselves. (An instructor's disk, available from the publisher, contains solutions to all programming problems in the labs and in the text.) The following titles suggest the theme of each lab:

Lab #1    Editing Files
Lab #2    Terminal Emulation
Lab #3    Introduction to the 68KMB
Lab #4    The 68KMB Programming Environment
Lab #5    Programming Problems
Lab #6    Character I/O
Lab #7    Interface to Switches and LEDs
Lab #8    Interface to a 7-Segment LED
Lab #9    Interface to a 4-Digit Display
Lab #10   Interface to an 8-Digit Display
Lab #11   Interface to a Hexadecimal Keypad

A number of individuals have assisted in numerous ways throughout the preparation of this manuscript. At Motorola, Michael Leung, was very helpful in providing numerous technical documents and valuable information of the current state of affairs in the world of the 68000. Marlin Mickle at URDA, Inc. was a constant source of good ideas on the shape and form of "the package," in particular the 68KMB and the interface boards. Mark DiVecchio of Athena Systems Development Group and Richard Whiffen of Enertec, Inc. were both extremely generous in allowing their company's software to be included on the enclosed disk free-of-charge for educational use. In my department at the University of Guelph, I am the beneficiary of ongoing high-quality technical support from Dave Calvert, Rick Macklem, Blair Nonnecke, and Tony VanRoon, and very generous administrative support from Pam Varga, Greta Krusch, and Bonnie Miller. More subtle, but equally appreciated, is the moral support and encouragement I receive from faculty colleagues Dilip Banerji, Jay Majithia, Tom Wilson, and Dave Swayne at the University of Guelph, and Bob Dueck, Len Klochek, and Ben Shefler at Seneca College. Shawn Zhang did a meticulous job of proofreading an early draft of the manuscript and pointed out numerous pedagogical lapses that needed to be cleaned up. And, of course, lots of thanks are due to my wife, Jean, for always being there when it counted, and to our boys, Bruce, Billy, and Andrew for making every day a new adventure.

# Brief Table of Contents

# Table of Contents

## Chapter 0

### Foundations

# Chapter 1

## Microcomputer Concepts

# Chapter 2

## The 68000 Microprocessor

## Chapter 3

## Instruction Set

# Chapter 4

## Assembly-Language Programming

# Chapter 5

## Programming Examples

# Chapter 6

## Privilege States, Exceptions, Reset

# Chapter 7

## Input/Output

# Chapter 8

## The 68KMB

# Chapter 9

# Interface Examples

# Chapter 10

# Beyond the 68000

# Appendices

# 0. *Foundations*

## 0.1. INTRODUCTION

In keeping with the tradition of counting from zero in the binary system—the number system upon which computers are based—we begin this text with Chapter 0. The focus initially is on introductory topics, which support subsequent chapters in this text. The topics chosen for this chapter could easily expand to a complete text; however, discussions are limited to the most crucial issues students must understand before venturing deeper into the 68000 microprocessor and other topics in computer organization. Readers with a good foundation in Boolean algebra and digital logic may skip ahead to Chapter 1.

## 0.2. REPRESENTATION OF INFORMATION

Computers store, manipulate, and transform **information.** In its raw form, without an implied meaning, information is often called **data.** Data usually represent numbers or text. Before we delve into the storage, manipulation, and transformation of data or information, we need a system to represent it.

From an early age, most of us learn the decimal system for numbers and the Roman alphabet for text; however, these systems are not directly used or understood by computers. Computers, sometimes called digital computers, represent all information in binary, a system with two symbols. Most commonly, the binary symbols are the digits 0 and 1, but other possibilities exist, as shown in Table 0-1.

A single binary digit is called a **bit.** Within a computer, a bit is stored in an electronic circuit called a **flip flop.** The basic property of a flip flop is the ability to remember. Once a bit is stored in a flip flop, it is held for future retrieval. Usually, 0 is stored as a low voltage ($\approx$ 0 volts) and 1 is stored as a high voltage ($\approx$ 5 volts).

In the following sections, we will explore properties of the binary and decimal number systems, as well as the octal and hexadecimal systems commonly used with computer systems.

Table 0-1.  The Binary System

| One Symbol | The Other Symbol |
|---|---|
| 1 | 0 |
| True | False |
| High | Low |
| 5 Volts | 0 Volts |
| On | Off |
| Yes | No |
| Apple | Orange |
| ✔ | ✘ |

## 0.2.1.  *Number Systems*

Since binary uses only two symbols, it is called **base 2.** The base of a number system is also called the **radix.** The most common number system used by humans is the decimal system—base 10—using the digits 0 through 9. Quantities larger than 9 are represented with additional digits carrying a higher weight. For example, the number 135 contains three digits. The "5" carries a weight of $5 \times 1 = 5$, the "3" carries a weight of $3 \times 10 = 30$, and the "1" carries a weight of $1 \times 100 = 100$, for a total of 135. This is illustrated below.

$$
\begin{array}{rcr}
1 \times 100 & = & 100 \\
3 \times 10 & = & 30 \\
5 \times 1 & = & +\ 5 \\
\hline
135 & & 135
\end{array}
$$

When confusion is possible, the base of a number is explicitly indicated by a subscript suffix, as in $135_{10}$.

In general, the weight of each digit is $m^n$, where $m$ is the base (10 in this case) and $n$ is the position of the digit. The digit on the right is in position "0," the next digit is in position "1," and so on. This is illustrated below.

$$
\begin{array}{rcr}
1 \times 10^2 & = & 100 \\
3 \times 10^1 & = & 30 \\
5 \times 10^0 & = & +\ 5 \\
\hline
135 & & 135
\end{array}
$$

Table 0-2.    Binary, Octal, Decimal, and Hexadecimal Systems

| System | Base | Symbols | Understood by Humans? | Understood by Computers? |
|---|---|---|---|---|
| Binary | 2 | 0, 1 | With difficulty | Yes |
| Octal | 8 | 0, 1, 2, 3, 4, 5, 6, 7 | With difficulty | No |
| Decimal | 10 | 0, 1, 2, 3, 4, 5, 6, 7, 8, 9 | Yes | No |
| Hexadecimal | 16 | 0, 1, 2, 3, 4, 5, 6, 7, 8, 9, A, B, C, D, E, F | With difficulty | No |

The digit on the right carries the least weight and is called the **least-significant digit.**

As well as the decimal system, we must familiarize ourselves with the binary, octal, and hexadecimal systems. The important features of each are summarized in Table 0-2.

Octal, or base 8, uses the symbols 0 through 7. Hexadecimal, or base 16, uses sixteen symbols consisting of 0 through 9 and A through F. Symbols A through F represent the quantities ten through fifteen with A for 10, B for 11, C for 12, D for 13, E for 14, and F for 15.

The last two columns in Table 0-2 indicate that decimal is the preferred system for humans and that binary is the only system understood by computers. Why do we then bother with the octal or hexadecimal systems? It is a common misconception that computers understand and can operate on octal or hexadecimal numbers. This is not the case. The octal and hexadecimal systems are not understood by computers. Some interfaces accept information in octal or hexadecimal, however, conversion to binary is required before the information is stored in the computer's memory.

Octal and hexadecimal are used by humans because they are much easier to work with than binary. As we shall see, conversion between octal or hexadecimal and binary (or vice versa) is trivial.

## 0.2.2.   *Conversion between Bases*

Since we are concerned with four different bases, the twelve conversions in Figure 0-1 are possible.

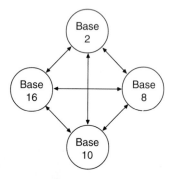

Figure 0-1.   Twelve conversions between four bases.

As a quick example, the number 13 in base 10 is shown below in each of the four bases:

$$13_{10} = 1101_2 = 15_8 = D_{16}$$

The conversion of a binary, octal, or hexadecimal number to decimal proceeds as illustrated previously. Multiply each digit (symbol) by its weight and form the sum. For the binary number above,

$$
\begin{aligned}
1 \times 2^3 &= 8 \\
1 \times 2^2 &= 4 \\
0 \times 2^1 &= 0 \\
1 \times 2^0 &= +1 \\
1101_2 &= 13_{10}
\end{aligned}
$$

For the octal number above,

$$
\begin{aligned}
1 \times 8^1 &= 8 \\
5 \times 8^0 &= +5 \\
15_8 &= 13_{10}
\end{aligned}
$$

For the hexadecimal number, 10A9, the conversion proceeds as follows:

$$
\begin{aligned}
1 \times 16^3 &= 4096 \\
0 \times 16^2 &= 0 \\
A \times 16^1 &= 160 \\
9 \times 16^0 &= +\;\;\;9 \\
10A9_{16} &= 4265_{10}
\end{aligned}
$$

To convert from decimal to binary, the following procedure is used: Continually divide the decimal number by two until the result is zero. Upon each division, keep track of the remainder (which is always 0 or 1). The number formed by combining the remainders is the binary equivalent of the original number. The first remainder is the **least-**

**significant bit** (LSB), on the right; and the last remainder is the **most-significant bit** (MSB), on the left. The following example sketches out the conversion of the decimal number 84 to binary.

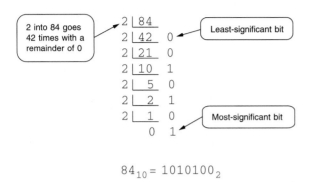

$$84_{10} = 1010100_2$$

Conversions from decimal to octal or from decimal to hexadecimal are similar to the example above. Convert from decimal to octal by continually dividing the decimal number by eight and keeping track of the remainder. The decimal number 93 is converted to octal as follows:

```
8 goes into 93         8 | 93
11 times with a        8 | 11   5
remainder of 5         8 |  1   3
                       8 |  0   1
```

$$93_{10} = 135_8$$

Using the same technique, the decimal number 9309 is converted to hexadecimal as follows:

```
16 goes into 9309      16| 9309
581 times with a       16|  581   D
remainder of 13_10     16|   36   5
or D_16                16|    2    4
                            0     2
```

$$9309_{10} = 245D_{16}$$

**Table 0-3.  Octal to Binary Conversion**

| Octal Digit | 3-bit Binary Code |
|---|---|
| 0 | 000 |
| 1 | 001 |
| 2 | 010 |
| 3 | 011 |
| 4 | 100 |
| 5 | 101 |
| 6 | 110 |
| 7 | 111 |

Conversions between the bases 2, 8, and 16 are extremely easy. Indeed, the only reason octal and hexadecimal are used is because of the straightforward conversions to binary.

A single octal digit represents three binary bits, as illustrated in Table 0-3.

To convert an octal number to binary, simply convert each octal digit to the corresponding 3-bit binary code. For example, $1075_8$ is converted to binary as follows:

```
Octal:    1   0   7   5

Binary: 001 000 111 101
```

The idea is the same for hexadecimal to binary conversions, except each hexadecimal digit corresponds to a 4-bit binary pattern. This is illustrated in Table 0-4.

To convert a hexadecimal number to binary, simply replace each hexadecimal digit by the corresponding 4-bit binary code. For example, the hexadecimal value A3F1C is converted to binary as follows:

```
Hexadecimal:    A    3    F    1    C

Binary:      1010 0011 1111 0001 1100
```

The conversion from binary to octal or from binary to hexadecimal is the reverse of the previous two examples. Just change the direction of the arrows above, and the opposite conversion is illus-

**Table 0-4.  Hexadecimal to Binary Conversion**

| Hexadecimal Digit | 4-bit Binary Code |
|---|---|
| 0 | 0000 |
| 1 | 0001 |
| 2 | 0010 |
| 3 | 0011 |
| 4 | 0100 |
| 5 | 0101 |
| 6 | 0110 |
| 7 | 0111 |
| 8 | 1000 |
| 9 | 1001 |
| A | 1010 |
| B | 1011 |
| C | 1100 |
| D | 1101 |
| E | 1110 |
| F | 1111 |

**Figure A.**

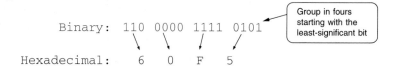

trated. Begin with the least-significant bit and group in threes for conversion to octal or in fours for conversion to hexadecimal. The binary value 10110111 is converted to octal as follows:

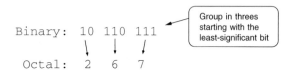

The binary value 110000011110101 is converted to hexadecimal as shown in Figure A. The only conversions remaining are from hexadecimal to octal and from octal to hexadecimal. These are easy if binary is used as an intermediary. That is, convert from hexadecimal to octal by first converting from hexadecimal to binary and then from binary to octal.

All conversions between the four bases have now been presented. They are summarized in Table 0-5.

**Example 0-1:** What is the largest possible decimal number that can be represented in (a) 8 bits, (b) 12 bits, (c) 16 bits, and (d) *n* bits?

**Solution:** (a) 255, (b) 4095, (c) 65,535, (d) $2^n - 1$

**Discussion:** The largest possible 8-bit binary number is 11111111. The solution to Example 0-1 can be found using the conversion procedure presented earlier, but there is an easier way. If 1 is added to the number 11111111 the result is 100000000 or $2^8$. Therefore, the answer is $2^8 - 1 = 255$.  ∎

**Example 0-2:** How many bits (minimum) are required to represent the decimal number 539?

**Solution:** 10 bits

**Discussion:** $2^9 = 512$, so 9 bits are not enough. $2^{10} = 1024$, so 10 bits minimum are sufficient to represent the number 539. The answer to this question is also found by taking the $\log_2 539$ and rounding up. $\log_2 539 = 9.074$, which rounds up to 10 bits.  ∎

## 0.2.3.  *Bytes and Kilobytes*

Many earlier computers and microprocessors handled data in 8-bit sizes. The term **byte** evolved to describe this convenient size of data. By most conventions, the bits in a byte are numbered from 0 to 7 with the least-significant bit—the bit on the right—as *bit 0* and the bit on the left as *bit 7*. This is

**Table 0-5.    Summary of Conversion Techniques**

| Conversion | Technique |
| --- | --- |
| Binary to Octal | Group bits in threes starting with LSB |
| Binary to Decimal | Multiply each bit by its weight and form the sum |
| Binary to Hexadecimal | Group bits in fours starting with LSB |
| Octal to Binary | Change each octal digit to its 3-bit binary code |
| Octal to Decimal | Multiply each octal digit by its weight and form the sum |
| Octal to Hexadecimal | Convert octal to binary and then binary to hexadecimal |
| Decimal to Binary | Continually divide by two and extract the remainders; the first remainder is the LSB |
| Decimal to Octal | Continually divide by eight and extract the remainders; the first remainder is the least-significant octal digit |
| Decimal to Hexadecimal | Continually divide by 16 and extract the remainders; the first remainder is the least-significant hexadecimal digit |
| Hexadecimal to Binary | Change each hexadecimal digit to its 4-bit binary code |
| Hexadecimal to Decimal | Multiply each hexadecimal digit by its weight and form the sum |
| Hexadecimal to Octal | Convert hexadecimal to binary and then binary to octal |

illustrated below.

```
Bit Number:  7 6 5 4 3 2 1 0
      Byte: |1|0|0|1|0|0|0|1|
```

A 2-byte or 16-bit value is often called a **word,** and a 4-byte or 32-bit value is often called a **long-word.** A **nibble** is a 4-bit value or half a byte. The term *word* is also used in a general sense, as the default data size of a computer.

The symbol $K$, for kilo, refers to $2^{10}$ or 1024. A **kilobyte,** therefore, is 1024 bytes—about a thousand bytes.

If a computer handles data in 8-bit sizes and uses a 16-bit address to store and retrieve data in memory, its address space contains $2^{16} = 65,536$ bytes. Since $2^{16}$ is the same as $2^6 \times 2^{10}$, the computer has an address space of 64K bytes.

> **Example 0-3:** How many bits are in 3K bytes?
> **Solution:** $3 \times 2^{10} \times 8 = 24,576$ ∎

It is also common to use the term $M$ or mega in place of $2^{20}$ or 1,048,576. A **megabyte,** therefore, is 1,048,576 bytes, or about a million bytes. A computer using a 24-bit address to store or retrieve bytes of data has a $2^4 \times 2^{20} = 16$ megabyte address space.

## 0.2.4.  1s *and 2s Complements*

The 1s and 2s complements of binary numbers are used to simplify subtraction and to represent negative numbers. Form the 1s complement of a binary number by complementing each bit. *Complementing* means change a 0 to a 1 or change a 1 to a 0. Here's an example:

```
Binary Number:   1 0 1 1 1 0 0
                 ↓ ↓ ↓ ↓ ↓ ↓ ↓
1s Complement:   0 1 0 0 0 1 1
```

Form the 2s complement of a binary number by taking the 1s complement and then adding 1. Here is an example:

```
Binary Number:   1 0 1 1 1 0 0
                 ↓ ↓ ↓ ↓ ↓ ↓ ↓
1s Complement:   0 1 0 0 0 1 1
      Add 1:   +             1
                 _____
2s Complement:   0 1 0 0 1 0 0
```

An interesting property is that taking the 2s complement twice yields the original number, as shown below.

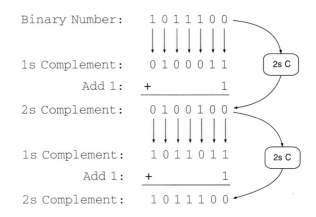

The idea of 1s and 2s complement has the following general interpretation: For any radix $m$, the $m - 1$'s complement is found by subtracting each digit from $m - 1$. The $m$'s complement is found by taking the $m - 1$'s complement and then adding 1. In base 10, for example, the 9s complement is found by subtracting each digit from 9. The 10s complement is the 9s complement plus 1. The 9s complement of $52_{10}$ is, therefore, $47_{10}$, and the 10s complement is $48_{10}$.

## 0.2.5.  *Signed Numbers*

Thus far we have discussed unsigned, or positive, numbers. In practice, we must also represent signed, or negative, numbers. Once we introduce signed numbers, it is important to pay attention to the *size* of the numbers. For example, an 8-bit computer stores numbers in 8-bit sizes. So, the number $5_{10}$ is represented as

$$00000101_2$$

The five zeros on the left are, of course, redundant in our usual way of writing numbers; bear in mind, however, that they are an important part of the internal storage of binary numbers within the computer.

A simple method of representing negative numbers is called **sign-magnitude.** Using sign-magnitude, the left bit in a binary number is the sign bit and the other bits are the magnitude. If the sign bit equals 1, the number is negative; if the sign bit is 0, the number is positive. Using an 8-bit, sign-magnitude representation, therefore, the values $+5_{10}$ and $-5_{10}$ are represented as follows:

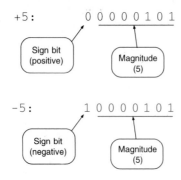

+5:    0 0 0 0 0 1 0 1

Sign bit (positive)    Magnitude (5)

-5:    1 0 0 0 0 1 0 1

Sign bit (negative)    Magnitude (5)

Oddly enough, there are two possible representations for zero using the sign-magnitude scheme, +0 and −0. The importance of size is evident in the example above. If we were simply to ask, *How is −5 represented as a sign-magnitude binary number?* then we cannot say, unless a size is given (or can be assumed).

**Example 0-4:** How is −5 represented as a sign-magnitude binary number on a computer that operates on 12-bit numbers?

**Solution:** 100000000101

**Discussion:** The sign bit is 1 and the low-order 11 bits hold the magnitude, 5.  ■

**Example 0-5:** What range of numbers can be expressed in 8 bits using a sign-magnitude scheme?

**Solution:** −127 to +127

**Discussion:** Using an $n$-bit sign-magnitude representation, the range of numbers is $-(2^{n-1} - 1)$ to $+(2^{n-1} - 1)$.  ■

A more common scheme of representing signed numbers is **2s complement.** Again, we must pay attention to the size of the numbers. Using an 8-bit, 2s complement representation, the values +5 and −5 are represented as follows:

+5:    0 0 0 0 0 1 0 1

-5:    1 1 1 1 1 0 1 1

2s complement of +5

Notice above that the most-significant bit—the bit on the left—is again the sign bit: 0 for positive numbers and 1 for negative numbers. The scheme presented earlier for converting binary numbers to decimal does not work for negative numbers represented in the 2s complement form. However, since taking the 2s complement of a number twice results in the original number, we need only take the 2s complement of a negative number to find the positive-equivalent of the number. For example, consider the following 16-bit number:

1111111111101011

If we are told the representation scheme is signed using the 2s complement method, and then asked, *What is the number?*, the answer is not obvious. The number is negative *something*, but what? We need only to take the 2s complement to get the positive-equivalent of the number. The 2s complement is

0000000000010101

which easily converts to $21_{10}$, so the original number is $-21_{10}$.

The following summarizes the range of numbers expressible using an 8-bit signed (2s complement) representation:

| Binary | Decimal |
|---|---|
| 1 0 0 0 0 0 0 0 | −128 |
| 1 0 0 0 0 0 0 1 | −127 |
| 1 0 0 0 0 0 1 0 | −126 |
| ⋮ | ⋮ |
| 1 1 1 1 1 1 1 0 | −2 |
| 1 1 1 1 1 1 1 1 | −1 |
| 0 0 0 0 0 0 0 0 | 0 |
| 0 0 0 0 0 0 0 1 | 1 |
| ⋮ | ⋮ |
| 0 1 1 1 1 1 1 0 | +126 |
| 0 1 1 1 1 1 1 1 | +127 |

In general, the range for $n$-bit signed numbers is from $-2^{n-1}$ to $+2^{n-1} - 1$.

The pattern of bits for 2s complement negative numbers seems strange at first, but the system is elegant. For example, note above that if we were to add 1 to the binary representation of −127 using the standard technique for addition, we would get −126, as expected. This is not the case for the sign-magnitude representation. Another powerful feature of 2s complement is that it greatly simplifies the addition and subtraction of signed numbers.

> **Example 0-6:** What is the range of numbers that can be represented using 12-bit, signed (2s complement) notation?
>
> **Solution:** −2048 to +2047
>
> **Discussion:** $n = 12$, $-2^{n-1} = -2^{11} = -2048$, $+2^{n-1} - 1 = +2^{11} - 1 = +2047$ ∎

## 0.2.6. Real Numbers

The representation of real numbers in binary is a natural extension of the technique for integers. The weight of the bit on the right of the binary decimal place is $2^{-1}$, the weight of the next bit on the right is $2^{-2}$, and so on. For example, the conversion of the binary real number 10010.101101 to decimal is sketched out below.

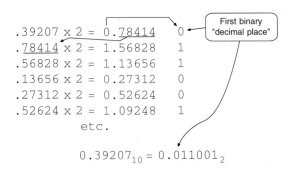

$$10010.101101_2 = 18.703125_{10}$$

The reverse conversion is trickier, but is still straightforward. The integer portion of the decimal number is converted as before. The fraction is converted by continually multiplying by 2 and extracting the integer portion of the result (the digit immediately to the left of the decimal place). The process is repeated until the result of the multiplication is zero or until the required precision is achieved. The conversion of 0.39207 to binary with six binary *decimal places* is sketched out below.

```
.39207 x 2 = 0.78414   0    First binary
.78414 x 2 = 1.56828   1   "decimal place"
.56828 x 2 = 1.13656   1
.13656 x 2 = 0.27312   0
.27312 x 2 = 0.52624   0
.52624 x 2 = 1.09248   1
        etc.
```

$$0.39207_{10} = 0.011001_2$$

Note, above, that the conversion could continue indefinitely since the original number was picked at random and is probably not expressible in a finite number of binary "decimal places."

## 0.2.7. Floating-Point Numbers

A more powerful scheme for representing real numbers is floating-point, which we present here briefly. Using floating-point notation, a number is expressed with an exponent, an implied base, and a fraction (also called the mantissa):

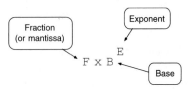

The fraction has an implied decimal point on the left. In binary, a sign bit is added to accommodate negative numbers. The decimal number 2.40625 is shown below in 12-bit floating-point format with a sign bit, an 8-bit fraction, and a 3-bit exponent.

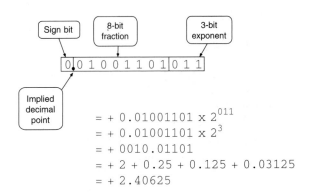

$$= + 0.01001101 \times 2^{011}$$
$$= + 0.01001101 \times 2^3$$
$$= + 0010.01101$$
$$= + 2 + 0.25 + 0.125 + 0.03125$$
$$= + 2.40625$$

The ability of the decimal point to "float" is seen above. Since the exponent is $011_2 = 3_{10}$, the fraction is multiplied by $2^3$. The effect is to shift the binary decimal point to the right three places.

There are numerous floating-point formats in use. In general, these involve trade-offs for precision and range. Most commonly, the fraction is normalized (the bit on the left is always 1), and the exponent is biased using *excess-n* notation. For example, a 3-bit excess-4 exponent is expressed as four greater than it really is. This is shown in Table 0-6.

Note in the right column that exponents range from −4 to +3. Biased or *excess-n* notation provides a convenient way to express negative exponents. It also complements the use of normalized fractions in achieving a good balance of precision and range.

**Table 0-6.    Excess-4 Notation**

| Excess-4 Notation | | |
|---|---|---|
| Binary | Decimal | Decimal – 4 |
| 000 | 0 | –4 |
| 001 | 1 | –3 |
| 010 | 2 | –2 |
| 011 | 3 | –1 |
| 100 | 4 | 0 |
| 101 | 5 | 1 |
| 110 | 6 | 2 |
| 111 | 7 | 3 |

The following example shows the decimal value 0.171875 expressed as a 12-bit floating-point number with a sign bit, an 8-bit normalized fraction, and a 3-bit excess-4 exponent.

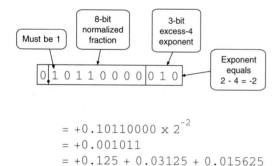

$$= +0.10110000 \times 2^{-2}$$
$$= +0.001011$$
$$= +0.125 + 0.03125 + 0.015625$$
$$= +0.171875$$

The amount of *excess* in the exponent will depend on its size. The idea is to provide about the same range of positive and negative exponents. For example, a format using an 8-bit exponent would likely use *excess-128* notation. This would allow exponents from $-128_{10}$ to $+127_{10}$.

## 0.2.8.    Binary-Coded Decimal

Considerable numeric information does not represent *quantities*—the sort of numbers that are used in arithmetic operations. Consider the number 8244120, which happens to be the telephone number for the University of Guelph. It is a decimal number, but to store it in a computer database as binary would be ludicrous. A common method to represent such numbers for storage in a computer's memory is called **packed decimal** or **binary-coded decimal (BCD)**. A BCD code stores each digit separately as a 4-bit binary code. This is shown in Table 0-7.

Note that the codes $1010_2$ to $1111_2$ are not used. The phone number for the University of

Guelph is represented in BCD as shown below.

BCD is also used to represent *quantities,* and so, BCD arithmetic is also required. Special circuits or computer instructions are used for BCD addition and subtraction (see Binary-Coded Decimal Instructions in Chapter 3).

## 0.2.9.    ASCII

Text is most commonly stored using the American Standard Code for Information Interchange—ASCII (pronounced "ass-key"). ASCII is a 7-bit code representing $2^7 = 128$ symbols or control operations. These are shown in Table 0-8.

Of the 128 ASCII codes, 95 are graphic codes and 33 are control codes. The graphic codes begin at $20_{16}$ (*space*) and go to $7E_{16}$ (~). The most common codes are, of course, the uppercase and lowercase alphabet and the digits. A variety of punctuation symbols are also represented.

The control codes begin at $00_{16}$ and go to $1F_{16}$. The last ASCII code, $7F_{16}$, is also a control code. Common control codes are CR for carriage return ($0D_{16}$), LF for line feed ($0A_{16}$), HT for horizontal tab ($09_{16}$), and so on.

The bits within an ASCII code are numbered from bit 1 on the right to bit 7 on the left. This is different from the usual numbering of binary codes (with the LSB as bit 0) and occasionally causes confusion. As an example, the ASCII code for lowercase *z* in binary is

```
Bit Number:  7 6 5 4 3 2 1
ASCII Code:  1 1 1 1 0 1 0
```

**Table 0-7.    Binary-Coded Decimal Codes**

| Binary-Coded Decimal | Decimal |
|---|---|
| 0000 | 0 |
| 0001 | 1 |
| 0010 | 2 |
| 0011 | 3 |
| 0100 | 4 |
| 0101 | 5 |
| 0110 | 6 |
| 0111 | 7 |
| 1000 | 8 |
| 1001 | 9 |

Table 0-8.   ASCII Codes

| Bit Positions 4321 | Bit Positions 765 | | | | | | | |
|---|---|---|---|---|---|---|---|---|
| | 000 | 001 | 010 | 011 | 100 | 101 | 110 | 111 |
| 0000 | NUL | DLE | SPACE | 0 | @ | P | ` | p |
| 0001 | SOH | DC1 | ! | 1 | A | Q | a | q |
| 0010 | STX | DC2 | " | 2 | B | R | b | r |
| 0011 | ETX | DC3 | # | 3 | C | S | c | s |
| 0100 | EOT | DC4 | $ | 4 | D | T | d | t |
| 0101 | ENQ | NAK | % | 5 | E | U | e | u |
| 0110 | ACK | SYN | & | 6 | F | V | f | v |
| 0111 | BEL | ETB | ' | 7 | G | W | g | w |
| 1000 | BS | CAN | ( | 8 | H | X | h | x |
| 1001 | HT | EM | ) | 9 | I | Y | i | y |
| 1010 | LF | SUB | * | : | J | Z | j | z |
| 1011 | VT | ESC | + | ; | K | [ | k | { |
| 1100 | FF | FS | , | < | L | \ | l | l |
| 1101 | CR | GS | - | = | M | ] | m | } |
| 1110 | SO | RS | . | > | N | ^ | n | ~ |
| 1111 | SI | US | / | ? | O | _ | o | DEL |

Bit positions in ASCII code: | 7 | 6 | 5 | 4 | 3 | 2 | 1 |   e.g., A = $1000001_2$ = $41_{16}$ = $65_{10}$.

ASCII has some interesting properties. Note that the digits 0 through 9 are given the codes $30_{16}$ to $39_{16}$. If the upper 3 bits of these codes are stripped off, then the result is the BCD equivalent of the corresponding digit.

Uppercase and lowercase characters differ only in bit 6, as illustrated below for *A* and *a*.

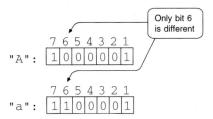

Uppercase *A* is the ASCII code $41_{16}$, and lowercase *a* is $61_{16}$. The *shift* operation, implemented as a modifier key on most keyboards, simply inhibits (clears) bit 6 in transforming a lowercase character to uppercase. With some keyboards, the shift key complements bit 6; so, if *caps lock* is in effect, keys entered with the shift key depressed will revert to lowercase.

Most computer keyboards implement a *control* function in a manner similar to the shift function. For example *control-s* is often used to suspend the transmission of output to a device (pause) while *control-q* resumes transmission. The control function is often implemented by inhibiting bits 6 and 7 in the ASCII code. From the ASCII table, *s* is $73_{16}$, so control-s generates the code $13_{16}$, as illus-

trated below:

"s":  7 6 5 4 3 2 1  | 1 | 1 | 1 | 0 | 0 | 1 | 1 |

"control-s":  7 6 5 4 3 2 1  | 0 | 0 | 1 | 0 | 0 | 1 | 1 |
Bits 6 and 7 are inhibited

The code $13_{16}$, above, is one of the 33 control codes in ASCII. In Table 0-8, it is called DC3 for *device code 3*. This is a special device control code that has been standardized to fulfill the function *transmission off* (usually called *XOFF*). The control code $11_{16}$, called DC1 or XON, is the resume transmission control code. XON and XOFF codes are also used for controlling the flow of information along communications lines using modems. This is often called *XON/XOFF handshaking*. The ASCII control codes are used for numerous other communications purposes; however, we will not elaborate on these here.

**Example 0-7:** Convert the postal code *N1G 2W1* to binary and hexadecimal ASCII codes.

**Solution:**

| Symbol | Hexadecimal | Binary |
|---|---|---|
| N | 4E | 1001110 |
| 1 | 31 | 0110001 |
| G | 47 | 1000111 |
| space | 20 | 0100000 |
| 2 | 32 | 0110010 |
| W | 57 | 1010111 |
| 1 | 31 | 0110001 |

**Example 0-8:** What control code is generated by entering *control-m* on a typical computer keyboard?

**Solution:** $0D_{16}$ (CR = carriage return)

**Discussion:** Control-m is an alternate way to generate the *return* or *enter* function on most keyboards. This is a handy trick to keep in mind in the event the RETURN key breaks.  ■

## 0.3.  BINARY ARITHMETIC

In this section, we present the pencil-and-paper techniques for binary addition, subtraction, multiplication, and division.

### 0.3.1.  Addition

With an understanding of number systems, particularly binary, we now investigate how numbers are added and subtracted in computers. Before looking at the circuits for addition and subtraction, we will work through the binary operations.

Addition involves an augend, an addend, and a sum, as shown below:

```
Augend:    A
Addend:  + B
   Sum:    C
```

Addition in binary is much the same as in decimal. In decimal, a carry results when a sum exceeds 9. In binary, a carry results when a sum exceeds 1. (There is no symbol for 2!) So, in binary, if two 1-bit values are added, only four possibilities exist:

```
                              carry
                                 1
   0      0      1      1      1 plus 1 is
 + 0    + 1    + 0    + 1      0 with a carry of 1
 ───    ───    ───    ────
   0      1      1     10
```

Multi-bit numbers are added as expected. Carries propagate to the next higher bit position,

as illustrated below.

```
  1 1 1
  1011
+ 0110
──────
10001
```

We can verify the example above by converting to decimal. The augend is $1011_2 = 11_{10}$. The addend is $0110_2 = 6_{10}$. The sum of 11 plus 6 is $17_{10} = 10001_2$, the answer shown above.

### 0.3.2.  Simple Subtraction

Subtraction involves a minuend, a subtrahend, and a difference, as shown below:

```
 Minuend:    A
Subtrahend: -B
Difference:  C
```

Binary numbers are subtracted using the same technique common with decimal numbers. *Zero subtract one*, of course, requires a borrow. An example follows:

```
  1001
- 0100
──────
  0101
```

In decimal, the example above is 9 − 4 = 5. In practice, computers use a much more elegant scheme for subtraction—using 2s complement addition.

### 0.3.3.  Addition and Subtraction Using 2s Complement

Using a 2s complement representation, both positive and negative numbers are added or subtracted without introducing a new technique. For example, consider adding −3 to 7 to get 4. If −3 is represented in 2s complement form, then we just add in the usual way. This is sketched out below using an 8-bit representation.

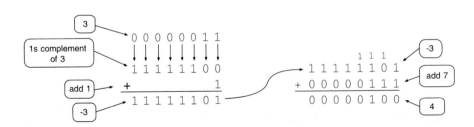

**Figure B.**

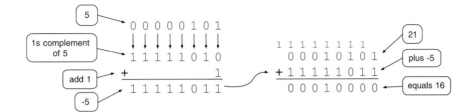

The traditional method of subtraction is not needed if negative numbers are represented using the 2s complement scheme. Subtraction is performed using a very simple and powerful method which we call *subtraction by addition.* To perform the operation

$$A - B$$

we simply add the 2s complement of B. This works because of the following simple relationship:

$$A - B = A + (-B)$$

The decimal operation $21 - 5 = 16$ is sketched out in Figure B to illustrate this technique. The first step (on the left, in Figure B) is to convert the subtrahend (+5) to its 2s complement form (−5). It is then added to the minuend (21).

This method is valid for numbers of any radix or base. If $A$ and $B$ are in base 10, then

```
A - B = A + "the 10s
        complement of B"
```

As we shall see later, building digital logic circuits to implement binary addition and subtraction as just shown is very straightforward.

### 0.3.4.  *Multiplication*

Binary multiplication is very similar to decimal multiplication. Multiplication involves a multiplicand, a multiplier, and a product, as shown below.

```
Multiplicand:    A
  Multiplier:  x B
     Product:    C
```

Partial products are formed by a shift-and-add

technique, as shown below.

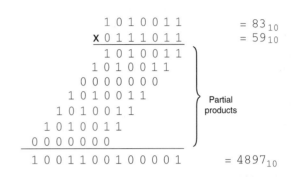

### 0.3.5.  *Division*

Division involves a quotient, a dividend, and a divisor, as shown below.

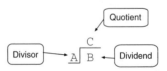

To perform binary division, the following steps are used:

1. Initialize the quotient to zero.
2. Subtract the divisor from the dividend to get a partial remainder (PR).
    If PR $\geq$ 0, increment quotient, continue.
    If PR $<$ 0, stop.
3. The PR becomes the dividend. Go to step 2.

For example, the operation $100/50 = 2$ is sketched out in binary in Figure C.

---

## 0.4.  LOGIC GATES AND BOOLEAN ALGEBRA

In this section we shift our focus to the circuits that computers are made from. For the most part these are logic circuits (also called digital circuits)

Figure C.

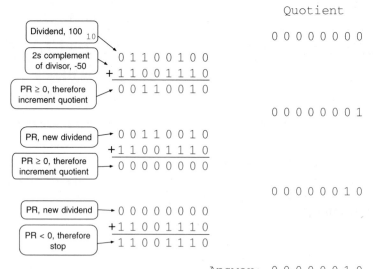

since they operate on binary data where 0 is represented by a low voltage (≈ 0 volts) and a 1 is represented by a high voltage (≈ 5 volts).

### 0.4.1.    *The Switch as a Logical Operator*

The idea underlying logic circuits is introduced by considering a simple electronic circuit with a switch controlling a light-emitting diode (LED).

The circuit in Figure 0-2 has four components: a 5-volt battery, a single-pole double-throw switch, an LED, and a resistor.

When a complete path exists for current to flow around the circuit, the LED turns on; otherwise the LED is off. When the switch is *up* (as shown), such a path exists and the LED is on. When the switch is *down* (dashed line), the circuit is *open* and current does not flow: The LED is off. The value of the resistor controls the brightness of the LED. The

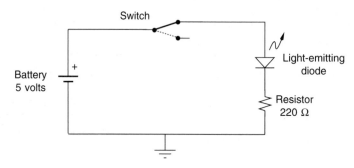

**Figure 0-2.    A switch controlling an LED.**

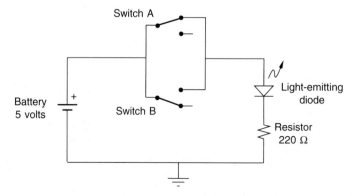

**Figure 0-3.    Two switches implementing the OR function.**

Table 0-9.   Operation of OR Circuit in Figure 0-3

| Switch A | Switch B | LED |
|---|---|---|
| down | down | off |
| down | up | on |
| up | down | on |
| up | up | on |

Table 0-10.   Operation of AND Circuit in Figure 0-4

| Switch A | Switch B | LED |
|---|---|---|
| down | down | off |
| down | up | off |
| up | down | off |
| up | up | on |

lower the resistance, the more current that flows, and the brighter the LED shines.

The idea of a logic circuit is illustrated by adding a second switch, as shown in Figure 0-3.

If switch A *or* switch B is *up,* a path exists for current to flow and the LED turns on. This is the logical OR function. The possibilities for the LED and the two switches are summarized in Table 0-9.

If the switches are arranged as in Figure 0-4, the logical AND function is implemented. As evident, switch A *and* switch B must be up before a path exists. If either switch is down, the circuit is open and current does not flow, thus keeping the LED off.

The possibilities for the LED and the two switches are summarized in Table 0-10.

The mathematical system used by computer scientists to describe the operation of logic circuits is called **Boolean algebra.** We need only introduce a simple level of abstraction to proceed. Let's call the LED *Z* and let 1 correspond to *LED on* and 0 correspond to *LED off*. Call the switches *A* and *B* with 1 corresponding to *up* and 0 corresponding to *down*. The relationship between *Z*, *A*, and *B* can be described by a **truth table.** For the AND circuit just described (Figure 0-4, Table 0-10), the truth table is

```
A     B   | Z
0     0   | 0
0     1   | 0
1     0   | 0
1     1   | 1
```

The OR function is represented in Boolean algebra with the symbol $\vee$ and the AND function with the symbol $\wedge$. So,

$$Z = A \vee B$$

is a mathematical expression for the OR function shown in Figure 0-3, and

$$Z = A \wedge B$$

is a mathematical expression for the AND function shown in Figure 0-4.

**Example 0-9:** When an LED is on, it exhibits a voltage drop of about 1.7 volts. Knowing this, what is the current through the LED in Figure 0-2 when the switch is up?

**Solution:** 15 mA

**Discussion:** This question requires a basic knowledge of Ohm's law. With a 5-volt power supply and a 1.7-volt drop across the LED, the voltage across the resistor is $5 - 1.7 = 3.3$ volts. Using $I$ (electron current) = $V/R$, the current through the resistor is $3.3/220 = 0.015$ amps = 15 milliamps. Since the resistor is in series with the LED, the current through the LED is the same, 15 mA.  ■

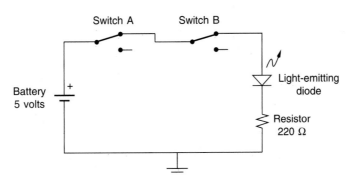

Figure 0-4.   Two switches implementing the AND function.

## 0.4.2.  *Basic Gates*

With this introduction, we illustrate the circuits that implement the basic set of logic operations. These circuits, commonly called **logic gates,** are shown in Table 0-11.

The column labeled *Operation* gives the usual name for each function. In addition to the OR and AND functions discussed earlier, there are also the NAND, NOR, EXOR, EXNOR, and the INVERTER (also called NOT) functions.

The column labeled *Symbol* shows the graphic symbol for each logic gate. Templates are available from bookstores to facilitate the pencil-and-paper design of logic circuits.

The column labeled *TTL Part #* gives an example part number of an integrated circuit (IC) for each logic function. *TTL* stands for *transistor-transistor logic*—a common technology for implementing logic circuits. Each part number begins with *74* to identify it as a member of the TTL family. The designation *LS* stands for *low-power Schottky*, referring to

**Table 0-11.   Basic Logic Gates**

| Operation | Symbol | TTL Part # | Equation | Truth Table |
|---|---|---|---|---|
| INVERTER | | 74LS04 | $Z = \overline{A}$ | A\|Z / 0\|1 / 1\|0 |
| OR | | 74LS32 | $Z = A+B$ / $Z = A \vee B$ | A B\|Z / 0 0\|0 / 0 1\|1 / 1 0\|1 / 1 1\|1 |
| AND | | 74LS08 | $Z = A \cdot B$ / $Z = A \wedge B$ | A B\|Z / 0 0\|0 / 0 1\|0 / 1 0\|0 / 1 1\|1 |
| NOR | | 74LS02 | $Z = \overline{A+B}$ / $Z = \overline{A \vee B}$ | A B\|Z / 0 0\|1 / 0 1\|0 / 1 0\|0 / 1 1\|0 |
| NAND | | 74LS00 | $Z = \overline{A \cdot B}$ / $Z = \overline{A \wedge B}$ | A B\|Z / 0 0\|1 / 0 1\|1 / 1 0\|1 / 1 1\|0 |
| EXOR | | 74LS86 | $Z = A \oplus B$ / $Z = A \veebar B$ | A B\|Z / 0 0\|0 / 0 1\|1 / 1 0\|1 / 1 1\|0 |
| EXNOR | | 74LS266 (O.C.) | $Z = \overline{A \oplus B}$ / $Z = \overline{A \veebar B}$ | A B\|Z / 0 0\|1 / 0 1\|0 / 1 0\|0 / 1 1\|1 |

a subfamily within the TTL family. Generally, subfamilies differ in speed and power requirements. The final digits identify the particular device.

The column labeled *Equation* gives the algebraic formula that describes the function of each gate. Note the use of a bar above a variable (or expression) to indicate logical inversion, or negation. Each equation has two common forms. When confusion with arithmetic operations is not likely, the top equation may be used. The logical OR function can be expressed as

$$Z = A + B$$

or as

$$Z = A \lor B$$

the latter conforming to traditional Boolean algebra. In fact, it is common to call the OR function the *logical sum* and the AND function the *logical product*. It is also common to omit the operation symbol altogether for the AND function (i.e., $A \cdot B = AB$).

The right-hand column, labeled *Truth Table*, expresses, in Boolean terms, all possible combinations for the input variables (A and B, above) with the resulting condition on the output variable.

As an example, the *74LS00* is a low-power Schottky TTL logic circuit that implements the logical NAND function. It contains four 2-input NAND gates in a 14-pin integrated circuit, as shown in Figure 0-5. Note that twelve of the pins provide connections to the inputs and outputs of the gates ($3 \times 4 = 12$), while two are for power connections. Pin 14 connects to the +5-volt supply and pin 7 connects to ground.

### 0.4.3.  Extension to Three or More Inputs

Although the AND, NAND, OR, and NOR gates are shown in Table 0-11 with two inputs, these functions can extend to any number of inputs. For example, the 74LS30 is a TTL NAND gate with eight inputs (see Figure 0-6).

With eight inputs, a truth table for this device has $2^8 = 256$ rows. (We won't bother to show it here.) The output is high for each input combination except when all inputs equal 1 (high). Algebraically this is

$$Z = \overline{A \cdot B \cdot C \cdot D \cdot E \cdot F \cdot G \cdot H}$$

In theory, any number of inputs is possible for the AND, NAND, OR, and NOR functions. In practice, designers must choose from a variety of devices available in a particular family of integrated circuits. Examples of common TTL devices are shown in Table 0-12.

Two entries in the table are for *buffers*. Buffers have one input and one output—like an inverter without the inversion. They are used to increase the output drive capability of a signal and to alter the electrical characteristics of a signal (e.g., higher current, three-state output). The column labeled *Type of Output* is discussed later in this chapter.

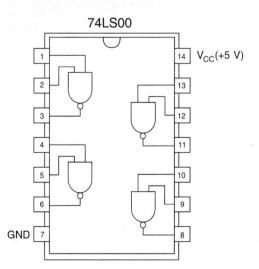

**Figure 0-5.   Pin connections for a 74LS00.**

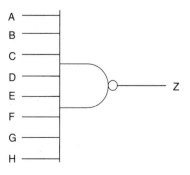

**Figure 0-6.   74LS30 8-input NAND gate.**

Table 0-12.   Common TTL Gates

| Device | Type of Gate | Number of Gates | Number of Pins | Type of Output |
|--------|--------------|-----------------|----------------|----------------|
| 7400 | 2-input NAND | 4 | 14 | totem pole |
| 7401 | 2-input NAND | 4 | 14 | open collector |
| 7402 | 2-input NOR | 4 | 14 | totem pole |
| 7404 | inverter | 6 | 14 | totem pole |
| 7405 | inverter | 6 | 14 | open collector |
| 7407 | buffer | 6 | 14 | open collector |
| 7408 | 2-input AND | 4 | 14 | totem pole |
| 7410 | 3-input NAND | 3 | 14 | totem pole |
| 7420 | 4-input NAND | 2 | 14 | totem pole |
| 7430 | 8-input NAND | 1 | 14 | totem pole |
| 7432 | 2-input OR | 4 | 14 | totem pole |
| 74LS240 | inverter | 8 | 20 | three-state |
| 74LS244 | buffer | 8 | 20 | three-state |

### 0.4.4.   EXOR *and* EXNOR *Gates*

The exclusive OR (EXOR) and exclusive NOR (EXNOR) gates have some unique properties. The EXOR function can be expressed using OR, AND, and NOT operations as follows:

$$A \oplus B = (\overline{A} \cdot B) + (A \cdot \overline{B})$$

It follows that the EXOR operation can be implemented with OR, AND, and NOT gates, as shown in Figure 0-7.

The idea of more than two inputs for the EXOR and EXNOR functions requires special consideration. It is common to think of the EXOR function as follows:

*The output is high if one or the other input is high, but not both.*

or

*The output is high if the inputs are different.*

This is evident by inspecting the truth table in Table 0-11. Obviously, these phrases don't extend beyond two input variables. However, the EXOR function can also be thought of as follows:

*The output is high if an <u>odd</u> number of inputs are high.*

From Table 0-11, the EXOR output is low when *zero* or *two* inputs are high, and is high when *one* input is high. Zero and 2 are even numbers, 1 is an odd number. From this, the extension to three or more inputs is apparent. We illustrate this in Figure 0-8 with two 2-input EXOR gates.

If we label the intermediate output Z′, then the truth table in Table 0-13 applies.

Comparing Z with inputs A, B, and C, we see that Z is 1 if *one* or *three* inputs are high or 0 if *zero* or *two* inputs are high, thus confirming our earlier statement. For three inputs then,

$$Z = A \oplus B \oplus C$$

By extension, the exclusive NOR function is expressed by the phrase, *The output is high if an <u>even</u> number of inputs are high.*

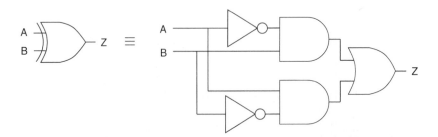

Figure 0-7.   EXOR implementation with standard gates.

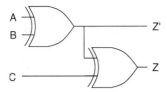

Figure 0-8. Implementing a 3-input EXOR function.

Table 0-13. Truth Table for 3-input EXOR Function in Figure 0-8

| | Inputs | | Outputs | |
|---|---|---|---|---|
| A | B | C | Z' | Z |
| 0 | 0 | 0 | 0 | 0 |
| 0 | 0 | 1 | 0 | 1 |
| 0 | 1 | 0 | 1 | 1 |
| 0 | 1 | 1 | 1 | 0 |
| 1 | 0 | 0 | 1 | 1 |
| 1 | 0 | 1 | 1 | 0 |
| 1 | 1 | 0 | 0 | 0 |
| 1 | 1 | 1 | 0 | 1 |

## 0.4.5. *DeMorgan Transformations*

DeMorgan's theorem is an interesting and powerful property in Boolean algebra. It is usually expressed as the following identities for the NAND and NOR operations:

$$\text{NAND:}\quad \overline{A \cdot B} = \overline{A} + \overline{B}$$
$$\text{NOR:}\quad \overline{A + B} = \overline{A} \cdot \overline{B}$$

Similar identities follow for the AND and OR operations:

$$\text{AND:}\quad A \cdot B = \overline{\overline{A} + \overline{B}}$$
$$\text{OR:}\quad A + B = \overline{\overline{A} \cdot \overline{B}}$$

To explain DeMorgan's theorem, let's first consider the following two sentences:

*Wear a hat if it is raining or if it is cold.*

*Don't wear a hat if it is not raining and it is not cold.*

These sentences achieve the same result in very different ways. Have a close look at these. Can you see that the first sentence is like an OR operation and that the second sentence is like the DeMorgan-equivalent of an OR operation? Similarly the AND, NAND, OR, and NOR functions can be transformed to give a slightly different perspective to the same logical operation. Consider the NAND operation as sketched out in Figure 0-9.

We introduce the verbal phrase *1s AND to give 0* as a handy way to think of the NAND operation. The three components of this phrase are shown on the left in Figure 0-9. We say *1s* because there are no bubbles at the inputs. We say *AND* because

the gate, forgetting about bubbles, looks like an AND gate. Finally, we say *to give 0* because of the bubble at the output. This is seen easily in the truth table for the NAND gate in Figure 0-9, where the three components of the verbal phrase are joined. This idea extends easily to the AND, OR, and NOR operations, which we will present shortly. First, however, we will transform the NAND operation using DeMorgan's theorem. This is sketched out in Figure 0-10.

Each of the three components of the operation has changed: *1s* has changed to *0s*, *AND* has changed to *OR*, and *to give 0* has changed to *to give 1*. Furthermore, the symbol has changed dramatically to reflect the transformation. Note on the right in Figure 0-10, however, the truth table is exactly the same. Now, the phrase captures the conditions yielding a 1 at the output. This is DeMorgan's transformation. The trick is to change each of the three components of the verbal phrase that describes the operation. Do this and any of the AND, OR, NAND, or NOR functions is transformed in the same manner. It is a powerful and simple technique that avoids the more formal academic treatment of DeMorgan's theorem.

We will not elaborate in detail on the importance of having two different ways to express the same thing, except to note that one or the other symbol is usually more appropriate. Using the appropriate symbol facilitates proper thinking about

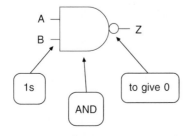
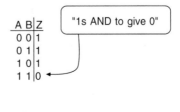

Figure 0-9.   Verbal description of a NAND gate.

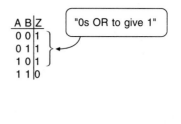

**Figure 0-10.   Verbal description of NAND gate with DeMorgan transformation.**

a logic circuit's operation. Table 0-14 summarizes the DeMorgan transformations for the AND, NAND, OR, and NOR functions.

Note in the table that the standard form of the NAND operation is shown with the following equation:

$$\overline{Z} = A \cdot B$$

This equation closely mimics the standard symbol with the bubble (inversion) at the output. Of course, it is the same as the more common form of the NAND equation

$$Z = \overline{A \cdot B}$$

## 0.4.6.   Universality of NAND *and* NOR *Gates*

Any logic function can be created using only NAND gates. This property is called the *universality*

Table 0-14. DeMorgan Transformations of Logic Gates

| Operation | Standard Form | DeMorgan-Equivalent Form |
|---|---|---|
| AND | $Z = A \cdot B$  "1s AND to give 1" | $\overline{Z} = \overline{A} + \overline{B}$  "0s OR to give 0" |
| NAND | $\overline{Z} = A \cdot B$  "1s AND to give 0" | $Z = \overline{A} + \overline{B}$  "0s OR to give 1" |
| OR | $Z = A + B$  "1s OR to give 1" | $\overline{Z} = \overline{A} \cdot \overline{B}$  "0s AND to give 0" |
| NOR | $\overline{Z} = A + B$  "1s OR to give 0" | $Z = \overline{A} \cdot \overline{B}$  "0s AND to give 1" |

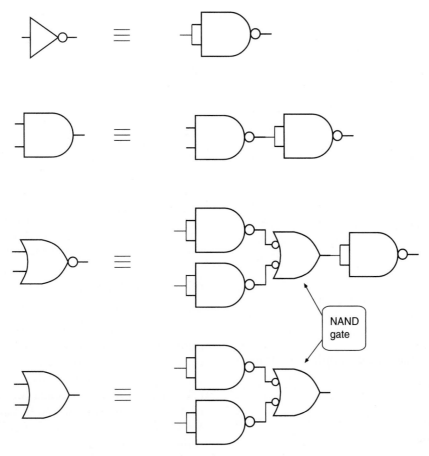

Figure 0-11.   Universality of the NAND gate.

*of the NAND gate.* Figure 0-11 illustrates the NOT, AND, NOR, and OR functions implemented with NAND gates.

We have taken the liberty to show the NOR and OR implementations with a DeMorgan-equivalent NAND symbol. It is still a NAND gate, but the transformed symbol more clearly shows the operation.

Since the EXOR and EXNOR operations can be implemented with standard gates, we have not bothered to include them in Figure 0-11. (See Question 15 at the end of this chapter.)

It is also possible to implement any logic operation with NOR gates. (See Question 19 at the end of this chapter.)

### 0.4.7.   Boolean Identities

Our earlier discussions of the EXOR function and the universality of the NAND and NOR gates used a variety of fundamental relationships, or *identities*, in Boolean algebra. These are formally presented in Table 0-15.

All the Boolean identities can be illustrated with logic gates. For example, the eight identities at the top of Table 0-15 are shown in Figure 0-12 as logic circuits.

The input states labeled "0" and "1" are

achieved by tying the input to ground (0 volts) for a logic 0 or to +5 volts for logic 1.

### 0.4.8.   *Algebraic Manipulation*

Armed with the assorted Boolean identities in Table 0-15, it is possible to build and manipulate complex equations describing myriad logic functions. The goal is to minimize the number of gates

Table 0-15.   Boolean Identities

| | |
|---|---|
| $X + 0 = X$ | $X \bullet 0 = 0$ |
| $X + 1 = 1$ | $X \bullet 1 = X$ |
| $X + X = X$ | $X \bullet X = X$ |
| $X + \overline{X} = 1$ | $X \bullet \overline{X} = 0$ |
| $\overline{\overline{X}} = X$ | |
| $X + Y = Y + X$ | Commutative rule |
| $X \bullet Y = Y \bullet X$ | |
| $X + (Y + Z) = (X + Y) + Z$ | Associative rule |
| $X \bullet (Y \bullet Z) = (X \bullet Y) \bullet Z$ | |
| $X \bullet (Y + Z) = X \bullet Y + X \bullet Z$ | Distributive rule |
| $X + (Y \bullet Z) = (X + Y) \bullet (X + Z)$ | |
| $\overline{X + Y} = \overline{X} \bullet \overline{Y}$ | DeMorgan's theorem |
| $\overline{X \bullet Y} = \overline{X} + \overline{Y}$ | |

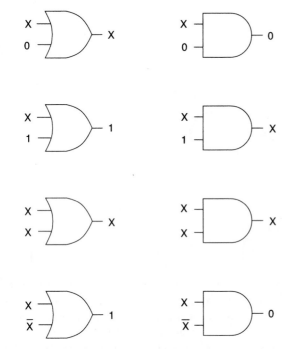

**Figure 0-12. Logic gate implementation of Boolean identities.**

required to build the circuit. For example, consider the Boolean equation

$$F = \overline{A}BC + \overline{A}B\overline{C} + AC$$

Without thinking too hard about it, we see that the circuit in Figure 0-13 is one possible implementation.

However, if we manipulate the terms using Boolean identities, the equation can be simplified. This is shown below.

```
F = ĀBC + ĀBC̄ + AC
  = ĀB(C + C̄) + AC (distributive  rule)
  = ĀB(1) + AC
  = ĀB + AC
```

The logic circuit in Figure 0-14 is equivalent to our first attempt (Figure 0-13), but is clearly superior since it uses fewer gates.

A variety of techniques exist to minimize logic equations (most notably, Karnaugh maps); however, these will not be presented in this text.

### 0.4.9. Timings

Although we usually think of the operation of logic circuits in a static sense—using truth tables or Boolean equations—it is also important to consider how logic circuits behave dynamically—as inputs change over time. This is particularly important when sequential circuits (or flip flops) are introduced. As a simple example, consider a 2-input NAND gate with inputs changing over time as shown in Figure 0-15.

The challenge is to determine the state of the output $Z$ given the inputs $A$ and $B$ changing as shown. Recall that a NAND gate's operation is captured by the phrase *1s AND to give 0*. We therefore scan the input timings, looking for two *1s*. At such times, the output is low, while at other times the output is high. There are only two places when the

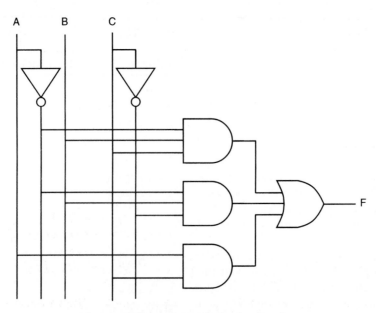

**Figure 0-13.    Example logic circuit.**

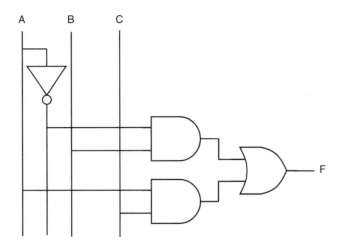

Figure 0-14.   Example logic circuit (after minimization).

inputs are high simultaneously, so there are only two places where the output is low. This is shown in Figure 0-16.

Of course, the timings are much more complex when the circuit involves several (or several dozen) gates. (See Question 20 at the end of this chapter.)

A timescale is not shown in the timing diagram in Figure 0-16. Input changes are shown as instantaneous (vertical lines), and input-to-output delays are shown as zero. In practice, there are small but significant delays. Figure 0-17 illustrates the measurement of input-to-output propagation delays. The parameter $t_{PHL}$ is the *high-to-low propagation*

*time,* which is the time between specified reference points in the input and output waveforms with the output changing from high to low. The reference point for 74LS-series devices is 1.3 volts. Similarly, $t_{PLH}$ is the time between specified reference points in the input and output waveforms with the output changing from low to high. Typically, input-to-output propagation delays are on the order of 10 ns for 74LS devices (*ns* is for nanosecond, or $10^{-9}$ seconds).

### 0.4.10.   *Types of Outputs*

Earlier, in Table 0-12, we listed a variety of TTL gates and identified the type of output as **totem**

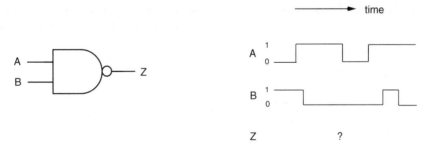

Figure 0-15.   Timing example for NAND gate.

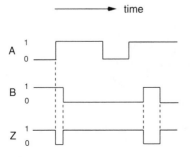

Figure 0-16.   Timing example for NAND gate (solved).

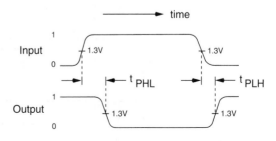

Figure 0-17.   High-to-low and low-to-high propagation times.

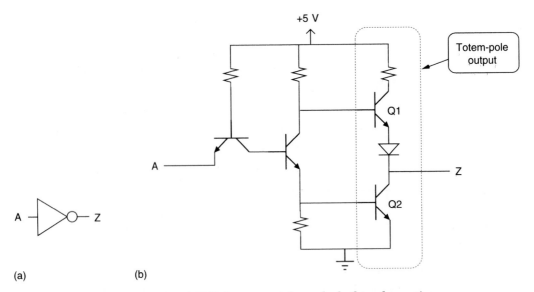

(a)                    (b)

Figure 0-18.   A TTL inverter. (a) symbol, (b) schematic.

**pole, open collector,** or **three-state.** A detailed discussion of these usually occurs under the topic *electrical properties of logic devices.* Our treatment here is brief.

**Totem Pole Outputs**   To begin, we present a typical TTL inverter, such as a 7404. The symbol is shown in Figure 0-18a and the electronic schematic of the internal components is shown in Figure 0-18b.

The output stage of this device is within the dotted line. The term **totem pole** simply refers to the vertical alignment of components. We can think of the two transistors, Q1 and Q2, as switches controlled by the input, $A$. One transistor is always ON while the other is OFF. If Q1 is ON, the output $Z$ is pulled high—toward +5 volts (logic 1). If Q2 is ON, the output $Z$ is pulled low—toward 0 volts (logic 0). Q1 is called the *pull-up transistor,* and Q2 is called the *pull-down transistor.* The relationship between $A$, Q1, Q2, and $Z$ is summarized in Table 0-16.

Table 0-16 is complete: At no time are the output transistors both ON or both OFF. There is a practical implication of this when designing logic circuits. Although it is common to join inputs of

Table 0-16.    Internal Operation of a TTL Inverter

| Input (A) | Transistor | | Output (Z) |
|---|---|---|---|
| | Q1 | Q2 | |
| 0 | ON | OFF | 1 |
| 1 | OFF | ON | 0 |

logic gates, it is not possible to join totem pole outputs. This is illustrated in Figure 0-19.

The problem arises when input conditions generate a high at one gate's output and a low at the other's. At such times, Q1 is ON for one gate and Q2 is ON for the other. This creates a low-resistance path from $V_{CC}$ (+5 volts) to ground. The electron current flow through the gates will be very high and one or the other of the gates will burn out.

**Three-State Outputs**   The vast majority of TTL devices have totem pole outputs. In the design of computer systems, however, it is necessary to connect the outputs of logic gates together when interfacing to a **bus.** (Buses are discussed in detail in Chapter 1.) To accomplish this, a logic device must electrically disconnect its output when it is not

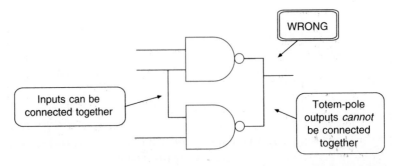

Figure 0-19.   Totem-pole outputs cannot be connected together.

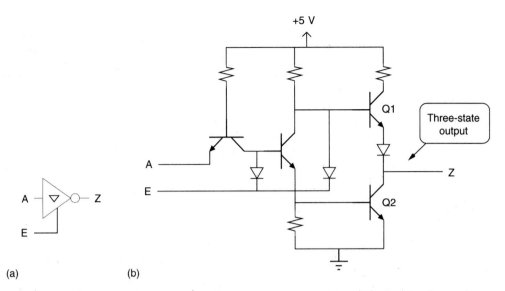

Figure 0-20.   An inverter with a three-state output. (a) symbol, (b) schematic.

*driving the bus.* By considering the totem pole output in Figure 0-18, this would occur if both Q1 and Q2 are OFF. Through a control input, a simple mechanism is introduced to provide such a *third state* for logic gates. This is illustrated in Figure 0-20, showing a three-state inverter with a control input. The small triangle within the symbol indicates **three-state output.**

The extra input, *E*, for *enable*, controls two diodes that alter the internal operation of the gate. Simply put, if $E = 0$, both Q1 and Q2 are prevented from turning ON, regardless of the state of the input, *A*. If $E = 1$, however, the circuit operates as before. Since the device operates *normally* when

$E = 1$, it is said to have an *active-high enable input.* This is illustrated in Table 0-17.

Table 0-17.   Operation of a Three-State Inverter with Active-High Enable

| | | Transistor | | |
|---|---|---|---|---|
| Enable (E) | Input (A) | Q1 | Q2 | Output (Z) |
| 1 | 0 | ON | OFF | 1 |
| 1 | 1 | OFF | ON | 0 |
| 0 | x | OFF | OFF | high impedance |

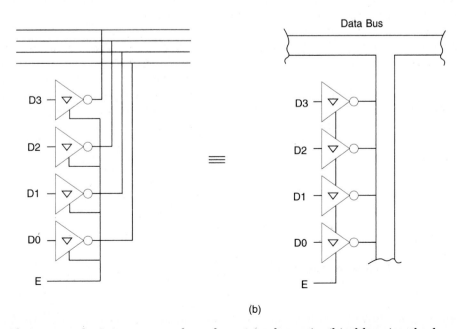

Figure 0-21.   Three-state devices connected to a bus. (a) schematic, (b) abbreviated schematic.

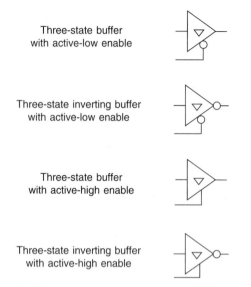

Three-state buffer
with active-low enable

Three-state inverting buffer
with active-low enable

Three-state buffer
with active-high enable

Three-state inverting buffer
with active-high enable

**Figure 0-22.   Four common types of three-state buffers.**

The last column in the table illustrates the third state. When $E = 0$, regardless of the input ($A = $ *don't care*), both transistors are OFF and the output ($Z$) is in the high impedance state, or Hi-Z state. *High impedance* refers to the high resistance path between the output and $V_{CC}$ (Q1 is OFF) *and* between the output and ground (Q2 is OFF). This is also called the *off* state.[1] If the output is connected to a bus line, the Hi-Z state allows the device to disconnect itself electrically from the bus.

---

[1] Three-state outputs are sometimes called "tri-state outputs." "Tri-state" is a registered trademark of National Semiconductor Corp.

Presumably, some other device is driving the bus lines at such times. Four three-state inverters driving a bus are shown in Figure 0-21.

Since the 4-bit data value probably originates from a single *device* (perhaps a memory), the control is a single enable line. The complete schematic in Figure 0-21a is usually abbreviated as in Figure 0-21b.

The three-state device in Figure 0-20 and Figure 0-21 is called a *three-state inverting buffer with active-high enable*. Other possibilities are shown in Figure 0-22.

**Open Collector Outputs**   The third type of output common in interfaces to computer buses is called an **open collector.** As with three-state outputs, open collector outputs allow multiple logic devices to drive the same line. An inverter with an open collector output is shown in Figure 0-23. Four common symbols are shown in Figure 0-23a and the electronic schematic is shown in Figure 0-23b.

In the schematic, the output has a pull-down transistor, Q2, but no pull-up transistor. The top terminal of the transistor—the collector—connects directly to the output $Z$, hence the term **open collector.** Since the pull-up transistor is missing, the circuit only has the capability of pulling a signal *down*—toward ground (0 volts). An external pull-up resistor is needed to pull the signal *up*—toward $V_{CC}$ (+5 volts)—when Q2 is OFF. This is illustrated in Figure 0-24, showing four open collector inverters driving a common signal, $Z$.

If any input $A$, $B$, $C$, or $D$ is high, the output $Z$ is pulled low. If all inputs are low, $Z$ is pulled high by the external pull-up resistor. Algebraically, this is

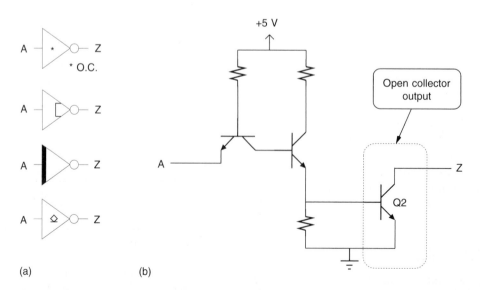

**Figure 0-23.   Inverter with an open collector output. (a) common symbols, (b) schematic.**

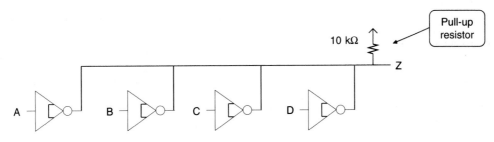

**Figure 0-24.   Four open collector inverters connected together.**

$$\overline{Z} = A + B + C + D$$

Since the logical OR function is achieved by connecting, or wiring, the outputs of the devices together, it is called a **wired-OR connection.** As noted earlier, in Table 0-12, open collector buffers are available in both the inverting and non-inverting varieties.

A common use of open collector devices is to drive the interrupt inputs on a computer bus. This is discussed in detail in Chapter 7.

## 0.5.   COMBINATIONAL LOGIC

A circuit that is built from logic gates and whose operation is characterized by a truth table is called a **combinational logic** circuit. Combinational logic is contrasted with **sequential logic** which has a clock input, making its operation dependent on current and previous conditions.

Since our purpose is to introduce topics in computer organization and the 68000 microprocessor, our treatment of this subject is not exhaustive. In the following sections we will illustrate a few types of combinational logic, including

- adders
- subtracters
- decoders

### 0.5.1. *Half Adder*

When two 1-bit numbers are added, only four possibilities exist. If the numbers are $A$ and $B$ and the outputs are $S$ (sum) and $C$ (carry), then Table 0-18 illustrates the possibilities.

A circuit to implement this truth table is called a **half adder.** As shown in Figure 0-25, only two gates are required.

### 0.5.2.   *Full Adder*

When adding multi-bit binary numbers, for each position, $n$, we need a *carry-in* bit as well as $A_n$ and

$B_n$. Consider the addition of $5_{10} + 4_{10} = 9_{10}$, as sketched out below in binary.

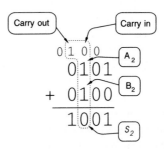

Four 1-bit additions are required. The dotted line encompasses the addition of bit #2 in the $A$ and $B$ words. In all, three bits are added: $A_2$, $B_2$, and the carry-in from bit #1. Two result bits are generated: $S_2$ and the carry-out. Since three bits are added, the eight possibilities in Table 0-19 occur.

A logic circuit to implement this truth table is called a **full adder.** A common configuration is shown in Figure 0-26a in schematic form and in Figure 0-26b in symbolic form.

### 0.5.3.   *4-bit Adder*

The addition of two 4-bit values requires four full adders. Obviously, a *carry-in* to bit #0 can never occur, so $C_i$ can be tied to ground for bit #0. *Carry-out* of bit #0, however, must propagate to $C_i$ of bit #1, and so on. The connections are shown in Figure

**Table 0-18.   Addition of Two 1-bit Numbers**

| Inputs | | Outputs | |
|---|---|---|---|
| A | B | S (sum) | C (carry) |
| 0 | 0 | 0 | 0 |
| 0 | 1 | 1 | 0 |
| 1 | 0 | 1 | 0 |
| 1 | 1 | 0 | 1 |

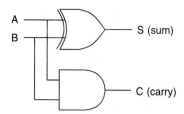

Figure 0-25.   Half adder.

0-27a and the symbolic representation of the entire circuit is shown in Figure 0-27b.

## 0.5.4.   4-bit Adder/Subtracter

As noted earlier, the 2s complement method of representing negative numbers allows for *subtraction by addition;* that is, $A - B = A + (-B)$. With a few extra gates it is possible to expand the 4-bit adder in Figure 0-27 into a 4-bit adder/subtracter. A control input selects between the *add* and *subtract* instructions. EXOR gates provide the mechanism for doing so, as illustrated in Figure 0-28.

The control input allows an input variable to pass through *as is* or inverted. This is precisely what is needed for an adder/subtracter. For addition, the addend is left as is ($B \oplus 0 = B$); and for subtraction, the addend is transformed into its 2s complement. EXOR gates transform the addend into its 1s complement form ($B \oplus 1 = \overline{B}$) and a final +1 is achieved through the unused *carry-in* of bit #0. The complete design is illustrated in Figure 0-29.

Table 0-19.   Addition of Two 1-bit Numbers with Carry-In

| Inputs | | | Outputs | |
| --- | --- | --- | --- | --- |
| $A_n$ | $B_n$ | Carry-In | $S_n$ | Carry-Out |
| 0 | 0 | 0 | 0 | 0 |
| 0 | 0 | 1 | 1 | 0 |
| 0 | 1 | 0 | 1 | 0 |
| 0 | 1 | 1 | 0 | 1 |
| 1 | 0 | 0 | 1 | 0 |
| 1 | 0 | 1 | 0 | 1 |
| 1 | 1 | 0 | 0 | 1 |
| 1 | 1 | 1 | 1 | 1 |

The control input is appropriately labeled $\overline{ADD}$/SUBTRACT to imply its operation. When $\overline{ADD}$/SUBTRACT = 0, $C_i = 0$ and $B$ passes through the EXOR gates unchanged; so, the operation is add: $A + B$. When $\overline{ADD}$/SUBTRACT = 1, $C_i = 1$ and each bit of $B$ is complemented; so, the operation is subtract: $A + (-B)$.

Before proceeding, there are a few general implications of the ideas just presented. We can think of the control input in Figure 0-29 as a 1-bit **instruction word,** selecting 1 of $2^1 = 2$ instructions. A 2-bit instruction word could select 1 of $2^2 = 4$ instructions, and so on. In support of this idea, the logic in Figure 0-29 could expand to implement many more instructions (multiply, divide, increment, OR, AND, etc.). Such a circuit is called an **arithmetic and logic unit (ALU).** If an ALU implements $n$ instructions the instruction code must be $\log_2 n$ bits. For example, a microprocessor with 256 instructions requires $\log_2 256 = 8$ bits for its

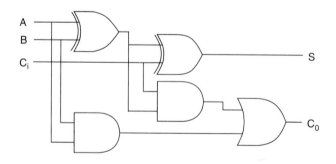

(a)

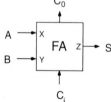

(b)

Figure 0-26.   Full adder. (a) schematic, (b) symbol.

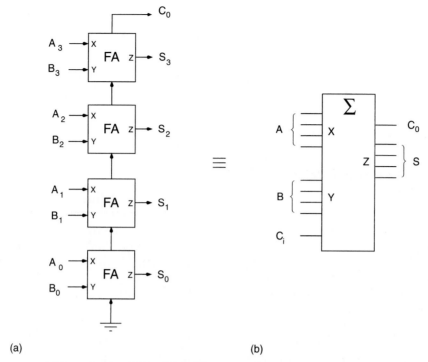

Figure 0-27.   Four-bit adder. (a) schematic, (b) symbol.

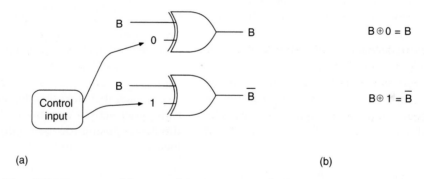

Figure 0-28.   EXOR gates with control input. (a) symbols, (b) Boolean equations.

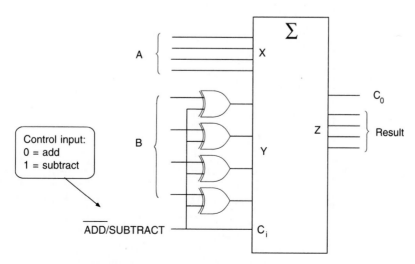

Figure 0-29.   Four-bit adder/subtracter.

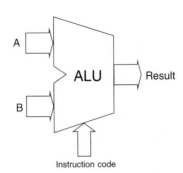

Figure 0-30.   Generalized ALU.

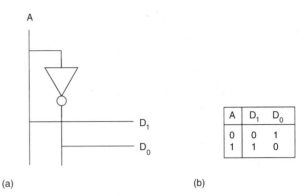

(a)                                     (b)

Figure 0-31.   1-line to 2-line decoder. (a) circuit,

instruction code. The general idea is shown in Figure 0-30.

## 0.5.5.   Decoders

One of the most common logic operations is selecting from 1 of $2^n$ choices given an $n$-bit binary code. A combinational logic circuit that performs this function is called a **decoder**. At the very least, a decoder has $n$ inputs and $2^n$ outputs. The idea is that the input represents an address, and one output *activates,* or *selects* that address, while the other outputs are *deselected,* or *inactive.*

For the trivial case of $n = 1$, the decoder has 1 input and $2^1 = 2$ outputs. The circuit and truth table are shown in Figure 0-31.

For $n = 2$, the decoder has 2 inputs and $2^2 = 4$ outputs (see Figure 0-32).

An example of a 3-line to 8-line decoder is the 74LS138. It is further characterized by having active-low outputs and three enable inputs. The 74LS138 is shown in Figure 0-33a (symbol) and Figure 0-33b (truth table).

The first three rows in the truth table (Figure 0-33b) illustrate the enable function. If any of the three enable inputs is inactive, the device is *disabled* and all outputs remain inactive (high). If all three enable inputs are active (last eight rows in the truth table), then the device operates as expected. The three address inputs—C, B, and A—determine which output goes active; the other seven outputs are inactive.

**Opcode Decoding within a CPU**   There are numerous applications of decoders. One was hinted at earlier. If a computer has an $n$-bit instruction word, then an $n$-line to $2^n$-line decoder is needed to identify the current instruction. This is illustrated in Figure 0-34 for a hypothetical 8-bit computer.

For each instruction code, one output of the decoder goes active. The decoded outputs connect to the ALU, causing the instruction to execute via the logic circuitry within the ALU.

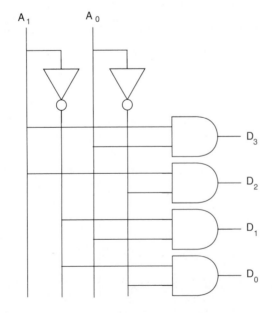

(a)                                     (b)

Figure 0-32.   2-line to 4-line decoder. (a) circuit, (b) truth table.

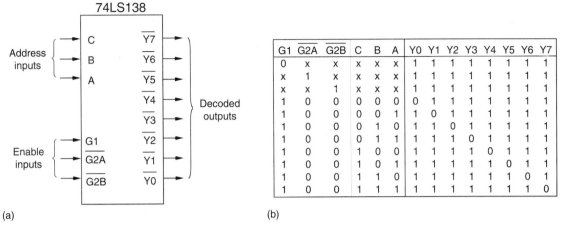

Figure 0-33.   The 74LS138 3-line to 8-line decoder. (a) symbol, (b) truth table.

| G1 | $\overline{G2A}$ | $\overline{G2B}$ | C | B | A | Y0 | Y1 | Y2 | Y3 | Y4 | Y5 | Y6 | Y7 |
|----|------|------|---|---|---|----|----|----|----|----|----|----|----|
| 0 | x | x | x | x | x | 1 | 1 | 1 | 1 | 1 | 1 | 1 | 1 |
| x | 1 | x | x | x | x | 1 | 1 | 1 | 1 | 1 | 1 | 1 | 1 |
| x | x | 1 | x | x | x | 1 | 1 | 1 | 1 | 1 | 1 | 1 | 1 |
| 1 | 0 | 0 | 0 | 0 | 0 | 0 | 1 | 1 | 1 | 1 | 1 | 1 | 1 |
| 1 | 0 | 0 | 0 | 0 | 1 | 1 | 0 | 1 | 1 | 1 | 1 | 1 | 1 |
| 1 | 0 | 0 | 0 | 1 | 0 | 1 | 1 | 0 | 1 | 1 | 1 | 1 | 1 |
| 1 | 0 | 0 | 0 | 1 | 1 | 1 | 1 | 1 | 0 | 1 | 1 | 1 | 1 |
| 1 | 0 | 0 | 1 | 0 | 0 | 1 | 1 | 1 | 1 | 0 | 1 | 1 | 1 |
| 1 | 0 | 0 | 1 | 0 | 1 | 1 | 1 | 1 | 1 | 1 | 0 | 1 | 1 |
| 1 | 0 | 0 | 1 | 1 | 0 | 1 | 1 | 1 | 1 | 1 | 1 | 0 | 1 |
| 1 | 0 | 0 | 1 | 1 | 1 | 1 | 1 | 1 | 1 | 1 | 1 | 1 | 0 |

**Address Decoding**  Usually the decoding of an instruction code occurs within the internal circuitry of a microprocessor IC or other processing unit. An example where decoder ICs, such as the 74LS138, are frequently used is interfacing memory ICs to a microprocessor. Although we defer detailed discussions of memory addressing to Chapter 1, the following brief example illustrates a common application of decoders. In Figure 0-35, an interface is shown between two RAMs and a typical 8-bit central processing unit (CPU), such as the 6800 8-bit microprocessor.

The interface uses a 74LS139—a 2-line to 4-line decoder with active-low enable and active-low outputs. The CPU, as shown, has an 8-bit data bus, a 16-bit address bus, and two control signals (E for enable, and $R/\overline{W}$ for read/write). The upper two bits of the CPU's address bus (A15 & A14) are attached to the address inputs of the decoder. The lower 14 bits are attached to the RAMs' address inputs (A0–A13). The $\overline{0}$ and $\overline{1}$ outputs of the decoder attach to the RAMs' chip select ($\overline{CS}$) inputs. The RAM selected by $\overline{0}$ is selected when A15 = 0 and A14 = 0. The RAM selected by $\overline{1}$ is selected when A15 = 0 and A14 = 1. The $\overline{2}$ and $\overline{3}$ outputs of the decoder are available for memory expansion. Each decoder output is active when the CPU accesses an address within a range of addresses. Figure 0-36 illustrates the decomposition of the CPU's address for this example.

The range of addresses selected for each decoder output is identified in Table 0-20.

Any memory read cycle or memory write cycle to an address in the range $0000_{16}$ to $3FFF_{16}$ will access the RAM on the left in Figure 0-35 (selected by the decoder's $\overline{0}$ output). Similarly, the RAM on the right is selected only when the CPU accesses an address in the range $4000_{16}$ to $7FFF_{16}$.

The CPU's control signal E (enable) is a synchronizing clock that connects (via an inverter) to the decoder's active-low enable input. This control signal is only activated by the CPU when a valid and stable address is on the address bus, thus preventing *spurious selections* that might otherwise occur when the address changes.

There are numerous other topics in combinational logic that we will not pursue at the present time. The concepts treated above will enter into discussions later in this text.

## 0.6.   SEQUENTIAL LOGIC

A logic circuit whose operation is determined by a synchronizing clock pulse is called a **sequential logic** circuit. The operation of a sequential circuit is described by a **function table** (as opposed to a truth table). As with combinational logic, our

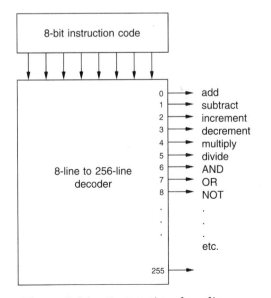

Figure 0-34.   Instruction decoding.

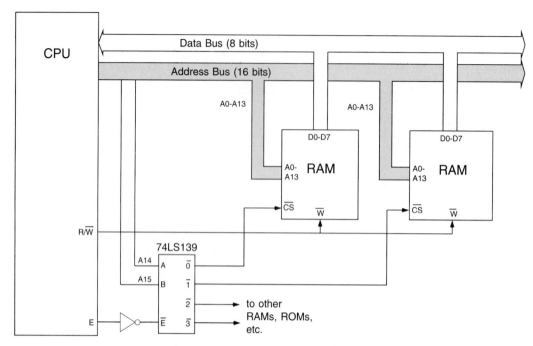

Figure 0-35.    Interface between RAMs and a CPU.

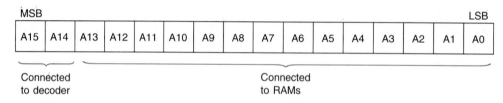

Figure 0-36.    Address decomposition for decoder example.

treatment of sequential logic is brief. The goal is to familiarize the reader with a few simple concepts in sequential logic that resurface later in this text. These include

- flip flops, or latches
- registers

## 0.6.1.   *Flip Flops*

A logic cell capable of maintaining a state after inputs change is called a **flip flop,** or **latch.** Since *maintaining a state* is like *remembering,* a flip flop is also a **memory cell.**

There are several varieties of flip flops, the most basic of which is the **SR latch** (see Figure 0-37).

The SR latch has two inputs—S for *set* and R for *reset*—and two outputs—Q and its complement $\overline{Q}$.

The phrase *the flip flop is set* implies that Q = 1. Conversely, the phrase *the flip flop is reset* implies Q = 0. By definition, Q and $\overline{Q}$ are the complement of one another. The usual state of S and R is inactive, or 0. When S is activated (1), the flip flop becomes set. When S returns to the inactive state (0), the flip remains set. This is the fundamental characteristic of a flip flop: the ability to remember, or retain, its state. When R is activated (1), the flip flop will be reset. It will remain reset after R returns to the inactive state, until such time that the S input is again activated. The condition S = R = 1 is not allowed because Q and $\overline{Q}$ are both set.

The description above is extremely brief; however, it is sufficient to understand the operation of the SR latch. The reader is invited to verify this through a timing diagram. Use a pencil and eraser

Table 0-20.    Address Ranges for Decoder Outputs

| Decoder Inputs | | Active | | Hexadecimal |
|---|---|---|---|---|
| A15 | A14 | Output | Binary Address | Address |
| 0 | 0 | $\overline{0}$ | 00xx xxxx xxxx xxxx | 0000 - 3FFF |
| 0 | 1 | $\overline{1}$ | 01xx xxxx xxxx xxxx | 4000 - 7FFF |
| 1 | 0 | $\overline{2}$ | 10xx xxxx xxxx xxxx | 8000 - BFFF |
| 1 | 1 | $\overline{3}$ | 11xx xxxx xxxx xxxx | C000 - FFFF |

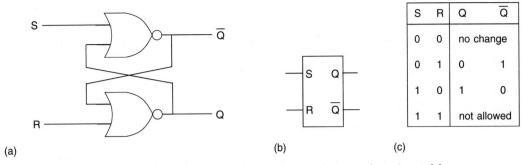

Figure 0-37. SR latch. (a) circuit, (b) symbol, (c) function table.

| S | R | Q | $\overline{Q}$ |
|---|---|---|---|
| 0 | 0 | no change | |
| 0 | 1 | 0 | 1 |
| 1 | 0 | 1 | 0 |
| 1 | 1 | not allowed | |

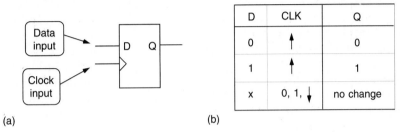

Figure 0-38. Type-D latch. (a) symbol, (b) function table.

| D | CLK | Q |
|---|---|---|
| 0 | ↑ | 0 |
| 1 | ↑ | 1 |
| x | 0, 1, ↓ | no change |

to mark signal levels on the schematic and work the device through its paces.

Another important type of flip flop is the **type-D latch** (see Figure 0-38).

The *up-arrow* symbol in the function table represents a 0-to-1, or positive-edge, transition on the clock input, while *down-arrow* represents a 1-to-0, or negative-edge, transition. The *arrow head* at the clock input (Figure 0-38a) implies that the clock input is positive-edge triggered. (If a bubble also appears, it is negative-edge triggered.) Note that

for a steady-state 0 or 1 on the clock input, no change occurs at the Q output (last row in the table). The clocking of data into the latch is shown in the first two rows. For example, if D = 0 when a positive-edge occurs on CLK, a 0 is clocked into the latch and appears at Q.

### 0.6.2. Registers

One of the most common uses of flip flops—particularly the type-D—is to hold a data value. If the

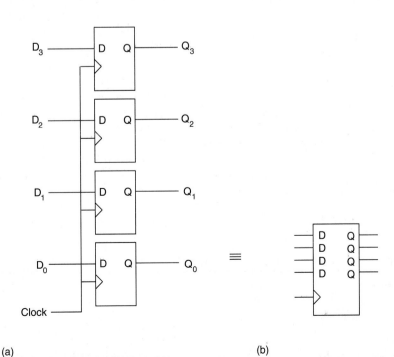

Figure 0-39. 4-bit data register. (a) flip flops, (b) symbol.

data value is, say, a byte, then eight type-D latches are needed. Since the entire data value is stored in a single operation, only one clock input is needed. This is illustrated in Figure 0-39a for a 4-bit latch, or register. The usual symbol for a 4-bit register is shown in Figure 0-39b.

An example of a common latch is the 74LS374 octal (8-bit) latch with three-state outputs (see Figure 0-40).

## 0.7. SEMICONDUCTOR MEMORY DEVICES

The flip flop is the basic element in semiconductor memory devices. Figure 0-41 shows a memory cell made from an SR latch.

A few extra gates are added for selecting the cell and reading from or writing to the cell. Each of the cell's three functions is described briefly below.

Deselect    When Row Select is held low (1st row in function table), both AND outputs driving the latch inputs are low. This prevents the latch from being set or reset. Data cannot be written into the latch. Furthermore, a low on Row Select keeps the Data Out line low. Data cannot be read from the latch.

Write    Assuming the cell is selected (Row Select = 1), if Read/Write = 0 a write cycle is in effect. The value on Data In (1/0) will present a high either on S (Data In = 1) or on R (Data In = 0) and the latch is set or reset accordingly. However, a low on Read/Write keeps Data Out low.

Read    Assuming the cell is selected (Row Select = 1), if Read/Write = 1 a read cycle is in effect. The inverted state of Read/Write is presented to the AND gates at the inputs of the SR latch. The effect is to ensure S = R = 0, thus the latch state cannot change. However, the high presented to the AND gate driving Data Out (in conjunction with Row Select = 1), allows the state of the latch (Q) to pass through to the Data Out line.

### 0.7.1. RAM

A memory IC containing cells similar to that in Figure 0-41 is called a **static RAM (SRAM).** *RAM* is for random access memory. RAMs contain thousands, even millions, of cells. The mechanism for combining cells into a complete RAM IC is presented in Figure 0-42 for a 16-bit static RAM.

Once again, we see a decoder in a very important role: selecting rows of RAM cells. Of

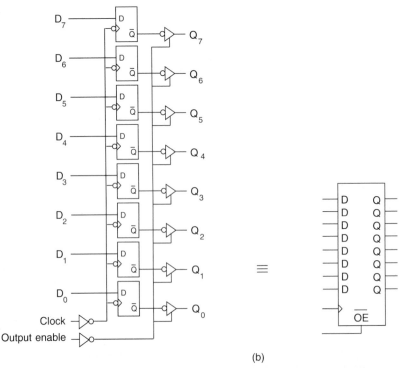

(a)                                                    (b)

**Figure 0-40.** 74LS374 octal latch with three-state outputs. (a) schematic, (b) symbol.

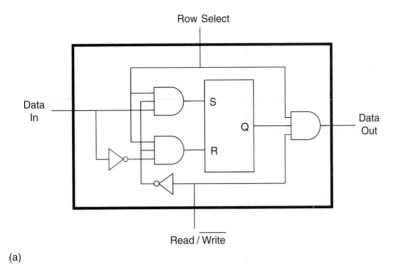

(a)

(b)

| Row Select | Read/ Write | Data In | Q | Data Out | Function |
|---|---|---|---|---|---|
| 0 | x | x | x | 0 | deselect |
| 1 | 0 | 1/0 | 1/0 | 0 | write |
| 1 | 1 | x | 1/0 | 1/0 | read |

Figure 0-41. Memory cell made from an **SR** latch. (a) schematic, (b) function table.

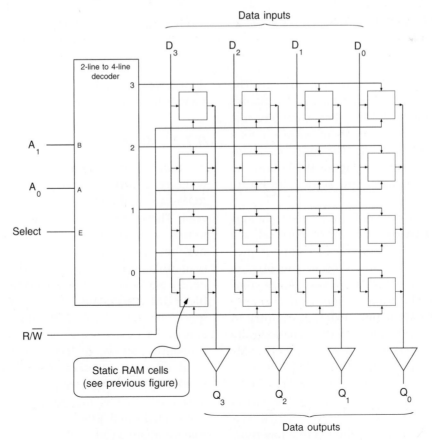

Figure 0-42. Static **RAM IC**.

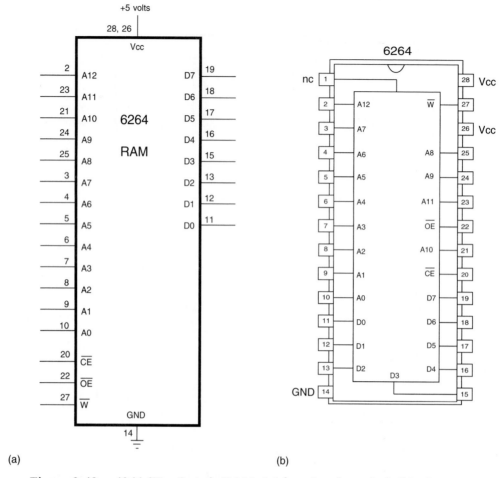

Figure 0-43.   6264 8K × 8 static RAM. (a) functional symbol, (b) pinouts.

course, 16 bits of RAM doesn't go very far. The structure of the RAM cell in Figure 0-42 extends easily to very large RAMs. For example, the 6264 SRAM contains 8K bytes of RAM—a total of $8 \times 2^{10} \times 8 = 65,536$ cells. The functional symbol for this IC is shown in Figure 0-43a and the pin connections (pinouts) are shown in Figure 0-43b.

Another common type of RAM device is the **dynamic RAM (DRAM).** In a DRAM, each cell is a capacitor that stores a 1 or 0 as a charge or no-charge. Only one transistor is needed to provide access to the cell, so DRAMs are very dense compared to SRAMs which require four or five transistors per cell. DRAMs require external circuitry to refresh (i.e., recharge) the capacitors periodically to prevent loss of data. On a per-bit basis, DRAMs are less expensive than SRAMs; however they are more difficult to design into a system because of the additional circuitry needed to support refresh cycles. Generally, SRAMs are used when a system's RAM requirements are limited to a few hun-

dred kilobytes or less. Larger systems with many megabytes of RAM use DRAMs.

## 0.7.2.   ROM

Another important type of semiconductor memory is the **read-only memory (ROM).** Unlike RAMs, ROMs are written *once* and thereafter can only be read. There are many varieties of ROM, differing mostly in how they are written and whether or not they can be rewritten. A **factory-mask ROM** is manufactured with a special mask that permanently places a 1 or 0 in each cell. A **programmable ROM (PROM)** is user programmable through special hardware. Variations exist that permit data erasure by exposing the device to ultraviolet light **(erasable PROM, EPROM)** or by a special electrical erase cycle **(electrically erasable PROM, EEPROM).** EPROMs are particularly popular since they are reusable, inexpensive, and easy to program. PC-hosted EPROM programmers are available for about $150.

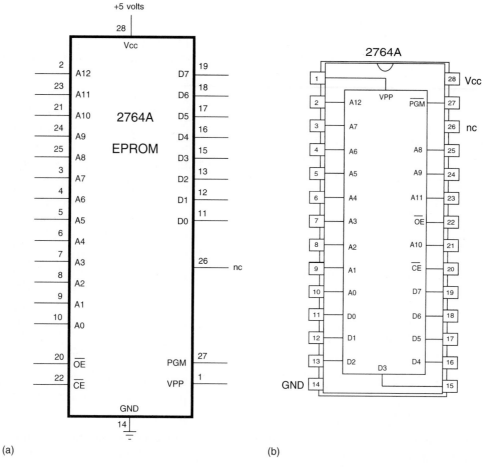

Figure 0-44.  2764A 8K byte EPROM. (a) functional symbol, (b) pinouts.

EPROMs (and other ROMs) are most commonly used to store programs that must be accessed frequently in computer systems. These include, for example, input/output subroutines or the bootstrap loader that loads the first track from disk into RAM. The use of an EPROM in the latter case is essential because the bootstrap program must be present in memory when the system is powered-on. Obviously RAMs cannot serve this purpose since they are volatile and lose their content when power is removed. The term **firmware** has evolved with reference to software stored in EPROM (or other ROMs).

One of the most popular ROMs is the 2764A 8K × 8 EPROM. The functional symbol is given in Figure 0-44a and the pinouts in Figure 0-44b.

This concludes our brief tour through the foundations of computer organization. In Chapter 1 the architecture of microcomputers and microprocessors is introduced.

## 0.8.  QUESTIONS

1.  Perform the following conversions:

| FROM | TO |
| --- | --- |
| 5-bit Signed Binary 10110 | Decimal |
| BCD 0010010011 | Decimal |
| Fixed Point Binary 10101.0101 | Decimal |
| Binary 111101011011 | Hexadecimal |
| Binary 111101011011 | Octal |
| Hexadecimal FEA | Binary |
| Hexadecimal C57 | Decimal |
| ASCII Code 110000 | ASCII Character |
| Decimal Integer -21 | 8-bit Signed Binary |
| Decimal Real 19.0125 | Fixed Point Binary |

2. What is the range of numbers that can be represented in 5-bit signed (2s C) notation?

3. What is the range of numbers that can be represented in 7-bit unsigned notation?

4. What is the range of numbers that can be represented in 14-bit signed (2s C) notation?

5. What decimal value is represented by the binary code 1100110? There are at least two answers to this question. Explain why.

6. Convert the number −27 to an 8-bit signed (2s C) number.

7. Convert the number −27 to a 10-bit signed (2s C) number.

8. If we assume the use of a 10-bit 2s complement representation, what is the maximum number that can be added to $0000011110_2$? Give your answer in binary and decimal.

9. If we assume a 10-bit unsigned representation, what is the maximum number that can be added to $0000011110_2$? Give your answer in binary and decimal.

10. What is the minimum number of bits required to represent the decimal number 5000 in unsigned binary?

11. What is the minimum number of bits required to represent the decimal number 50,000 in signed (2s C) binary?

12. Design a circuit with two switches (similar to Figure 0-3) that implements the EXOR function.

13. With reference to Figure 0-2, what standard value of resistor will set the LED operating current to 10 mA maximum? (Note: Standard resistor values begin with 10, 12, 15, 18, 22, 27, 33, 39, 47, 56, 68, or 82; e.g., 820 Ω, 8200 Ω.)

14. Illustrate how to implement a 2-input EXNOR function using 2-input NOR gates.

15. Illustrate how to implement a 2-input EXOR function with four 2-input NAND gates.

16. Construct sentences that describe the operation of the circuits in Figure 0-3 and Figure 0-4. Construct two sentences for each by using DeMorgan's theorem.

17. Illustrate two ways to draw the symbol for a 3-input AND function.

18. Figure 0-11 illustrates one way to implement the inverter function with a NAND gate. What is another?

19. Illustrate the universality of the NOR gate by implementing the NOT, OR, NAND, and AND functions with 2-input NOR gates only.

20. Complete the timing diagram for the logic circuit shown in Figure 0-45.

21. Simplify the following Boolean equations:

   (a) $Z = A \bullet B \bullet C + \overline{A} \bullet B + A \bullet B \bullet \overline{C}$

   (b) $Z = A \bullet B + A \bullet (D \bullet C + D \bullet \overline{C})$

   (c) $Z = \overline{A} \bullet B \bullet C + A \bullet C$

22. Construct a truth table for the 74LS139 (see Figure 0-35). Also, for each output give the Boolean equation describing its operation.

23. A certain static RAM has a capacity of 32K bytes of data.

   (a) How many 1-bit cells are in this IC?

   (b) How many address lines are on this IC? (Assume the device has 8 data lines.)

24. What is firmware?

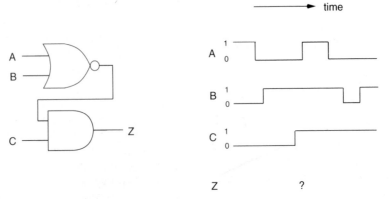

Figure 0-45. Circuit for question 20.

# 1. Microcomputer Concepts

## 1.1. INTRODUCTION

In this chapter, general concepts and terminology in computer organization are introduced. To begin, we define some important terms.

**Computer architecture** is defined as the attributes and behavior of a computer as seen by a machine language programmer. This definition includes the instruction set, instruction formats, operation codes, addressing modes, and all registers and memory locations that may be directly manipulated by a machine language programmer.[1]

Computer architecture is contrasted with an **implementation,** which is defined as the hardware structure, logic design, and data-path organization of a particular embodiment of the architecture. An architecture may have many implementations, while an implementation is a realization of an architecture. In general, an implementation will have a much shorter life cycle than an architecture.

**Computer organization** is the hardware and software characteristics of complete computer systems, encompassing computer architectures and their implementations, as well as the interface circuitry, devices, and components peripheral to the CPU. The latter include random access memory (RAM), read-only memory (ROM), and other semiconductor technologies, as well as input/output devices such as video display terminals (VDTs), printers, or magnetic and optical disks. Obviously, the study of computer organization sets out very ambitious goals.

A **computer** is a functional unit capable of (a) being programmed to operate on data without human intervention, and (b) storing and retrieving data.

A **central processing unit** (CPU) is a functional unit that interprets and executes instructions.

A **microprocessor** is a CPU packaged in a single integrated circuit (IC).

A **computer system** is a computer, complete with CPU, memory, peripheral devices, and programs.

A **microcomputer** is a computer system with a microprocessor as the CPU.

## 1.2. BLOCK DIAGRAM OF A MICROCOMPUTER

To explore computer systems in more detail, Figure 1-1 shows the functional blocks of a typical microcomputer.

The absence of detail in the figure is deliberate, making it representative of most computer systems. As shown, a computer system contains a CPU connected to RAM, ROM, interface circuitry, and peripheral devices. The connections are via three *buses:* an address bus, a data bus, and a control bus. Let's discuss this block diagram in detail.

### 1.2.1. The Central Processing Unit (CPU)

The CPU is the main component of a microcomputer. Through a complex weave of logic circuits, its primary purpose is to perform two fundamental operations: fetching instructions and executing instructions. The CPU has the ability to decode and execute instructions based on a set of binary codes, each with the ability to perform a simple operation. These instructions are usually arithmetic (add, subtract, multiply, divide), logic (AND, OR, NOT, etc.), data movement, or branch operations, and are represented by a set of binary codes called the **instruction set.**

Figure 1-2 is an extremely simplified view of the inside of a CPU. It shows a set of registers for the temporary storage of information, an **arithmetic and logic unit** (ALU) for performing operations on this information, and an **instruction decode and control unit** that determines the operation to perform and sets in motion the necessary actions to perform it. Two additional registers are shown. The **instruction register** (IR) holds the binary code for each instruction as it is executed, and the **program counter** (PC) holds the memory address of the next instruction to be executed.

[1]This definition is from R. L. Sites, 1993, *Communications of the ACM,* Vol. 36, No. 2, p. 33.

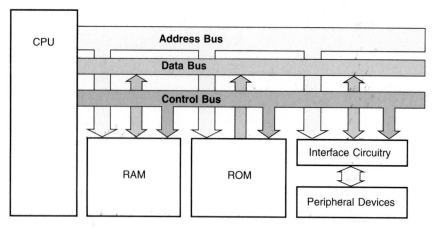

Figure 1-1.   Microcomputer block diagram.

***Opcode Fetch*** Fetching an instruction from the system RAM is one of the most fundamental operations performed by a CPU. This is called an **opcode fetch.** The following steps are required:

1. The content of the program counter is placed on the address bus.
2. A READ control signal is activated.
3a. Data (the instruction opcode) are read from RAM and placed on the data bus.
3b. The program counter is incremented to prepare for the next fetch from memory.
4. The opcode is latched into the CPU's internal instruction register.

Figure 1-3 illustrates the flow of information for an opcode fetch.

Note in step 1, the content of the program counter is copied to a special latch (not shown) which drives the address bus. Incrementing the program counter, identified by step 3b, occurs in parallel with the opcode fetch. This speeds up memory accesses if a second instruction word is read immediately after the opcode fetch. It also means that the program counter is already incremented when the instruction word is read; so PC-relative addressing must use an offset from the location *after* the current instruction.

The execution stage involves decoding (or deciphering) the opcode and generating control signals to gate internal registers in and out of the ALU and to signal the ALU to perform the specified operation. Due to the wide variety of possible operations, this explanation is very limited. It applies to a simple operation such as *increment register.* More complex instructions require more steps, such as reading additional words as data for the operation.

A series of instructions combined to perform a meaningful task is called a **program,** or **software,** and herein lies the real mystique. The degree to which tasks are efficiently and correctly carried out

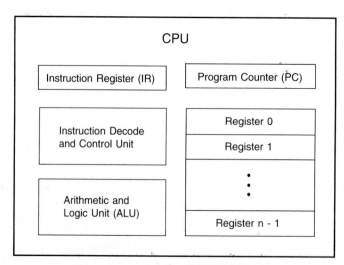

Figure 1-2.   CPU functional units.

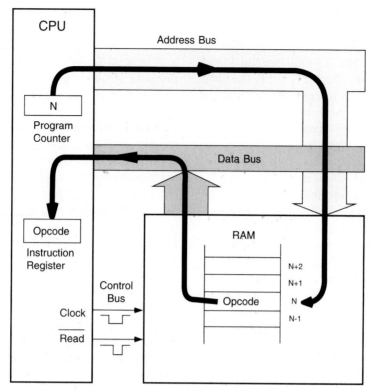

Figure 1-3.   Opcode fetch.

is determined for the most part by the quality of software, rather than by the sophistication of the CPU. Programs, then, *drive* the CPU, and in doing so they occasionally go amiss, mimicking the frailties of their authors. Phrases such as *The computer made a mistake!* are misleading. Although equipment breakdowns are inevitable, mistakes in results usually follow from poor programs.

## 1.2.2.   *Semiconductor Memory*: RAM *and* ROM

Programs and data are stored in memory. The variations of computer memory are so vast, their accompanying terms so plentiful, and technology breakthroughs so frequent, that extensive and continual study is required to keep abreast of the latest developments. The memory devices directly accessible by the CPU consist of semiconductor ICs called RAM and ROM. These are often called **main memory.**

**Random access memory (RAM)** is semiconductor memory capable of being read or written via software. RAM is **volatile,** meaning its contents are lost when power is removed from the device. RAM is *random access* since the time to retrieve data is independent of the location of the data (contrast with sequential memory, such as

magnetic tape, where each location is accessed following the previous location).

**Read-only memory (ROM)** is semiconductor memory that can be read, but not written. ROMs are programmed once (with the assistance of hardware) and maintain data thereafter, even in the absence of power. ROMs are **non-volatile.**

Most computer systems have a disk drive and a small amount of ROM, just enough to hold the short but frequently used software routines for input/output operations. User programs and data are stored on disk and are loaded into RAM for execution. With the continual drop in the per-byte cost of RAM, today's small computer systems often contain millions of locations of RAM.

The digital organization of RAMs was presented in the previous chapter.

## 1.2.3.   *The Buses*: *Address, Data, and Control*

A **bus** is a collection of wires with a common purpose. Access to the circuitry around the CPU is provided by three buses: the **address bus,** the **data bus,** and the **control bus.**

*Address Bus*   For each read or write operation, the CPU specifies the location by placing an address on the address bus, and then activates a signal on the control bus indicating whether the operation is a read or a write. Read operations retrieve a byte of data from memory at the location specified and place it on the data bus. The CPU reads the data and latches it in one of its internal registers. For a write operation, the CPU outputs data on the data bus. Because of the control signal, memory recognizes the operation as a write cycle and stores the data in the location specified.

Most small microcomputers have 16 or 20 address lines. Given $n$ address lines, each with the possibility of being high (1) or low (0), $2^n$ locations can be accessed. A 16-bit address, therefore, can access $2^{16} = 65,536$ locations, and a 20-bit address bus can access $2^{20} = 1,048,576$ locations. The abbreviation $K$ (for kilo) stands for $2^{10} = 1024$, therefore 16 bits can address $2^6 \times 2^{10} = 64K$ locations, while 20 bits can address 1024K (or 1 Meg) locations.

***Data Bus***   The data bus carries information between the CPU and memory or I/O devices. Extensive research has investigated the sort of activities that consume a computer's valuable execution time. Evidently computers expend up to two-thirds of their time simply moving data. Since the majority of move operations are between a CPU register and external RAM or ROM, the number of lines (the *width*) on the data bus is important for overall performance. This limitation-by-width is a bottleneck: There may be vast amounts of memory on the system, and the CPU may possess tremendous computational power, but access to the data—data movement between the memory and CPU via the data bus—is bottlenecked by the width of the data bus.

This trait is so important it has become common to add a prefix indicating the extent of this bottleneck. The phrase *16-bit computer* refers to a computer with 16 lines on its data bus.[2] Most computers fit the 4-bit, 8-bit, 16-bit, or 32-bit classification, with overall computing power increasing as the width of the data bus increases.

Note that the data bus in Figure 1-1 is bidirectional and the address bus is unidirectional. Address information is always supplied by the CPU (as indicated by the arrow in Figure 1-1), yet data may travel in either direction depending on whether a read or write operation is intended.

Address information is sometimes also provided by direct memory access (DMA) circuitry, as discussed in Chapter 7. Note also that the term *data* is used in a general sense: The *information* that travels on the data bus may be instructions of a program or data used by the program.

***Control Bus***   The control bus is a hodgepodge of signals, each having a specific role in the orderly control of system activity. As a rule, control signals are timing signals supplied by the CPU to external circuitry to synchronize the movement of information on the address and data buses. Although there are usually three signals, such as CLOCK, READ, and WRITE, for basic data movement between the CPU and memory, the names and operation of these signals are highly dependent on the specific CPU. The manufacturer's data sheets must be consulted for details.

The control bus also contains signals for system reset, hardware interrupts, bus errors, and DMA request/acknowledge handshaking. Specific details of these are provided in later chapters as necessary.

### 1.2.4.  *Peripheral Devices*

Input/output devices, or computer *peripherals,* provide the path for communications between the computer system and the *real world*. Without these, computer systems would be rather introverted machines, of little use to the people who use them. Three classes of I/O devices are **mass storage, human interface,** and **control/monitor.**

***Mass-Storage Devices***   Like semiconductor RAMs and ROMs, mass-storage devices are forms of memory technology—constantly growing, ever improving. As the name suggests, they hold large quantities of information (programs or data) that cannot fit into the computer's relatively small RAM or main memory. This information must be loaded into main memory before the CPU accesses it. Classified according to ease of access, mass-storage devices are either online or archival. Online storage, also called secondary memory, is available to the CPU without human intervention upon the request of a program, and archival storage holds data that are rarely needed and require manual loading onto the system. Archival storage is usually on magnetic tapes or disks, while online storage is on magnetic disk.

***Human Interface Devices***   The union of man and machine is realized by a multitude of human interface devices, the most common being the video

---

[2]There is by no means universal agreement with this phrase. Many implementations have a data bus that is narrower (e.g., 8 bits) than the registers inside the CPU (e.g., 16 bits). The phrase "pseudo 16-bit computer" is sometimes used in these instances.

display terminal (VDT) and printer. VDTs are really two devices, combining a keyboard for input and a CRT (cathode-ray tube) for output. An entire field of engineering called ergonomics or human factors has evolved from the necessity to design these peripherals (and other machines or equipment) with humans in mind, the goal being the safe, comfortable, and efficient mating of the characteristics of people with the machines they use. Indeed, there are more manufacturers of peripheral devices than computers. For most computer systems, there are at least three of these devices: a keyboard, CRT, and printer. Other human interface devices include the joystick, light pen, mouse, microphone, or loudspeaker.

***Control/Monitor Devices***  By way of control/monitor devices (and some meticulously designed interface electronics and software), computers are given the ability to perform myriad control-oriented tasks, and perform them unceasingly, without fatigue, far beyond the capabilities of humans. Applications such as temperature control of a building, home security, elevator control, home appliance control, and even welding parts of an automobile, are all made possible using these devices.

Control devices are outputs, or **actuators,** that affect the world around them when supplied with a voltage or current (e.g., motors, relays, and lights). Monitoring devices are inputs, or **sensors,** that are stimulated by heat, light, pressure, motion, and so on, and convert this to a voltage or current read by the computer (e.g., phototransistors, thermistors, and switches). The interface circuitry converts the voltage or current to binary data, or vice versa, and through software an orderly relationship between inputs and outputs is established.

A critical component in the interface to many control/monitor devices is the digital-to-analog converter (DAC) or the analog-to-digital converter (ADC). A DAC receives a binary word from the computer (e.g., 1001011) and translates it to an analog voltage (e.g., 5.439 volts) for controlling an output device. An ADC performs a similar but reverse operation.

## 1.3.  MEMORY ORGANIZATION AND HIERARCHY

Two very different kinds of memory were mentioned earlier: semiconductor memory and mass-storage memory. It is important to develop a strong understanding of the relationship between these and other types of memory and the terminology that accompanies them. Figure 1-4 is a hierarchical memory tree, categorizing the different forms of computer memory by technology. The figure is not exhaustive, but it covers the most common types of memory. The different

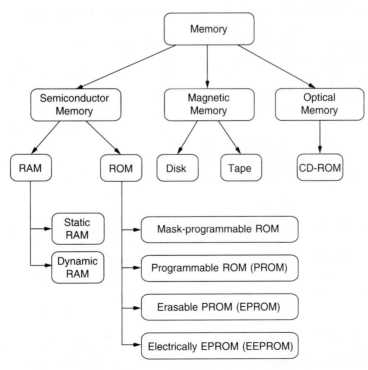

Figure 1-4.  Memory classification by technology.

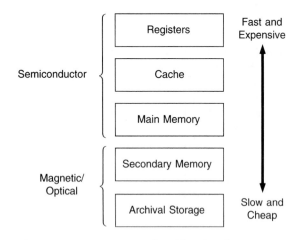

**Figure 1-5.   Memory classification by access.**

types of RAM and ROM were discussed in Chapter 0.

Figure 1-5 shows a different perspective, categorizing memory by how it is accessed in a computer system. The figure is ordered from fast and expensive memory at the top to slow and cheap memory at the bottom. The internal registers directly accessible by the CPU are, of course, the fastest type of memory because they are accessible without using the system's buses. Cache is a type of memory used on advanced microprocessors such as the 68040 or 80486. It is a high-speed RAM which is tightly linked to the CPU for fast access. During program execution, blocks of program and data memory are read from main memory into cache memory. The block transfers occur at very high rates and subsequent accesses use the cache memory to achieve the highest possible execution speed. Main memory is the semiconductor memory connected to the system's buses. Secondary and archival memory are magnetic disks, magnetic tapes, or optical disks, as noted earlier.

If we cross memory technology with memory access, Table 1-1 emerges. It shows which technologies are implemented for each access method

identified in Figure 1-5. It is easy to find exceptions to the table. However, the general idea of relating technology to access is important. An interesting intersection is between main memory and magnetic-disk technology. Virtual memory is a scheme whereby a system is given a very large virtual address space—much larger than the physical address bus permits. The virtual space extends into the system's disk storage. When an instruction fetch or a data reference occurs to a virtual address for which no mapping exists to physical memory, the reference is temporarily suspended. The required block of memory is transferred from disk to main memory and the mapping is updated. The memory reference resumes and program execution continues.

## 1.4.   THE MEMORY MAP

Typical 8-bit microprocessors, such as the Intel 8085 or Motorola 6802, have a 16-bit address bus and an 8-bit data bus. This defines a memory space of $2^{16} = 2^6 \times 2^{10} = 64K$ addresses with each address storing an 8-bit value. The memory space accessible by the CPU via the address bus is often depicted in a **memory map.** Within the memory space, regions may contain RAM, ROM, or perhaps nothing at all. Some of the memory addresses may contain registers and input/output ports for peripheral devices (see Chapter 7).

In this text, we show memory maps with address 0 at the *bottom* and the last memory address at the *top*. (Sometimes memory maps are shown in the reverse perspective.) For a 16-bit address bus, the first memory address is $0_{10}$ or $0000_{16}$ and the last address is $2^{16} - 1 = 65,535_{10}$ or $FFFF_{16}$. Each address references a byte value with bit 0 as the least-significant bit (LSB, on the right) and bit 7 as the most-significant bit (MSB, on the left). This is shown in Figure 1-6.

**Table 1-1.   Memory Access vs. Memory Technology**

| Memory Access | Memory Technology | | | | |
| --- | --- | --- | --- | --- | --- |
| | RAM | ROM | Disk | Tape | Optical |
| Registers | X | | | | |
| Cache | X | | | | |
| Main Memory | X | X | VM | | |
| Secondary Memory | | | X | | X |
| Archival Storage | | | | X | X |

VM = virtual memory

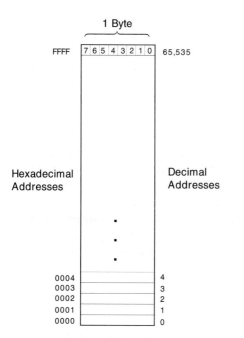

Figure 1-6.  Memory map.

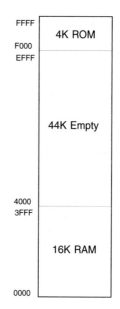

Figure 1-7.  A sample memory map.

Figure 1-6 shows the *space* accessible by the CPU through the usual memory references. The size of this memory space (e.g., 64K) indicates the *capability* of the system more so than the specific amount of memory present. For example, the once-popular Commodore *VIC-20* microcomputer was so called because it contained 20K of memory, even though its address space was 64K. Figure 1-7 illustrates this as a hypothetical memory map with a 64K space, containing 4K of ROM at the top of memory, 16K of RAM at the bottom of memory, and 44K of vacant space. Usually the empty locations are available for memory expansion or I/O interfaces (using memory-mapped I/O).

### 1.4.1.  *Dividing the Memory Space*

Note in Figure 1-7 that addresses are indicated for the beginning and ending of each section of memory. The 16K RAM begins at address 0 and ends at address 3FFF. Similarly, the 4K section of ROM begins at address F000 and ends at the top of memory at address FFFF. How are these addresses determined? This important question is easy to answer once a few basic ideas in memory addressing are presented. Figure 1-8a shows a 16-bit address with bit 0 as the LSB (on the right) and bit 15 as the MSB (on the left). Since binary is awkward, it is convenient to express addresses in hexadecimal as shown in Figure 1-8b.

To divide the memory space into subsections or **blocks** (as shown in Figure 1-7), we think of the

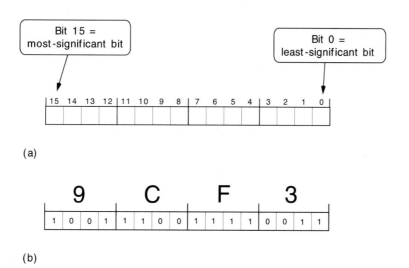

Figure 1-8.  16-bit addresses. (a) bit numbering, (b) address example.

```
Block      ******** Binary Addresses ********  *** Hex ***
Number          From                To          From   To
  0      00 00000000000000  00 11111111111111    0000  3FFF
  1      01 00000000000000  01 11111111111111    4000  7FFF
  2      10 00000000000000  10 11111111111111    8000  BFFF
  3      11 00000000000000  11 11111111111111    C000  FFFF
```

address as divided in two parts. The upper part identifies a **block number** and the lower part a **block address.** Once we determine where to divide the address, everything falls into place. Furthermore, if there are $m$ bits for the complete address, $n$ bits for the block number, and $p$ bits for the block address, then the following relationship must hold:

$$m = n + p$$

It also holds that

$$2^m = 2^n \times 2^p = 2^{n+p}$$

(See Figure 1-9.)

The next step is to decide on the size of each block or the number of blocks. Either way, the specification must be a power-of-two (at least initially) and must satisfy the equations above. For $m = 16$, the 64K memory space can be split into two blocks of 32K, four blocks of 16K, and so on. This is illustrated in Table 1-2.

A memory map can be constructed for each row in Table 1-2. (Figure 1-6 corresponds to the first row in the table.) The beginning and ending address of each block is obtained, first in binary by filling in the $n$ and $p$ fields, and then in hexadecimal for convenience. The block numbers start at *zero* (bottom of memory) and increment to $2^n - 1$ (top of memory). Within a block, the addresses start at *zero* and end at $2^p - 1$. It is easier to think of the block addresses as starting at *all 0s* and ending at *all 1s* in the $p$ field.

Let's work through an example with four blocks of 16K. This will illustrate how to obtain the final address for the 16K block of RAM in Figure 1-7. With four blocks, the block numbers are 0, 1, 2, and 3 decimal, or 00, 01, 10, and 11 binary ($n = 2$ bits). Within each block, the first address is 0 and

the last address is 16,383 ($p = 14$ bits, $2^p - 1 = 16,383$). In binary, the block addresses will range from 00000000000000 to 11111111111111. All that remains is to put the codes together and express the addresses in hexadecimal, as shown at the top of this page. The spaces inserted in the binary addresses serve only to highlight the division of the binary address into an $n$ field and a $p$ field. A memory map showing a 64K space divided into four blocks of 16K is shown in Figure 1-10.

When a block size is not a power-of-two, determining the address range is more difficult. Consider the following question:

*What is the last address of a 5K block of memory beginning at $8000_{16}$?*

Since 5K is not a power-of-two, the solution is not as neat as the example with four blocks of 16K. However, $5K = 4K + 1K$, so the problem reduces to two simple problems. For 4K blocks, $n = 4$ and $p = 12$ ($2^{12} = 4K$). A 4K block starting at

$$1000 \; 000000000000_2 = 8000_{16}$$

ends at

$$1000 \; 111111111111_2 = 8FFF_{16}$$

The address after $8FFF_{16}$ is $9000_{16}$, the beginning of the 1K block. For 1K blocks, $n = 6$ and $p = 10$ ($2^{10} = 1K$). If the first address is

$$100100 \; 0000000000_2 = 9000_{16}$$

then the last address is

$$100100 \; 1111111111_2 = 93FF_{16}$$

which is the answer to the question posed above.

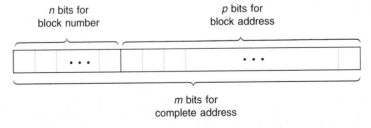

Figure 1-9.  Dividing a memory space into blocks.

Table 1-2.   Dividing a 64K Memory Space

| $n$ | $p$ | Number of Blocks ($2^n$) | Block Size ($2^p$) |
|---|---|---|---|
| 0 | 16 | 1 | 65536 |
| 1 | 15 | 2 | 32768 |
| 2 | 14 | 4 | 16384 |
| 3 | 13 | 8 | 8192 |
| 4 | 12 | 16 | 4096 |
| 5 | 11 | 32 | 2048 |
| 6 | 10 | 64 | 1024 |
| 7 | 9 | 128 | 512 |
| 8 | 8 | 256 | 256 |
| 9 | 7 | 512 | 128 |
| 10 | 6 | 1024 | 64 |
| 11 | 5 | 2048 | 32 |
| 12 | 4 | 4096 | 16 |
| 13 | 3 | 8192 | 8 |
| 14 | 2 | 16384 | 4 |
| 15 | 1 | 32768 | 2 |
| 16 | 0 | 65536 | 1 |

## 1.5.   THE DEVELOPMENT ENVIRONMENT

In this section, the process of developing micro-processor-based products is described. In progressing from concept to product, numerous steps are involved and numerous tools are used. The most common steps and tools are presented as found in typical design scenarios employing microprocessors such as the 8085, 6802, or 68000.

Designing is a highly creative activity, and in recognition of this we state at the outset that sub-stantial leeway is required for individuals or development teams. Such autonomy, however, may be difficult to achieve for very large or safety-critical projects. Admittedly, in such environments the management of the process and the validation of the results must satisfy a higher order. The present discussion pertains to the development of relatively small-scale products, such as controllers for microwave ovens, automobile dashboards, computer peripherals, electronic typewriters, games, or high-fidelity audio equipment.

The steps required and the tools and techniques available are presented and elaborated on and examples are given. Developing an understanding of the steps is important, but strict adherence to their sequence is not advocated. It is felt that forcing the development process along ordered, isolated activities is usually overstressed and probably wrong. Later in this section, we will present an all-in-one development scenario, where the available resources are known and called upon following the instinct of the designer. We begin by examining the steps in the development cycle.

### 1.5.1.   The Development Cycle

Proceeding from concept to product is usually shown in a flow diagram known as the **development cycle,** similar to that shown in Figure 1-11. The reader may notice that there is nothing particularly *cyclic* about the steps shown. Indeed, the figure shows the ideal and impossible scenario of *no breakdowns.* Of course, problems arise. **Debugging** (finding and correcting errors) is needed at every step in the development cycle with corrections introduced by re-engaging in an earlier activity. Depending on the severity of the error, the correction may be trivial or, in the extreme, may return the designer to the concept stage. Thus, there is an implied connection from the output of any step in the development cycle to any earlier step.

The steps along the top path in Figure 1-11 correspond to software development, while those along the bottom correspond to hardware development. The two paths meet at a critical and complicated step called *integrate and verify,* which leads to acceptance of the design as a *product.* The dotted line encloses a common loop of activity that is repeated many times during a complete design scenario. Not shown are various steps subsequent to acceptance of the design. These include, for example, manufacturing, testing, distribution, and marketing. We begin by examining the steps in software development.

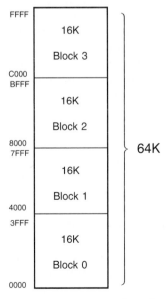

Figure 1-10.   Memory map showing four 16K blocks.

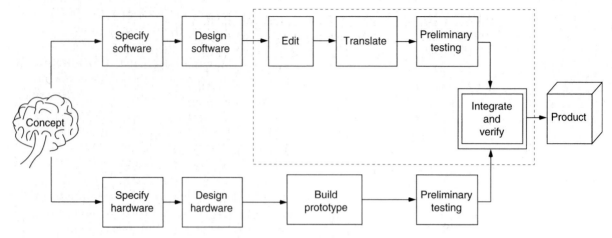

Figure 1-11.    The development cycle.

## 1.5.2.    *Software Development*

The steps in the top path in Figure 1-11 are discussed in this section, beginning with the specification of the application software.

***Specifying Software***    Specifying software is the task of explicitly stating what the software will do. This may be approached in several ways. At a superficial level, specifications may address the user interface; that is, how the user will interact with and control the system. (What effects will result from and be observed for each action taken?) If switches, dials, keyboards, CRTs, or audio or visual indicators are employed on the prototype hardware, the explicit purpose and operation of each should be stated.

Formal methods have been devised by computer scientists for specifying software requirements; however, they are not generally used in the design of microprocessor-based applications, which are small in comparison to application software destined for mainframe computers.

Software specifications may also address details of system operation below the user level. For example, a controller for a photocopier may monitor internal conditions necessary for normal or safe operation, such as temperature, current, voltage, or paper movement. These conditions are largely independent of the user interface, but still must be accommodated by software.

Specifications can be modularized by system function with entry and exit conditions defined to allow intermodule communication. Techniques will be described in Chapter 4 for documenting subroutines in this manner using comment blocks.

Interrupt-driven systems require careful planning and have unique characteristics that must be addressed at the specification stage. Activities without time-critical requirements occur in the fore-

ground loop or in a round-robin sequence for handling by timed interrupts. Time-critical activities generate high-priority interrupts that take over the system for immediate handling. Software specifications may emphasize execution time on such systems. How long does each subroutine or interrupt service routine (ISR) take to execute? How often is each ISR executed? ISRs that execute asynchronously (in response to an event) may take over the system at any time. It may be necessary to block them in some instances or to preempt (interrupt) them in others. Software specifications for such systems must address priority levels, polling sequences, and the possibility of dynamically reassigning priority levels or polling sequences within ISRs. Interrupts are presented in detail in Chapter 7.

***Designing Software***    Designing the software is a task designers often jump into without much planning.  There are two common techniques for designing software prior to coding: flowcharts and pseudo code. The simple example in Figure 1-12 shows a flowchart and a pseudo-code sketch for the problem of counting the number of negative bytes in a list.

***Editing and Translation***    The editing and translation of software occur, at least initially, in a tight cycle. Errors detected by the assembler are quickly-corrected by editing the source file and re-assembling. Since the assembler has no idea of the purpose of the program and checks only for *grammatical errors* (e.g., missing commas, undefined instructions), the errors detected are **syntax errors.** They are also called **assemble-time errors.**

***Preliminary Software Testing***    A **run-time error** does not surface until the program is executed by a

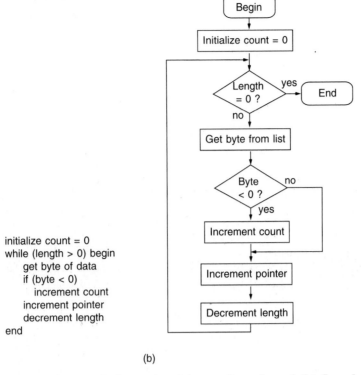

```
initialize count = 0
while (length > 0) begin
    get byte of data
    if (byte < 0)
        increment count
    increment pointer
    decrement length
end
```

(a)                    (b)

**Figure 1-12.**  Software design using (a) pseudo code and (b) flowchart.

simulator or in the target system. These errors may be elusive, requiring careful observation of CPU activity at each stage in the program. A **debugger** is a system program that executes a user program for the purpose of finding run-time errors. The debugger includes features such as executing the program until a certain address (a **breakpoint**) is reached, and **single-stepping** through instructions while displaying CPU registers, status bits, or input/output ports.

### 1.5.3. Hardware Development

For the most part this text does not emphasize hardware development. This is due both to the intended focus of the text and to the increased functionality of LSI circuits employed in today's computing systems. Such circuits include sophisticated features enabled through software, and embed much of the logic previously implemented in SSI and MSI devices.[3] The following is a brief description of the steps in hardware development.

**Specifying Hardware**  Specifying the hardware involves assigning quantitative data to system functions. For example, a robotic-arm project should be specified in terms of the number of articulations, reach, speed, accuracy, torque, power require-

ments, and so on. Designers are often required to provide a specifications sheet analogous to that accompanying an audio amplifier or VCR. Other hardware specifications include physical size and weight, CPU speed, amount and type of memory, memory map assignments, I/O ports, optional features, and so on.

**Designing Hardware**  The conventional method of hardware design, employing a pencil and logic template, is still widely used, but is often enhanced through computer-aided design (CAD) software. Although many CAD tools are for the mechanical or civil engineering disciplines, some are specifically geared for electronic or computer engineering. The two most common examples are tools for drawing schematic diagrams and tools for laying out printed circuit boards (PCBs). Although these programs have a long learning curve, the results are impressive. Some schematic drawing programs produce files that can be read by PCB programs to generate a layout automatically.

**Building the Prototype**  There are pathetically few shortcuts for the labors of prototyping. Whether bread-boarding a simple interface to a bus or port connector on a single-board computer (SBC), or wire-wrapping an entire microcomputer board, the techniques of prototyping are developed only with a great deal of practice. Large companies with large

---

[3]SSI = small-scale integrated; MSI = medium-scale integrated; LSI = large-scale integrated.

budgets often proceed directly to a printed circuit-board format, even for the first iteration of a design. Projects undertaken by small companies, students, or hobbyists, however, are more likely to use the traditional wire-wrapping method for prototypes.

***Preliminary Hardware Testing***   The first test of the hardware is undertaken in the absence of any application software. Step-wise testing is important: There is no point measuring a clock signal with an oscilloscope until the presence of DC power supply voltages is verified. The following sequence is suggested:

- visual checks
- continuity checks
- DC measurements
- AC measurements

Visual and continuity checks should occur before power is applied to the board. Ample lighting and a magnifying glass will help. Continuity checks using an ohmmeter should be conducted from the IC side of the prototype, from IC pin to IC pin. This way, the IC pin-to-socket and socket pin-to-wire connections are verified at each end. ICs should be removed when power is first applied to the prototype. DC voltages should be verified throughout the board with a voltmeter. Finally, AC measurements are made with the ICs installed to verify clock signals, and so on.

After verifying the connections, voltages, and clock signals, debugging becomes pragmatic: Is the prototype functioning as planned? If not, corrective action may take the designer back to the construction, design, or specification of the hardware.

If the design is a complete system with a CPU, a single wiring error may prevent the CPU from completing its reset sequence: The first instruction after reset may never execute! A powerful debugging trick is to drive the CPU's reset line with a low-frequency square wave ($\approx 1$ kHz) and observe (with an oscilloscope or logic analyzer) bus activity immediately following reset.

Functional testing of the board may require application software or a monitor program to *work* the board through its motions. It is at this stage that software must assist in completing the design.

## 1.5.4.   Integration and Verification

The most difficult stage in the development cycle occurs when hardware meets software. Some very subtle bugs that eluded simulation (if undertaken) emerge under real-time execution. The problem is confounded by the need for a full complement of resources: hardware such as the PC development system, target system, power supply, cables, and test equipment; and software such as the monitor program, operating system, and terminal emulation program.

We shall elaborate on the integration and verification step by first expanding the area within the dotted line in Figure 1-11. Figure 1-13 shows *utility programs* and *development tools* within circles, *user files* within squares, and *execution environments* within double-lined squares.

Editing a source file is straightforward. The translation step (from Figure 1-11) is shown in two stages. An assembler converts a source file to an object file and a linker/locator combines one or more relocatable object files into a single absolute object file for execution in a target system or simulator. The assembler and linker/locator also create listing files for printing or inspection using an editor.

The most common filename suffixes are shown in parentheses for each file type. Although any filename and suffix usually can be provided as an argument, assemblers vary in their choice of default suffixes.

If the program was written originally in a single file following an absolute format, linking and locating are not necessary. In this case, the alternate path in Figure 1-13 shows the assembler generating an absolute object file.

It is also possible (although not emphasized in this text) that high-level languages, such as C or Pascal, are used instead of, or in addition to, assembly language. Translation requires a **cross-compiler** to generate the relocatable object modules for linking and locating.

A **librarian** may also participate. Relocatable object modules (most likely subroutines) that are general purpose and useful for many projects are stored in libraries. The librarian program provides the facility to build library files consisting of a collection of relocatable object modules (subroutines). During linking and locating, the name of the library file is passed as an argument. The linker/locator searches the library for the code corresponding to previously declared external symbols that are not resolved at that point in linking/locating.

***Software Simulation***   Five execution environments are shown in Figure 1-13. Preliminary testing (see Figure 1-11) proceeds in the absence of the target system. This is shown in Figure 1-13 as

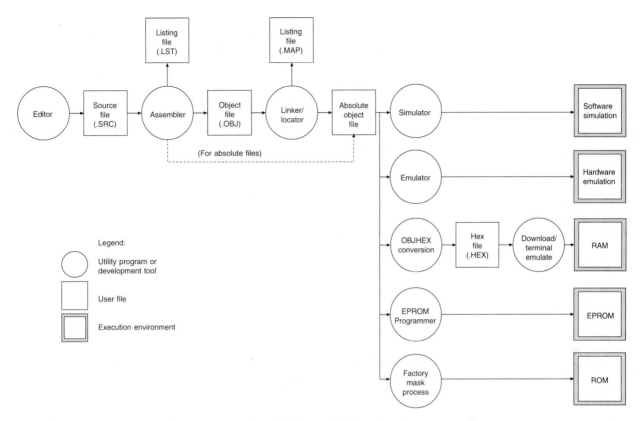

Figure 1-13.   Detailed steps in the development cycle.

software simulation. A **simulator** is a program that executes on the development system and imitates the architecture of the target system. A 68000 simulator, for example, would contain fictitious (or *simulated*) registers for each of the data and address registers, as well as for the program counter, status register, and so on. Programs are executed in simulation mode with progress presented on the development system's CRT display. Simulators are useful for early testing; however, portions of the program that are time-critical or that directly manipulate hardware must integrate with the target system for testing.

*Hardware Emulation*   A direct connection between the development system and the target system is possible through a **hardware emulator** (or **in-circuit emulator**). The emulator contains a processor that replaces the processor IC in the target system. The emulator processor, however, is under the direct control of the development system. This allows software to execute in the environment of the target system without leaving the development system. Commands are available to single-step the software, execute to a breakpoint (or the *n*th occurrence of a breakpoint), and so on. Furthermore, execution is at full speed, so time-

dependent bugs may surface that eluded debugging under simulation.

The main drawback of hardware emulation is cost. PC-hosted units sell in the $2,000–$7,000 (U.S.) range, which is beyond the budgets of most hobbyists and stretches the budgets of most colleges or universities (if equipping an entire laboratory, for example). Stand-alone units are even more expensive. Companies supporting professional development environments, however, will not hesitate to invest in hardware emulators. The benefit in accelerating the product development process easily justifies the cost.

*Execution from RAM*   An effective and simple scenario for testing software in the target system is possible, even if a hardware emulator is not available. The technique uses a *host system/target system* configuration where the host system is typically a PC/AT-type machine and the target system is a single-board computer (SBC). The connection between the two is serial, RS232C, using an asynchronous protocol. On the host computer, a terminal emulation program executes and turns the host computer into a *dumb* terminal. The host computer becomes the terminal for the SBC. The SBC will support a variety of commands; but, in particular, one will be called *LOAD* (or something similar) to receive a hexadecimal-ASCII dump of a program from the host computer. The terminal emulation program on the host computer will support a similar command (perhaps called DOWN-LOAD or FILE TRANSMIT). All programming and interface examples for this text were developed in a similar environment.

***Hexadecimal File Formats***   There are several formats for storing object programs in hexadecimal-ASCII form. The one used with Motorola CPUs such as the 68000 is called **S-records.** A small program is shown in Figure 1-14a as a series of S-records with the format of one record decomposed in Figure 1-14b.

A brief description of each field in an S-record follows:

Record Type
    S0 = first record (data bytes contain module name)
    S1 = data record (with 16-bit address)
    S2 = data record (with 24-bit address)
    S8 = end-of-file record (data bytes contain 24-bit address for program entry)
    S9 = end-of-file record (data bytes contain 16-bit address for program entry)

Byte Count
    The hexadecimal count of the number of bytes that follow in the current record. In Figure 1-14b, $13_{16}$ = 16 + 3 = 19.

Load Address
    First memory address for data bytes in current record

Data Bytes
    Hexadecimal data for current record (see Record Type)

Checksum
    A value that, when EXORed to the sum of the preceding bytes (mod 256, excluding the Record Type), yields FF.

Note that the data bytes in a data record usually contain instruction bytes of a program (i.e., data in the general sense).

***Execution from EPROM***   Once a satisfactory degree of performance is obtained through execution in RAM (or through in-circuit emulation), the software can be burned into EPROM and installed in the system as **firmware.** This is an extremely inexpensive and popular execution environment. EPROMs, such as the 2764A storing 8K bytes of data, cost only a few dollars, and are reusable. When necessary to change the program, the EPROM is removed from the target system and placed in an EPROM eraser for about 30 minutes. The eraser contains a special ultraviolet light that changes the electrical property of the transistors that store data inside the EPROM. A blank, or erased, EPROM contains all 1s.

***The Factory Mask Process***   If a final design is destined for mass production, then a more cost-effective alternative to EPROM is a factory mask ROM. A factory mask ROM is programmed during the manufacturing of the device using a *mask*—a photographic plate that passes or masks light during a stage of manufacturing the IC.

The choice of ROM vs. EPROM is largely economic. A factory mask device is cheaper than the

```
S00900006D796E616D656F
S11320003C3C000A327C201661000020534666F4F2
S11320101E3C00E44E4E53636F7474204D61634B59
S10C2020656E7A6965200D0A0061
S113202A1E3C00F81019670000064E4E60F64E7505
S9030000FC
```

(a)

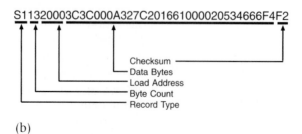

(b)

Figure 1-14.   Motorola S-records. (a) file format, (b) field format.

EPROM device; however, there is a large setup fee to produce the mask and initiate a custom manufacturing cycle. A trade-off point can be identified to determine the feasibility of each approach. For example, if ROMs cost $1 plus a $5,000 setup fee, and EPROMs cost $5, then the breakeven point is

$$5n = 1n + 5000$$

$$4n = 5000$$

$$n = 1250$$

A production run of 1,250 units or more would justify the use of a ROM over an EPROM.

### 1.5.5. Commands and Environments

In this section, the overall development environment is considered. We present the notion that at any time the designer is working within an *environment* with commands doing the work. The central environment is the operating system on the host computer, which is most likely MS-DOS running on a member of the PC family of microcomputers. As suggested in Figure 1-15, some commands return to MS-DOS upon completion while others evoke a new environment.

*Invoking Commands*  Commands in the host development system are either **internal** or **external.** An internal command is in memory at all times, ready for execution (e.g., DIR). An external command is an executable disk file that is loaded into memory for execution (e.g., FORMAT).

Application programs are similar to external commands in that they exist as an executable disk file and are invoked from the MS-DOS prompt. However, there are still many possibilities. Commands or applications may be invoked as part of a batch file, by a function key, or from a menu-driven user interface acting as a front end for MS-DOS.

If command arguments are needed, there are many possibilities again. Although arguments are typically entered on the invocation line following the command, some commands have default values for arguments, or prompt the user for arguments. Unfortunately, there is no standard mechanism, such as the dialog box on the Apple *Macintosh,* to retrieve extra information needed for a command or application.

Some applications, such as editors, *take over* the system and bring the user into a new environment for subsequent activities.

*Environments*  As evident in Figure 1-15, some software tools such as the simulator, in-circuit emulator, or EPROM programmer evoke their own environment. Learning the nuances of each takes time, due to the great variety of techniques for directing the activities of the environment: cursor keys, function keys, first-letter commands, menu highlighting, default paths, and so on. It is often

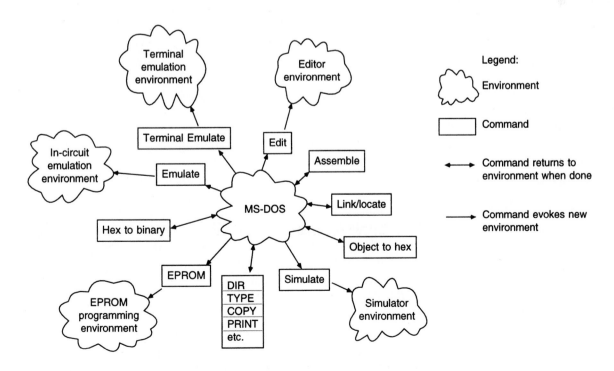

possible to switch among environments while leaving them active. For example, terminal emulators and editors usually allow switching to DOS momentarily to execute commands. The MS-DOS command EXIT immediately brings back the suspended environment.

*Methodology*   As research in artificial intelligence and cognitive science has discovered, modeling human *problem solving* is a slippery business. Humans appear to approach the elements of a situation in parallel, simultaneously weighing the possible actions and proceeding by intuition. The methodology suggested here recognizes this human ability. The steps in the development cycle and the tools and techniques afforded by the development environment should be clearly understood, but the overall process should support substantial freedom.

Commands can be categorized as *translate, view,* or *evoke* (a new environment). The results of translation should be viewed to verify results. We can take the attitude of not believing the outcome of any translation (assembling, EPROM programming, etc.) and verify by viewing the results. Tools for viewing are commands such as DIR (Were the expected output files created? How big are they?), TYPE (What's in an output file?), EDIT, PRINT, and so on.

## 1.6.  SUMMARY

This chapter has introduced many of the general concepts of microprocessors, microcomputers, and system design. There is no substitute for experience, however. Success in design requires considerable intuition, a valuable commodity that cannot be delivered in a textbook. The age-old expression *trial and error* still rings true as the main technique employed by students for learning about microcomputers and for turning ideas into products.

## 1.7.  QUESTIONS

1. One of the first minicomputers, the PDP-8, had a 12-bit address bus. What was the last address in this computer's memory space? Give the answer in decimal, binary, octal, and hexadecimal.

2. Draw a memory map of a system with a 12-bit address bus, dividing the memory space into 2K blocks. Indicate the hexadecimal address of the first and last address in each block.

3. The 68000 microprocessor has a 24-bit address bus. Into how many 64K blocks can the 68000's memory space be divided?

4. What are the first and last addresses of the 1Meg block of memory at the top of the 68000's address space?

5. What is the last address of a 1K block of memory beginning at address $C000_{16}$?

6. If a 64K memory space is divided into 8K blocks, what are the beginning and ending addresses of block #3? (Remember, the block starting at address 0 is block #0.)

7. A certain computer has a 4Meg address space. How many bits wide is this computer's address bus?

8. A popular microcontroller is the MCS-51 from Intel Corp. Two versions are the 8751 with an on-chip EPROM and the 8051 with an on-chip mask-programmed ROM. Assume the 8751 sells for $30 in any quantity and the 8051 sells for $3 plus a $10,000 setup fee.

   (a) How many units are necessary to justify use of an 8051 device?

   (b) What is the savings for projected sales of 3,000 units of the final product if an 8051 is used instead of an 8751?

9. Below is a 68000 program shown as a series of S-records.

```
S00A00006D796E616D65323C
S11331003C3C000A327C31166100002A534666F4C6
S11331101E3C00E44E4E53636F7474204D61634B48
S1133120656E7A696520286D6F64696666696554429CE
S1133130200D0A0010196700000861000000660F401
S11331404E751E3900010040020700026 7F413C0E7
S1093150000010042 4E756F
S9030000FC
```

   (a) What is the starting address of the program?

   (b) What is the length of the program?

   (c) What is the last address of the program?

10. The following is a single line from a hexadecimal file containing S-records. The checksum appears in the last two characters as "00." It is incorrect. What is the correct checksum?

```
S11320500061143C007B101F000000206000000400
```

# 2. The 68000 Microprocessor

## 2.1. INTRODUCTION

In 1979, Motorola Inc. introduced the first implementation of the M68000 16/32-bit microprocessor architecture—the MC68000. The MC68000, with a 16-bit data bus and a 24-bit address bus, was the first in a family of processors to implement a comprehensive, fully expandable computer architecture. Since 1979, many new members have been added to the 68000 family (see Figure 2-1). The clock frequency of the initial device was 4 MHz, as identified by the suffix "L4" in Motorola's part number. Versions were introduced soon after with clock speeds of 6, 8, 10, and 12 MHz. Additionally, the 68008 is an economical version with a scaled-down 8-bit data bus, and the 68HC000 is a complementary metal-oxide semiconductor (CMOS) version that operates with about one-tenth the power consumption. Clock speeds continued to increase as new members were added with significant performance-boosting enhancements. These include the 68010 introduced in 1983 supporting virtual memory, the 68020 (1984) with full 32-bit data and address buses and cache memory, the 68030 (1987) with separate instruction and data caches, and the 68040 (1990) with many advanced features, such as multiple internal execution units and an on-chip floating-point unit. Typically, the 68040 is three times faster than the 68030.

Processors from the 68000 family are found in a variety of commercial products, including popular microcomputers such as the Apple *Macintosh* and the Commodore *Amiga,* and the *Genesis* home entertainment system from Sega Enterprises, Ltd. Many industrial controllers use a microprocessor from the 68000 family. These include products for process control in oil refineries, assembly-line robotics and image processing, and telecommunications.

The 68000 architecture is also a favorite choice for college and university curricula in computer organization and computer engineering due to its highly consistent architecture. One factor often cited is the 68000's *linear address space.* From beginning to end, the address space is continuous. There is no segmentation of the address space (unlike Intel counterparts) to complicate a student's initial exposure to the architecture.

This chapter introduces the architecture of the MC68000 microprocessor (hereafter the "68000"). All details of the 68000 implementation are upward compatible to the other 68000-family devices. We begin with a look at the 68000 programmer's model.

## 2.2. PROGRAMMER'S MODEL

A CPU **programming model** includes all registers under control of the programmer. The model contains general-purpose registers, a program counter, a stack pointer, and a status register. Other components of the CPU, such as the instruction register, ALU, instruction decode and control unit, and so on, are not shown since they are not under direct control of the programmer. The 68000 programmer's model is shown in Figure 2-2.

The programmer's model contains:

- eight 32-bit data registers (D0–D7)
- eight 32-bit address registers (A0–A7)
- a 32-bit program counter (PC)
- a 16-bit condition and status register (SR)

The distinction between the user stack pointer (A7) and the supervisor stack pointer (also A7) will be discussed below when we examine the status register in more detail.

Although an in-depth discussion of the 68000's instructions is deferred to the next chapter, some general comments on the programmer's model are given below using simple instruction examples.

### 2.2.1. Data Registers

In Figure 2-2, the data registers are shown with dashed lines identifying boundaries for byte (bits 0–7), word (bits 0–15), and longword (bits 0–31) operands. The instruction set supports all three operand sizes. Many instruction mnemonics can include a suffix of .B, .W, or .L to define data sizes

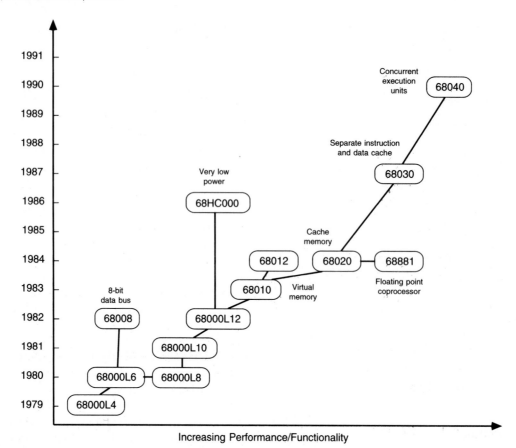

Figure 2-1.   68000 genealogy.

of byte, word, or longword respectively. For example, the instruction

```
        MOVE.B  #$5F,D3
```

moves the 8-bit value $5F into the low byte of D3, leaving the upper 24 bits unchanged.[1] The instruction

```
        MOVE.W  #$5F,D3
```

moves the 16-bit value $005F into the low word of D3, leaving the upper 16 bits unchanged. Since *word* is the default size for the MOVE instruction, the suffix ".W" is not needed in the example above.[2] The instruction

```
        MOVE.L  #$5F,D3
```

moves the 32-bit quantity $0000005F into D3.

---

[1]As consistent with Motorola conventions, hexadecimal values are identified with a leading dollar sign ("$"). The number sign ("#") preceding $5F indicates *immediate addressing*. Addressing modes are discussed later in this chapter.

[2]The notion of a default size for an instruction operand is a feature of the assembler. It has nothing to do with the architecture of the 68000 per se.

## 2.2.2.  Address Registers

Many instructions on the 68000 can use address registers or data registers in the same way. Additionally, some instructions operate specifically on address registers. Byte operations on address registers are not permitted. When a word-size operation is specified, the result is sign-extended to form a 32-bit quantity. For example, the instruction

```
        MOVEA.W  #$1000,A4
```

moves the value $00001000 to A4, whereas the instruction

```
        MOVEA.W  #$8000,A4
```

moves the value $FFFF8000 to A4. Since the 68000's address bus is 24 bits, only 24 of the 32 bits in address registers are used in accessing physical memory. When referring to physical memory locations, we will generally only provide a 24-bit address. When referring to values in address registers, 32-bit values will be cited.

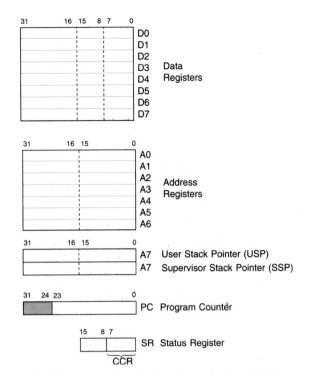

Figure 2-2.   68000 programmer's model.

### 2.2.3.   Program Counter

Even though the program counter (PC) is shown as 32 bits in Figure 2-2, only 24 bits are used in addressing memory. A 24-bit PC can address $2^{24}$ or 16 Mbytes of memory. Since the 68000 data bus is 16 bits wide, all instruction words are 16 bits. Furthermore, all word addresses on the 68000 must be *even* ($000000, $000002, $000004, etc.). This point will become more apparent when we discuss the memory organization of the 68000 later in this chapter. An odd value in the PC is illegal and causes a bus error. Bus errors are discussed in Chapter 6.

### 2.2.4.   Stack Pointer

The stack pointer (SP) is A7 on the 68000. For many instructions, A7 is no different from the other registers. For example, the following two instructions

```
MOVEA  #100,A6
MOVEA  #100,A7
```

explicitly name address registers as the destination registers. The second instruction moves a value into A7, which happens to be the stack pointer. Most assemblers allow "SP" to be substituted for A7 for clarity.

The following instructions implicitly use A7 as a pointer to the stack:

BSR — branch to subroutine
ILLEGAL — take illegal instruction trap
JSR — jump to subroutine
LINK — link and allocate stack space
PEA — push effective address
RTE — return from exception
RTR — return and restore condition codes
RTS — return from subroutine
TRAP — trap
TRAPV — trap on overflow
UNLK — unlink

The 68000 stack is a *pre-decrement-write stack*, which is to say (a) the stack grows *down* as items are pushed on it, and (b) at any moment the stack pointer points to the last item pushed on the stack (as opposed to the next vacant location to receive an item). *Down*, in this sense, corresponds to a mental model of memory whereby the *bottom* is address $000000 and the *top* is address $FFFFFE. This is illustrated in Figure 2-3, showing the 68000 memory space and a hypothetical stack.

A typical use of the stack is to save the program counter when branching to a subroutine. When a BSR instruction executes, the program counter is *pushed* on the stack prior to the branch. It is *pulled* from the stack by the RTS instruction at the end of the subroutine. The BSR and RTS instructions are presented in detail in Chapter 3.

### 2.2.5.   Status Register

The 68000 status register (SR) is 16 bits. The upper byte is the **system byte** and the lower byte is the

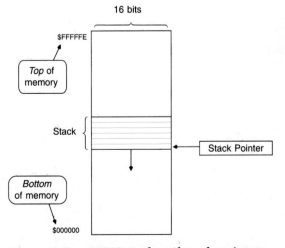

Figure 2-3.   68000 stack and stack pointer.

**user byte,** also called the **condition code register** (CCR). Only ten of the 16 bits are defined, as shown in Figure 2-4.

*Supervisor Mode Bit*    The 68000 executes instructions either in **user mode** or **supervisor mode.** The active mode is set by bit 13 in the status register, the supervisor state bit (S). If S = 0, the active mode is user. If S = 1, the active mode is supervisor. The *active mode* is also called the *privilege state.* There are three differences for supervisor mode: (1) a second stack pointer is used for instructions using A7, (2) the full 16 bits of the status register are accessible, and (3) all instructions are available. In user mode, the user stack pointer is active, only the lower byte of the status register is accessible, and some instructions are restricted and cannot be executed. Privilege states are discussed in detail in Chapter 6.

*Trace Bit*    Bit 15 of the status register is the trace bit (T), which is accessible only while executing in supervisor mode. Normally the trace bit is cleared and instructions execute one after another in the usual way. If the trace bit is set to one, the 68000 executes in trace mode, or **single-step mode.** After each instruction, a trace exception occurs and the processor executes a special debugging routine. Typically, the trace exception dumps the CPU's registers to a terminal. The programmer responds by changing the values in registers or memory locations, or by directing the system to execute the next instruction, and so on.

*Interrupt Mask Bits*    Bits 8–10 of the status register are the interrupt mask bits. These bits are configurable in supervisor mode to set the level of the lowest priority interrupt that the CPU will respond to. The 68000 has eight interrupt priority levels, with 0 as the lowest and 7 as the highest. In fact, the normal interrupt priority level presented to the CPU is level 0, which corresponds to *no interrupt.* Interrupt level 1 is the lowest priority *executable* interrupt; interrupt level 2 is the next lowest, and so on. Interrupt priority level 7 is special; it is the highest priority interrupt and can never be inhibited by the interrupt mask bits. Level 7 interrupts are often called **non-maskable interrupts.**

For example, the following instruction sets the interrupt level to three:

```
MOVE.W #$2300,SR
```

The instruction above can only execute while the CPU is in supervisor state. To leave the CPU in supervisor state as well, bit 13 is set in the immediate data above. Bits 10, 9, and 8 in the immediate data are set to $011_2$, thereby setting the CPU's interrupt mask level to "3." Subsequent interrupts at levels 1 and 2 are ignored. Interrupts at levels 3 through 7 are permitted, however, and will be responded to in the manner described in Chapter 7.

*Condition Code Bits*    The status bits of primary concern to programmers are those in the CCR. The CCR bits are available regardless of the privilege state of the CPU. Each of the CCR bits is defined below.

| | |
|---|---|
| X (extend) | Set to the value of C for arithmetic operations. Otherwise not affected or set to a specified result. |
| N (negative) | Set if the most-significant bit of the result is set. Cleared otherwise. |
| Z (zero) | Set if the result is zero. Cleared otherwise. |
| V (overflow) | Set if an arithmetic overflow occurs. This implies the result cannot be represented in the operand size. Cleared otherwise. |
| C (carry) | Set if a carry out of the most-significant bit occurs for an addition. Set if a borrow occurs in a subtraction. Cleared otherwise. |

As an example of how the condition code bits are affected, we will work through the computation of the CCR bits in detail for a typical add instruction. Consider the following instruction along with the *before* and *after* conditions for the status register and D1. The challenge is to determine the contents of the two registers *after* the add instruction executes. All values are in hexadecimal.

```
Instruction:      ADD.B #$19,D1

Before:           SR =      0000
                  D1 = 00000070
```

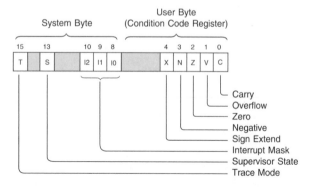

Figure 2-4.    The 68000 status register.

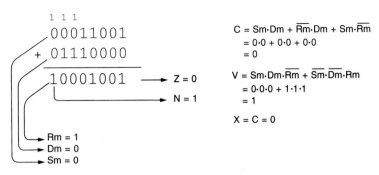

Figure 2-5.   Condition code computation.

After:            SR = _____
                   D1 = _____

The instruction adds the immediate byte $19 to the least-significant byte in D1 ($70). The immediate data value is the *source* and register D1 is the *destination*. The operation performed is

```
source + destination -> destination
```

The other 24 bits in D1 are unaffected. The addition is sketched out in Figure 2-5 in binary. The computation of the Z and N bits is straightforward. The entire result is *not* zero, therefore Z = 0 (false). The most-significant bit of the result is set, therefore N = 1.

The computation of the C and V bits uses Boolean expressions given in Appendix A for all 68000 instructions. The terms in the Boolean expressions represent the most-significant bit in the source (Sm), destination (Dm), and result (Rm). It is usually easier just to think of what is going on in the operation, rather than computing the Boolean expression. The carry bit is not set because there was no carry out of the MSB during the addition. The overflow bit is set because the result is out of range. This is easily seen in glancing at the numbers: Two positive numbers were added (MSB = 0), and a negative result was obtained (MSB = 1). The numbers added were $19 = 25_{10}$ and $70 = 112_{10}$. Eight-bit signed values are limited to the range

$-128$ to $127$; however $25 + 112 = 137$. This causes an overflow.

The X-bit receives a copy of the C-bit. The *after* values of the registers are D1 = \$00000089 and SR = \$000A.

As a final comment, note that the V-bit is always computed with the assumption that the values are signed. It is perfectly reasonable that the binary numbers above are unsigned numbers. (Only the programmer knows for sure!) In this case, the programmer probably does not care about the state of the V-bit. Eight-bit unsigned numbers have a range of 0 to $255_{10}$. The C-bit functions as an *overflow* if the data are unsigned.

A full understanding of the CCR lies both in the computation of the bits (as just illustrated) and in the testing of the bits. Testing of the CCR bits is accomplished through three instructions, Bcc, Scc, and DBcc (see Appendix A). As a brief example, consider the following: We want to add two signed numbers (as above) and continue in the program if the result is *in range*. If an overflow occurs, we want to branch to a special routine, called ERROR, that handles the abnormal condition. The instruction sequence in Figure 2-6 is used.

First, the add takes place (line 2), then a conditional branch instruction determines if an overflow occurred (line 3). BVS is the mnemonic for *branch if overflow set*. If V = 1, the branch takes place and the ERROR routine executes (line 7). If V = 0, the branch does not take place and the program continues (line 4).

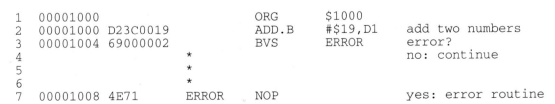

Figure 2-6.   Branch if overflow set (BVS) example.

## 2.3.   MEMORY ORGANIZATION

The address bus on the 68000 is 24 bits wide, so $2^{24} = 2^4 \times 2^{10} \times 2^{10} = 16$ megabytes of memory can be addressed. In this perspective, each location contains a byte of data so the memory map in Figure 2-7 applies. This is the *byte view* of the 68000's memory space.

The data bus on the 68000 is 16 bits wide, which is the default data size for read or write operations between the CPU and memory. However, the 68000 architecture supports operand sizes of bytes (8 bits), words (16 bits), or longwords (32 bits). Addressing considerations for these data sizes are now described.

First, note that addresses of 16-bit values (words) must be *even*. The first word in memory is at address $000000, the second is at $000002, the third is at $000004, and so on. Bytes, however, may be read at any address. The first byte in memory is at address $000000, the second is at $000001, the third is at $000002, and so on, as shown in Figure 2-7.

A 68000 memory map can also be constructed showing a *word view* of data. Addresses increment by two from each word to the next. This is very convenient since it allows both a byte and word view of memory without a conflict in addresses. For example, word address $000000 contains two bytes, the byte at address $000000 (on the left) and the byte at address $000001 (on the right), and so on. This is shown in Figure 2-8.

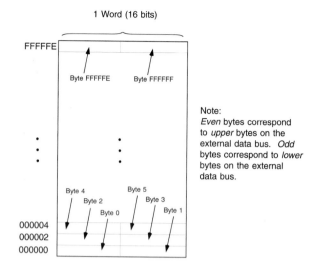

Note:
*Even* bytes correspond to *upper* bytes on the external data bus. *Odd* bytes correspond to *lower* bytes on the external data bus.

**Figure 2-8.   68000 memory map (word view).**

Longwords (32 bits) also have even addresses. Since a longword is two words, longword addresses are spaced at intervals of four. A longword can begin at any even address *n;* the next longword is at address *n* + 4, and so on. Figure 2-9 shows the *longword view* of the 68000's memory space.

When a longword is read or written, two memory cycles are required, since the physical width of the data bus is 16 bits. Bytes or words may be read or written in a single memory cycle. When reading or writing a word operand, the least-significant bit of the address bus is not used (since for even addresses, A0 = 0). When reading or writing a byte operand, the least-significant bit of the address determines whether the data transfer is over the high or low byte of the data bus.

## 2.4.   ADDRESSING MODES

Instructions for the 68000 contain two kinds of information: the type of function to be performed, and the location of the operand(s) on which to perform that function. The methods of locating the operand(s) are explained in this section. The 68000 supports 13 addressing modes, as summarized in Table 2-1.

Examples of each addressing mode are provided below using MOVE instructions. The general format of the MOVE instruction is

```
MOVE  source,destination
```

Both the source and destination of the move may be specified using a variety of addressing modes (subject to the constraints identified in

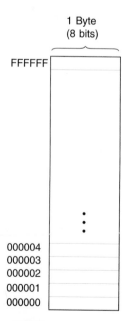

**Figure 2-7.   68000 memory map (byte view).**

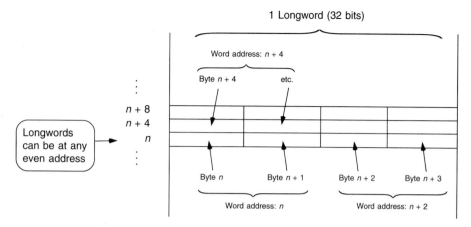

Figure 2-9. 68000 memory map (longword view).

Appendix B). As specified above, the instruction moves a 16-bit word of data from the source location to the destination location.

The following examples use a *before/after* approach to illustrate each addressing mode. The idea is to examine an instruction and its addressing modes in isolation of other instructions. The *before* conditions identify the contents of registers and memory locations just before the instruction executes. The *after* conditions identify the same registers and memory locations, illustrating the changes caused by the instruction.

An explicit operand size may be specified by ap-

pending .B (byte), .W (word), or .L (longword) to the mnemonic, as shown in the examples.

## 2.4.1. *Data Register Direct*

The data register direct addressing mode identifies a data register (D0–D7) as the source or destination of data. In Figure 2-10, data register direct is the addressing mode for both the source and destination of the data. Since ".B" is appended to the MOVE mnemonic, only the low byte (bits 0–7) of the destination data register is affected.

## Table 2-1. 68000 Addressing Modes

| Mode | Assembler Syntax | Effective Address Generation |
|---|---|---|
| Data Register Direct | Dn | EA = Dn |
| Address Register Direct | An | EA = An |
| Absolute Short | xxx.S or <xxx | EA = (next word) |
| Absolute Long | xxx.L or >xxx | EA = (next two words) |
| Register Indirect | (An) | EA = (An) |
| Postincrement Register Indirect | (An)+ | EA = (An), An ← An + N |
| Predecrement Register Indirect | −(An) | An ← An − N, EA = (An) |
| Register Indirect with Offset | d16(An) | EA = (An) + d16 |
| Register Indirect with Index and Offset | d8(An,Xn) | EA = (An) + (Xn) + d8 |
| PC-Relative with Offset | d16(PC) | EA = (PC) + d16 |
| PC-Relative with Index and Offset | d8(PC,Xn) | EA = (PC) + (Xn) + d8 |
| Immediate | #data | DATA = next word(s) |
| Implied Register | CCR, SR, USP, SSP, PC | EA = CCR, SR, USP, SSP, PC |

*Notes:*

EA = effective address
An = address register
Dn = data register
Xn = address or data register used as index register
CCR = condition code register
SR = status register
USP = user stack pointer
SSP = supervisor stack pointer

PC = program counter
( ) = contents of
d8 = 8-bit offset (displacement)
d16 = 16-bit offset (displacement)
N = 1 for byte, 2 for word, 4 for longword. (If An is the stack pointer and the operand size is byte, N = 2 to keep the stack pointer on a word boundary.)
← = is replaced by

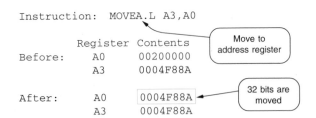

Figure 2-10. Data register direct addressing mode.

Figure 2-11. Address register direct addressing mode.

## 2.4.2. Address Register Direct

An important variation of the move instruction is MOVEA, which moves data to an address register. The destination must be an address register. As coded in Figure 2-11, the move is 32 bits since ".L" is appended to MOVEA.

Moving data to an address register is treated differently from moving data to a data register. Only word or longword operands may be specified. (Byte moves to an address register are not supported.) If the operand size is word, then a 16-bit source operand is read from the source effective address and then *sign-extended* to form a 32-bit operand when writing to the destination address register. *Sign-extending* means that the most-significant bit of the source operand is copied to the left to fill out the destination operand. This is illustrated in Figure 2-12 by repeating the previous example and specifying a 16-bit operand.

Without any suffix, MOVEA works with a 16-bit source operand, bits 0–15 of A3:

$$1111\ 1000\ 1000\ 1010_2 = F88A_{16}$$

The MSB of the source operand is 1, therefore the sign-extended 32-bit result has bits 16–31 equal to 1:

$$1111\ 1111\ 1111\ 1111\ 1111\ 1000\ 1000\ 1010_2 = FFFFF88A_{16}$$

## 2.4.3. Absolute Short

Using absolute addressing, the source or destination is a memory location whose address is specified in one or two extension words of the instruction. There are two variations of absolute addressing: absolute short and absolute long.

With absolute short addressing, a single extension word is appended to the instruction to provide bits 0–15 of the address. The upper bits are formed when the instruction is executed by sign-extending bit 15 of the extension word to bits 16–31. (On the 68000, only 24 bits, bits 0–23, are actually used in addressing physical memory.)

If the 32-bit address of the data, as represented in the assembly language instruction, has the upper 17 bits all equal to zero or all equal to one, then absolute short addressing can be used.

The mode is explicitly set to absolute short by appending ".S" to the address, as in

```
MOVE.B  #5,$F00.S
```

or by preceding the address with " < ", as in

```
MOVE.B  #5, < $F00
```

The syntax may slightly vary from one assembler to the next (see Table 2-1).

The example in Figure 2-13 uses immediate addressing (discussed below) for the source operand, and absolute short addressing for the destination of the move.

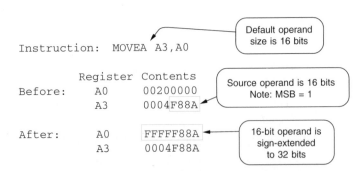

Figure 2-12.   Writing a word to an address register.

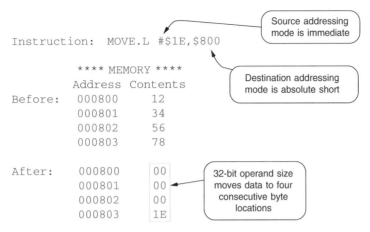

Figure 2-13. Absolute short addressing mode.

As a final note, do not confuse the size of the absolute address with the size of the operand. In Figure 2-13, the operand is 32 bits (because .L is appended to the mnemonic), but the address is specified in the instruction as 16 bits (absolute short).

## 2.4.4. Absolute Long

Instructions using absolute long addressing include two extension words specifying a 32-bit address of a source or destination operand. This is illustrated in Figure 2-14.

The mode may be explicitly set to absolute long by appending ".L" to the address, as in

        MOVE.B  #5,$F00.L

or by preceding the address with " > ", as in

        MOVE.B  #5,>$F00

The syntax may vary slightly from one assembler to the next (see Table 2-1).

Often, the distinction between absolute short addressing and absolute long addressing is transparent to the programmer, since memory addresses may be expressed using predefined labels. If the value of the label (i.e., the memory address) is in the range 0–$7FFF (bits 15–31 = 0, bottom

32K) or $FF8000–$FFFFFF (bits 15–31 = 1, top 32K), then the assembler will code the addressing mode as absolute short. If the memory address is in the range $008000–$FF7FFF, the assembler will code the addressing mode as absolute long. The range of addresses applicable to absolute short and absolute long addressing is illustrated in Figure 2-15.

An excerpt from a listing file is given in Figure 2-16 to illustrate how instructions using variations of absolute addressing are encoded by a typical 68000 assembler.

A few comments regarding Figure 2-16 are in order. In line 2, the MOVE instruction is converted into two words. The instruction word, $3A38, completely specifies the operation and the addressing modes for the source and destination operands. (A detailed discussion of the encoding of instruction words is presented in Chapter 3.) The source addressing mode is absolute short; so a single source extension word ($7000) appears as the second word in the instruction. When the instruction executes, a word value is read from address $007000 and placed in D5.

The MOVE in line 3 assembles using absolute long addressing for the source operand. Since the source address was specified as $8000 (which is the same as $00008000), absolute long addressing was required to correctly specify the address. The

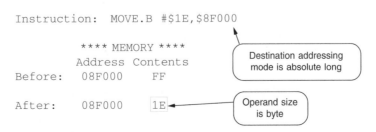

Figure 2-14. Absolute long addressing mode.

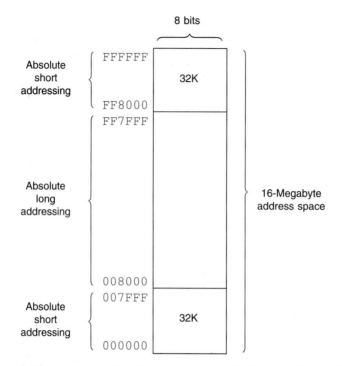

**Figure 2-15.**   Address ranges for absolute short and absolute long addressing.

instruction is three words long, consisting of the instruction word and two words for the absolute long address of the source operand.

The third instruction (line 4) provides a source address with the upper 17 bits equal to one; so the assembler used the absolute short form of the instruction. The address presented in the single extension word ($8000) will sign-extend to $FFFF8000 when the instruction executes. On the 68000, this is truncated to the 24-bit physical address $FF8000.

The fourth MOVE (line 5) uses a special assembler symbol (">") to force absolute long addressing, even though the address could be correctly expressed in 16 bits. This is a special feature of many assemblers that is useful for debugging or in implementing memory management. With some assemblers, absolute long addressing is specified by appending ".L" to the address.

The last instruction uses absolute long addressing to specify both the source and destination

operands. The assembled instruction is five words long.

## 2.4.5.   Register Indirect

With register indirect addressing, an address register contains the address of the source or destination operand. Only address registers may be used. Indirection is indicated by enclosing the address register in parentheses. In Figure 2-17, the source operand is specified using data register direct addressing and the destination is specified using register indirect addressing. The instruction moves a longword (32 bits) from D0 to the memory location specified by the address in A0. Note that the content of the address register does not change.

## 2.4.6.   Postincrement Register Indirect

The postincrement and predecrement variations of register indirect addressing are important additions

```
1  00001000                 ORG      $1000
2  00001000  3A387000       MOVE     $7000,D5
3  00001004  3A390000       MOVE     $8000,D5
   00001008  8000
4  0000100A  3A388000       MOVE     $FFFF8000,D5
5  0000100E  3A390000       MOVE     >$7000,D5
   00001012  7000
6  00001014  33F91234       MOVE     $12345678,$ABCDEF01
   00001018  5678ABCD
   0000101C  EF01
```

**Figure 2-16.**   Assembler treatment of absolute addressing.

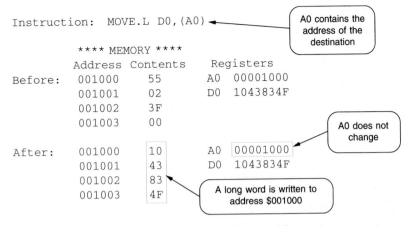

Figure 2-17.  Register indirect addressing.

to the 68000 addressing modes. They complement one another and allow for powerful programming operations on lists, strings, arrays, matrices, and so forth. An example is given in Figure 2-18.

The postincrement variation is indicated by a plus sign (" + ") after the parentheses enclosing the address register. Whether used to specify the source or destination location, the read or write of data takes place *before* the address register is incremented. After reading or writing data, the address register is incremented by the number of bytes in the operand, as follows:

| Operand Size | Incremented by. . . |
|---|---|
| byte | 1 |
| word | 2 |
| longword | 4 |

An exception to the above rule occurs when using A7 as an address register. Since A7 functions as the stack pointer, *word alignment* must be maintained; that is, A7 must always contain an even value. If a byte operand is read from or written to the stack, A7 is incremented (or decremented) by two to maintain word alignment.

### 2.4.7.  Predecrement Register Indirect

The predecrement variation of register indirect addressing is indicated by preceding the parentheses with a minus sign (" – "). In Figure 2-19, a word value is saved on the stack. The value of the stack pointer (A7) is decremented by two *before* the move takes place.

### 2.4.8.  Register Indirect with Offset

Register indirect with offset is a variation of register indirect addressing that includes a 16-bit offset (or displacement) as an extension word in the instruction. The sign-extended offset is added to the address register to form the effective address of the source or destination. Note in Figure 2-20 that the content of the address register does not change.

### 2.4.9.  Register Indirect with Index and Offset

Register indirect with index and offset is another variation of register indirect addressing. As well as an offset, an *index register* is used. The offset is an 8-

```
Instruction:  MOVE.W (A5)+,D0

        **** MEMORY ****
        Address Contents  Registers
Before: 001000   45       A5  00001000
        001001   67       D0  0000FFFF
        001002   89
        001003   AB

After:  001000   45       A5  00001002
        001001   67       D0  00004567
        001002   89
        001003   AB
```

Figure 2-18.  Postincrement address register indirect addressing.

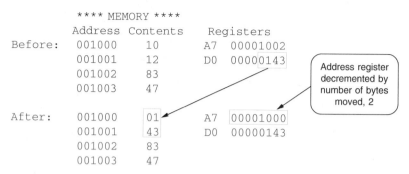

Figure 2-19.   Predecrement address register indirect addressing.

bit signed integer in the low-byte of the extension word. The high-byte of the extension word specifies the index register. The format of the extension word is shown in Figure 2-21.

The effective address is formed by adding the sign-extended offset, the content of the index register, and the content of the address register. As noted in the W/L field in Figure 2-21, the index register can be treated as a word or longword index. If a word index is used, it is sign-extended to 32 bits when the effective address is calculated. Any data or address register may be specified as the index register. An example is given in Figure 2-22.

### 2.4.10.   PC-Relative with Offset

This addressing mode uses a 16-bit offset (or displacement) which is added to the PC to form the effective address. The value in the PC when the calculation takes place is the address of the extension word. The offset is usually specified as a label representing the effective address; the assembler computes the offset by subtracting the PC from the address represented by the label. This addressing mode is only available for source operands (see Appendix B). An example is given in Figure 2-23.

The example given in Figure 2-23 is illustrated further in Figure 2-24 as a program listing. Note that the offset appearing in the extension word for

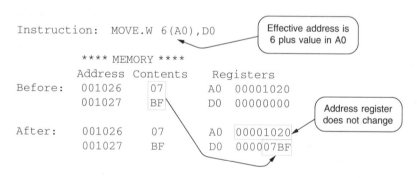

Figure 2-20.   Register indirect with offset addressing.

| 15 | 14 | 13 | 12 | 11 | 10 | 9 | 8 | 7 | 6 | 5 | 4 | 3 | 2 | 1 | 0 |
|----|----|----|----|----|----|---|---|---|---|---|---|---|---|---|---|
| D/A | Register | | | W/L | 0 | 0 | 0 | | Displacement Integer | | | | | | |

D/A field:
  0 = data register
  1 = address register
Register field:
  register number
W/L field:
  0 = sign-extended, low-order word integer in index register
  1 = longword value in index register

**Figure 2-21.   Extension word for register indirect with index and offset addressing.**

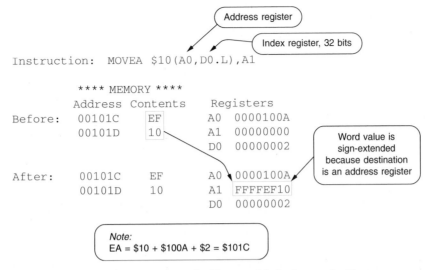

Figure 2-22.   Register indirect with index and offset.

the MOVE.W instruction (line 2) is $001E. The address of the extension word is $1000 + 2 = $1002, and the address represented by the label COUNT is $1020. The extension word (offset) is calculated as follows:

$$\$001020 - \$001002 = \$001E$$

## 2.4.11.   PC-Relative with Index and Offset

This addressing mode is similar to PC-relative with offset except the offset is limited to 8 bits and an index register is also used in computing the effective address of the source operand. The offset is an 8-bit signed integer in the low-byte of the extension word. The high-byte of the extension word

specifies the index register. The format of the extension word is shown in Figure 2-25.

The effective address is formed by adding the sign-extended offset, the content of the index register, and the content of the program counter. As noted in the W/L field in Figure 2-25, the index register can be treated as a word or longword index. If a word index is used, it is sign-extended to 32 bits when the effective address is calculated. Any data or address register may be specified as the index register. An example is given in Figure 2-26.

One of the great benefits in using PC-relative addressing is in designing **position-independent code.** Position-independent code can be loaded at any address and executed. Obviously, references to absolute memory locations must be avoided. This

```
Instruction:   MOVE.W $1020(PC),D5

                **** MEMORY ****
                Address  Contents    Registers
        Before:  001020    AB        PC  00001000
                 001021    CD        D5  12345678

        After:   001020    AB        PC  00001004
                 001021    CD        D5  1234ABCD
```

Instruction is two words long, so PC is incremented by four

Figure 2-23.   PC-relative with offset.

```
1 00001000                       ORG        $1000
2 00001000 3A3A001E              MOVE.W     COUNT(PC),D5
3 00001020                       ORG        $1020
4 00001020 ABCD        COUNT     DC.W       $ABCD
```

Figure 2-24.   Listing example of PC-relative with offset addressing.

| 15 | 14 | 13 | 12 | 11 | 10 | 9 | 8 | 7 | 6 | 5 | 4 | 3 | 2 | 1 | 0 |
|----|----|----|----|----|----|---|---|---|---|---|---|---|---|---|---|
| D/A | Register | | | W/L | 0 | 0 | 0 | Displacement Integer | | | | | | | |

D/A field:
 0 = data register
 1 = address register
Register field:
 index register number
W/L field:
 0 = sign-extended, low-order word integer in index register
 1 = longword value in index register

**Figure 2-25.   Extension word for PC-relative with index and offset addressing.**

is illustrated in Figure 2-27 in a subroutine that computes the square of any integer from 0 to 10 using a table look-up method. The table is located immediately after the subroutine and access to the table uses PC-relative addressing with an index register and offset. A call to the subroutine to compute the square of 5 is shown in lines 2 and 3.

All the work is performed in the single MOVE.B instruction (line 5). Using D0 as an index into the table, the square of the value in D0 is read from the table and replaces the value in D0. The following instruction (line 6) returns from the subroutine to the main program. Note that computation of the square is quite fast as implemented above. Using a multiply instruction will take much longer to perform the same operation. Table look-up can be used to implement many other functions as well.

Even though the example in Figure 2-27 is *ORG-ed* to execute at $2000, the code is completely position-independent and could be loaded at any memory address and executed.

## 2.4.12.  Immediate Addressing

Immediate addressing uses one or two extension words to hold the source operand. For byte or word operations, a single extension word is used (byte values are stored in bits 0–7). Longword operations require two extension words with the high-order word first and the low-order word second. An example is given in Figure 2-28.

The base of the immediate data may be specified in decimal, hexadecimal, octal, or binary, as shown in Figure 2-28. ASCII codes may be used by enclosing characters in single quotes.

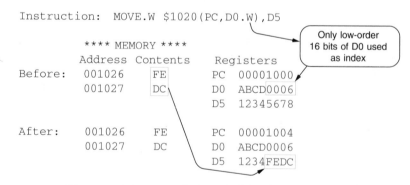

**Figure 2-26.   PC-relative with index and offset.**

```
1 00002000                       ORG      $2000
2 00002000 303C0005              MOVE.W   #5,D0
3 00002004 6102         BSR.S    SQUARE
4 00002006 60FE         BRA      *
5 00002008 103B0004     SQUARE   MOVE.B   TABLE(PC,D0.W),D0
6 0000200C 4E75                  RTS
7 0000200E 00010409     TABLE    DC.B     0,1,4,9,16,25
  00002012 1019
8 00002014 24314051              DC.B     36,49,64,81,100
  00002018 64
```

**Figure 2-27.   Listing example of PC-relative with index and offset.**

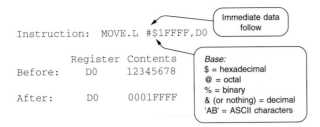

**Figure 2-28.** Immediate addressing.

A few examples are shown in Figure 2-29 in a program listing.

A variation of immediate addressing is *quick immediate*. This mode is available with the following instructions:

MOVEQ    move quick
ADDQ     add quick
SUBQ     subtract quick

MOVEQ includes an 8-bit signed integer in the low-byte (bits 0–7) of the instruction word. The data constant moved, however, is 32 bits; so the 8-bit value is sign-extended prior to the move. Most assemblers will automatically code a MOVE instruction as MOVEQ if the following conditions exist: (1) the size of the move is specified as long, and (2) the immediate data appearing in the instruction can be encoded in 8 bits. This is illustrated in Figure 2-30. The first instruction is MOVE.L and the assembler encoded it as expected—using two extension words for the 32-bit immediate data. The second instruction is also a MOVE.L. Since the immediate data can be encoded in 8 bits, the assembler chose the more efficient MOVEQ form of the instruction. The 8-bit immedi-

ate constant ($1F) appears in the low-byte of the instruction word. The third instruction, which is exactly the same operation as the second, is explicitly coded as MOVEQ.

ADDQ and SUBQ are slightly different from MOVEQ. Both ADDQ and SUBQ operate on byte, word, or longword data sizes; however, the immediate data value must be in the range 1 to 8. The data constant is encoded in a 3-bit field in the instruction word using $001_2 - 111_2$ as $1 - 7$ and $000_2$ as 8.

More detailed descriptions of these instructions are found in Appendix B. The encoding of instruction words is presented in Appendix C.

### 2.4.13. Implied Register

A few instructions implicitly use a register as a source or destination operand or in computing the effective address for branching. For example, the instruction

```
MOVE.B   #1,CCR
```

sets bit 0—the carry bit—in the condition code register and clears the other bits. The destination addressing mode is *implied register* since no field is present in the instruction word identifying the CCR: It is implicitly encoded in the instruction word. More examples of implied addressing can be found in Appendix B.

### 2.4.14. Relative Addressing

The 68000 includes several variations of branch instructions that use **relative addressing.** Since an

```
1 00001000                      ORG          $1000
2 00001000 203C0001             MOVE.L       #$1FFFF,D0
  00001004 FFFF
3 00001006 303C005A             MOVE.W       #'Z',D0
4 0000100A 103C00FD             MOVE.B       #-3,D0
5 0000100E 303CFFFD             MOVE.W       #-3,D0
6 00001012 103C000A             MOVE.B       #%1010,D0
7 00001016 203C0001             MOVE.L       #$1FFFF,D0
  0000101A FFFF
8 0000101C 701F                 MOVE.L       #$1F,D0
9 0000101E 701F                 MOVEQ        #$1F,D0
```

**Figure 2-29.** Listing example of immediate addressing.

```
7   00001016  203C0001          MOVE.L       #$1FFFF,D0
    0000101A  FFFF
8   0000101C  701F              MOVE.L       #$1F,D0
9   0000101E  701F              MOVEQ        #$1F,D0
```

**Figure 2-30.** Listing example of MOVEQ.

operand is not read or written, an addressing mode is not present in the conventional sense. Nevertheless, it is important to know how the destination address for the branch is computed. The technique is very similar to PC-relative with offset, except the assembly coding of the instruction does not reference the PC in the operand field. The following branch instructions use relative addressing:

BRA       branch always
Bcc       branch conditional
BSR       branch to subroutine
DBcc      test condition, decrement and branch

There are two variations of relative addressing: (a) using an 8-bit offset in the low-byte of the instruction word, or (b) using a 16-bit offset in an extension word. This is best illustrated through examples. See Figure 2-31.

Figure 2-31 includes two branch instructions (BRAs). The first BRA has $6000 as the instruction word. Since the low-byte is zero, an extension word is used as a 16-bit displacement in computing the branch destination. The value in the PC when the computation takes place is the address immediately following the instruction word, which, in this case, is the address of the extension word, $2000 + 2 = $2002. The branch destination is the label AHEAD at address $2020. The following equation is used:

```
PC + offset = branch destination
```

In this example, we have

```
$00002002 + $0000001E = $00002020
```

The second BRA uses a special assembler symbol as the branch destination. The asterisk ("*") means *the current location;* so the effect is a *branch to itself* instruction. An 8-bit offset appears in the low-byte of the instruction word ($FE). Since the branch instruction is in location $2022, the PC will contain $2024 when the branch destination is computed. The computation uses 32-bit arithmetic

```
1   00002000                        ORG    $2000
2   00002000   6000001E             BRA    AHEAD
3   00002020                        ORG    $2020
4   00002020   4E71       AHEAD     NOP
5   00002022   60FE                 BRA    *
```

Figure 2-31. Listing example of relative addressing.

```
1   00002000                        ORG    $2000
2   00002000   601E                 BRA.S  AHEAD
3   00002020                        ORG    $2020
4   00002020   4E71       AHEAD     NOP
5   00002022   60FE                 BRA    *
```

Figure 2-32. Forcing short form of relative addressing.

(as above); so, the 8-bit offset must be sign-extended as follows:

```
$00002024 + $FFFFFFFE = $00002022
```

An interesting observation about the first branch instruction in Figure 2-31 (line 2) is that a 16-bit displacement was used even though the branch destination was easily within the 8-bit range of −128 to +127. This occurred because the assembler could not determine the value of the label AHEAD when the instruction BRA AHEAD was assembled. (This occurs when branching forward in a program.) Therefore, the assembler used the form of the instruction with a 16-bit offset.[3] Obviously, the result is an inefficient machine language program. To avoid this, most assemblers include a mechanism to force the use of short (.S) or long (.L) forms of the instruction. Of course, it rests with the programmer to ensure that the branch destinations are *in range;* otherwise the assembler will generate an error message. To illustrate this, the example is repeated in Figure 2-32, forcing a short offset for the first branch instruction. The short form of BRA was forced by appending .S to the BRA mnemonic. This saves one word of memory and, therefore, reduces the execution time of the program.

The Bcc, DBcc, and BSR instructions (see Appendix A) are identical to BRA with respect to the offsets and the computation of the branch destination.

## 2.4.15. Addressing Mode Categories

Not all addressing modes are available for all instructions. To help identify which addressing modes are valid for each instruction, the addressing modes are placed in the categories identified in Table 2-2.

There is, of course, some basis underlying each category. The *data* category consists of addressing modes that may identify a data operand, as op-

---

[3]This is a common side effect of most two-pass assemblers. Two-pass assemblers are discussed in Chapter 4.

Table 2-2. Addressing Mode Categories

| Addressing Mode | Data | Memory | Control | Alterable | Data Alterable | Memory Alterable | Control Alterable | All |
|---|---|---|---|---|---|---|---|---|
| Data Register Direct | • | | | | • | • | | • |
| Address Register Direct | | | | | • | | | • |
| Address Register Indirect | • | • | • | | • | • | • | • |
| Postincrement Address Register Indirect | • | • | | | • | • | | • |
| Predecrement Address Register Indirect | • | • | | | • | • | | • |
| Address Reg. Indirect with Offset | • | • | • | | • | • | • | • |
| Address Reg. Indirect with Index and Offset | • | • | • | | • | • | • | • |
| Absolute Long | • | • | • | | • | • | • | • |
| Absolute Short | • | • | • | | • | • | • | • |
| PC-Relative with Offset | • | • | • | | | | | • |
| PC-Relative with Index and Offset | • | • | • | | | | | • |
| Immediate | • | • | • | | | | | • |

posed to an address operand. So, address register indirect is excluded from the data category. The *memory* category applies to any operand in a memory location (as opposed to a register). The *control* category identifies memory addresses without an associated size. The postincrement and predecrement modes are excluded since they alter a pointer register by the size of the operand (1, 2, or 4). The *alterable* modes refer to any operand that is writable. The alterable mode intent is to discourage programmers from writing *self-modifying code,* such as incrementing an absolute address within an instruction. For example, a memory location may not be written to use either of the PC-relative addressing modes.

Each of the data, control, and memory categories is combined with the alterable category to form a subset category. Each subset is the union of two categories. *Data alterable* modes, for example, are those that are valid both for the *data* and the *alterable* categories. The categories in Table 2-2 are mentioned throughout Appendix B wherever <*ea*> appears as the source or destination addressing mode. A few examples follow.

| | | |
|---|---|---|
| TST | <ea> | Only data alterable modes are allowed. |
| SUB | <ea>,Dn | Only memory alterable modes are allowed. |
| MOVEA | <ea>,An | All addressing modes are allowed. |
| JMP | <ea> | Only control addressing modes are allowed. |

## 2.5. HARDWARE SUMMARY

In this section, the hardware structure of the 68000 microprocessor is introduced. We will not discuss electrical properties or specific timing parameters for bus operations. These are given in the 68000 data sheet in Appendix G. Our discussion begins with the pin definitions on the 68000 IC. Figure 2-33 shows the pinouts grouped by function. The general operation of each signal is described in the following paragraphs. To see how the signals work together in a complete 68000-based system, see Chapter 8.

### 2.5.1. *Address Bus*

The 68000 has a 24-bit address bus. The 23 lines A1 through A23 encode a word address. The 24th line, A0, is not available externally. It appears implicitly as the upper data strobe ($\overline{\text{UDS}}$) and lower data strobe ($\overline{\text{LDS}}$) (see below) to identify even or odd bytes for 8-bit transfers. In total, the 24 address lines provide a memory space of $2^{24} = 16$ megabytes. In hexadecimal, addresses range from $000000 to $FFFFFF.

The address bus is unidirectional, three-state, and provides an address for all CPU cycles except the interrupt acknowledge cycle. In the latter case, A1, A2, and A3 provide the level of the interrupt being acknowledged and lines A4–A23 are driven high. Interrupts are discussed in detail in Chapter 7.

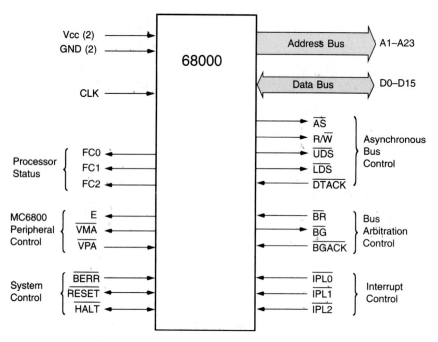

Figure 2-33.   68000 input/output signals.

## 2.5.2.   Data Bus

This bidirectional, three-state bus is the general-purpose data path between the CPU and external circuitry (RAM, ROM, I/O devices, etc.). It is 16 bits wide. However, byte transfers are also supported. During interrupt acknowledge cycles, the external device supplies the vector number on data lines D0–D7.

## 2.5.3.   Address Strobe

The address strobe ($\overline{AS}$) line is a three-state output which is driven low to indicate that the information on the address bus is a valid address. $\overline{AS}$ is the primary control signal to synchronize the address decoding circuitry for memory ICs or peripheral devices.

## 2.5.4.   Read/Write

The READ/$\overline{WRITE}$ (R/$\overline{W}$) line is a three-state output which is driven high when the data bus transfer is a read cycle (R/$\overline{W}$ = 1) or driven low to indicate that the data bus transfer is a write cycle (R/$\overline{W}$ = 0). The terms *read* and *write* are always with respect to the CPU. That is, a read operation transfers data from external circuitry (usually memory) into the CPU, and a write operation transfers data from inside the CPU (usually a register) to external memory or I/O devices.

## 2.5.5.   Upper and Lower Data Strobes

The upper data strobe ($\overline{UDS}$) and lower data strobe ($\overline{LDS}$) lines implicitly encode the internal state of the least-significant address line, A0, and, additionally provide for byte transfers on the 68000's 16-bit data bus. The relationship between $\overline{UDS}$, $\overline{LDS}$, and the internal signals A0 and WORD/$\overline{BYTE}$ is illustrated in Figure 2-34.

When the 68000 reads or writes a word of data (WORD/$\overline{BYTE}$ = 1), both $\overline{UDS}$ and $\overline{LDS}$ are driven low. If, however, the transfer is only 8 bits (WORD/$\overline{BYTE}$ = 0), A0 controls the state of $\overline{UDS}$ and $\overline{LDS}$. If A0 = 0, a byte at an even address is transferred ($\overline{UDS}$ = 0); or if A0 = 1, a byte at an odd address is transferred ($\overline{LDS}$ = 0). Longword (32-bit) transfers are also possible; however, these are realized as two consecutive word transfers.

The interface between the 68000 and *byte-wide* RAMs, such as the 8K-by-8 6264 discussed in Chapter 0 is straightforward. In Figure 2-35, the RAM connected to D8–D15 is designated the *upper RAM*, or *even RAM*, and the RAM connected to D0–D7 is designated the *lower RAM*, or *odd RAM*. The chip select ($\overline{CS}$) signal for the upper RAM is qualified with $\overline{UDS}$, while the chip select input for the lower RAM is qualified with $\overline{LDS}$.

## 2.5.6.   Data Transfer Acknowledge

The input signal $\overline{DTACK}$ indicates the completion of a data transfer. When the CPU receives a low on

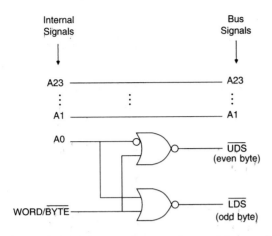

Figure 2-34. Upper data strobe and lower data strobe. (a) logic, (b) truth table.

| WORD/BYTE | A0 | UDS | LDS |
|-----------|-----|-----|-----|
| 1 | X | 0 | 0 |
| 0 | 0 | 0 | 1 |
| 0 | 1 | 1 | 0 |

DTACK during a read cycle, data are latched in the destination register inside the CPU and the cycle is terminated. When the CPU receives a low on DTACK during a write cycle, the cycle is terminated with the assumption that the destination (usually a memory IC) has received the data.

DTACK is often generated through the address decode circuitry that selects memory ICs or I/O devices. For slow memory ICs or I/O devices, this circuitry can be designed to delay the generation of DTACK as appropriate to ensure a successful transfer. The amount of delay is often quoted as a number of CPU clock cycles. For a delay of one CPU clock cycle, the memory is said to include one **wait state,** and so on. Memory interfaces with zero wait states can operate as fast as the CPU.

DTACK is usually driven by a device such as the 7407 open-collector buffer. This allows multiple memory ICs or I/O devices to drive DTACK, as shown in Figure 2-36. This type of connection is called a *wire-OR*, since it implements a logical OR operation through a common wired connection.

(The wire-OR connection was discussed in Types of Outputs in Chapter 0.)

## 2.5.7. Bus Request

The input signal BR indicates to the CPU that a device needs to become the bus master. Bus requests can be issued at any time during a cycle or between cycles. As with DTACK, BR can be wire-ORed to allow multiple devices to generate bus requests.

## 2.5.8. Bus Grant

The signal BG is an output from the CPU to all other potential bus-master devices indicating that the processor will relinquish bus control at the end of the current bus cycle.

## 2.5.9. Bus Grant Acknowledge

The input signal BGACK indicates that a device has become the bus master. This signal should not be asserted until the following conditions exist:

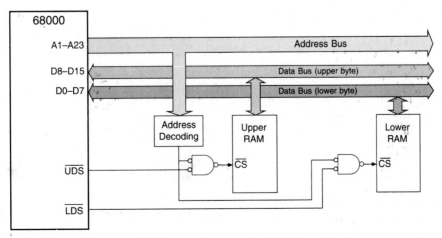

Figure 2-35. Decoding with UDS and LDS.

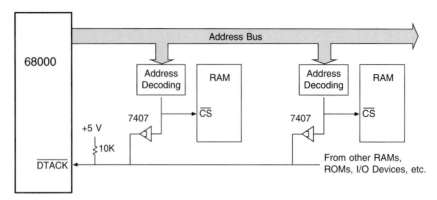

Figure 2-36.    Generation of DTACK.

- BG is active, indicating the CPU is prepared to relinquish the bus.
- AS is inactive, indicating the CPU is not using the bus.
- DTACK is inactive, indicating that neither memory nor peripherals are using the bus.
- BGACK is inactive, indicating no other device is still a bus master.

## 2.5.10.    Interrupt Priority Level

The input signals IPL0, IPL1, and IPL2 serve two purposes: to indicate an interrupt request from the peripheral device and to encode the interrupt priority level of the interrupting device. If any of these signals is driven low, an interrupt request is made pending. Furthermore, the combined state of these signals indicates the priority level of the interrupting device.

A level-0 interrupt (all three signals high) is the lowest priority level and indicates no interrupt request is pending. A level-7 interrupt (all three signals low) is the highest priority interrupt. Since interrupt requests are not latched, the interrupt priority level must be maintained on these signals until the CPU executes an interrupt acknowledge cycle. Interrupts are discussed in detail in Chapter 7.

## 2.5.11.    Bus Error

The input signal BERR indicates a problem in the current bus cycle. The problem may be:

- no response from a device
- no interrupt vector number received during interrupt acknowledge cycle
- an illegal access request through a memory management unit
- some other implementation-dependent error

No response from a device usually means that DTACK was not generated during an attempt to access a memory address. Regardless, circuitry must be provided to generate BERR. If the CPU does not receive a response on either DTACK, VPA, or BERR during a memory reference, the system hangs.

When a bus error occurs, the CPU either retries the bus cycle or initiates exception processing, as determined by the interaction between BERR and HALT.

A watchdog timer is often used to handle a bus cycle that does not terminate properly with DTACK. One possible implementation is shown in Figure 2-37 using a 74HC393 binary counter. Between bus cycles, AS is high, so the counter remains *clear*. Through the inverter on $Q_C$, BERR is driven high (inactive). At the beginning of each bus cycle, AS goes low, enabling the 74HC393 to count. Counting occurs through E, which pulses freely at one-tenth the CPU clock frequency. If the cycle is not terminated, AS will remain low and on the fourth E-clock (after about 40 CPU clocks), $Q_C$ goes high, driving BERR low. This creates a *bus error* condition. If, on the other hand, the cycle is terminated normally, AS returns high, thus clearing the counter and preventing a bus error condition.

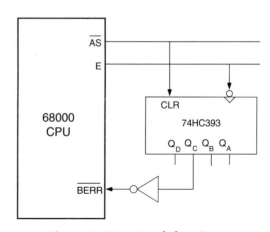

Figure 2-37.    Watchdog timer.

Through exception processing, it is often possible to determine the error and recover gracefully. Since the PC and SR are saved on the stack during exception processing, it is possible to determine where the program was executing when the error occurred, and, perhaps, determine which memory address was incorrectly referenced.

## 2.5.12. *Reset*

The external assertion of $\overline{RESET}$ along with the assertion of $\overline{HALT}$ starts a system reset to initialize both the CPU and external devices. $\overline{RESET}$ is a bidirectional signal. The CPU asserts $\overline{RESET}$ when the RESET instruction is executed. In this case, all external devices on the system are reset, but the internal state of the CPU is maintained. The reset operation is described in detail in Chapter 6.

## 2.5.13. *Halt*

When the input signal $\overline{HALT}$ is asserted, the CPU stops all bus activity at the end of the current bus cycle. All control signals enter the inactive state and all three-state lines enter the high-impedance state.

$\overline{HALT}$ is bidirectional. The CPU asserts $\overline{HALT}$ in certain instances (e.g., a double bus fault) to indicate the condition to external devices.

## 2.5.14. *Enable*

The 68000 architecture includes three control bus signals specifically for interfacing to peripheral devices that are compatible with the 68000's 8-bit predecessor—the 6800. These signals are enable (E), valid peripheral address ($\overline{VPA}$), and valid memory address ($\overline{VMA}$). Enable (E) is the clock signal to which the data and address information are synchronized during read or write transfers between the CPU and 6800-compatible peripherals.

Enable (E) is generated by an internal ring counter that may come up in any state upon power-up. Its phase relationship with the clock input (CLK) is indeterminate. Enable is a free-running clock that runs regardless of the CPU state. Detail timing diagrams are given in Appendix G.

## 2.5.15. *Valid Peripheral Address*

The assertion of the input signal $\overline{VPA}$ indicates that the device addressed is a 6800 device and that data transfers should be synchronized with enable (E).

A second use of $\overline{VPA}$ is during an interrupt acknowledge cycle. If $\overline{VPA}$ is asserted instead of $\overline{DTACK}$ during an interrupt acknowledge cycle, it indicates that the CPU should generate an auto-

vector for the pending interrupt. Interrupts are discussed in detail in Chapter 7.

## 2.5.16. *Valid Memory Address*

The output signal $\overline{VMA}$ indicates to 6800 peripheral devices that the address on the address bus is valid and that the CPU is synchronized to the enable (E) signal. $\overline{VMA}$ is asserted only in response to a $\overline{VPA}$ input that identifies a 6800 device. In most interfaces to 6800 peripherals, the $\overline{VMA}$ signal can be ignored.

## 2.5.17. *Processor Function Codes*

The function code outputs FC0, FC1, and FC2 indicate the current mode of execution (user or supervisor) and the type of address space currently being accessed (see Table 2-3). The function code outputs are valid whenever address strobe ($\overline{AS}$) is active.

As illustrated later in this chapter in the timings for read and write cycles, the function code lines are valid whenever the CPU is accessing memory ($\overline{AS}$ = 0). Note that FC2 indicates whether the current mode of operation is user (FC2 = 0) or supervisor (FC2 = 1). Similarly, FC1 indicates whether the current bus cycle is accessing a data operand (FC1 = 0) or an instruction word (FC1 = 1). Data accesses using PC-relative addressing will also yield FC1 = 1, since the operand is a data constant embedded in the program (e.g., an entry in a look-up table).

During interrupt acknowledge cycles, all function code outputs equal one. This condition in conjunction with address lines A1–A3 (which indicate the level of the interrupt being responded to), signals external devices that their interrupt request is being responded to. See Chapter 7 and Chapter 8 for implementation examples.

One use of the function code outputs is implementing memory management or memory protection logic. If a certain region of the system's mem-

Table 2-3.  Function Code Outputs

| Function Code | | | |
| --- | --- | --- | --- |
| FC2 | FC1 | FC0 | Address Space Type |
| 0 | 0 | 0 | (Undefined, reserved) |
| 0 | 0 | 1 | User Data |
| 0 | 1 | 0 | User Program |
| 0 | 1 | 1 | (Undefined, reserved) |
| 1 | 0 | 0 | (Undefined, reserved) |
| 1 | 0 | 1 | Supervisor Data |
| 1 | 1 | 0 | Supervisor Program |
| 1 | 1 | 1 | CPU Space (Interrupt Acknowledge) |

ory space is for user programs, while another region is for system programs, then the function code outputs can be used to prevent user programs from accessing the system space. An *access violation* signal can be implemented to signal a memory reference to an address in the system region while FC2 = 1.

### 2.5.18.   Clock

The clock input is a TTL-compatible signal that is internally buffered for development of the internal clocks needed by the CPU. This clock signal must be a constant frequency square wave and must not be gated off at any time. The clock signal must conform to minimum and maximum pulse-width times listed in 68000's data sheet (see Appendix G).

### 2.5.19.   Power and Ground

A power supply ($V_{CC}$) of +5 volts is presented to two pins on the 68000 IC. A ground connection (GND) is also required on two pins. The power requirements and dissipation characteristics of the 68000 are given in Appendix G. Under most circumstances, the power supply current drawn by the 68000 IC is less than 750 mA.

### 2.5.20.   Signal Summary

Table 2-4 summarizes the 68000 address, data, and control signals presented in the preceding pages.

## 2.6.   DATA TRANSFER TIMINGS

The following paragraphs describe the data bus, address bus, and control bus timings for data transfer operations. To keep our discussions simple, specific timing parameters are not discussed. These are found in Appendix G. The transfer of data between the CPU and memory ICs or peripheral devices involves the following signals:

- address bus lines A1–A23
- data bus lines D0–D15
- control bus lines $\overline{AS}$, $\overline{UDS}$, $\overline{LDS}$, R/$\overline{W}$, and $\overline{DTACK}$

The address and data buses are separate parallel buses using an asynchronous bus structure. *Asynchronous*, in this sense, means that there is no common clock signal used by both devices (the CPU and memory) to coordinate the transfer. The two main types of bus cycles are the **read cycle** and the **write cycle.** Although the data bus is 16 bits wide, transfers of 8 bits or 16 bits are supported. Longword (32-bit) transfers are supported in the 68000's instruction set; however, these require two consecutive 16-bit transfers. A longword transfer is in all respects identical to two word transfers and is not discussed further in this section.

Table 2-4.   Signal Summary

| Signal Name | Mnemonic | Input/Output | Active State |
| --- | --- | --- | --- |
| Address Bus | A1–A23 | Output | High |
| Data Bus | D0–D15 | I/O | High |
| Address Strobe | $\overline{AS}$ | Output | Low |
| Read/Write | R/$\overline{W}$ | Output | Read-High Write-Low |
| Upper Data Strobe | $\overline{UDS}$ | Output | Low |
| Lower Data Strobe | $\overline{LDS}$ | Output | Low |
| Data Transfer Acknowledge | $\overline{DTACK}$ | Input | Low |
| Bus Request | $\overline{BR}$ | Input | Low |
| Bus Grant | $\overline{BG}$ | Output | Low |
| Bus Grant Acknowledge | $\overline{BGACK}$ | Input | Low |
| Interrupt Priority Level | $\overline{IPL0}$, $\overline{IPL1}$, $\overline{IPL2}$ | Input | Low |
| Bus Error | $\overline{BERR}$ | Input | Low |
| Reset | $\overline{RESET}$ | I/O | Low |
| Halt | $\overline{HALT}$ | I/O | Low |
| Enable | E | Output | High |
| Valid Memory Address | $\overline{VMA}$ | Output | Low |
| Valid Peripheral Address | $\overline{VPA}$ | Input | Low |
| Function Codes | FC0,FC1,FC2 | Output | High |
| Clock | CLK | Input | High |

## 2.6.1. Read Cycle

During a read cycle, the CPU receives either one or two bytes of data from the memory or peripheral device. If the instruction specifies a word transfer, both the upper data strobe ($\overline{UDS}$) and the lower data strobe ($\overline{LDS}$) are asserted (driven low) by the CPU. When the instruction specifies a byte transfer, the CPU uses the internal signal A0 to determine which byte to read (even or odd) and generates the appropriate data strobe. If A0 = 0, an even byte is transferred across lines D8–D15 and $\overline{UDS}$ is asserted. If A0 = 1, an odd byte is transferred across lines D0–D7 and $\overline{LDS}$ is asserted. The read-cycle timing for a word transfer is shown in Figure 2-38.

Note in the figure that a read cycle takes four cycles of the CPU's clock signal, CLK. One period of the CPU's clock is called a **machine cycle.** Each half of a machine cycle is identified as a *state*—S0, S1, and so on. If, for example, the CPU is operating with a 10 MHz clock, then the clock period is 0.1 μs = 100 ns, and the total time for the read cycle in Figure 2-38 is $4 \times 100 = 400$ ns.

The key to understanding the timings lies in distinguishing the input signals from the output signals. For a read cycle, all the signals shown in Figure 2-38 are outputs from the CPU except $\overline{DTACK}$ and the data bus lines, D0–D15. The timings for the output signals show what the CPU *gen-*

*erates.* The timings for the input signals show what the CPU *expects.* The following is a state-by-state description of the read-cycle timing:

S0    The CPU places a valid function code on FC0–FC2 indicating the type of cycle, and drives R/$\overline{W}$ high to indicate a read cycle.

S1    The CPU places a valid address on lines A1–A23.

S2    The CPU asserts $\overline{AS}$, $\overline{UDS}$, and $\overline{LDS}$. (Since the timing in Figure 2-38 is for a word transfer, both $\overline{UDS}$ and $\overline{LDS}$ are asserted.)

S3    No bus signals are altered.

S4    The CPU waits for the memory or peripheral to respond by placing data on lines D0–D15 and asserting $\overline{DTACK}$.

S5    No bus signals are altered.

S6    State 6 is entered only when the CPU has received $\overline{DTACK}$ (or $\overline{BERR}$ or $\overline{VPA}$) in S4. It is assumed that valid data are on lines D0–D15.

S7    The CPU latches data into an internal register on the falling edge of CLK as it enters S7. At the same time, the CPU negates (de-asserts) $\overline{AS}$, $\overline{UDS}$, and $\overline{LDS}$. At the end of S7 (rising edge of CLK), the CPU places the address bus in the high-impedance state. The memory or peripheral can de-assert $\overline{DTACK}$ at this time.

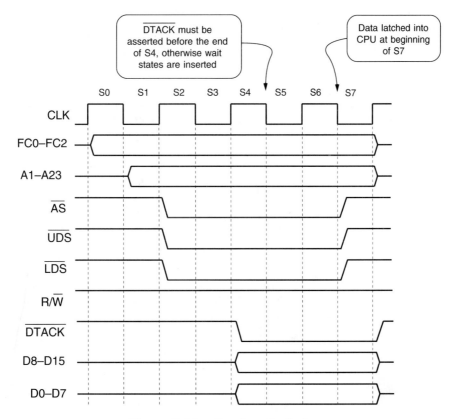

**Figure 2-38.    Read-cycle timing.**

State 4 is critical. If the CPU does not receive $\overline{\text{DTACK}}$ by the end of S4, it will insert wait states consisting of whole clock cycles (S4 + S5) until it detects a low on $\overline{\text{DTACK}}$. Alternately, $\overline{\text{VPA}}$ may be asserted if the access is to a 6800 peripheral that requires the special timings afforded by the signals enable (E) and $\overline{\text{VMA}}$. Another possibility is for the cycle to terminate by asserting $\overline{\text{BERR}}$, in which case the CPU will proceed to re-try the current bus cycle or will initiate exception processing. In the worst case, neither $\overline{\text{DTACK}}$, $\overline{\text{VPA}}$, nor $\overline{\text{BERR}}$ are received: The CPU will hang. A watchdog timer is often used to ensure this never occurs (see Figure 2-37).

> **Example 2-1:** If a 68000 is operating from a 4 MHz clock, what is the duration of a read cycle with (a) zero wait states, (b) 1 wait state, or (c) n wait states?
>
> **Solution:** (a) 1 μs, (b) 1.25 μs, (c) (1 + n × 0.25) μs
>
> **Discussion:** At CLK = 4 MHz, $t_C = 1/4$ μs = 0.25 μs. Since a read cycle takes 4 cycles of CLK, the answer for (a) is 4 × 0.25 = 1 μs. Each wait state adds one clock period, or 0.25 μs, to the read-cycle time; so, the answer for (b) is 1 + 0.25 = 1.25 μs, and for (c) (1 + n × 0.25) μs.  ∎

For byte transfers into the CPU, the timing is the same as shown in Figure 2-38 except only one of $\overline{\text{UDS}}$ or $\overline{\text{LDS}}$ is asserted and only 8 bits of data are latched internally. When reading a byte from an odd address, data are read on lines D0–D7 and lines D8–D15 are ignored. When reading a byte from an even address, data are read on lines D8–D15 and lines D0–D7 are ignored.

## 2.6.2.  Write Cycle

During a write cycle, the CPU sends data from an internal register to an external memory IC or peripheral device. The assertion of $\overline{\text{UDS}}$ or $\overline{\text{LDS}}$ with respect to byte vs. word transfers is identical to the read-cycle timing. The write-cycle timing for a word transfer is shown in Figure 2-39.

For a write cycle, all the signals shown in Figure 2-39 are outputs from the CPU except $\overline{\text{DTACK}}$. The following is a state-by-state description of the write-cycle timing:

S0   The CPU places a valid function code on FC0–FC2 and drives R/$\overline{\text{W}}$ high (just in case the preceding cycle has left R/$\overline{\text{W}}$ low).

S1   The CPU places a valid address on lines A1–A23.

S2   The CPU asserts $\overline{\text{AS}}$ and drives R/$\overline{\text{W}}$ low indicating a write cycle.

S3   The data bus lines are taken out of the high-impedance state and the data to be written are placed on lines D0–D15.

S4   The CPU asserts $\overline{\text{UDS}}$ and $\overline{\text{LDS}}$ at the beginning of S4 (rising edge of CLK) and waits for $\overline{\text{DTACK}}$ as a cycle termination signal. (Alternately, $\overline{\text{VPA}}$ or $\overline{\text{BERR}}$ can terminate the cycle, as with the read cycle.) The CPU will insert wait states (full clock cycles; S4 + S5) until a termination signal is received.

S5   No bus signals are altered.

S6   No bus signals are altered.

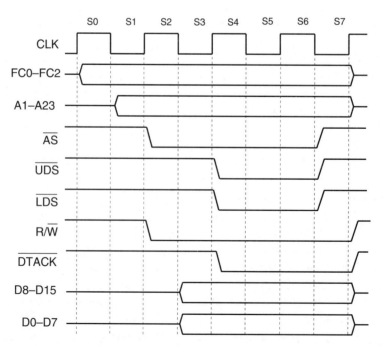

**Figure 2-39.   Write-cycle timing.**

S7  At the beginning of S7 (falling edge of CLK), the CPU de-asserts $\overline{AS}$, $\overline{UDS}$, and $\overline{LDS}$. At the end of S7 (rising edge of CLK), the CPU places the address bus and data bus in the high-impedance state and drives R/$\overline{W}$ high. The memory or peripheral device may de-assert $\overline{DTACK}$ at this time.

## 2.7. SUMMARY

This chapter has introduced the 68000 microprocessor's programming model, hardware structure, and memory addressing capabilities. The examples were limited to simple instructions, primarily MOVE. In the next chapter we will examine the 68000's instruction set and present more advanced programming examples.

## 2.8. QUESTIONS

1. How many bits are defined in the 68000 status register? Which bits are available in user mode?

2. D5 contains $FFFFF000 just before the instruction MOVE.W #$F3,D0 executes. What is the value in D5 after this instruction?

3. A3 contains $12345678 just before the instruction MOVEA.W #$1000,A3 executes. What is the value in A3 after this instruction?

4. A7 contains $00002000 just before the instruction BSR $3000 executes. What is the value in A7 after this instruction?

5. D7 contains $FFFFFFFF just before the instruction ADD.B #1,D7 executes. What are the contents of D7 and the condition code register after this instruction?

6. The condition code register contains $15 just before the instruction BGT $3000 executes. Does the branch take place?

7. The condition code register contains $1B and the PC contains $2FF0 just before the instruction BLT.S $3000 executes. What is the content of the PC after this instruction?

8. If the 68000 memory map is split exactly in half, what is the last hexadecimal address in the first half? What is the first hexadecimal address in the second half?

9. What is the maximum number of 64K by 8 RAMs that could be interfaced to the 68000?

10. A longword variable is stored in memory at address $001F00. What is the address of the longword variable immediately following this variable?

11. What is wrong with the instruction MOVE.W #100,$FFFF?

12. What is wrong with the instruction MOVEA.B #$55,A5?

13. What is wrong with the instruction MOVE.L #%1010,$10(PC,D2.L)?

14. What is the hexadecimal content of D7 after the instruction MOVE.L #%11110,D7 executes?

15. A0 contains $00002000 just before the instruction MOVE.B #1,(A0)+ executes. What is the value of A0 after this instruction?

16. A7 contains $00002000 just before the instruction MOVE.B #1,(A7)+ executes. What is the value of A7 after this instruction?

17. A4 contains $00010000 just before the instruction MOVE.L #1,−(A4) executes. What is the value of A4 after this instruction?

18. What is the source extension word for the instruction MOVEA $10(A0,D7.L),A1?

19. If the instruction MOVE.W $2040(PC),D4 is in memory at address $002030, what is the extension word for the source operand?

20. If the instruction MOVE.B $F0000(PC,D5.W), D2 is in memory at address $00F0040, what is the extension word for the source operand?

21. D5 contains $AAAAAAAA just before the instruction MOVEQ #1,D5 executes. What is the value in D5 after this instruction?

22. D5 contains $AAAAAAAA just before the instruction MOVE #1,D5 executes. What is the value in D5 after this instruction?

23. Assume the instruction BRA AHEAD is in memory location $004030 and the label AHEAD represents the instruction at address $4040. What is the offset for this instruction? Will the offset be stored as an 8-bit or 16-bit value by a typical assembler? Why?

24. The instruction BRA $4000 is in memory location $005000. What is the offset for this instruction?

25. Devise five questions similar to questions 11–13. Use instructions that are plausible except for a minor mistake that a careless programmer might overlook. Provide answers to your questions.

26. What is wrong with the instruction MOVE #%1011,A8?

27. An EPROM at the bottom of the 68000's memory space contains the following data:

| Address | Contents |
|---------|----------|
| 000000  | 0040     |
| 000002  | 0000     |
| 000004  | 0006     |
| 000006  | 0000     |
| 000008  | ABCD     |

   (a) From which address is the first instruction fetched following a power-on reset?
   (b) What is the value of the supervisor stack pointer immediately following a power-on reset?

28. What happens if, during a memory read cycle, the CPU does not receive a response on $\overline{\text{DTACK}}$, $\overline{\text{VPA}}$, or $\overline{\text{BERR}}$?

29. What is the difference between the following two instructions?

   MOVE.L $1000,D7    MOVE.L #$1000,D7

30. Identify the addressing modes for the source and destination operands in the following instructions:

   (a)  MOVE.L   D0,$0400
   (b)  MOVE.B   #−25,(A4)
   (c)  MOVE.B   $8000,LIST(A4)
   (d)  MOVE.W   TABLE(PC),$FF8000
   (e)  MOVE.W   #$FFFF,OFFSET(A0,A1)
   (f)  MOVE.L   LOOKUP(PC,D7.W),$123456
   (g)  MOVE.W   TEMP1,TEMP2
   (h)  MOVE.W   #1,−1(A4,D5.W)
   (i)  MOVE.W   (A4),−(A7)
   (j)  MOVE.B   $100,(A6)+

31. Under what conditions will the effect of the following instructions be the same?

   MOVE   D0,$1234

   MOVE   D0,(A0)

   MOVE   D0,8(A7)

   MOVE   D0,0(A4,D5,W)

   MOVE   D0,−(A6)

   MOVE   D0,(A0)+

   MOVE   D0,−16(A5)

# 3. Instruction Set

## 3.1 INTRODUCTION

This chapter introduces the 68000 instruction set. Eight categories of instructions are identified and selected examples are given. Many details of the instruction set are also uncovered by examining the *binary encoding* of instruction words and the *timings* and *bus activity* during execution. For the most part, this chapter should be viewed as *supplemental* information to explain through examples. The primary references for the 68000 instruction set are Appendix A through Appendix D, as summarized in Table 3-1.

***Condition Code Bits*** The way condition code bits are affected is critical to understanding the operation of each instruction. Where appropriate in the examples that follow, calculations are shown in binary for each CCR bit; however, the before/after values are shown in hexadecimal. The binary position of each bit in the CCR is shown in Figure 3-1 as a reminder of this relationship.

***Incremental Learning*** To assist students, Table 3-2 is a guide to incremental learning of the 68000's instruction set. Instructions labeled *introductory* will be familiar to anyone who has studied 8-bit microprocessors. The reader should strive to learn these instructions in detail on a *first-pass* through the instruction set. Many useful and powerful programs can be written only by using these instructions.

Instructions identified as *intermediate* are slightly more complex, introducing operations that most 8-bit microprocessors do not have. In particular, *exception processing* is introduced with the TRAP and RTE instructions. The reader is advised to learn the intermediate instructions only when comfortable with basic 68000 operations.

Finally, nine instructions are listed as *advanced*. Some of these are very straightforward (e.g., RESET); however, none is essential for the most common 68000 programming problems. The reader may defer studying these instructions until comfortable with the 68000 architecture and the introductory and intermediate instructions.

The labels *Introductory, Intermediate,* and *Advanced* appear throughout the next section where individual instructions are discussed. These are added to help students and teachers chart an appropriate course of study. A reasonable approach, for example, would be to defer studying the intermediate and advanced instructions until an appropriate time later.

## 3.2 INSTRUCTION CATEGORIES

The 68000 instruction set implements a rich assortment of operations. These are categorized as follows:

- data movement
- integer arithmetic
- Boolean
- shift and rotate
- bit manipulation
- binary-coded decimal
- program flow
- system control

### 3.2.1 Data-Movement Instructions

Data-movement instructions provide the facility to move operands (data) among memory locations or registers. Operands may be bytes (8 bits), words (16 bits), or longwords (32 bits). The size of operand available to each instruction is specified in Appendix B. Table 3-3 summarizes the data-movement instructions.

***MOVE, MOVEA, and MOVEQ*** **(Introductory)**
The MOVE instruction was used extensively in the examples in Chapter 2, so we will not dwell on it here. MOVEA is used when the destination is an address register. Only word or longword operands are supported, and if a word is specified, it is sign-extended to 32 bits when writing to the address register.

MOVEQ is a one-word variation of MOVE that encodes an 8-bit immediate source operand in the low-byte of the instruction word. The destina-

Table 3-1.    Instruction Set Appendices.

| Appendix | Content |
|---|---|
| A | Condition Codes Computation |
| B | Instruction Definitions |
| C | Machine Language Summary |
| D | Instruction Execution Times |

Table 3-2.    Incremental Learning of 68000 Instructions.

| Introductory Instructions | | Intermediate Instructions | Advanced Instructions |
|---|---|---|---|
| ABCD | MOVE | BCHG | CHK |
| ADD | MOVEA | BCLR | ILLEGAL |
| AND | MOVEQ | BSET | LINK |
| ASL, ASR | NEG | BTST | MOVEP |
| Bcc | NOP | DIV | RESET |
| BRA | NOT | EXT | STOP |
| BSR | OR | LEA | TAS |
| CLR | ROR, ROL | MOVEM | TRAPV |
| CMP | ROXR, ROXL | MUL | UNLK |
| EOR | RTS | PEA | |
| EXG | SBCD | RTE | |
| JMP | SUB | RTR | |
| JSR | SWAP | Scc | |
| LSL, LSR | TST | TRAP | |
| | | DBcc | |

tion for MOVEQ must be a 32-bit data register. Most assemblers automatically convert MOVE to MOVEA or MOVEQ as appropriate, depending on the specification of the source and destination operands.

### MOVEM                                    (Intermediate)
MOVEM moves multiple registers to or from memory locations. Any of the data or address registers may be specified. For example,

```
MOVEM.W  D3-D5/A2,-(A7)
```

moves the low words of registers D3, D4, D5, and A2 to the stack (see Figure 3-2a). The dash indicates a range of registers, so D3–D5 means D3, D4, and D5. A forward slash separates individual registers. The registers are identified in a **register list mask** following the instruction word (Figure 3-2b). The same set of registers can be restored later with

```
MOVEM.W  (A7)+,D3-D5/A2
```

The bit sequence for the register bit mask is reversed when restoring registers (see Appendix B).

### MOVEP                                    (Advanced)
MOVEP facilitates word or longword transfers to 8-bit peripherals. Since 8-bit peripherals only have eight data lines, the interface to the 68000 uses either the upper byte (D8–D15) or the lower byte (D0–D7) of the data bus. Peripheral interface ICs usually contain many registers, so the addresses are either consecutive odd bytes or consecutive even bytes in the memory space. This poses a problem for multi-byte transfers. MOVEP solves

this by transferring either a word or longword operand over consecutive even or odd bytes in the memory space. For example, if we assume A0 = $0000C001 and D0 = $12345678, then

```
MOVEP.W  D0,0(A0)
```

transfers the byte $56 to address $00C001 and the byte $78 to address $00C003. This is illustrated in Figure 3-3. MOVEP uses a data register for either the source or destination operand. The other operand is specified using register indirect addressing with a 16-bit offset.

### LEA and PEA                             (Intermediate)
LEA (load effective address) transfers the source operand's address (rather than its contents) to a destination address register. Thus, the following two instructions are the same:

```
MOVEA.L  #ARRAY,A5
LEA      ARRAY,A5
```

Table 3-3.    Data-Movement Instructions.

| Instruction | Operation |
|---|---|
| EXG | Exchange registers |
| LEA | Load effective address |
| LINK | Link and allocate stack |
| MOVE | Move source to destination |
| MOVEA | Move source to address register |
| MOVEM | Move multiple registers |
| MOVEP | Move to peripheral |
| MOVEQ | Move short data to destination |
| PEA | Push effective address |
| UNLK | Unlink stack |

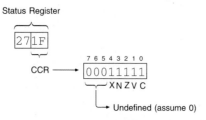

Figure 3-1.    CCR bit positions.

Instruction: MOVEM.W D3-D5/A2,-(A7)

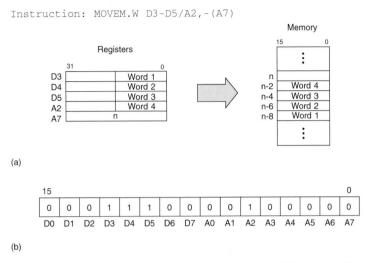

(a)

(b)

Figure 3-2.   MOVEM example. (a) data movement, (b) register list mask.

LEA usually appears when adjusting a pointer by an index or offset, or both. For example,

```
LEA        6(A0,D5.L),A0
```

loads A0 with the effective address represented by 6(A0,D5.L). The new value of A0 is the old value + 6 + the content of D5.

PEA (push effective address) is similar to LEA in that it moves an effective address rather than the operand specified by the effective address. However, PEA moves the effective address to the active stack (user or supervisor) rather than to an address register. One use of PEA is passing a pointer to a subroutine. The pointer can point to a parameter list for use in the subroutine. Just before calling the subroutine, the pointer is saved on the stack as follows:

```
PEA        PARAMS
BSR        SUBRTNE
```

Within the subroutine, the variables are accessed after initializing an address register with the address of the parameters. For example,

```
MOVEA.L   4(SP),A5
```

Instruction: MOVEP.W D0,0(A0)

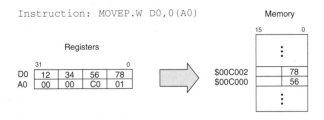

Figure 3-3.   MOVEP example.

### LINK and UNLK                          (Advanced)

The LINK (link and allocate) and UNLK (unlink) instructions work together. LINK has two purposes: to create a pointer to a parameter list (while saving the old pointer), and to create temporary storage for local variables within subroutines. LINK takes two arguments: an address register, called a **frame pointer,** and a data constant. For example,

```
LINK  An,#data
```

pushes *An* onto the stack, copies the stack pointer (SP) into *An,* then adds *data* to the SP. To allocate space for local variables, the immediate data constant must be negative and must equal the number of bytes of storage to allocate. The allocated space is called a **frame.** In the subroutine, the *An* acts as a pointer to the local variables or parameters passed to the subroutine. UNLK takes the address register (the frame pointer) as an operand and deallocates the storage occupied by the local variables and restores the old value of the pointer. The deallocation occurs simply by reloading the SP with the address pointed at by the frame pointer.

The best way to learn about LINK and UNLK is through a simple example. In Figure 3-4, two parameters are pushed on the stack and then a subroutine is called in the usual way. The state of the stack immediately after the subroutine call is illustrated at "1." The first instruction in the subroutine is LINK A5,# −12. A5 becomes the frame pointer and 12 bytes of storage are allocated for local use. The state of the stack immediately after LINK executes is illustrated at "2." Within the subroutine, parameters passed to the subroutine are accessed using address register indirect addressing with the appropriate offset. Access to parameter P2 is illus-

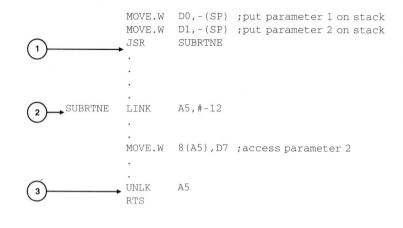

```
            MOVE.W   D0,-(SP)  ;put parameter 1 on stack
            MOVE.W   D1,-(SP)  ;put parameter 2 on stack
 (1)        JSR      SUBRTNE
              .
              .
              .
              .
 (2)  SUBRTNE LINK    A5,#-12
              .
              .
            MOVE.W   8(A5),D7  ;access parameter 2
              .
              .
 (3)        UNLK     A5
            RTS
```

(a)

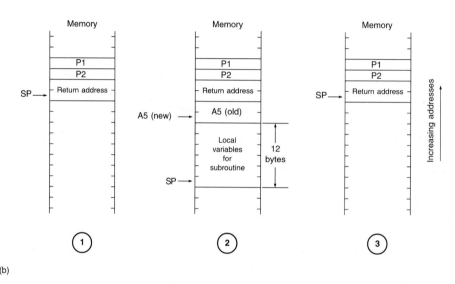

(b)

Figure 3-4.   LINK/UNLK example. (a) program listing, (b) memory allocation.

trated in Figure 3-4a. The effective address of P2 is 8(A5), which can be determined by counting up (in bytes) from *A5 (new)* in Figure 3-4b. Just before returning to the main program, the frame is deallocated and the SP and the old frame pointer are restored. The state of the stack immediately after UNLK executes is illustrated at "3." Notice that the stack is returned to the state it was in just before LINK executed, illustrated at "1."

### *EXG*                          (Introductory)
The EXG (exchange registers) instruction exchanges the contents of two registers. Either data or address registers may be specified. The entire 32-bit contents of both registers are exchanged.

### 3.2.2  *Integer-Arithmetic Instructions*

The 68000 supports a variety of integer-arithmetic operations on byte, word, or longword operands (see Table 3-4).

### *Add and Subtract Instructions*      (Introductory)
An example of the ADD instruction was given in Chapter 2 to illustrate the computation of the CCR bits. ADDX and SUBX permit multi-precision addition and subtraction operations by adding or subtracting the X-bit as well as the two operands. It is assumed that the X-bit holds the carry from a previous operation on lower-order operands.

Both operands must be specified either using data register direct addressing or predecrement address register indirect addressing. For example, if D0/D1 and D2/D3 each contain 64-bit integers (with the high-order longword in the first register and the low-order longword in the second register), then the 64-bit sum is computed as follows:

```
            ADD.L    D1,D3
            ADDX.L   D0,D2
```

The 16-bit sum is left in D2/D3. An important feature of ADDX (and SUBX) is the treatment of

Table 3-4. Integer Arithmetic Instructions.

| Instruction | Operation |
|---|---|
| ADD | Add source to destination |
| ADDA | Add source to address register |
| ADDI | Add immediate data to destination |
| ADDQ | Add short data to destination |
| ADDX | Add with extend bit to destination |
| CLR | Clear operand |
| CMP | Compare source to destination |
| CMPA | Compare source to address register |
| CMPM | Compare memory |
| DIVS | Signed divide |
| DIVU | Unsigned divide |
| EXT | Sign extend |
| EXTB | Sign extend byte |
| MULS | Signed multiply |
| MULU | Unsigned multiply |
| NEG | Negate |
| NEGX | Negate with extend |
| SUB | Subtract source from destination |
| SUBA | Subtract source from address register |
| SUBI | Subtract immediate from destination |
| SUBQ | Subtract short from destination |
| SUBX | Subtract with extend bit from destination |

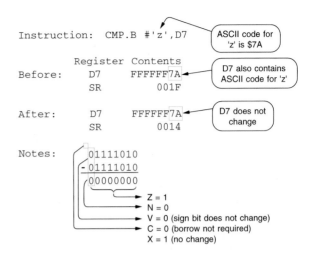

Figure 3-5. CMP example.

the Z-bit in the CCR. Appendix B describes the Z-bit computation for these instructions as *Cleared if the result is non-zero. Unchanged otherwise* (see page 272 and page 357). So, for multi-precision operations, Z is set after the final operation only if all operations yielded a result of zero. If any operation yielded a non-zero result, Z is clear after the final operation. This is important for multi-precision operations because it allows Z to reflect the state of the *entire result*, rather than the state of the high-order operand only.

### *Compare Instructions* (Introductory)

The CMP (compare) instruction is very similar to the subtract instruction (see Figure 3-5). The main difference is that the result of the subtraction is ignored with the compare instruction.

The sole purpose of the compare instruction is to set or clear bits in the condition code register so that a subsequent conditional branch can take an appropriate action. In Figure 3-5, perhaps an ASCII character was read from a terminal and placed in D7. Suppose further that the letter *z* is special in some way. If there is an appropriate action for D7 = *z* (ISZ) and an alternate action for D7 ≠ *z* (ISNOTZ), then the instruction sequence in Figure 3-6 could be used. The appropriate test is *branch if equal zero* (BEQ). If D7 contains the ASCII code for the letter *z* ($7A), then the Z-bit in the CCR is set immediately after the CMP instruction (as in Figure 3-5) and the branch takes place. Otherwise, the branch does not occur and the program continues with the next instruction.

As a further example of the CMP instruction, consider the subroutine in Figure 3-7 called ISDIGIT, which tests D7 to determine if it contains an ASCII code for a decimal digit (0 to 9). The subroutine uses the C-bit in the CCR as a *status flag* to return the result of the test to the calling program. If D7 is in the range "0" to "9" (i.e., $30 to $39),

```
          Address  Contents ******************* CH3-1.SRC *********************
       1  00001000                       ORG     $1000
       2  00001000 BE3C007A              CMP.B   #'z',D7  ;character = z?
       3  00001004 67000008              BEQ     ISZ      ;yes: execute ISZ
       4  00001008 4E71       ISNOTZ     NOP              ;no: execute ISNOTZ
       5                      *
       6                      * Do something if D7 != "z"
       7                      *
       8  0000100A 60000004              BRA     SKIP
       9  0000100E 4E71       ISZ        NOP
      10                      *
      11                      * Do something else if D7 = "z"
      12                      *
      13  00001010 4E71       SKIP       NOP              ;continue with program
      14  00001012                       END
```

Figure 3-6. Check for ASCII character.

```
        Address  Contents   ******************* CH3-2.SRC **************************
      1                     * ISDIGIT - Is D7 in the range $30 to $39?
      2                     *           Yes: return with C = 1
      3                     *           No:  return with C = 0
      4                     *
      5 00001000                       ORG    $1000
      6 00001000 BE3C0030   ISDIGIT    CMP.B  #'0',D7      ;compare: D7 - $30
      7 00001004 65000008              BCS    NO           ;If D7 < '0', not digit
      8 00001008 BE3C003A              CMP.B  #'9'+1,D7    ;compare: D7 - $3A
      9 0000100C 4E75                  RTS                 ;C set/clear correctly here
     10 0000100E 023C00FE   NO         ANDI   #$FE,CCR     ;if no, clear C bit
     11 00001012 4E75                  RTS                 ;return to calling program
     12 00001014                       END
```

**Figure 3-7.   ISDIGIT subroutine.**

the subroutine returns with C = 1. Otherwise, the subroutine returns with C = 0. If the ASCII code in D7 is less than "0" ($30), the first compare finishes with C = 1. The BCS instruction branches ahead to the ANDI instruction which clears C. The following RTS instruction returns to the calling program with C = 0, indicating the character in D7 is *not* a digit. If D7 ≥ "0," it remains uncertain whether D7 contains a digit; therefore, a second CMP.B is needed. This time the compare is against "9" + 1 ($3A); so C is set only if D7 is a digit. C is clear if D7 > "9." The RTS immediately after the second compare returns with C correctly set or clear.

### Multiply and Divide   (Intermediate)

DIVS (signed divide) is illustrated through an example. In Figure 3-8, the integer $14_{10}$ is divided by $-3_{10}$. The correct decimal answer is $-4$ with a remainder of 2. The DIVS instruction works with a 32-bit dividend (the destination operand) and a 16-bit divisor (the source operand). The dividend must be a data register. The operands are treated as signed integers, such that

```
destination / source -> destination
```

The 16-bit result is stored in the low word of the destination. The 16-bit remainder is stored in the high word. The CCR bits are affected as described in Appendix A.

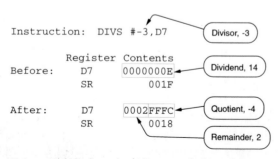

```
Notes: 14 / -3 = -4 with a remainder of 2
```

**Figure 3-8.   DIVS example.**

DIVU (unsigned divide) is the same as DIVS except both the dividend and the divisor are treated as unsigned integers. Both DIVU and DIVS generate a divide-by-zero trap in the event the dividend is zero.

MULU (unsigned multiply) multiplies two 16-bit unsigned integers and generates a 32-bit product. All 32 bits of the product are saved in the destination data register. MULS is the same except the numbers are treated as 16-bit signed integers.

### CLR and NEG   (Introductory)

CLR (clear) writes zeros into the destination operand. Byte, word, and longword data sizes are supported. NEG (negate) performs a 2s complement operation on destination data. The arithmetic effect is

```
0 - destination -> destination
```

Obviously, the effect is to turn a positive number into a negative number or vice versa. Note that for byte operands, an overflow only occurs if the original value is $80, since this is the only value ($-128_{10}$) for which the sign-reversed result is out of range ($+128_{10}$ cannot be represented as an 8-bit signed integer!). A similar condition applies for word ($8000) and longword ($80000000) operands.

NEGX subtracts the destination *and the X-bit in the CCR* from zero and stores the result in the destination. If, for example, NUMBER is the address of a 64-bit signed integer (first longword in the first address), then the sign of NUMBER is reversed as follows:

```
NEG.L     NUMBER+4
NEGX.L    NUMBER
```

The first operation negates the low-order 32 bits at the address NUMBER + 4 (four bytes past

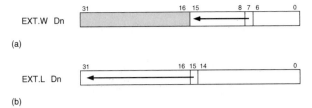

(a)

(b)

**Figure 3-9.** EXT example. (a) byte-to-word, (b) word-to-longword.

NUMBER). The second operation includes the borrow from the first operation (if one occurred) in the negation of the high-order 32 bits at the address NUMBER.

As with ADDX, the Z-bit is cleared if the result is non-zero, or is unchanged otherwise. This permits a correct test-for-zero after a multi-precision negate operation.

### EXT                                    (Intermediate)
EXT (sign-extend) is used to increase the bit size of a signed integer. There are two forms: EXT.W converts an 8-bit integer to 16 bits, and EXT.L converts a 16-bit integer to 32 bits. The destination operand must be a data register. The conversion is performed by copying the high-order bit in the original data through to the left to fill out the new value (see Figure 3-9). For example, if D5 contains $00000080 initially, EXT.W D5 leaves D5 with $0000FF80.

### 3.2.3  Boolean Instructions

The 68000's Boolean instructions implement the standard set of logical operations (see Table 3-5).

### Logical Instructions                  (Introductory)
The EOR (exclusive OR) instruction in Figure 3-10 performs a 32-bit exclusive OR operation on two

longword operands. Although the operation is shown in hexadecimal, 32 1-bit EXOR operations have taken place.

A common use of the logical AND instruction is to clear, or *mask*, certain bits in a destination operand. For example, if the low-byte in D0 contains an ASCII character in bits 0–6 and a parity bit in bit 7, then the parity bit can be stripped off as follows:

```
        ANDI.B  #%01111111,D0
```

This instruction leaves the low-order 7 bits *as is* and clears the high-order bit. (Recall from Chapter 0 that $X \cdot 1 = X$ and $X \cdot 0 = 0$.)

Similarly, the logical OR instruction is often used to set certain bits in a destination operand. If, for example, the low-order byte in D0 is known to contain an ASCII character in the range *A–Z*, then the character can be converted to lowercase as follows:

```
        ORI.B  #%00100000,D0
```

Uppercase and lowercase ASCII characters differ only in the bit position where the 1 appears above; for example, $A = 01000001_2$ and $a = 01100001_2$. By setting the bit indicated, the code is converted to lowercase.

### Scc                                    (Intermediate)
The set conditional instruction (SCC) tests the condition codes bits and then writes 1s (condition true) or 0s (condition false) to the destination. Only byte-size operands are supported.

### TST                                    (Introductory)
The test instruction, TST, is the same as CMP #0, destination.

### 3.2.4  Shift and Rotate Instructions

The 68000 supports a variety of shift and rotate instructions (see Table 3-6). If the data are in a register, a shift count determines the number of bit positions to shift. Data in memory locations may be shifted one position only.

### Arithmetic-Shift Instructions         (Introductory)
Arithmetic shift instructions treat data as signed integers. Shifting is analogous to multiplication by powers-of-two (ASL) or division by powers-of-two (ASR). Consider the value 4 represented as an 8-

**Table 3-5.  Boolean Instructions.**

| Instruction | Operation |
|---|---|
| AND | AND source to destination |
| ANDI | AND immediate data to destination |
| EOR ✓ | Exclusive OR source to destination |
| EORI | Exclusive OR immediate data to destination |
| NOT | Complement destination |
| OR | OR source to destination |
| ORI | OR immediate data to destination |
| Scc | Test condition codes and set operand |
| TST | Test operand and set condition codes |

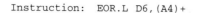

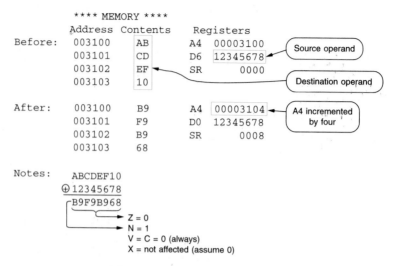

```
Instruction:   EOR.L  D6,(A4)+

                        **** MEMORY ****
                        Address  Contents      Registers
          Before:       003100     AB       A4   00003100          Source operand
                        003101     CD       D6   12345678
                        003102     EF       SR      0000           Destination operand
                        003103     10

          After:        003100     B9       A4   00003104          A4 incremented
                        003101     F9       D0   12345678            by four
                        003102     B9       SR      0008
                        003103     68

          Notes:        ABCDEF10
                      ⊕ 12345678
                        B9F9B968
                                        Z = 0
                                        N = 1
                                        V = C = 0 (always)
                                        X = not affected (assume 0)
```

Figure 3-10.  EOR example.

bit binary variable, $00000100_2$. Shifting left by one position yields $00001000_2 = 8_{10}$ which is the same as multiplication by two. Shifting left by $n$ positions is the same as multiplication by $2^n$.

In Figure 3-11, a count of two is used in an arithmetic shift of the byte variable $\$68 = 104_{10}$. An arithmetic shift right by two bit positions corresponds to division by four. The final result of $1A_{16} = 26_{10}$ is the correct answer to $104_{10} / 4$.

### Logical-Shift Instructions    (Introductory)

Logical shift instructions treat data as Boolean variables. One or more bits are lost, depending on the

shift count. If the shift is left, bits are lost from the most-significant side of the operand. If the shift is right, bits are lost from the least-significant side.

### Rotate Instructions    (Introductory)

Rotate instructions keep all bits by performing a circular operation. The circular rotate may include only the destination operand (ROR, ROL) or may also include the X-bit in the CCR (ROXR, ROXL). The following instruction has the effect of reversing the nibbles in the low-byte in D0:

```
ROR.B  #4,D0
```

If, for example, D0 contains $12345678 initially, the ROR instruction above leaves D0 with $12345687. Since ".B" is specified, only the low-order byte is affected.

### SWAP    (Introductory)

A swap instruction is also available to exchange the upper and lower words in a 32-bit operand. Although this is equivalent to a longword rotate with a shift count of 16, SWAP is much faster. Note in Appendix D that the execution time for the shift and rotate instructions increases with the shift count.

## 3.2.5  Bit-Manipulation Instructions

The 68000's bit manipulation instructions provide the capability to set, clear, complement, or test individual bits in a destination operand (see Table 3-7).

```
Instruction:   ASR.B  D3,D2
                                        Arithmetic shift
                                        right: sign bit
                                        does not change!

               Register  Contents
     Before:     D3      00000002       Shift count in D3
                 D2      00000068
                 SR          001F       Shift data in D2

     After:      D3      00000002
                 D2      0000001A
                 SR          0000

     Notes:     01101000

                00110100

                00011010   0
                                        C = X = 0
                                        Z = 0
                                        N = 0
                                        V = 0 (always)
```

Figure 3-11.  ASR example.

**Table 3-6. Shift and Rotate Instructions.**

| Instruction | Operation | Bit Movement |
|---|---|---|
| ASL | Arithmetic shift left | |
| ASR | Arithmetic shift right | |
| LSL | Logical shift left | |
| LSR | Logical shift right | |
| ROL | Rotate left | |
| ROR | Rotate right | |
| ROXL | Rotate left with extend bit | |
| ROXR | Rotate right with extend bit | |
| SWAP | Swap words of a longword | |

**BST** **(Intermediate)**

In Figure 3-12, the bit test instruction (BTST) tests a bit in a destination operand and sets the Z-bit in the CCR if the bit is zero or clears the Z-bit if the bit is 1. When using the bit-manipulation instructions, bear in mind that the least-significant bit in an operand (the bit on the right) is bit number *zero*.

## 3.2.6 *Binary-Coded Decimal Instructions*

Three binary-coded decimal (BCD) instructions are included in the 68000 instruction set. Only byte operands are supported and the addressing modes are limited to register direct and predecrement ad-

**Table 3-7.   Bit-Manipulation Instructions.**

| Instruction | Operation |
|---|---|
| BCHG | Change bit |
| BCLR | Clear bit |
| BSET | Set bit |
| BTST | Test bit |

**Table 3-8.   Binary-Coded Decimal Instructions.**

| Instruction | Operation |
|---|---|
| ABCD | Add source to destination |
| NBCD | Negate destination |
| SBCD | Subtract source from destination |

dress register indirect. The BCD instructions are summarized in Table 3-8.

***ABCD***                                                  **(Introductory)**

The ABCD instruction adds two binary-coded decimal bytes plus the X-bit in the condition code register. The result replaces the destination operand:

$$source_{10} + destination_{10} + X -> destination$$

The ABCD instruction in Figure 3-13 uses predecrement address register indirect addressing for both the source and destination operands. The concept of **decimal adjust** appears in the example. The initial result of the binary addition is $11101101_2$. Since the low nibble ($1101_2$) is greater than nine, it is adjusted by adding six (the difference between base 16 and base 10). The result is then $11110011_2$. A second adjustment is needed on the upper nibble if it, too, is greater than nine *or* if a **half carry** occurred. A half carry is a carry-out of bit 3. In the example, both these conditions exist, so a second adjustment of $60_{16}$ is added. The final result of $01010011_2$ with $C = X = 1$ is the correct decimal answer of 153. On the 68000, this adjustment occurs in a single operation because the ALU logic includes the appropriate carry look-ahead logic. For the most part, the adjustment is transparent to the programmer.[1]

The N and V bits are undefined after BCD operations. For convenience, they are coded as zero in Figure 3-13. The X-bit plays an important role in BCD (and binary) arithmetic. If the entire operation is limited to decimal values between 0 and 99, then X is not used and should be explicitly cleared prior to the ABCD instruction. After the addition, X (and C) indicates if the result is greater than $99_{10}$ (as in Figure 3-13). If, however, the operation is on larger variables (stored in consecutive byte locations), then X provides the mechanism to propagate carries from one byte operation to the next.

The X-bit can be explicitly cleared using an AND operation with a mask byte having bit 4 = 0:

```
ANDI   #%11101111,CCR
```

Figure 3-14 illustrates how multi-precision BCD operations are implemented on the 68000. If two 4-digit BCD variables in RAM are to be added, two ABCD instructions are required. If A0 and A1 act as pointers to the variables, they must be aligned initially to point to the byte locations just past the least-significant bytes of the BCD variables. With these initial conditions, the addition proceeds as shown in Figure 3-14. The first instruction explicitly clears X just in case it is set from a previous operation. The first ABCD instruction adds the two least-significant bytes (two digits each) and sets X if the result is greater than $99_{10}$. The second ABCD instruction adds the two most-significant bytes as well as X, thus propagating the carry from the low byte to the high byte of the operation.

### 3.2.7   Program-Flow Instructions

The 68000's program flow instructions branch (perhaps conditionally) to an instruction other than the one immediately following the current instruction (see Table 3-9). This operation may be necessary as part of the usual decisions within a program, or to branch to subroutines, to return from subroutines, or to return from interrupts or exceptions.

***BRA***                                                  **(Introductory)**

BRA (branch always) implements an unconditional branch operation. All the 68000's branch in-

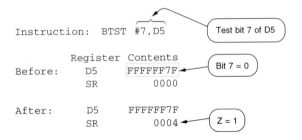

```
Instruction:   BTST  #7,D5              Test bit 7 of D5

               Register  Contents
Before:        D5        FFFFFF7F       Bit 7 = 0
               SR        0000

After:         D5        FFFFFF7F
               SR        0004           Z = 1
```

**Figure 3-12.   BTST example.**

---

[1]Many microprocessors (e.g., 8085, 6809, 8051) do not have BCD instructions. A decimal adjust instruction must immediately follow binary addition to achieve the same effect.

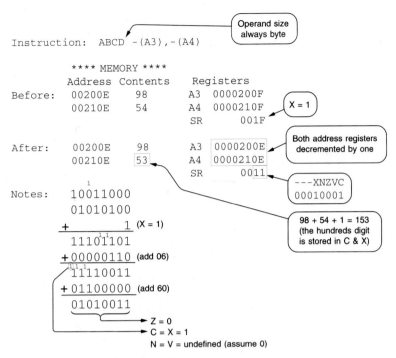

Figure 3-13.  ABCD example.

structions use PC-relative addressing. The offset is expressed either as an 8-bit signed integer or as a 16-bit signed integer, depending on the distance to the branch destination. If the branch destination is within −128 or +127 bytes of the address following the first word in the branch instruction, then an 8-bit offset can be used, as shown in Figure 3-15. If the branch destination is outside this range but within −32768 or +32767, then a 16-bit offset can be used. If the destination is outside this range, then a branch instruction cannot be used.

*Bcc*                                          **(Introductory)**
Bcc (branch conditional) is used whenever program execution must follow one of two paths depending on the result of a previous operation. There are 14 variations of Bcc, as outlined in Appendix A (Table A-2). The destination of Bcc is usually specified with a label. As explained in Chapter 2, the instruction uses PC-relative addressing with an 8-bit signed offset or a 16-bit

signed offset, depending on the distance to the destination.

Bcc instructions often follow compare (CMP) instructions in determining whether one number is *higher* or *lower* than another. In these instances, the form of Bcc depends on whether the numbers are treated as signed or unsigned. For example, to branch to D1GREATER if D1 is greater than D0, the sequence

```
CMP.L  D0,D1
BHI    D1GREATER
```

is used if the numbers are *unsigned*. However, the sequence

```
CMP.L  D0,D1
BGT    D1GREATER
```

is used if the numbers are *signed* (see Appendix A, Table A-2).

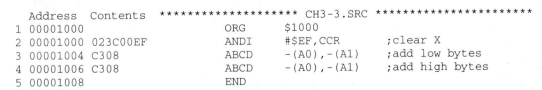

Figure 3-14.  Multi-precision BCD addition.

Table 3-9.    Program Flow Instructions.

| Instruction | Operation |
|---|---|
| Bcc | Branch conditionally |
| BRA | Branch always |
| BSR | Branch to subroutine |
| DBcc | Test, decrement, and branch |
| JMP | Jump to address |
| JSR | Jump to subroutine |
| NOP | No operation |
| RTE[†] | Return and deallocate stack |
| RTR | Return and restore condition codes |
| RTS | Return from subroutine |

[†]privileged instruction

### BSR and RTS    (Introductory)

The BSR instruction branches to a subroutine. BSR and BRA are identical except for one detail: BSR saves the PC on the stack before loading the PC with the new value. RTS is used to return from the subroutine by restoring the PC from the stack. A full 32-bit value is saved/restored. Figure 3-16 sketches the progress of a main program which branches to a subroutine and then returns back to the main program. Before and after conditions are given for the BSR instruction in the main program and the RTS instruction in the subroutine. Note in Figure 3-16 that A7 is the stack pointer. If the current execution mode is *user,* the user stack pointer (USP) is used. If the current execution mode is *supervisor,* the supervisor stack pointer (SSP) is used.

### RTR    (Intermediate)

RTR (return and restore) is a variation of RTS that pulls the PC *and the CCR* from the stack. Restoring the CCR is useful when the subroutine must keep the CCR bits intact for use in the main program. Since BSR does not save the CCR bits when branching to a subroutine, the responsibility lies with the subroutine. This requires the subroutine

to begin by saving the CCR bits on the stack. The following sequence is typical:

```
SUBRTNE  MOVE  SR,-(SP)
              .
              .
              .
         RTR
```

Since there is no instruction to move just the CCR bits to the stack, the entire status register is pushed onto the stack. Note that the move instruction above is *not* a privileged instruction. When the 16-bit status register is pulled from the stack by RTR, the high-byte is ignored. The low-byte is put into the CCR.

### RTE    (Intermediate)

RTE (return from exception) is similar to RTS. It is used as the last instruction in an exception routine to pull the old value of the PC *and the SR* from the stack. Execution continues where it left off before the exception occurred. If the system state was *user* before the exception occurred, then the state will be restored to *user* after RTE executes.

RTE is a privileged instruction. If it is executed while the system is in user mode, a *privilege violation* occurs and exception processing begins at vector #8 (address $000020).

### JMP and JSR    (Introductory)

The JMP (jump) instruction specifies the destination using one of several *effective addresses,* as given in Appendix B. These allow for destinations anywhere in the 68000's memory space. The simplest use of JMP employs a label as the jump destination. The assembler will code the instruction using absolute-short or absolute-long addressing, as appropriate. JSR is the same as JMP except the PC is saved on the stack prior to the jump.

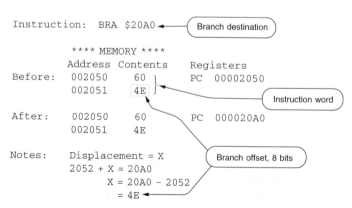

Figure 3-15.   BRA example.

# BSR $40F2

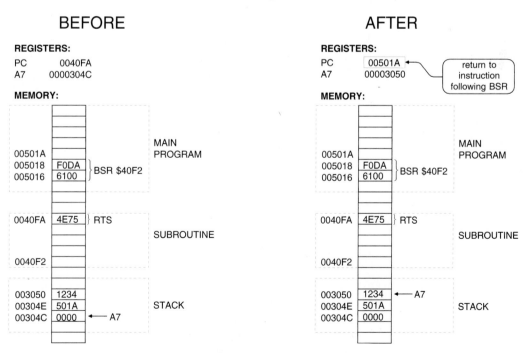

Figure 3-16.   BSR/RTS example.

**Figure A.**

```
        BCS.S      AHEAD    ;branch ahead if carry set
        SUBQ       #1,D7    ;decrement D7
        BPL.S      LOOP     ;if 0 or positive, branch to loop
AHEAD                       ;next instruction
```

### DBcc                                    (Intermediate)

The DBcc (test condition, decrement, and branch) instruction combines two conditional tests in one instruction. The instruction has the form

```
        DBcc       Dn,label
```

First the condition specified by *cc* in the mnemonic is tested. If the condition is true, execution proceeds with the following instruction. If the condition is false, then the data register specified in the instruction is decremented. If the result is *not -1*, the branch takes place. Otherwise execution proceeds with the following instruction. This is illustrated in Figure 3-17.

If we consider a *cc* condition such as carry set (CS), then it is apparent that

```
        DBCS       D7,LOOP
```

is equivalent to the instructions shown in Figure A.

Three lines of source code are reduced to one using DBcc. DBcc is always two words long, so the savings in object code is less dramatic than on first-look. The three-instruction sequence above is three words long, so the difference is only one word.

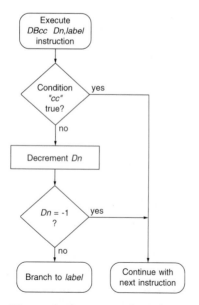

Figure 3-17.   DBcc flowchart.

One common variation of DBcc is DBF, where *F*, for false, explicitly forces the first test to fail. Without the first test, the instruction is equivalent to *decrement and branch if not −1*. DBF is commonly coded as DBRA. This is a convenient looping primitive; however, since DBRA is always two words, there is no savings over the following similar instruction sequence:

```
        SUBQ       #1,Dn    ;1 word
        BPL.S      LOOP     ;1 word
```

Note that loop control with DBRA must use a count one less than the number of loop iterations desired (except as noted below).

One special use of DBRA deserves mention. Many programming situations require an operation to be performed *count* times. A typical implementation is

```
            MOVE.W      #COUNT,D7
LOOP        .
            .
            .
            SUBQ.W      #1,D7
            BNE         LOOP
```

If COUNT = 0, this program fails because D7 is decremented to −1 *before* the first execution of BNE. In many situations the variable COUNT is passed through a subroutine call, so the magnitude of COUNT is unknown. DBRA conveniently avoids this problem as follows:

```
            MOVE.W      #COUNT,D7
            BRA.S       AHEAD
LOOP        .
            .
            .
AHEAD       DBRA        D7,LOOP
```

The loop is entered at the DBRA instruction, so if COUNT = 0, it is decremented right away to −1 and the loop instructions never execute. Note that this arrangement precludes the usual adjustment of initializing the counter with *COUNT-1*. See Appendix B for more details on DBcc and DBRA.

### NOP                                    (Introductory)

Every student's favorite, NOP (no operation) is a one-word instruction that performs no operation and does not affect any of the condition code bits. The PC is incremented (by two) and execution continues with the next instruction. NOPs are sometimes useful for debugging or to introduce a time delay between surrounding instructions. The latter is illustrated in Chapter 9 in controlling the width of an output pulse created through software.

### 3.2.8   System-Control Instructions

A miscellaneous group of instructions is known as system-control instructions. These instructions control basic operating details of the 68000 CPU (see Table 3-10).

***Status Register and***
***CCR Instructions***                              **(Introductory)**
Unique variations of MOVE, AND, OR, and EOR are provided to alter bits in the status register. Either the SR or the CCR can be specified as operands; however, if the SR is specified, the instruction is privileged and can only execute while the system is in supervisor mode. Any attempt to alter the entire SR while in user mode causes a *privilege violation* trap.

***TRAP***                                        **(Intermediate)**
One of the more common system-control instructions is TRAP. The TRAP instruction is very simple in operation. It (a) pushes the PC and the Status Register on the system stack, (b) sets the execution mode to *supervisor*, and (c) loads the PC with a new value read from a vector table.

Supervisor mode is indicated by a 1 in bit 13 of the status register. The vector table for traps starts at address $000080, near the bottom of the 68000's memory space (see Table 6-2 in Chapter 6). TRAP takes a vector number between 0 and 15 as an immediate operand. For TRAP #0, the PC is loaded with the address read from longword address $80. For TRAP #1, the PC is loaded with the address read from longword address $84, and so on. TRAP #5 is illustrated in Figure 3-18.

A trap is considered an **exception** to normal processing. Executing instructions in response to traps is called **exception processing**. After processing the exception, the instruction RTE (return from exception) is executed. This restores the SR and PC from the system stack, and restores the execution mode to its previous value (user or supervisor). See Chapter 6 for more details on exception processing.

***TRAPV and CHK***                                   **(Advanced)**
TRAPV and CHK initiate exception processing conditionally. TRAPV tests for an overflow condition. If $V = 1$, exception processing begins using vector #7 (address $00001C). If $V = 0$, no operation takes place and execution continues with the next instruction. CHK compares a source operand against the content of a data register. The source operand is a 16-bit signed *upper bound* against which the data register is checked. If the content of the data register is less than zero or greater than the upper bound, exception processing begins using vector #6 (address $000018). CHK is used to ensure that array indices do not exceed the bounds of the array or that stack limits are not exceeded.

***TAS***                                              **(Advanced)**
TAS (test and set) is used to implement task synchronization in multi-tasking or multi-processing environments. The instruction tests a destination byte and then sets the most-significant bit in the destination byte. The most-significant bit (MSB) in the tested byte plays the role of a **semaphore**. A

Table 3-10.   System-Control Instructions.

| Instruction | Operation |
|---|---|
| ANDI[††] | AND immediate to status register/condition code register |
| CHK | Trap on upper out-of-bounds operand |
| EORI[††] | Exclusive OR immediate to status register/condition code register |
| ILLEGAL | Illegal instruction trap |
| MOVE[††] | Move to/from status register/condition code register |
| ORI[††] | OR immediate to status register/condition code register |
| RESET[†] | Assert RESET line |
| STOP[†] | Stop processor |
| TAS | Test and set operand |
| TRAP | Trap unconditionally |
| TRAPV | Trap on overflow |

[†]privileged instruction
[††]privileged instruction if SR specified (except MOVE from SR)

Instruction: TRAP #5

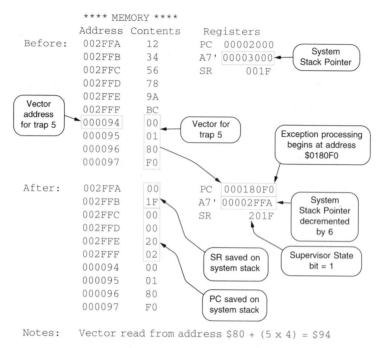

Figure 3-18.   TRAP example.

semaphore is a flag that provides access to certain *resources* in the system. To access the resource, the flag must be clear, meaning the resource is available. TAS usually occurs in a sequence such as appears in Figure B below. If SEMAPHORE was clear when TAS executed, the BNE branch test fails and the program continues on to utilize the resource. Either way, the flag is set to indicate that the resource is being requested or is about to be used. After using the resource, the semaphore is cleared, freeing the resource. TAS is *indivisible*: the instruction performs a *read-modify-write* operation that cannot be halted midstream through a bus request. This is an important trait of semaphores that prevents false testing of the flag.

An example of a resource that might be implemented using TAS is a seat query in an airline reservation system. To prevent multiple seat bookings, agent inquiries must block other inquires temporarily while a decision is made on booking a seat.

### STOP, RESET, and ILLEGAL   (Advanced)

The STOP instruction loads the SR with an immediate operand and stops the CPU. The conditions under which the CPU subsequently begins instruction execution are specified in Appendix B. RESET asserts the CPU's $\overline{\text{RESET}}$ line for 124 clock cycles. System implementations with the 68000 should use the $\overline{\text{RESET}}$ signal to reset peripheral devices. If the STOP or RESET instruction is executed while the system is in user mode, a *privilege violation* occurs.

ILLEGAL is the mnemonic for the instruction code $4AFC. If this instruction is executed, an *illegal instruction* trap occurs. There are other instruction codes that are undefined on the 68000, and if these are executed, an illegal instruction trap also occurs. Note that some of the *undefined* codes on the 68000 are valid on subsequent processors in the 68000 family. The ILLEGAL instruction code ($4AFC) is *illegal* on all processors in the 68000 family.

```
Figure B.   WAIT    TAS      SEMAPHORE   ;resource available?
                    BNE      WAIT        ;no: check again
                    .                    ;yes: use requested resource
                    .
                    .
                    CLR.B    SEMAPHORE   ;clear semaphore, free resource
```

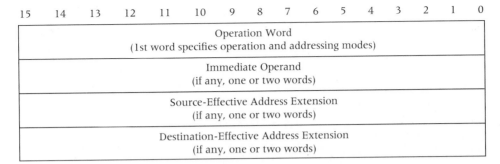

Figure 3-19.   68000 instruction format.

## 3.3   MACHINE-LANGUAGE FORMAT

It is important in studying computer organization to examine the binary encoding of instructions. The binary, or machine language, form of instructions reveals many details of the characteristics, limits, and possibilities of an architecture. All aspects of the instruction are specified, including (a) the operation performed, (b) the location of the source operand, (c) the location of the destination operand, (d) the size of the operands, and (e) special modifiers for the operation.

. Each 68000 instruction is coded in binary as one to five 16-bit words. The length of the instruction and the operation are specified in the first word—the **operation word** (or **opcode**). The remaining words further specify the operands as either immediate data or as effective address-extension words. The instruction format is shown in Figure 3-19.

The format of the first instruction word determines not only the operation, but the number of operands and the location of the operands. Three general categories of instructions are single-operand instructions, double-operand instructions, and conditional branch instructions (see Figure 3-20).

**Single-Operand Format**   Many 68000 instructions require one operand only. Examples include CLR, NOT, or TST. The machine-language format is shown in Figure 3-20a. Single-operand instructions use three fields to specify the instruction, the operand size, and the effective address of the operand. The 2-bit size field indicates whether the operand is a byte ($00_2$), word ($01_2$), or longword ($10_2$). The effective-address field contains a mode subfield and a register subfield. The possibilities for the effective-address field are given in Table C-2 in Appendix C, which is repeated in Table 3-11 for convenience. The mode subfield identifies the addressing mode and the register subfield identifies which register is used or which non-register addressing mode is used.

**Double-Operand Format**   Many instructions, such as ADD or SUB, require a source and a destination operand. The format in Figure 3-20b specifies the operation and two operands. For most double operand instructions, one operand must be in a register. The 1-bit D-field indicates whether the source or destination operand is a data register, as follows:

```
D = 0  <ea>  OP  <Dn>  -->  <Dn>
D = 1  <Dn>  QP  <ea>  -->  <ea>
```

Collectively, the D and size fields are called the *op-mode* field.

**Conditional Branch Format**   The 68000 includes three conditional branch instructions: Bcc, Scc, and DBcc. The format in Figure 3-20c specifies the instruction, the condition, and the 8-bit displacement of the branch destination. If the 8-bit displacement is zero, then a 16-bit displacement is read from the following instruction word.

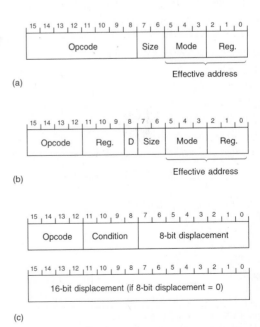

Figure 3-20.   Instruction formats. (a) single-operand, (b) double-operand, (c) conditional branch.

Table 3-11.   Effective Address Encoding Summary.

| Addressing Mode | Mode Bits | Register Bits |
|---|---|---|
| Data Register Direct | 000 | register number |
| Address Register Direct | 001 | register number |
| Address Register Indirect | 010 | register number |
| Address Register Indirect with Postincrement | 011 | register number |
| Address Register Indirect with Predecrement | 100 | register number |
| Address Register Indirect with Displacement[†] | 101 | register number |
| Address Register Indirect with Index[*] | 110 | register number |
| Absolute Short[†] | 111 | 000 |
| Absolute Long[††] | 111 | 001 |
| Program Counter with Displacement[†] | 111 | 010 |
| Program Counter with Index[*] | 111 | 011 |
| Immediate or Status Register[†††] | 111 | 100 |

[†]One extension word required
[††]Two extension words required
[†††]For Immediate addressing, one or two extension words required depending on the size of the operation
[*]One extension word required; see Table C-3 in Appendix C for the encoding

With a 4-bit condition field, 16 conditions are possible. These are identified in Table A-2 in Appendix A, which is repeated in Table 3-12 for convenience.

### 3.3.1   Hand Assembly

The best way to illustrate instruction encoding is by converting 68000 assembly-language instructions to machine language (binary). We call this process **hand assembly** to distinguish it from the automatic conversion that an assembler performs. Appendix C is the main reference source for this conversion. The process involves first determining

Table 3-12.   Conditional Tests.

| Mnemonic | Condition | Encoding | Test |
|---|---|---|---|
| T[†] | true | 0000 | 1 |
| F[†] | false | 0001 | 0 |
| HI | high | 0010 | $\overline{C} \cdot \overline{Z}$ |
| LS | low or same | 0011 | $C + Z$ |
| CC(HS) | carry clear | 0100 | $\overline{C}$ |
| CS(LO) | carry set | 0101 | $C$ |
| NE | not equal | 0110 | $\overline{Z}$ |
| EQ | equal | 0111 | $Z$ |
| VC[††] | overflow clear | 1000 | $\overline{V}$ |
| VS[††] | overflow set | 1001 | $V$ |
| PL[††] | plus | 1010 | $\overline{N}$ |
| MI[††] | minus | 1011 | $N$ |
| GE[††] | greater or equal | 1100 | $N \cdot V + \overline{N} \cdot \overline{V}$ |
| LT[††] | less than | 1101 | $N \cdot \overline{V} + \overline{N} \cdot V$ |
| GT[††] | greater than | 1110 | $N \cdot V \cdot \overline{Z} + \overline{N} \cdot \overline{V} \cdot \overline{Z}$ |
| LE[††] | less or equal | 1111 | $Z + N \cdot \overline{V} + \overline{N} \cdot V$ |

[†] Not available for Bcc instruction
[††]Twos complement arithmetic, signed numbers
• = Boolean AND
+ = Boolean OR

the general category of instruction from the op-code map derived from upper four bits in the instruction word. The possibilities are given in Table C-1 in Appendix C, which is repeated in Table 3-13 for convenience.

**Example 3-1.** Convert the following 68000 assembly-language instruction to machine language:

    ADD.W   #512,D2

**Solution:**

    D47C (1st instruction word)
    0200 (2nd instruction word)

**Discussion:** The first step is to look up the opcode bits 15–12 in Table 3-13. For ADD instructions, bits 15–12 are $1101_2$. The second step is to look up the full opcode in Appendix C, pages 366 to 377. These pages tabulate all 68000 instructions, sorted numerically by the binary code. On page 376, the ADD instruction is found with the encoding shown in Figure 3-21. ■

Bits 0–11 contain three fields of information. The data register field is coded as $010_2$, since the destination register in our example is D2. The op-mode field identifies the variations of the instruction. Our example is a word operation of the form

```
<ea> + <Dn> -> Dn
```

so the op-mode field is coded as $001_2$. The effective address field contains two subfields: mode and register (see Table 3-11). Since the source operand in the example is a word and is specified using immediate mode addressing, the mode subfield is $111_2$ and the register subfield is $100_2$. A single extension

Table 3-13.   Opcode Map.

| Bits 15 through 12 | Operation |
| --- | --- |
| 0000 | Bit Manipulation/MOVEP/Immediate |
| 0001 | Move Byte |
| 0010 | Move Long |
| 0011 | Move Word |
| 0100 | Miscellaneous |
| 0101 | ADDQ/SUBQ/Scc/DBcc |
| 0110 | Bcc/BSR |
| 0111 | MOVEQ |
| 1000 | OR/DIV/SBCD |
| 1001 | SUB/SUBX |
| 1010 | (Unassigned) |
| 1011 | CMP/EOR |
| 1100 | AND/MUL/ABCD/EXG |
| 1101 | ADD/ADDX |
| 1110 | Shift/Rotate |
| 1111 | (Unassigned) |

word is required for the 16-bit source operand ($512_{10} = 0200_{16}$).

The first word is the instruction word, the second word is a source extension containing the 16-bit immediate data. The binary encoding of the instruction word is summarized in Figure 3-22.

**Example 3-2.** Convert the following 68000 assembly-language instruction to machine language. Assume the instruction is in memory location $2050.

```
BGE.S $2000
```

**Solution:**

```
6CAE
```

**Discussion:** The ".S" suffix to the mnemonic indicates that the offset is encoded as a short (8-bit) PC-relative value. BGE (branch if greater or equal) is a conditional branch instruction (Bcc). In Table 3-13, bits 15–12 of the operation word are indicated as $0110_2$ for Bcc instructions. The encoding on page 373 in Appendix C is reproduced in Figure 3-23.  ■

The 4-bit condition field must be filled out to specify the *greater than or equal* condition. The encoding of this field is given in Table 3-12. As seen in the fourth from the last row, the required encoding is $1100_2$. The low-byte of the instruction word contains the 8-bit offset for the instruction. If this field contains zero, it indicates that a 16-bit offset is found in the next instruction word. In our example, the 8-bit offset is calculated as follows:

```
$00002052 + offset = $00002000
offset = $00002000 - $00002052 = $FFFFFFAE
```

Only the low-byte ($AE) of the offset is used.

**Example 3-3.** Convert the following 68000 assembly-language instruction to machine language:

```
MOVE.L  0(A3,D4),D7
```

**Solution:**

```
2E33 (1st instruction word)
4000 (2nd instruction word)
```

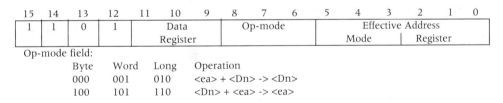

Figure 3-21.   Encoding of ADD instruction.

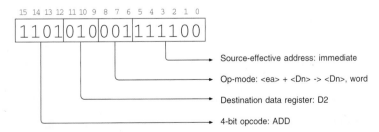

Figure 3-22.   Solution to Example 3-1.

† See Table 3-12 or Table A-2

**Figure 3-23.   Encoding of Bcc instruction.**

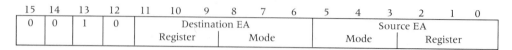

**Figure 3-24.   Encoding of MOVE.L instruction.**

**Discussion:** From Table 3-13, bits 15–12 of the instruction word are $0010_2$. In Appendix C, the complete encoding of the instruction is given on page 368. This is repeated in Figure 3-24 for convenience. ■

Both the source and destination operands are specified in 6-bit mode/register subfields. (Note the order of the subfields in Figure 3-24.) The destination addressing mode is data register direct; so, from Table 3-11, the encoding is mode = $000_2$ and register = $111_2$. The source-addressing mode is address register indirect with index; so the encoding is mode = $110_2$ and register = $011_2$. The register field specifies the address register (A3). Note in Table 3-11 that an extension word is required to further specify the index register and displacement. This is provided in Table C-3 in Appendix C, which is repeated in Figure 3-25 for convenience.

Since the index register (D4) is a data register, the D/A field is coded with 0 and the register field with $100_2$. The W/L field indicates whether the index is a word or a longword. This can be specified explicitly by appending ".W" or ".L" to the register in the assembly-language instruction. Since no designation was provided, a word-size index is assumed and the W/L field is coded with 0. The displacement integer is coded as $00000000_2$, as given in the instruction.

**Example 3-4.** Convert the following 68000 assembly-language instruction to machine language:

```
MOVEM.L  D0-D7/A0,-(A7)
```

**Solution:**

```
48E7 (1st instruction word)
FF80 (2nd instruction word)
```

**Discussion:** This instruction saves nine 32-bit registers on the stack, D0 through D7, and A0. The second instruction word is a register list mask that identifies the registers (see Appendix C). For register-to-memory transfers, the upper-byte identifies the data registers (bit 15 for D0, bit 14 for D1, etc.) and the lower-byte identifies the address registers (bit 7 for A0, bit 6 for A1, etc.). If a bit is set in the register mask, the corresponding register is saved, otherwise the register is not saved. ■

### 3.3.2   Disassembly

Disassembly is the reverse process of assembly. One starts with a binary code and converts to the equivalent assembly-language instruction.

**Example 3-5.** Convert the 68000 machine-language instruction $91D4_{16}$ to assembly language.

**Solution:**

```
SUBA.L  (A4),A0
```

| 15 | 14 | 13 | 12 | 11 | 10 | 9 | 8 | 7 | 6 | 5 | 4 | 3 | 2 | 1 | 0 |
|----|----|----|----|----|----|---|---|---|---|---|---|---|---|---|---|
| D/A | | Register | | W/L | 0 | 0 | 0 | | | | Displacement Integer | | | | |

D/A field:
   0 = use a data register as the index
   1 = use an address register as the index
Register field:
   register number
W/L field:
   0 = sign-extended, low order word integer in index register
   1 = long value in index register
Displacement Integer Field:
   8-bit signed offset, sign-extended to 32 bits

**Figure 3-25.   Extension word to specify index register and displacement.**

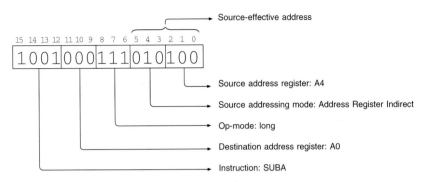

Figure 3-26.   Solution to Example 3-5.

**Discussion:** Bits 15–12, $1001_2$, identify the category of instruction. In Table 3-13 this is shown as SUB/SUBX. From page 374 in Appendix C the encoding of these instructions is given. A process of elimination is used to choose among the possibilities and determine the size of the operand(s) and the source and destination addressing modes. For example, SUBX has bit 4 = 0 (see page 374). Since bit 4 = 1 in the code $91D4_{16}$, SUBX is eliminated as a possibility. The decomposition of the binary code is shown in Figure 3-26. ∎

**Example 3-6.** Convert the 68000 machine-language instruction $003C_{16}$ to assembly language.

**Solution:**

```
ORI  #data,CCR
```

**Discussion:** The first four bits of the operation, $0000_2$, delimit the possibilities to instructions on pages 366–368 in Appendix C. Again, a process of elimination is used to narrow in on the correct instruction. For example, AND immediate has bit 9 = 1. Since, bit 9 = 0 in the code $003C_{16}$, AND immediate is eliminated. The decomposition of the binary code is shown in Figure 3-27. Since the example only provides the first instruction word, the immediate data cannot be specified in the assembly-language form. ∎

---

## 3.4   INSTRUCTION TIMINGS

Minimizing the execution time of a program is important in many situations. Overall system perfor-mance is affected by the speed of execution of system programs; therefore, the consequences of speeding up frequently executed routines can be critical. In real-time systems it may be necessary to perform certain operations within a specified time interval. Again, squeezing every last cycle out of a program may be very important. Alternatively, it may be necessary for certain operations to occur at regular, timed intervals.

Each instruction on the 68000 takes a specific amount of time to execute.[2] The execution time is related to two parameters:

$n$   the number of CPU clock cycles in an instruction

$t_C$   the period of the CPU clock

The latter is simply the reciprocal of the CPU clock frequency. With an 8 MHz clock, for example, $t_C = 1/8 = 0.125 \ \mu s = 125$ ns.[3] As we learned in Chapter 2, much of the 68000's activity is memory-read cycles or memory-write cycles. Each takes four CPU clock cycles, assuming the memory interface uses zero wait states. If one wait state is included (to accommodate slow memory ICs), a read or write cycle takes $4 + 1 = 5$ CPU clock cycles, and so on.

The number of clock cycles in a complete instruction is trickier to determine, but still straight-forward. Appendix D is our main reference. It tab-ulates the number of clock cycles for all 68000 instructions. Since there are so many variations (because of the variety of addressing modes), more than one table is often needed. A few examples will illustrate the use of Appendix D.

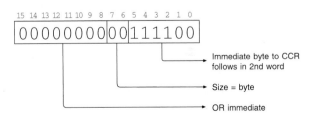

Figure 3-27.   Solution to Example 3-6.

---

[2]There are a few exceptions to this. The execution time for MUL, for ex-ample, depends on the pattern of 1s and 0s in the multiplier.

[3]μs is a microsecond or $10^{-6}$ seconds. ns is a nanosecond or $10^{-9}$ seconds.

**Example 3-7.** How long does the following instruction take to execute, assuming a CPU clock frequency of 10 MHz?

    MOVE.B #5,D1

**Solution:** 800 ns

**Discussion:** At 10 MHz, $t_C = 1/10 = 0.1$ μs = 100 ns. The number of clock cycles is found in Table D-2 in Appendix D for all move byte and move word instructions. When moving an immediate byte to a data register, the number of cycles is given as 8(2/0). This means a total of eight clock cycles, composed of two memory-read cycles and zero memory-write cycles. Therefore, the execution time is 8 × 100 = 800 ns. ■

It is worthwhile to gain a sense not only of the total execution time for instructions, but for the decomposition of the instruction into memory-read and write cycles. For example, the move instruction in Example 3-7 takes 8 cycles, consisting of an opcode fetch (4 clocks) and a memory read (4 clocks). An opcode fetch is a type of memory read. The second memory read is to retrieve the second instruction word—the immediate data value moved into the D1. This is illustrated in Figure 3-28.

**Example 3-8.** If a 68000 is operating from a 16-MHz clock, how long does the following instruction take to execute?

    NOT.L $1000

**Solution:** 1.5 μs

**Discussion:** At 16 MHz, $t_C = 1/16 = 0.0625$ μs = 62.5 ns. The instruction logically complements a longword in a memory location. From Table D-6 in Appendix D, the number of CPU cycles is given as 12(1/2)+ . The number of cycles is 12 (1 read, 2 writes) *plus* additional cycles for the addressing mode to specify the memory location. The addressing mode is absolute short; so, from Table D-1 an additional 12 cycles are added, for a total of 24 cycles. The execution time, therefore, is 24 × 0.0625 = 1.5 μs. ■

The instruction NOT.L $1000 takes 24 CPU clock cycles, consisting of four memory-read cycles and two memory-write cycles. Since the instruction is two words long, the first two memory-read cycles retrieve the opcode and the absolute short address. Then, the longword operand is read. This takes two more memory-read cycles. Finally, the complement of the 32-bit value just read is written back to the same memory location. This takes two memory write cycles. The timing is illustrated in Figure 3-29.

**Example 3-9.** How long does the following instruction take to execute, assuming a CPU clock frequency of 10 MHz and a value of 5 in D0?

    ROR.L D0,D1

**Solution:** 1.8 μs

**Discussion:** This instruction rotates the 32-bit contents of D1 right five positions. The number of CPU clock cycles is given in Table D-7 in Appendix D as $8 + 2n(1/0)$, where $n$ is the number of positions to rotate. Only one memory-read cycle is required. The rest of the clock cycles are for the internal execution of the instruction. With $n = 5$, the total number of clock cycles is $8 + 2 × 5 = 18$. At a clock frequency of 10 MHz, $t_C = 0.1$ μs, so the execution time is $0.1 × 18 = 1.8$ μs. ■

Although ROR.L D0,D1 takes 18 clocks cycles, only one memory-read cycle is required. During the last 14 clock cycles, the CPU buses are inactive while the content of D1 is internally rotated five positions right. The timing is illustrated in Figure 3-30.

**Example 3-10.** The subroutine in Figure 3-31 adds a list of 16-bit values and returns the sum in D7. Parameters are passed to the subroutine as follows: The address of the list is in A0, the count is in D0. Assuming a count of $25_{10}$, how long will this subroutine take to execute on a 10 MHz 68000?

**Solution:** 56.8 μs

**Discussion:** The number of cycles for each instruction is given in Appendix D. These are summarized below.

| | | |
|---|---|---|
| CLR.W | 4(1/0) | $n_1 = 4$ |
| ADD.W | 4(1/0) + 4(1/0) | $n_2 = 8$ |
| SUBQ.B | 4(1/0) | $n_3 = 4$ |
| BNE.S | 10(2/0) branch taken | $n_4 = 10$ |
| | 8(1/0) branch not taken | $n_5 = 8$ |
| RTS | 16(4/0) | $n_6 = 16$ |

This program includes a loop, so the calculation is tricky. The CLR and RTS instructions execute once only. The loop consists of the ADD, SUBQ, and BNE instructions. Each of these executes COUNT times. BNE takes 10 cycles if the branch is taken, 8 cycles if the branch is not taken. With COUNT = 25, the branch is taken 24 times. The

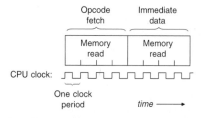

**Figure 3-28.    Timing for MOVE.B #data,Dn.**

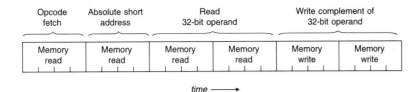

Figure 3-29. Timing for NOT.L $1000.

twenty-fifth time through the loop, the count reaches zero, the branch test fails, and execution falls through to the RTS instruction. The total number of cycles is

$$
\begin{aligned}
n &= n_1 + \text{COUNT}(n_2 + n_3) + (\text{COUNT} - 1)n_4 \\
&\quad + n_5 + n_6 \\
&= 4 + 25(8 + 4) + 24(10) + 8 + 16 \\
&= 568
\end{aligned}
$$

At 10 MHz, the subroutine takes $0.1 \times 568 = 56.8\ \mu s$ to execute. ∎

In the event the interface to the memory ICs includes wait states, an adjustment is necessary. For each memory-read cycle or memory-write cycle in an instruction, add one clock cycle for each wait state. For example, the NOT instruction in Example 3-8 has six memory references (see Figure 3-29). If the memory interface includes one wait state, the number of CPU cycles increases by six, to 30. On the other hand, the ROR instruction in Example 3-9 has only one memory reference (see Figure 3-30); so a memory interface with one wait state increases the number of CPU cycles by one, to 19. (See Question 6 at the end of this chapter.)

Example 3-11. The RAM interface on a 10 MHz 68000 system inserts one wait state for each read or write cycle. How long will the following instruction take to execute on this system?

```
        BSR.S     COSINE
```

Solution: $2.2\ \mu s$

Discussion: From Table D-9 in Appendix D, the BSR instruction takes 18(2/2) cycles to execute. Since there are four memory references (2 read cycles, 2 write cycles), four extra cycles are required for the wait states, for a total of $18 + 4 = 22$ cycles. At 10 MHz, $t_C = 100$ ns, so the execution time is $22 \times 100 = 2200$ ns $= 2.2\ \mu s$. ∎

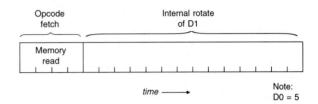

Figure 3-30. Timing for ROR.L D0,D1.

An interesting observation about this instruction is that the execution time is 18(2/2) cycles regardless of whether a byte or word offset is used (see Appendix D). If a byte offset is used, the instruction is one word only; if a word offset is used, the instruction is two words. Evidently, the 68000 CPU does not fully benefit from the short form of this instruction: There is a size benefit, but no speed benefit. The second read cycle in BSR.S is a *dummy* read; it takes place (because of implementation reasons) but the value is discarded.

---

## 3.5  SUMMARY

This chapter has introduced the instruction set of the 68000 microprocessor, including the assembling and disassembling of instructions and instruction timings. The reader is now well prepared to embark on 68000 assembly-language programming. In Chapter 4, we will present some of the broader concepts in assembly-language programming, such as the use of an assembler and a linker/locator.

---

## 3.6  QUESTIONS

1. The similarity between the SUB (subtract) and CMP (compare) instructions was noted

```
1 00001000                  ORG      $1000
2 00001000 4247   ADDLIST   CLR.W    D7
3 00001002 DE58   LOOP      ADD.W    (A0)+,D7
4 00001004 5300             SUBQ.B   #1,D0
5 00001006 66FA             BNE.S    LOOP
6 00001008 4E75             RTS
7 0000100A                  END
```

Figure 3-31. ADDLIST subroutine.

earlier in this chapter. Besides the fact that the result of the comparison (i.e., subtraction) is discarded with CMP, name two other differences between these two instructions.

2. Convert the following 68000 assembly-language instructions to machine language:

   (a)  MOVE.B  #-3,D7

   (b)  CMP.L  >$F000,D7

   (c)  BSR.L  $F1000 (instruction is at $F1A50)

   (d)  ASR.W  $4000

   (e)  MOVE.B  5(A2,D7),$12000

   (f)  MOVEM  D3-D7,-(A7)

3. Considering only the first instruction word, how many possible instructions can the 68000 implement? Based on Table 3-13, how many of these are implemented? How many are not implemented?

4. Convert the following 68000 instruction words (shown in hexadecimal) to assembly language. Interpret each word as a separate instruction. If more than one word is required for the complete instruction, indicate the number of words and the purpose of the words following the instruction word.

   (a)  327C

   (b)  C2C0

   (c)  6700

   (d)  4E4E

   (e)  1019

   (f)  4E75

   (g)  027C

5. If a 68000 is operating at 4 MHz, determine the execution time of the following instructions:

   (a)  MOVE.L  (A6)+,D0

   (b)  MOVEM.W  (A7)+,A3/A6

   (c)  BTST  #3,25(A0)

   (e)  CLR.W  100(A2,D3)

6. A fast 68000 system operates at 33 MHz; but the RAMs are slow and require two wait states for any read or write cycle. How long will the subroutine in Example 3-10 take to execute on this system? Assume a count of $50_{10}$ is passed to the subroutine.

7. As noted in Example 3-9, the CPU buses are inactive during 14 cycles while D1 is rotated. What logic levels are found on the 68000 control signals $\overline{AS}$, $\overline{RD}$, and $\overline{WR}$ during these 14 cycles?

8. The BSR.S instruction in Example 3-11 executes in 18 machine cycles, including two memory-read cycles and two memory-write cycles. What is the purpose of the two memory-write cycles?

9. What are seven ways (one instruction each) to clear the 32-bit contents of D0?

10. Each of the following is a machine code for the TST instruction:

   (a)  4A38

   (b)  4A78

   (c)  4AB8

   (d)  4A50

   (e)  4A68

   (f)  4A70

   (g)  4A64

Translate each instruction into mnemonic form.

11. Write a two-instruction sequence that will save the 68000's data registers to memory locations $009000 to $00901F. D0 is to go in longword address $009000, D1 is to go in longword address $0090004, and so on.

12. What are the contents of D6 and D7 following the instruction sequence below?

   MOVE.L  #$12345678,D6

   MOVE.L  #$87654321,D7

   SWAP  D7

   EXG  D6,D7

13. What are the contents of D0 and D1 following the instruction sequence below?

   MOVE.B  #-1,D0

   MOVE.L  #$AAAA5555,D1

   EXT.W  D0

   MOVE.B  D1,D0

14. Write an instruction sequence to reverse the 32-bit pattern in D0. For example, if D0 contains $00000012 beforehand, it should change to $48000000.

15. What is the difference between the JMP and BRA instructions?

16. Write an instruction sequence to reverse the nibbles in each byte in a 32-bit variable stored in D0. For example, if D0 contains $12345678 initially, the instruction sequence should leave D0 with $21436587.

17. Write an instruction sequence to sign-extend the low-order byte in D7 to 32 bits.

# 4. Assembly-Language Programming

## 4.1. INTRODUCTION

Assembly language is a computer language lying between the extremes of machine language and high-level language. Typical high-level languages, like Pascal or C, use words and statements that are easily understood by humans, although still remote from natural language. Machine language is the binary language of computers. A machine-language program is a series of binary codes representing instructions a computer can execute.

Assembly language replaces the binary codes of machine language with easy-to-remember **mnemonics** that facilitate programming. For example, an addition instruction in machine language might be represented by the code "10110011." It might be represented in assembly language by the mnemonic "ADD." Programming with mnemonics is obviously preferable to programming with binary codes.

Of course this is not the whole story. Instructions operate on data, and the location of the data is specified by various **addressing modes** embedded in the binary code of the assembly-language instruction. Therefore, there may be several variations of the ADD instruction depending on what is added. The rules for specifying these variations are central to the theme of assembly-language programming.

An assembly-language program is not executable by a computer. Once written, the program must undergo translation to machine language. In the example above, the mnemonic "ADD" is translated to the binary code "10110011." Depending on the complexity of the programming environment, this translation may involve one or more steps before an executable machine-language program results. As a minimum, a program called an **assembler** is required to translate instruction mnemonics to machine-language binary codes. A further step may require a *linker* to combine portions of programs from separate files and to set the address in memory where the program executes. We begin with a few definitions.

An **assembly language program** is a program using labels, mnemonics, and so on, in which each statement corresponds to a machine instruction. Assembly-language programs, often called **source code** or **symbolic code,** are not executable by a computer.

A **machine-language program** is a program containing binary codes that represent instructions to a computer. Machine-language programs, often called **object code,** are executable by a computer.

An **assembler** is a program that translates an assembly-language program into a machine-language program. Machine-language programs are either *absolute* or *relocatable*. In the latter case, *linking* is required to set the absolute address for execution.

A **cross assembler** is an assembler that runs on a computer system with a different CPU from the target computer. An example is a 68000 cross assembler that runs on a *PC/AT*. The *PC/AT* CPU is an Intel 80386 (or compatible) and cannot execute 68000 programs.

A **host computer** is a computer system used to develop programs. Generally the programs do not (or cannot) execute on the host computer.

A **target computer** is a computer system upon which a program executes.

A **linker** is a program that combines relocatable object programs (modules) and produces an absolute object program that is executable by a target computer. A linker is sometimes called a *linker/locator* to reflect its separate functions of combining relocatable modules (linking) and setting the address for execution (locating).

A **segment** is a unit of code or data memory. Segments are relocatable or absolute. A relocatable segment has a name, type, and other attributes that allow the linker to combine it with other partial segments, if required, and to locate correctly the segment.

A **module** contains one or more segments or partial segments. A module has a name assigned by the user. The module definition determines the scope of local symbols. An object file contains one or more modules. A module may be thought of as a *file* in many instances.

A **program** is a single absolute module, merging all absolute and relocatable segments from all input modules. A program contains only the binary codes for instructions (with addresses and data constants) that are understood by a computer.

## 4.2.  ASSEMBLER OPERATION

There are many assembler programs and other support programs to facilitate the development of applications for microprocessors such as the 68000. The assembler used to develop the program examples for this text is A68K by Enertec, Inc.[1] Although details vary slightly among assemblers, the general idea is the same. Mastering an assembler such as A68K will facilitate learning any new assembler in the future. A68K is a relocatable assembler, supporting the development of both absolute program modules and relocatable program modules. In the latter case, a linker is required to combine and locate modules. XLINK, also by Enertec, is used for this purpose. A librarian called XLIB is also available to permit linking with existing user-created subroutines stored in a library file. An exhaustive description of all commands and options supported by A68K, XLINK, and XLIB is not included here. Our goal is to present the general concepts in the use of assemblers and linker/locators.

---

[1]Available from URDA, Inc., 1811 Jancey Street, Suite 200, Pittsburgh, PA, USA (1-800-338-0517).

### 4.2.1.  *Assembler Invocation*

The assembler program receives a single source program as input and generates an object code output file and a listing output file. This is illustrated in Figure 4-1a. Common suffixes are ".SRC" for the source file, ".OBJ" for the object file, and ".LST" for the listing file.

The assembler is executed, or invoked, from the system prompt by entering its name, followed by arguments identifying files and options. In Figure 4-1b, an invocation line for A68K is illustrated. The first argument following the command identifies the source input file, the second identifies the object file, and the third identifies the object code output file.

Numerous options are supported as well. The option "X" directs the assembler to place a cross reference listing of symbols and a symbol table in the listing file. The option "S" directs the assembler to place a symbol table in the object file for subsequent use by a linker or debugger.

Commas are important in the invocation line, since they separate arguments. Assemblers vary considerably in their use of default suffixes or missing arguments. For example, with A68K, the invocation

```
A68K TEST.SRC
```

assembles TEST.SRC and creates an object code output file called TEST.R01. No listing file is created. The user's manual provides complete details of the syntax, arguments, and options supported by each assembler.

**Example 4-1.** A 68000 assembly-language program is written using an editor and saved in a file called PROJECT.SRC. What invocation line

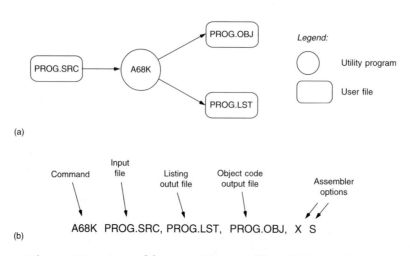

Figure 4-1.   Assembler operation. (a) files, (b) invocation.

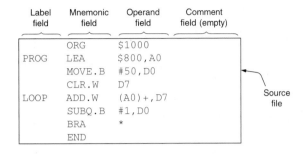

(a)

(b)

Figure 4-2.   Assembler files. (a) source file, (b) listing file.

is used with A68K to assemble this program and place the object code in PROJECT.OBJ and the listing file in PROJECT.LST? Include symbol tables in both the object and listing files.

**Solution:**

```
A68K PROJECT.SRC, PROJECT.LST, PROJECT.OBJ,
                 X S
```

**Discussion:** The command A68K is followed by the source, listing, and object filenames in sequence, and then by options X and S to place symbol tables in the output files. ∎

Figure 4-2 illustrates the contents of a typical source file and listing file. Each line in the source program is divided into four fields. These are discussed below. The listing file is abbreviated in the figure. Along with the assembled source program, the listing file contains header information at the beginning (e.g., name of file, date, time) and perhaps a symbol table and cross reference listing at the end.

For convenience, it is useful to execute the assembler from an MS-DOS batch file. For example, if the following line is placed in a file called A.BAT,

```
A68K %1.SRC,%1.LST,%1.OBJ,X S
```

then the file PROG.SRC is assembled by entering

```
A PROG
```

The first argument (PROG) is substituted for each occurence of "%1" in the batch file.

Since most assemblers scan the source program twice in performing the translation to machine language, they are described as **two-pass assemblers.** The assembler uses a **location counter** as the address of instructions and the value for labels. The action of each pass is described below.

### 4.2.2.   Pass One

During the first pass, the source file is scanned line by line and a **symbol table** is built. The location counter defaults to 0 (on the first appearance of each segment) or is set by the ORG (set origin) directive. As the file is scanned, the location counter is incremented by the size of each instruction (in bytes). Define constant (DC) directives increment the location counter by the number of bytes defined. In a data segment, define storage (DS) directives increment the location counter by the number of bytes reserved.

When a label is found at the beginning of a line, it is placed in the symbol table along with the current value of the location counter. Symbols defined using equate (EQU) directives are placed in the symbol table along with the *equated* value. The symbol table is saved and used during pass two.

### 4.2.3.   Pass Two

During the second pass, the object and listing files are created. Mnemonics are converted to opcodes and placed in the output files. Operands are evaluated and placed within or after the instruction op-codes (depending on the instruction). Where symbols appear in the operand field, their values are retrieved from the symbol table (created during pass one) and used in calculating the correct data or addresses for the instructions.

Since two passes are performed, the source program may use **forward references,** that is, use a symbol before it is defined. This would occur, for example, when branching ahead in a program.

The object file, if it is absolute, contains only the binary codes of a machine-language program (00–FF). A relocatable object file will also contain a symbol table and other information for linking and locating. The listing file contains the ASCII text codes for both the source program and the hexadecimal bytes in the machine-language program.

A good demonstration of the distinction between an object file and a listing file is to display each on the host computer's CRT using, for example, the MS-DOS command TYPE. The listing file clearly displays, with each line of output containing an address, hexadecimal opcode, and perhaps data, followed by the program statement from the source file. Displaying the object file is a problem, however. The output will appear as *garbage* since the object file contains binary codes of a machine-language program, rather than ASCII text codes.

A sketch of a 68000 two-pass assembler is shown in Figure 4-3 written in a pseudo code computer language (similar to Pascal or C) to enhance readability. The pseudo code hides the fine details of the assembler's operation; nevertheless, it could serve as a framework for the more ambitious reader to write a 68000 cross assembler in C or Pascal.

## 4.3.   ASSEMBLY-LANGUAGE PROGRAM FORMAT

This section describes the format of source programs in assembly language. Each line of an

```
BEGIN /* pass 1 */
  LC = 0;  /* LC = location counter */
  mnemonic = null;
  WHILE (mnemonic <> end) DO BEGIN
    get_line();
    scan_line();
    IF (got_label AND mnemonic <> end)
      enter_in_symbol_table(label, LC);
    CASE mnemonic OF BEGIN
      null, comment, end: ; /* do nothing */
      ORG: LC = operand_value;
      EQU: enter_in_symbol_table(label, oprnd_value);
      DC: WHILE (got_operand) DO increment_LC;
      DS: LC = LC + operand_value;
      length1_instruction: LC = LC + 2;
      length2_instruction: LC = LC + 4;
      length3_instruction: LC = LC + 6;
      length4_instruction: LC = LC + 8
      length5_instruction: LC = LC + 10;
    END
  END
  /* pass 2 */
  rewind_source_file;
  LC = 0;
  mnemonic = null;
  WHILE (mnemonic <> end) DO BEGIN
    get_line();
    scan_line();
    CASE mnemonic OF BEGIN
      null, comment, equ, end: ; /* do nothing */
      ORG: LC = operand_value;
      DC: WHILE (operand) BEGIN
          put_in_object_file(operand);
          LC = LC + 1;
        END
      DS: LC = LC + operand;
      instruction: WHILE (inst_length > 0) BEGIN
          put_in_object_file(inst_code);
          LC = LC + 1;
        END
    END
  END
END
```

Figure 4-3.   Operation of a two-pass assembler.

assembly-language program contains one of the following:

- a machine instruction
- an assembler directive
- a comment

**Machine instructions** are the familiar mnemonics of executable instructions (e.g., ADD). **Assembler directives** are instructions to the assembler program to define program structure, symbols, data, constants, and so on (e.g., ORG). **Comments** enhance the readability of programs by explaining the purpose and operation of instruction sequences.

Those lines containing machine instructions or assembler directives must conform to rules—the syntax—understood by the assembler. Each line is divided into *fields* separated by space or tab characters. The format for each line follows:

```
[label]  mnemonic  [operand]  [comment]
```

Only the mnemonic field is mandatory. The placement of each field within a source program was illustrated in Figure 4-2a. One or more operands may be permitted, depending on the instruction or directive. The fields are described below.

### 4.3.1.  Label Field

A label represents the address of the instruction (or data) that follows. When branching to this instruction, this label is used in the operand field of the branch or jump instruction (e.g., BEQ SKIP).

Since the label field is optional, most assemblers require that the label begins in the first column. The absence of a label is therefore signaled by a space or tab character at the beginning of a line. The first non-space or non-tab character signals the beginning of the mnemonic.

Whereas the term *label* always represents an address, the term *symbol* is more general. Symbols can be labels as well as names corresponding to equated values, segments, and so on.

A symbol (or label) is up to 132 characters long. The first character must be a letter (a–z, A–Z), "?", "@", or "_". The following characters may also include digits (0–9).[2] Instruction mnemonics and names of registers are reserved and not allowed as symbols.

### 4.3.2.  Mnemonic Field

Instruction mnemonics or assembler directives go in the mnemonic field. The mnemonic field follows the label field by at least one space or tab character. Examples of instruction mnemonics are ADD, MOVE, ASL, or CMP. Examples of assembler directives are ORG, EQU, or DC. Assembler directives are described later in this chapter.

### 4.3.3.  Operand Field

The operand field follows the mnemonic field. This field contains the address or data used by the instruction. Labels can represent addresses of the data; symbols can represent data constants. The possibilities for the operand field are largely dependent on the operation. Some instructions have no operand (e.g., RTS), while others allow for multiple operands separated by commas. The possibilities for the operand field are numerous, and we shall elaborate on these at length. But first, the comment field.

### 4.3.4.  Comment Field

Remarks to clarify the program go in the comment field at the end of each line. Entire lines may be comments by beginning them with an asterisk ("*") or semicolon (";"), depending on the assembler. Subroutines and large sections of a program generally begin with a comment block—several lines of comments that explain the general properties of the section of software that follows. Some assemblers require a semicolon at the beginning of a comment that follows on the same line as an operand.

## 4.4.  SPECIAL ASSEMBLER SYMBOLS

Special assembler symbols appear in the operand field to identify CPU registers, addressing modes, and so on. The examples that follow are given in source format only. The hexadecimal (assembled) form of the instructions is given in Figure 4-4, later in this section.

### 4.4.1.  The Location Counter

An asterisk ("*") in the operand field refers to the current value of the assembler's location counter. For example, the instruction

```
BRA   *+8
```

---

[2]The required format for labels and symbols is one area, in particular, that varies from one assembler to the next. The format given is for A68K and may be different from other assemblers.

means branch always (BRA) to the location eight bytes beyond the branch instruction (*+8). A *branch to itself* instruction is

```
            BRA         *
```

Of course this example could be coded as

```
    HERE      BRA         HERE
```

with the assembler computing the offset to use in the instruction.

## 4.4.2.  Indirect Address

When a 68000 address register is used as the address of an operand, it indirectly references the operand. This is a powerful feature of most microprocessor's instruction sets. Stepping through lists of data is also possible using postincrement or predecrement indirect addressing. For example, the instruction

```
        MOVE.B      (A3)+,D4
```

moves a byte of data from memory to D4. A3 is used as the address of the data.  After the data byte is retrieved, A3 is increment by 1 so that it points to the next byte in the list. See Chapter 2 for more details on indirect addressing.

## 4.4.3.  Immediate Data Constants

Instructions using immediate addressing include a data constant in the operand field. The data become part of the binary code of the instruction. Immediate data are preceded by a number sign ("#"). For example

```
    COUNT     EQU         100
              MOVE.W      #COUNT,D5
```

defines the symbol COUNT as 100 and then moves the value into D5. Note that the assembler converts 100 from decimal to binary. In the listing file the constant appears in hexadecimal.

Values other than decimal are used by preceding them with a dollar sign ("$") for hexadecimal, commercial at sign ("@") for octal, or a percent sign ("%") for binary.[3] For example, the following instructions are the same:

```
MOVE.W   #100,D5         decimal constant
MOVE.W   #$64,D5         hexadecimal constant
MOVE.W   #@144,D5        octal constant
MOVE.W   #%01100100,D5   binary constant
```

Negative values are also possible. The assembler converts the binary operand to 2s complement form in the appropriate size for the instruction. For example, the following two instructions are the same:

```
    MOVE.W      #-5,D7
    MOVE.W      #$FFFB,D7
```

## 4.4.4.  Data Address

Many instructions access memory locations using a direct, or absolute, address. The address may be specified in a symbolic form or using a constant. For example, the following instruction

```
        MOVE        $F000,D5
```

moves 16 bits of data from memory location $00F000 to register D5. (Recall that ".W" is the default operand size for MOVE.) The same effect could be achieved using

```
    PORT      EQU         $F000
              MOVE        PORT,D5
```

## 4.4.5.  Code Address

A code address is used in the operand field of branch or jump instructions, or as the immediate operand when loading an address register. Code addresses are usually specified using a label, as in

```
    HERE      .
              .
              .
              BEQ         HERE
```

The branch-if-equal-zero instruction uses relative addressing. The assembler computes the relative address by subtracting the value of the symbol HERE from the address following the BEQ instruction (location counter + 2).

It is instructive to review the preceding examples after translation by an assembler. Although the sequence of instructions in Figure 4-4 is meaningless, the hexadecimal form reveals important characteristics of the relationship between assem-

---

[3]A68K represents octal numbers with a trailing "Q" (i.e., 144Q, not @144).

```
 1  00001000                   ORG     $1000
 2  00001000 6006              BRA     *+8              ;"*" location counter
 3  00001002 60FE              BRA     *                ;branch to itself
 4  00001004 6000FFFE  HERE    BRA     HERE             ;branch to itself
 5  00001008 181B              MOVE.B  (A3)+,D4         ;indirect addressing
 6  00000064  COUNT    EQU     100                      ;equate symbol to value
 7  0000100A 3A3C0064          MOVE.W  #COUNT,D5        ;symbol as immed. data
 8  0000100E 3A3C0064          MOVE.W  #100,D5          ;decimal
 9  00001012 3A3C0064          MOVE.W  #$64,D5          ;hexadecimal
10  00001016 3A3C0064          MOVE.W  #144Q,D5         ;octal (A68K format)
11  0000101A 3A3C0064          MOVE.W  #%01100100,D5    ;binary
12  0000101E 3E3CFFFB          MOVE.W  #-5,D7           ;negative number, decimal
13  00001022 3E3CFFFB          MOVE.W  #$FFFB,D7        ;negative number, hexadecimal
14  00001026 3A390000          MOVE    $F000,D5         ;data address
    0000102A F000
15  0000F000          PORT     EQU     $F000            ;equate symbol as address
16  0000102C 3A390000          MOVE    PORT,D5          ;data address (symbol)
    00001030 F000
17  00001032 4E71     BACK     NOP                      ;code address (NOP =
18  00001034 4E71              NOP                      ;   no operation)
19  00001036 67FA              BEQ     BACK
20  00001038                   END
```

Figure 4-4.   Listing form of examples in section 4.4

bly language and machine language. Note in line 14, for example, that the assembler used absolute long addressing when the address was specified only as $F000. Although $F000 is a 16-bit value, had absolute short addressing been used, the address would sign-extend to $FFF000 at run-time, which is probably *not* the intent.

## 4.5. ASSEMBLE-TIME EXPRESSIONS

Values and constants in the operand field are expressed three ways: (a) explicitly (e.g., $F3), (b) with a predefined symbol (e.g., LOOP), or (c) using an expression (e.g., 3+5). Expressions provide a powerful technique for making assembly-language programs more readable and more flexible. When an expression is used, the assembler calculates a value and inserts it into the instruction. Since the expressions are evaluated when the program is assembled, they are called **assemble-time expressions.** Do not confuse these with 68000 instructions that perform similar operations. For example, the 68000 instruction AND performs a logical AND on two variables at *run-time;* whereas the assemble-time operator .AND. is evaluated by the assembler program as the program is assembled. The result is a numeric constant which is inserted in the instruction.

All assemble-time expressions are evaluated using 32-bit arithmetic; however, either 8, 16, or 32 bits are inserted into the instruction as appropriate. Table 4-1 summarizes the most common expressions supported by 68000 assemblers. As noted earlier, the syntax may vary from one assembler to the next.

Unary operators take one argument (e.g., -3), whereas binary operators take two (e.g., 4 * 5). Operations are evaluated according to the precedence indicated (or left-to-right, for equal precedence). Parentheses override precedence in the usual way. The last eight operators are *relational,* yielding a result of all 1s (true) or all 0s (false).

Some examples are given in Figure 4-5. The unary minus operator appears in line 3. The instruction uses an immediate word operand; so the expression "−1" is converted to the 16-bit constant $FFFF_{16}$ and appears in the second instruction word. The first instruction word is the opcode ($3A3C_{16}$).

**Example 4-2.** A large integer is assigned to the symbol COUNT using the equate directive. Illustrate an instruction that will initialize D5 with the number of *thousands* in COUNT. For example, if COUNT = $4792_{10}$, D5 is loaded with 4.

**Solution:** See Figure A.

**Figure A.**
```
1  00001A85          COUNT    EQU     6789
2  00001000                   ORG     $1000
3  00001000 7A06              MOVE.L  #COUNT/1000,D5
```

Table 4-1.    Assemble-Time Operators.

| Operator[†] | Function | Precedence | Type |
|---|---|---|---|
| – | Unary minus | 1 | Unary |
| .NOT. | Logical NOT | 1 | Unary |
| .LOW. | Low byte of | 1 | Unary |
| .HIGH. | High byte of | 1 | Unary |
| .LWRD. | Low word of | 1 | Unary |
| .HWRD. | High word of | 1 | Unary |
| * | Multiplication | 3 | Binary |
| / | Division | 3 | Binary |
| + | Addition | 4 | Binary |
| – | Subtraction | 4 | Binary |
| .MOD. | Modulo | 3 | Binary |
| .SHR. | Logical shift right | 3 | Binary |
| .SHL. | Logical shift left | 3 | Binary |
| .AND. | Logical AND | 5 | Binary |
| .OR. | Logical OR | 6 | Binary |
| .XOR. | Logical XOR | 6 | Binary |
| .EQ. | Equal[††] | 7 | Binary |
| .NE. | Not Equal[††] | 7 | Binary |
| .GE. | Greater or equal[††] | 7 | Binary |
| .LE. | Less or equal[††] | 7 | Binary |
| .GT. | Greater than[††] | 7 | Binary |
| .LT. | Less than[††] | 7 | Binary |
| .UGT. | Unsigned greater than[††] | 7 | Binary |
| .ULT. | Unsigned less than[††] | 7 | Binary |

[†]Operators apply to A68K. Different assemblers may support different operators.
[††]Relational operators return 1s (true) or 0s (false)

```
 1 00000064                    COUNT    EQU    100
 2 00002000                             ORG    $2000
 3 00002000 3A3CFFFF                     MOVE   #-1,D5
 4 00002004 3A3C0009                     MOVE   #4+50/10,D5
 5 00002008 3A3C0001                     MOVE   #25.mod.6,D5
 6 0000200C 3A3C0400                     MOVE   #$8000.shr.5,D5
 7 00002010 3A3C0040                     MOVE   #$45&$F0,D5
 8 00002014 3A3C0041                     MOVE   #.high.'AB',D5
 9 00002018 3A3CFFFF                     MOVE   #5.gt.4,D5
10 0000201C 3A3C0032                     MOVE   #COUNT/2,D5
11 00002020                              END
```

Figure 4-5.    Examples of assemble-time operators.

**Discussion:** This example uses the assemble-time operation for division (/). The result of 6789/1000 is 6. (The remainder is discarded.) The assembled instruction includes $06 in the low byte of the instruction word. Note that the assembler used the MOVEQ form of the instruction since the size is ".L" and the immediate data constant is expressible in 8 bits. ∎

**Example 4-3.** A 32-bit binary value is equated to the symbol KEY in a data encryption program. Illustrate instructions to initialize data registers D0 though D3 with one byte of the key each. D0 gets bits 0–7, D1 gets bits 8–15, D2 gets bits 16–23, and D3 gets bits 24–31. Place eight bits of the key in the low byte of each data register and clear bits 8–31. This is illustrated in Figure 4-6 using $12345678 as an example KEY.

**Solution:** See Figure B.

**Figure B.**

```
1 00001000                  ORG    $1000
2 12345678         KEY       EQU    $12345678
3 00001000 7078              MOVE.L #.LOW.KEY,D0
4 00001002 7256              MOVE.L #(.LWRD.KEY).SHR.8,D1
5 00001004 7434              MOVE.L #(.HWRD.KEY).AND.$FF,D2
6 00001006 7612              MOVE.L #(.HWRD.KEY).SHR.8,D3
```

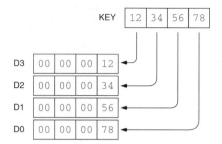

Figure 4-6.   Bit positions for KEY example.

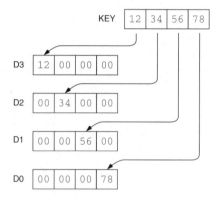

Figure 4-7.   Bit positions for modified KEY example.

**Discussion:** This example uses the assemble-time operators .LOW., .LWRD., .HWRD., .AND., and .SHR. (see Table 4-1). All four instructions assembled into the MOVEQ form. The low-byte of each instruction word contains the 8 bits extracted from the key. ■

**Example 4-4.** Repeat the previous example, except place the bits in the same position of the data register as in the original key (e.g., bits 0–23 of D3 are cleared and bits 24–31 are loaded with bits 24–31 of KEY). This is illustrated in Figure 4-7.

**Solution:** See Figure C.

**Discussion:** Only the first move benefits from the MOVEQ form. The others include the 32-bit immediate data in the second and third instruction words. Note that the position of each 8-bit pattern is the same in the immediate data as in the original key. ■

**Example 4-5.** A program to add a list of 16-bit numbers uses the label COUNT as the number of entries in the list. The entries are placed in the program using DC.W directives. Illustrate how to define COUNT to receive automatically the correct value, regardless of the size of the list.

**Solution:**

```
1 00001000                ORG   $1000
2 00001000 007B   LIST   DC.W   123
3 00001002 002D          DC.W   45
4 00001004 1A85          DC.W   6789
5 00001006 000A          DC.W   10
6 00001008 09A4          DC.W   2468
7 00000005      COUNT   EQU    (*-LIST)/2
8 0000100A               END
```

**Discussion:** In line 7, the label COUNT is automatically assigned the value 5, which is the number of entries in the list. The assemble-time expression "(*-LIST)/2" provides a convenient way of defining COUNT without explicitly specifying the number of entries. The first part of the expression subtracts the address of the start of the list (LIST) from the value of the location count (*, the address after the last entry). Division by two converts this to a word count. ■

There is no substitute for practice. The assembler expressions are best learned by constructing examples in a source program and observing the results in the listing file. See Question 1 at the end of this chapter.

## 4.6.   ASSEMBLER DIRECTIVES

Assembler directives are instructions to the assembler program. Although they appear in the mnemonic field of the program, they are *not* assembly-language instructions executable by the target microprocessor. With the exception of DC, they have no direct effect on the contents of memory. Some directives also require a label. Some require one or more arguments.

A variety of functions are fulfilled by assembler directives, including (a) defining symbols and as-

Figure C.
```
1 00001000                      ORG    $1000
2 12345678        KEY    EQU    $12345678
3 00001000 7078          MOVE.L #KEY.AND.$000000FF,D0
4 00001002 223C0000       MOVE.L #KEY.AND.$0000FF00,D1
  00001006 5600
5 00001008 243C0034       MOVE.L #KEY.AND.$00FF0000,D2
  0000100C 0000
6 0000100E 263C1200       MOVE.L #KEY.AND.$FF000000,D3
  00001012 0000
```

signing them values, (b) controlling the flow of execution for the assembler, and (c) setting the format and content of the object file and listing file.

The most important assembler directives are shown in Table 4-2. Each is described in the following paragraphs and short examples are given in source format. The listing form of the examples appears in Figure 4-8 near the end of this section.

## 4.6.1. ORG

The ORG (origin) directive sets the address in memory for the instructions or data constants that follow. A label is not permitted. An address is required as an argument.

Assembler format:

```
          ORG          address
```

Example:

```
          ORG          $1000
START     MOVE.B       #100,D5
```

In this example, the hexadecimal address $1000 is set as the starting address for the instructions that follow. The opcode for the MOVE.B instruction goes in address $1000; the second word of MOVE.B goes in address $1002, and so on.

Note that instructions on the 68000 (and most other 16-bit microprocessors) must be *word aligned*. If $1001 is used in the ORG directive above, the address $1001 will be unassigned and the following instruction will be assembled at address $1002. Remember, word addresses on the 68000 have "0" as the least-significant bit.

## 4.6.2. EQU

The EQU (equate) directive assigns a value to a symbol. The symbol is used later in the program in place of the value.

Assembler format:

```
symbol    EQU          value
```

Example:

```
COUNT     EQU          100
          ORG          $2000
HERE      MOVE.B       #COUNT,D5
```

The symbol COUNT is assigned the decimal value 100.

Equate directives are very powerful, and generous use of them is encouraged. There are two main benefits in using equate directives. First, they make programs easier to read. In the example above, the name COUNT gives the reader a sense of how the value 100 is used in the program.

Second, equate directives make programs easier to maintain and change. It is possible to use a defined symbol many times in a program. If the value of the symbol must change, it is only changed in the single line where it is defined (equated) and then the program is reassembled. All uses of the symbol within the program are updated with the new value.

A well-written assembly-language program contains very few data constants as arguments in instructions. Instead, a group of equate directives will appear near the top of the source program defining the constants within the program.

## 4.6.3. END

The END directive is used at the end of the source program. Statements following the END directive are not processed by the assembler.

Assembler format:

```
          END          [label]
```

Then END directive may be followed by a label. The label represents the entry point for the pro-

Table 4-2.   Assembler Directives.

| Directive | Operation | | Syntax | |
|---|---|---|---|---|
| ORG | set program origin | | ORG | value |
| EQU | equate value to symbol | symbol | EQU | value |
| END | end of source program | | END | label |
| DC | define data constant | [label] | DC | number[,number][...] |
| DS | define RAM storage | [label] | DS | count |
| RSEG | begin relocatable segment | | RSEG | name |
| EXTERN | define external symbol | | EXTERN | symbol[,symbol][...] |
| PUBLIC | define public symbol | | PUBLIC | symbol[,symbol][...] |

gram. The address of the entry point is used by de-buggers, loaders, conversion utilities, and so on, to identify the starting address of the program.

## 4.6.4.  DC

The DC (define constant) directive places data constants within a program. An optional label may be used. Multiple constants are defined by separating them with commas. There are several variations of the DC directive to control the size of data constants. Constants may be bytes (DC.B), words (DC.W), or longwords (DC.L). Word is the default size (DC). As well, ASCII codes can be defined as a series of bytes by including the characters within single quotation marks (e.g., 'hello').

Assembler format:

```
[label]  DC  number[,number][...]
```

Example:

```
CR    EQU   $0D      define a symbol
      ORG   $3000    set origin
NUM   DC    5,-1     word-size default
MORE  DC.B  5,-1     byte-size constants
NAME  DC.B  'JOHN'   ASCII string
      DC.B  CR,0     CR is a symbol
```

The memory assignments for the directives above are given later in Figure 4-8.

For word or longword constants, the assembler adjusts the address forward, if necessary, to achieve the proper alignment. For example,

```
      ORG   $4001
VALUE DC    15       decimal constant
```

leaves $4001 unassigned and assigns the word $000F to word address $4002.

If a single ASCII character is defined as a word constant, it is left-justified within the word. For example,

```
      ORG   $5000
      DC.W  'a'
```

assigns the value $6100 to the word address $005000.

## 4.6.5.  DS

The DS (define storage) directive reserves RAM storage for use during execution of the program. As with DC, storage may be reserved in byte (DS.B), word (DS.W), or longword (DS.L) increments. The default is DS.W if no suffix is provided.

Assembler format:

```
[label]  DS  count
```

Example:

```
LENGTH  EQU   80
        ORG   $6000
BUFFER  DS.B  LENGTH
TEMP    DS.B  1
```

Eighty bytes of RAM storage are defined to begin at the address $006000 and a single byte named TEMP is defined at address $006000 + 80_{10} = $006050. The label BUFFER represents the address of the first byte. To initialize the buffer with zeros, the instructions shown in Figure D could be used:

## 4.6.6.  RSEG

The directive RSEG (relocatable segment) declares that the following instructions are placed in a relocatable segment identified with the name provided as an argument.

Assembler format:

```
        RSEG  name
```

Example:

```
        RSEG  EPROM
BEGIN   MOVE.B  #44,D5
```

```
Figure D.      ORG    $7000
               MOVE.L  #LENGTH,D1   use D1 as counter
               MOVEA   #BUFFER,A1   A1 points to buffer
        LOOP   MOVE.B  #0,(A1)+     clear location
               SUBQ.B  #1,D1        done?
               BNE     LOOP         no: clear again
```

```
 1    00001000                             ORG         $1000
 2    00001000 1A3C0064      START         MOVE.B      #100,D5
 3    00000064              COUNT          EQU         100
 4    00002000                             ORG         $2000
 5    00002000 1A3C0064      HERE          MOVE.B      #COUNT,D5
 6    0000000D              CR             EQU         $0D           define a symbol
 7    00003000                             ORG         $3000         set origin
 8    00003000 0005FFFF     NUM            DC          5,-1          word-size default
 9    00003004 05FF         MORE           DC.B        5,-1          byte-size constants
10    00003006 4A4F484E     NAME           DC.B        'JOHN'        ASCII string
11    0000300A 0D00                        DC.B        CR,0          CR is a symbol
12    00004001                             ORG         $4001
13    00004002 000F         VALUE          DC          15            decimal constant
14    00005000                             ORG         $5000
15    00005000 6100                        DC.W        'a'
16    00000050              LENGTH         EQU         80
17    00006000                             ORG         $6000
18    00006000              BUFFER         DS.B        LENGTH
19    00006050              TEMP           DS.B        1
20    00007000                             ORG         $7000
21    00007000 7250                        MOVE.L      #LENGTH,D1    use R1 as counter
22    00007002 327C6000                    MOVEA       #BUFFER,A1    A1 points to buff
23    00007006 12FC0000     LOOP           MOVE.B      #0,(A1)+      clear location
24    0000700A 5301                        SUBQ.B      #1,D1         done?
25    0000700C 66F8                        BNE         LOOP          no: clear again
26    00000000                             RSEG        EPROM
27    00000000 1A3C002C     BEGIN          MOVE.B      #44,D5
28    00000004                             END
```

Figure 4-8.    Listing form of examples in section 4.6.

A segment named EPROM is defined and the instructions that follow are placed in this segment when the program modules are linked together.

RSEG is used in lieu of ORG when writing relocatable program modules. Instead of taking an address as an argument (like ORG), RSEG takes a name. The name and address are used later as arguments to the linker.

Note that the same segment name may appear many times within a module or in different modules. When the modules are linked together, segments with the same names are joined together in the order they appear in when linked. The address provided to the linker is the first address of the first instance of the segment.

The examples presented in this section are repeated in Figure 4-8 in listing form. Although the instruction sequence is meaningless, the figure illustrates important properties of the relationship between assembly language and machine language.

**Example 4-6.** A table look-up scheme requires data constants in memory beginning at an address that is a multiple of 32. Illustrate an ORG directive that will *bump-up* the assembler's location counter to the next multiple-of-32.

**Solution:** See Figure E.

**Discussion:** The second ORG directive (line 3) is the answer to this problem. First, 32 is added to the location counter to bring it past the next multiple-of-32 boundary. Then, the lower five bits are cleared to reduce the location counter to the multiple-of-32 address just past its original value, as shown in the address column on the left. ∎

**Example 4-7.** An 8-bit peripheral interface adapter (PIA) resides in the 68000's memory space at addresses $00F000 through $00F006. It includes the following 8-bit registers:

CONTROL    at address $00F000
STATUS     at address $00F002
INPUT      at address $00F004
OUTPUT     at address $00F006

(a) Define these registers using EQU directives so that a change to the PIA's base address requires only one change in the source program.

(b) Write the value $F5 to the output port using address register indirect addressing with an offset.

**Solution:** See Figure F.

**Figure E.**
```
1 00123456                  ORG    $123456
2 00123456  4E71            NOP
3 00123460                  ORG    (*+32).AND.$FFFFE0
4 00123460  0025    TABLE   DC.W   $25         ;etc.
```

**Figure F.**    (a)

```
1 00001000                        ORG       $1000
2 0000F000              PIA       EQU       $00F000
3 0000F000              CONTROL   EQU       0
4 0000F002              STATUS    EQU       2
5 0000F004              INPUT     EQU       4
6 0000F006              OUTPUT    EQU       6
```

(b)

```
7 00001000 207C0000              MOVEA.L   #PIA,A0
  00001004 F000
8 00001006 10BC00F5              MOVE.B    #$F5,OUTPUT(A0)
9 0000100A                       END
```

**Discussion:** (a) If the PIA is relocated to a different address, only the first equate needs updating (line 2). In (b), note that the longword form of MOVEA is used (line 7). This is essential. If the suffix ".L" is omitted, the word form is assumed and the 16-bit address $F000 appears in the instruction. When the instruction executes, the address sign-extends to $FFFFF000, which is *not* the address of the PIA. Using MOVEA.L prevents this because a full 32-bit address ($0000F000) appears in the instruction. The output register in the PIA is initialized in line 8 using register indirect addressing with OUTPUT as an offset. ∎

## 4.6.7. EXTERN *and* PUBLIC

The EXTERN and PUBLIC directives are used when a program is split over multiple files (modules). They provide the mechanism for symbols to appear in one module but be defined in another.

Assembler format:

```
EXTERN   symbol[,symbol][...]
PUBLIC   symbol[,symbol][...]
```

Example:

Consider a subroutine called SQRT that finds the square root of the integer in D7. The technique to define the subroutine in one module (a file called MATH.SRC) and use it in another (PROG.SRC) is given in Figure 4-9.

When PROG.SRC is assembled, no error message is generated for the BSR instruction even though the subroutine is not found in the file. EXTERN and PUBLIC are important when developing a large program split among multiple modules, as discussed in the next section.

---

## 4.7. MODULAR PROGRAMMING

**Modular programming** is a program development technique whereby a large programming problem is decomposed into smaller problems. For the purpose of this discussion, a module is a *file;* therefore, each module is a separate file containing a portion of the complete program. Before the program is executed, the modules are assembled in the usual way, and then combined, or linked, into a single module.

Modular programming offers several important advantages over *monolithic programming* (placing the entire program in a single file). These include (a) assembling and maintaining each module separately, (b) using the same label in different modules without conflict, (c) using modules in different programs without reassembling the modules, and (d) a faster *build* (assemble/link) of a program since only the modules that change need reassembling.

### 4.7.1. *Inter-Module Communication*

Modules must communicate with each other, which is to say that branching between modules (e.g., calling subroutines) or using data constants defined in other modules is necessary. This is accomplished by using external and public symbols. An **external symbol** is a symbol used in the current module but defined in another. A **public symbol** is a symbol that is defined in the current

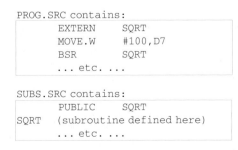

Figure 4-9.    EXTERN/PUBLIC example.

module and used in other modules. The assembler directives EXTERN and PUBLIC define external and public symbols.

When a module with an external symbol is assembled, the assembler has no knowledge of the value of the symbol (e.g., the address of a subroutine that is called). However, no error message is generated. Instead, the assembler leaves a *hole* in the output object file (module) and flags the location as external. A table containing the location (offset from start of module) and name of the external symbol is appended to the object module. The correct value is calculated and substituted later by the linker when the modules for the entire program are combined. One of the main functions of the linker is to **resolve external references** between modules. Obviously, the symbol must exist as a public symbol in another module linked, otherwise an **unresolved external symbol** message is generated by the linker.

## 4.7.2.  Segments

A concept closely connected with modular programming is that of **segments.** Most commonly, there is a **code segment** and a **data segment.** A code segment contains program instructions and/or data constants such as ASCII strings. Data constants are included in a program using the DC (define constant) assembler directive. Code segments are *read-only.*

A data segment is an area of RAM storage used to store and retrieve data values during the execution of a program. These locations are defined using the DS (define storage) assembler directive. Data segments are *read/write.*

In many implementations, the code segment is destined for EPROM and the data segment is destined for RAM. Note that a module may contain both code and data segments.

## 4.7.3.  Relocation

Another concept closely connected with modular programming is that of **relocation.** Previously, we learned that the ORG directive sets the address in memory where the program executes. In modular programming, this is generally not possible because the starting addresses of modules are not known until the modules are combined by the linker. Furthermore, it may be desirable to allow the entire program to be assembled without explicitly setting the absolute address for execution. Using relocatable segments permits this.

Instead of ORG, the directive RSEG is used to begin a relocatable segment. Whereas the ORG directive takes an address as an argument, the RSEG directive requires a name. The name identifies the segment and is used subsequently as an argument to the linker. Only at *link time* is an address provided for the named segment. The process of fixing the absolute address for code and data segments at link time is known as *locating.* Some linkers are therefore referred to as *linker/locators.*

## 4.7.4.  Linker Invocation

When all modules can be assembled without errors, the program is then *built* by combining the modules into a single absolute module. A linker performs this operation (see Figure 4-10).

The figure shows a linker (XLINK, by Enertec) receiving four input files and generating two output files. PROG.HEX is the executable program, formatted in Motorola S-records. (S-records were presented in Chapter 1.) PROG.MAP is the **link map.** A link map is similar to an assembler's listing file; it identifies the name, starting address, and size of all segments and the name and value of all symbols.

Linker invocations vary slightly from one product to the next. XLINK requires a CPU-type as an argument since it is a universal linker, capable of linking object modules for many different CPUs. The absolute output file in Figure 4-10 is formatted in S-records. In practice, many linkers output a binary program, ready for execution. If downloading to a target system's RAM is required, then the binary program file is first converted to hex-ASCII format using a separate conversion utility.

A very important omission from Figure 4-10b is the identification of segments and the specification of absolute addresses for the segments. These are entered as command line arguments. In their absence, the linker combines segments starting at address $000000. Since linker commands are often lengthy, execution from a batch file or a custom command file is the norm. This is illustrated in the following annotated example of modular programming.

## 4.7.5.  Annotated Example

Many of the concepts introduced in this chapter are now brought together in an annotated example of a simple 68000 program. The source code is split over two files and uses symbols declared as EXTERN and PUBLIC to allow inter-file communication. Each file is a module—one named ECHO,

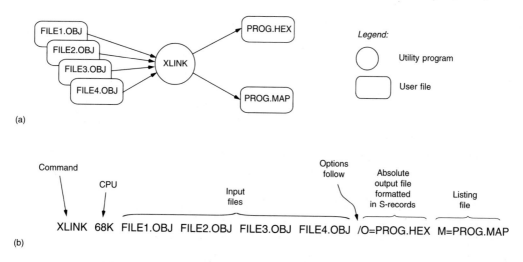

Figure 4-10.    Linker operation. (a) files, (b) invocation.

the other named MYLIB. The program contains a relocatable code segment named EPROM and a relocatable data segment named RAM. Working with multiple files, modules, and segments is essential for large programming projects. A careful examination of the example that follows will strengthen these core concepts and prepare the reader to embark on practical 68000-based programming tasks.

Our example is a simple input/output program intended to run on a 68000 single-board computer such as the 68000 Mini-Board (68KMB) dis-

```
 1                   ***********************************************************
 2                   * ECHO.SRC - prompt with a command line, echo input      *
 3                   *            line to output, repeat until 'q' is entered  *
 4                   ***********************************************************
 5   0000000D        CR       EQU     $0D
 6   0000000A        LF       EQU     $0A
 7   00000000                 EXTERN  OUTSTR,INLINE,OUTLINE
 8   00000000                 EXTERN  BUFFER,TOUPPR
 9                   ***********************************************************
10                   * Put in a code segment called 'EPROM'                    *
11                   ***********************************************************
12   00000000                 RSEG    EPROM
13   00000000 227C0000 LOOP    MOVEA.L #PROMPT,A1  ;A1 points to prompt string
     00000004 0030
14   00000006 4EB90000         JSR     >OUTSTR     ;output prompt string
     0000000A 0000
15   0000000C 4EB90000         JSR     >INLINE     ;get input from keyboard
     00000010 0000
16   00000012 227C0000         MOVEA.L #BUFFER,A1  ;check for quit character
     00000016 0000
17   00000018 1019             MOVE.B  (A1)+,D0    ;put 1st char in D0
18   0000001A 4EB90000         JSR     >TOUPPR     ;convert to uppercase
     0000001E 0000
19   00000020 B03C0051         CMP.B   #'Q',D0     ;Q?
20   00000024 6708             BEQ.S   EXIT        ;yes: exit
21   00000026 4EB90000         JSR     >OUTLINE    ;no:  output line
     0000002A 0000
22   0000002C 60D2             BRA.S   LOOP
23   0000002E 4E4E     EXIT    TRAP    #14         ;return to MON68K
24
25   00000030 0D0A456E PROMPT  DC.B    CR,LF,'Enter a command: ',0
     00000034 74657220
     00000038 6120636F
     0000003C 6D6D616E
     00000040 643A2000
26   00000044                  END     LOOP
```

Figure 4-11.    Linker example: ECHO.LST.

```
 1                              ************************************************************
 2                              *MYLIB.SRC - Library of useful subroutines              *
 3                              ************************************************************
 4   0000C001       DUART      EQU       $C001        ;68681 serial interface IC
 5   00000002       SRA        EQU       1*2          ;status register A
 6   00000006       TBA        EQU       3*2          ;transmit buffer A
 7   00000006       RBA        EQU       3*2          ;receive buffer A
 8   0000000D       CR         EQU       $0D          ;carriage return
 9   0000000A       LF         EQU       $0A          ;line feed
10   00000028       LENGTH     EQU       40           ;length of input buffer
11   00000000                  PUBLIC    OUTCHR,INCHR,OUTSTR,INLINE
12   00000000                  PUBLIC    OUTLINE,BUFFER,TOUPPR
13   00000000                  RSEG      EPROM
14                              ************************************************************
15                              * OUTCHR - output character in D0 to serial port         *
16                              ************************************************************
17   00000000 2F08  OUTCHR     MOVE.L    A0,-(A7)           ;save A0
18   00000002 3F07             MOVE.W    D7,-(A7)           ;save D7
19   00000004 207C0000         MOVEA.L   #DUART,A0          ;A0 points to 68681
     00000008 C001
20   0000000A 1E280002 OUTCHR2 MOVE.B    SRA(A0),D7
21   0000000E 02070004         ANDI.B    #4,D7
22   00000012 67F6             BEQ.S     OUTCHR2
23   00000014 11400006         MOVE.B    D0,TBA(A0)
24   00000018 3E1F             MOVE.W    (A7)+,D7           ;restore D7
25   0000001A 205F             MOVE.L    (A7)+,A0           ;restore A0
26   0000001C 4E75             RTS
27
28                              ************************************************************
29                              * INCHR - input character in D0 from serial port         *
30                              ************************************************************
31   0000001E 2F08  INCHR      MOVE.L    A0,-(A7)           ;save A0
32   00000020 3F07             MOVE.W    D7,-(A7)           ;save D7
33   00000022 207C0000         MOVEA.L   #DUART,A0          ;A0 points to 68681
     00000026 C001
34   00000028 1E280002 INCHR2  MOVE.B    SRA(A0),D7
35   0000002C 02070001         ANDI.B    #1,D7
36   00000030 67F6             BEQ.S     INCHR2
37   00000032 10280006         MOVE.B    RBA(A0),D0
38   00000036 0200007F         ANDI.B    #$7F,D0            ;ensure bit 7 = 0
39   0000003A 3E1F             MOVE.W    (A7)+,D7           ;restore D7
40   0000003C 205F             MOVEA.L   (A7)+,A0           ;restore A7
41   0000003E 4E75             RTS
42
43                              ************************************************************
44                              * OUTSTR - output null-terminated string to serial port  *
45                              *        - Entry: A1 points to string                    *
46                              ************************************************************
47   00000040 2F00  OUTSTR     MOVE.L    D0,-(A7)           ;save D0 on stack
48   00000042 1019  OUTSTR2    MOVE.B    (A1)+,D0
49   00000044 6704             BEQ.S     OUTSTR3
50   00000046 61B8             BSR.S     OUTCHR
51   00000048 60F8             BRA.S     OUTSTR2
52   0000004A 201F  OUTSTR3    MOVE.L    (A7)+,D0           ;restore D0
53   0000004C 4E75             RTS                          ;yes: done
54
55                              ************************************************************
56                              * INLINE - input line from serial port, put in buffer    *
57                              ************************************************************
58   0000004E 227C0000 INLINE  MOVEA.L   #BUFFER,A1
     00000052 0000
59   00000054 61C8  INLINE2    BSR.S     INCHR              ;input character
60   00000056 12C0             MOVE.B    D0,(A1)+           ;put in buffer
61   00000058 61A6             BSR.S     OUTCHR             ;echo character
62   0000005A B03C000D         CMP.B     #CR,D0             ;character = CR?
63   0000005E 66F4             BNE.S     INLINE2            ;no: repeat
64   00000060 12FC0000         MOVE.B    #0,(A1)+           ;yes: put null at end and
65   00000064 4E75             RTS                          ;     return
66
67                              ************************************************************
68                              * Define a buffer in data segment                        *
69                              ************************************************************
70   00000000                  RSEG      RAM                ;begin a data segment
71   00000000       BUFFER     DS.B      LENGTH
72
```

continued

Figure 4-12.    Linker example: MYLIB.LST.

```
73                      ************************************************
74                      * OUTLINE - output line to serial port        *
75                      ************************************************
76   00000066                   RSEG    EPROM          ;restart code segment
77   00000066 103C000A  OUTLINE  MOVE.B  #LF,D0
78   0000006A 6194               BSR.S   OUTCHR         ;first begin a new line
79   0000006C 227C0000           MOVEA.L #BUFFER,A1     ;init A1 to point to string
     00000070 0000
80   00000072 1019      AGAIN    MOVE.B  (A1)+,D0       ;get char., inc pointer
81   00000074 6704               BEQ.S   EXIT           ;character = 0?
82   00000076 6188               BSR.S   OUTCHR         ;no:  send it and
83   00000078 60F8               BRA.S   AGAIN          ;     get next char
84   0000007A 4E75      EXIT     RTS                    ;yes: done
85
86                      ************************************************
87                      * TOUPPR - convert ASCII code in D0 to uppercase *
88                      ************************************************
89   0000007C 6108      TOUPPR   BSR.S   ISALPH         ;is ASCII code alpha?
90   0000007E 6404               BCC.S   SKIP           ;no:  exit
91   00000080 C03C00DF           AND.B   #%11011111,D0  ;yes: ensure uppercase
92   00000084 4E75      SKIP     RTS
93
94                      ************************************************
95                      * ISALPH - return with C=1 if code in D0 is ASCII alpha *
96                      *          Note: Alpha codes in range a-z or A-Z        *
97                      ************************************************
98   00000086 B03C0061  ISALPH   CMP.B   #'a',D0
99   0000008A 6506               BCS.S   SKIP3
100  0000008C B03C007B           CMP.B   #'z'+1,D0
101  00000090 6512               BCS.S   YES
102  00000092 B03C0041  SKIP3    CMP.B   #'A',D0
103  00000096 6506               BCS.S   SKIP4
104  00000098 B03C005B           CMP.B   #'Z'+1,D0
105  0000009C 6506               BCS.S   YES
106  0000009E 023C00FE  SKIP4    ANDI    #$FE,CCR       ;clear C if not alpha
107  000000A2 4E75               RTS
108  000000A4 003C0001  YES      ORI     #1,CCR         ;set C if alpha
109  000000A8 4E75               RTS
110  000000AA                    END
```

**Figure 4-12. Continued.**

cussed in Chapter 8. It is assumed a terminal (or a host computer running a terminal emulation program) is attached to the serial port. A trap instruction at the end returns control to the monitor program.

The program does the following:

1. Output the prompt *Enter a command:*
2. Input a line from the keyboard, echoing each character as it is entered and storing the characters in a buffer.
3. Check the first character entered.
4. If the first character is "q" or "Q," quit.
5. Otherwise, echo the entire line again. Go to step 1.

The rest of our example describes the content of five files:

ECHO.LST    listing of ECHO module containing main program

MYLIB.LST    listing of MYLIB module containing subroutines

ECHO.XLK    linker command file

ECHO.MAP    link map

ECHO.HEX    absolute program in hex-ASCII format (S-records)

***ECHO.LST***   The main program loop is contained in ECHO.SRC. The 26 lines of source code were assembled without errors and appear in listing form as ECHO.LST in Figure 4-11. The program uses two equated symbols (lines 5–6) and five external symbols (lines 7–8). The ORG directive was not used. Instead, RSEG appears in line 12 declaring EPROM as the name of the segment that follows. Note, the address is $00000000 in the line following RSEG. Since the segment is relocatable, the assembler starts the segment at zero. The actual address is provided later as an argument to the linker.

The program begins in line 13. The first use of an external symbol is a jump to the subroutine OUTSTR to send the prompt string to the terminal (line 14). The absolute long address of OUTSTR is coded as $00000000. Since the assembler has no knowledge of the location of OUTSTR, it puts zeros in the instruction. This is a so-called *hole* in the relocatable object module. The symbol OUTSTR will appear in a table at the end of the object module with an entry of $00000008, since the hole appears eight bytes from the beginning of the segment. Other holes appear in lines 15, 16, 18, and 21 where other external symbols are used. The linker will fix these by computing the correct absolute address once all program modules are processed.

Line 13 must be fixed by the linker as well. The immediate operand PROMPT appears in the second and third instruction words as $00000030. In line 25 we see the prompt string does indeed begin at address $00000030; however, this address is relative to $00000000, the temporary starting address of the module. The address of PROMPT is adjusted, as with OUTSTR, by the linker.

***MYLIB.LST***   The subroutines for the example program are separate from the main program loop. MYLIB.LST in Figure 4-12 contains seven subroutines plus the definition of a buffer to hold the characters for the input line.

Seven symbols are equated in lines 4–10 and seven symbols are declared PUBLIC in lines 11–12. In a table at the end of the object module (MYLIB.OBJ), these symbols appear along with an entry indicating where they are defined relative to the beginning of the module.

The code for the subroutines is also destined for the code segment EPROM, as declared in line 13 with the RSEG directive.

In lines 70 and 71, the RAM buffer is defined. Line 70 terminates the EPROM segment and initiates a new segment named RAM. In line 71, the RAM segment begins with an address of $00000000 and the buffer is defined with a DS directive. The EPROM segment is restarted in line 76 with another instance of RSEG. Note that the address continues at $00000066, right where it left off. The RAM declarations in lines 70–71 could just as easily be placed at the end of the program, if the programmer wishes to keep the code and

data segments separate in the source program. This is largely a matter of personal style.

***ECHO.XLK***   The relocatable object code for the ECHO and MYLIB files is found in ECHO.OBJ and MYLIB.OBJ. They are combined using a linker such as XLINK. Since the number of command-line arguments is often large, XLINK, and most other linkers, support *command files*. Figure 4-13 shows the contents of a command file called ECHO.XLK containing typical linker arguments.

Using this command file, the linker is invoked with

```
XLINK      @ECHO
```

The similarity with the command line approach is apparent. Additionally, the third and fourth lines in ECHO.XLK name segments and specify starting addresses. The EPROM code segment is destined for $008000 and the RAM data segment for $00A000.

***ECHO.MAP***   A link map provides essential information for debugging. Only through the link map is it possible to determine the physical addresses of the subroutines in the final program. Figure 4-14 shows the content of ECHO.MAP. The segments are identified first, along with their starting location and size. The symbol table that follows provides the vital information, *what is where*. For example, the subroutine OUTSTR is in the MYLIB module at physical address $008084.

***ECHO.HEX***   Finally, the absolute program module produced by XLINK is placed in ECHO.HEX in hex-ASCII format. All program bytes from Figure 4-11 and Figure 4-12 are found in Figure 4-15 with the adjustments made by the linker. The first JSR in ECHO.LST, discussed earlier, is shown in boldface type for convenience. Note the second and third instruction words—the hole—are re-

```
DEF-CPU      68K
LOAD         ECHO.OBJ MYLIB.OBJ
DEF-SEG      (EPROM)=8000
DEF-SEG      (RAM)=A000
MAP          ECHO.MAP
DUMP         ECHO.HEX
EXIT
```

Figure 4-13.   Linker example: ECHO.XLK.

placed with 00008084. This is the absolute address of the OUTSTR subroutine.

## 4.8.   PROGRAMMING STYLE

It is important to adopt a clear and consistent style in assembly-language programming. This is particularly important when working as part of a team, since team members must read and understand each other's programs.

The assembly-language solutions to problems up to this point were deliberately sketchy (with the exception of the annotated example just given). For larger programming tasks, however, a more critical approach is required. The following tips are offered to help improve assembly-language programming style.

### 4.8.1.   Labels

Use labels that are descriptive of the destination they represent. For example, when branching back to repeatedly perform an operation, use a label such as LOOP, BACK, MORE, and so on. When skipping over a few instructions in the program, use a label such as SKIP or AHEAD. When repeatedly checking a status bit, use a label such as CHECK, WAIT, or AGAIN.

The choice of labels is restricted somewhat when using a simple memory-resident or absolute assembler. These assemblers treat the entire program as a unit, thus limiting the use of common labels. Several techniques can circumvent this. Common labels can be sequentially numbered, such as SKIP1, SKIP2, SKIP3, and so on; or perhaps within a subroutine all labels can use the

| Segments | Loc | Siz | Typ | Org | P/N | Al |
|---|---|---|---|---|---|---|
| ======== | === | === | === | === | === | == |
| EPROM | 00008000 | 000000EE | Rel | Stc | Pos | 01 |
| RAM | 0000A000 | 00000028 | Rel | Stc | Pos | 01 |

| Modules/Entries | | Values |
|---|---|---|
| =============== | | ====== |
| echo | | |
| CR | L | 0000000D |
| LF | L | 0000000A |
| LOOP | L | 00008000 |
| EXIT | L | 0000802E |
| PROMPT | L | 00008030 |
| mylib | | |
| OUTCHR | E | 00008044 |
| INCHR | E | 00008062 |
| OUTSTR | E | 00008084 |
| INLINE | E | 00008092 |
| OUTLINE | E | 000080AA |
| BUFFER | E | 0000A000 |
| TOUPPR | E | 000080C0 |
| DUART | L | 0000C001 |
| SRA | L | 00000002 |
| TBA | L | 00000006 |
| RBA | L | 00000006 |
| CR | L | 0000000D |
| LF | L | 0000000A |
| LENGTH | L | 00000028 |
| OUTCHR2 | L | 0000804E |
| INCHR2 | L | 0000806C |
| OUTSTR2 | L | 00008086 |
| OUTSTR3 | L | 0000808E |
| INLINE2 | L | 00008098 |
| AGAIN | L | 000080B6 |
| EXIT | L | 000080BE |
| SKIP | L | 000080C8 |
| ISALPH | L | 000080CA |
| SKIP3 | L | 000080D6 |
| SKIP4 | L | 000080E2 |
| YES | L | 000080E8 |

Figure 4-14.   Linker example: ECHO.MAP.

```
S00700006563686F59
S1138000227C000080304EB9000080844EB900000C
S11380108092227C0000A00010194EB9000080C09C
S11380020B03C005167084EB9000080AA60D24E4EA1
S11380300D0A456E746572206120636F6D6D616E0B
S1078040643A20007A
S11380442F083F07207C0000C0011E2800020207FD
S1138054000467F6114000063E1F205F4E752F088A
S11380643F07207C0000C0011E2800020207000113
S113807467F6102800060200007F3E1F205F4E753D
S11380842F001019670461B860F8201F4E75227C14
S11380940000A00061C812C061A6B03C000D66F4E3
S10980A412FC00004E7501
S11380AA103C000A6194227C0000A00010196704A5
S11380BA618860F84E7561086404C03C00DF4E753F
S11380CAB03C00616506B03C007B6512B03C0041DF
S11380DA6506B03C005B6506023C00FE4E75003C3A
S10780EA00014E75CA
S90380007C
```

Figure 4-15.    Linker example: ECHO.HEX.

name of the subroutine followed by a number, such as SEND, SEND1, SEND2, and so on. There is an obvious loss of clarity here, since the labels SEND1 and SEND2 are not likely to reflect the skipping or looping action taking place.

### 4.8.2.  Comments

The use of comments cannot be overemphasized, particularly in assembly-language programming, which is inherently abstract. All lines of code, except those with truly obvious actions, should include a comment.

Conditional branch instructions are effectively commented using a question similar to the flow-chart question for a similar operation. The *yes* and *no* answers should appear in comments at the lines representing the *jump* and *no jump* actions. This is seen in the INLINE subroutine in Figure 4-12 (lines 62–64).

### 4.8.3.  Comment Blocks

Comment lines are essential at the beginning of each subroutine. Since subroutines perform well-defined tasks commonly needed throughout a program, they should be general-purpose and well documented. Each subroutine is preceded by a **comment block**—a series of comment lines that explicitly state:

- the name of the subroutine
- the operation performed
- entry conditions
- exit conditions
- name of other subroutines used (if any)
- name of registers affected by the subroutine (if any)

The comment blocks preceding the subroutines in Figure 4-12 were kept very short to minimize the size of the figure. An example of a well-documented subroutine is Figure 4-16. A good sense of the precise operation of the subroutine is gained just by reading the comment header. This is obviously preferable to probing the fine details of the subroutine to learn its operation.

### 4.8.4.  Saving Registers on the Stack

As applications grow in size and complexity, new subroutines are often written that build upon and use existing subroutines. Thus, subroutines are calling other subroutines which in turn call other subroutines, and so on. These are called **nested subroutines.** There is no danger in nesting subroutines so long as the stack has enough room to hold the return addresses. This is not a problem, since nesting beyond several levels is rare.[4]

A potential problem, however, lies in the use of registers within subroutines. As the hierarchy of subroutines grows, it becomes ever more difficult to remember what registers are affected by subroutines. A solid programming practice, therefore, is to save registers on the stack that are altered by a subroutine, and then restore them at the end of the subroutine. Note that the INLINE subroutine in Figure 4-12 (lines 55–65) does not do this: It destroys the contents of D0, D7, and A1. This is preventable by beginning the subroutine with

---

[4]An exception is a recursive subroutine—a subroutine that calls itself. The use of recursion usually requires a large stack to handle the numerous stacking operations.

```
 7              ********************************************************
 8              * ISHEX - IS character HEX-ascii?                     *
 9              *                                                     *
10              *     ENTER:   ASCII code in D0[0:7]                  *
11              *     EXIT:    C = 1 if code in range '0'-'9', 'A'-'F',*
12              *                   or 'a'-'f'                        *
13              *              C = 0 otherwise                        *
14              *              D0[8:31] cleared                       *
15              *     USES:    ISDIGIT                                *
16              ********************************************************
17  00000000 02800000  ISHEX    ANDI.L   #$7F,D0        ;clear bits 8-31
    00000004 007F
18  00000006 61000020           BSR      ISDIGIT
19  0000000A 6500001A           BCS      SKIP
20  0000000E 00000020           ORI.B    #$20,D0        ;convert to lowercase
21  00000012 0C000061           CMPI.B   #'a',D0
22  00000016 6500000A           BCS      SKIP2
23  0000001A 0C000067           CMPI.B   #'f'+1,D0
24  0000001E 65000006           BCS      SKIP
25  00000022 023C00FE  SKIP2    ANDI.B   #$FE,CCR       ;not hex
26  00000026 4E75      SKIP     RTS
```

Figure 4-16.  Subroutine documentation.

```
MOVEM.L    D0/D7/A1,-(A7)
```

and preceding RTS at the end with

```
MOVEM.L    (A7)+,D0/D7/A1
```

The registers within the subroutine are saved on the stack initially, and then restored before returning to the calling program.

### 4.8.5.  Equates

Defining constants with equate statements makes programs easier to read and maintain. Equates appear at the beginning of a program to define constants such as carriage return (CR) and line feed (LF), to define the size of buffers, addresses of registers within peripheral ICs, and so on.

The constant is used throughout the program by substituting the equated symbol for the value. When the program is assembled, the value is substituted for the symbol. If a constant must be changed, only one line needs editing—the line where the symbol is equated. When the program is reassembled, the new value is automatically substituted wherever the symbol is used.

### 4.8.6.  Subroutines

As programs grow, it is important to *divide and conquer;* that is, subdivide large and complex operations into small and simple operations. These small and simple operations are programmed as subroutines. Subroutines are hierarchical in that simple subroutines can be used by more complex subroutines, and so on. An example is the TOUPPR subroutine in Figure 4-12 (lines 86–92) which uses the low-level subroutine ISALPH (lines 94–109) to do much of its work.

### 4.8.7.  Program Organization

Although programs are often written piecemeal (i.e., subroutines are written separately from the main program), all programs should be consistent in their final organization. In general, the sections of a program are ordered as follows:

- equates
- initialization instructions
- main body of program
- subroutines
- data constants definitions (DC)
- RAM buffer definitions (DS)

All but the last item above are called the code segment, and the RAM definitions are called the data segment. Code and data segments are traditionally separate, since code is often destined for ROM or EPROM whereas data buffers are always destined for RAM. Note that data constants are defined using the DC directive and are part of the code segment since they are unchanging constants and, therefore, part of the program.

The organization advocated above is a general framework only. The creative element of programming is important, however, and individual styles are encouraged.

### 4.9.  SUMMARY

This chapter has introduced many important concepts in assembly-language programming, including advanced concepts supporting modular programming techniques.

## 4.10.   QUESTIONS

1. If D0 contains $12345678 before each of the following instructions executes, what is the value in D0 after each instruction executes?

```
MOVE      #-1,D0
MOVE.B    #-1,D0
MOVE      #5.SHL.1,D0
MOVE.B    #5/3,D0
MOVE      #5.MOD.3,D0
MOVE      #5.AND.$A,D0
MOVE      #5.OR.$A,D0
MOVE.B    #5.EQ.%101,D0
MOVE.L    #.HIGH.'AB',D0
MOVE.B    #'A'.GT.'B',D0
```

2. At a certain point in a program it is desired to move the assembler's location counter forward to the next 4K address boundary. (This might be useful, for example, to enter a code section that will begin in the next 4K EPROM.) Show an ORG directive with an appropriate operand to accomplish this.

3. Hand assemble the following program.

```
COUNT    EQU    25
         ORG    $002000
START    DC.B   'Hello'
FINISH   EQU    *
LENGTH   DC.W   FINISH-START
         DC.B   -COUNT
         DC.B   COUNT.LT.100
```

4. Identify the errors in the following assembly-language instructions.

```
MOVEA.L  #4,A8
EORQ     D0,D1
MOVE.B   #300,D0
MOVEA.W  A4,D2
ADD      D0,#25
```

5. Name two benefits in using EQU directives in an assembly-language program.

6. Answer the following questions with reference to Figure 4-14 and Figure 4-15.
   (a) What is the address of the beginning of the prompt string?
   (b) What is the first and last address of the program?
   (c) What is the first and last address of the RAM buffer used in the program?
   (d) What is the address of the INLINE subroutine?

7. Repeat Question 6 assuming the program was linked with the segment EPROM at $001F00 and the segment RAM at $004800.

8. Modify the ECHO/MYLIB program such that the first character of the input line is interpreted as a command. Change the prompt to *Sharon's program, Enter a command: .* (Use your name, please.) Continue to use a modular approach in the new program. Place the code to determine the command in ECHO2.SRC, but put all the code to execute the commands in subroutines in MYLIB2.SRC. The following commands should be supported:

Q   Quit to the monitor program (this is already supported)

U   Echo entire line in uppercase characters. Convert lowercase characters to uppercase characters. Leave graphic characters as is.

L   Echo entire line in lowercase characters. Convert uppercase characters to lowercase characters. Leave graphic characters as is.

F   Echo input line forwards

B   Echo input line backwards

?   Display a description of the commands supported

For any other command character, do not echo the line. (Reissue the prompt and repeat.) Recognize commands in both uppercase and lowercase.

# 5. Programming Examples

## 5.1. INTRODUCTION

This chapter presents a series of programming *case studies*. The programs are relatively simple, not exceeding 20 instructions. Our goal is to present, through small isolated examples, the most common 68000 instructions working together in complete programs.

Learning to program in assembly language is an incremental process. Prerequisite skills include a firm understanding of

1. the architecture of the target machine (e.g., the 68000)
2. addressing modes for moving data between CPU registers and memory
3. a subset of the target machine's instruction set
4. how to edit, assemble, load, and execute a program
5. how to use debugging features such as breakpoints and single-stepping

Step 1 is where we usually begin. Learning the architecture of a target CPU includes, for example, understanding the registers, memory organization, and data types of the CPU. Programmers are particularly interested in the operation of the general-purpose registers, the program counter, the stack pointer, and the status register.

Step 2 is critical in learning to program in assembly language. Passing too quickly through the topic of *addressing modes* usually bears serious consequences when programming. Many instructions operate on data. Properly organizing the storage and access of data (through addressing modes) is important in writing good assembly-language programs. To emphasize this point, consider the following two instructions:

```
MOVE    #$1000,D5
MOVE    $1000,D5
```

If the reader has any hesitation at all as to the difference between these two instructions, then writing 68000 assembly-language programs is not yet possible. The 68000's 14 addressing modes were presented in Chapter 2 along with numerous examples. Review these if necessary.

Once the mechanism for reading and writing data between CPU registers and memory is understood, it is necessary to acquire a repertoire of instructions to solve programming problems (Step 3). Consider the following analogy: Instructions are to programming as words are to writing. There's no point trying to write without a reasonable vocabulary of words. However, it is not necessary to know every word in the dictionary to write effectively. Similarly, assembly-language programming can begin once a reasonable subset of the CPU's instructions is understood. Combining words into sentences (writing) is analogous to combining instructions to form meaningful operations on data (programming). The 68000's instructions set was presented in Chapter 3.

Many readers will already have some experience with an 8-bit microprocessor. Since the 68000 includes many instructions with an 8-bit heritage, we can exploit this familiar territory in simple solutions to problems. However, as a 16-bit CPU, the 68000 also includes advanced features not generally found in 8-bit machines. To promote incremental learning, multiple solutions are given for many examples in this chapter. First, a simple solution using traditional techniques is shown; then an advanced feature is introduced in a new solution. The advanced feature may demonstrate a different instruction or addressing mode, or may adopt a completely new strategy to simplify the algorithm, reduce the length of the program, or shorten the execution time.

Step 4 pertains to the environment in which programming takes place. A good program development environment is, of course, important. Learning to use the programming environment is usually taught through student laboratory exercises.

Debugging (Step 5) is extremely difficult to teach. Debugging tools are particularly important now that complete programming problems are undertaken. Programmers learn to work through so-

Table 5-1.    Programming Examples in this Chapter.

| Example | Program Name | Description |
|---------|--------------|-------------|
| 5-1 | FLIP | Complement a number |
| 5-2 | LARGER | Find the larger of two numbers |
| 5-3 | ADD, ADD2, ADD3 | Add a list of numbers |
| 5-4 | ADD64 | 64-bit addition |
| 5-5 | BMOVE, BMOVE2 | Move a block of memory |
| 5-6 | NEG, NEG2 | Count negative entries in a list |
| 5-7 | ADDBCD | Add a series of BCD bytes |
| 5-8 | ADDBCD2 | Add a series of BCD words |
| 5-9 | ASCBIN | Convert ASCII digits to binary |
| 5-10 | SORT | Sort a list of bytes |
| 5-11 | SQRT | Square root of a 32-bit integer |

lutions step-by-step and consider the consequences of *each* operation. Debugging tools allow the programmer to compare *expected results* against *observed results*. This is achieved typically by single-stepping through critical sections of a program and observing the contents of registers or memory locations *after each instruction*. If the observed results are not as expected, a bug exists. As with programming tools, debugging tools are usually taught in a hands-on laboratory setting.

The examples presented in this chapter are summarized in Table 5-1.

***Format of Examples***    Each programming example contains the following parts:

| | |
|---|---|
| Problem description | The problem is described along with the name of the program. The requirements and structure of the source and destination data are described along with addresses, registers, and labels used in the program. |
| Sample conditions | The *before* data show an example of data that could be used with the program. The *after* data show the content of memory locations or registers after execution of the program. Both are in hexadecimal format. |
| Solution | A programming solution is given as a 68000 assembly-language program in listing format, as described in Chapter 4. |
| Discussion | Important points about the program are discussed. |

Sample data are embedded in the programs using define constant (DC) directives. Strictly speaking, this is not appropriate since DC directives are intended to define read-only data *constants* in a code segment, rather than read/write RAM locations in a data segment. However, the approach shown is useful since RAM locations are automatically initialized with sample data when the program is loaded. Note that it is important to manually change the sample data and rerun the program to test for different outcomes.

An alternate way to organize the data area is through define storage (DS) directives, as follows:

```
        ORG    DATA   ;data at $9000
NUMBER  DS.W   1      ;operate on this number
RESULT  DS.W   1      ;store result here
```

Using this scheme, data are loaded manually using monitor commands prior to executing the program.

The example programs discussed in this chapter begin at address $8000 and operate on data beginning at address $9000. Different addresses may be used depending on the memory organization of the target system.

The example programs terminate with TRAP #14. This is the mechanism to return to the monitor program on the 68000 system used to develop and test the examples for this chapter. Other systems may require different instructions to terminate a program.

---

## 5.2.  EXAMPLE PROGRAMS

### Example 5-1: Complement a Number

**Problem:**  Write a 68000 assembly-language program called FLIP that reads 16-bits of data from a location called NUMBER (at address

**Figure A.**

```
 1                          ***************************************************
 2                          * FLIP.SRC                                        *
 3                          ***************************************************
 4 00008000               CODE      EQU       $8000       ;program starts at $8000
 5 00009000               DATA      EQU       $9000       ;data starts at $9000
 6
 7 00008000                         ORG       CODE        ;program at $8000
 8 00008000 30390000 FLIP  MOVE.W    >NUMBER,D0  ;get 16-bit data
   00008004 9000
 9 00008006 4640                     NOT.W     D0          ;complement data
10 00008008 33C00000                 MOVE      D0,>INVERSE ;store complemented data
   0000800C 9002
11 0000800E 4E4E                     TRAP      #14         ;return to monitor
12                          *
13                          * Use DC directives to initialize RAM
14                          *
15 00009000                         ORG       DATA        ;data at $9000
16 00009000 1234   NUMBER   DC.W     $1234       ;read this data
17 00009002 0000   INVERSE  DC.W     0           ;store result here
18 00009004                 END      FLIP
```

$9000) and stores the complement of the data in a location called INVERSE (at address $9002).

Sample Conditions:

Before:

| Address | Contents |
|---------|----------|
| 009000  | 1234     |
| 009002  | 0000     |

After:

| Address | Contents |
|---------|----------|
| 009000  | 1234     |
| 009002  | EDCB     |

**Solution:** See Figure A.

**Discussion:** The program only requires four instructions. In line 8, the source data are read into D0. Absolute long addressing is forced by preceding NUMBER with ">". Since the address of NUMBER is $009000, absolute long addressing must be used, otherwise the 16-bit address $9000 is sign extended to $FF9000 (see Chapter 2). The data are complemented in line 9 using NOT.W and then written to INVERSE at address $009002 in line 10. The program

terminates with TRAP #14 in line 11, returning control to the monitor program. ■

### Example 5-2: Find the Larger of Two Numbers

**Problem:** Write a 68000 program called LARGER that compares two unsigned bytes. BYTE1 is at address $9000, and BYTE2 is at $9001. Store the larger of the two bytes in RESULT at address $9002.

Sample Conditions:

Before:

| Address | Contents |
|---------|----------|
| 009000  | 19       |
| 009001  | 23       |
| 009002  | 00       |

After:

| Address | Contents |
|---------|----------|
| 009000  | 19       |
| 009001  | 23       |
| 009002  | 23       |

**Solution:** See below.

```
 1                          ***************************************************
 2                          * LARGER.SRC                                      *
 3                          ***************************************************
 4 00008000               CODE      EQU       $8000       ;program starts at $8000
 5 00009000               DATA      EQU       $9000       ;data starts at $9000
 6
 7 00008000                         ORG       CODE        ;program at $8000
 8 00008000 207C0000 LARGER MOVEA.L  #BYTE1,A0   ;A0 points to bytes
   00008004 9000
 9 00008006 1018                     MOVE.B    (A0)+,D0    ;get 1st byte
10 00008008 1218                     MOVE.B    (A0)+,D1    ;get 2nd byte
11 0000800A B200                     CMP.B     D0,D1       ;second byte bigger?
12 0000800C 6202                     BHI.S     STORE       ;yes: store it
13 0000800E 1200                     MOVE.B    D0,D1       ;no: replace with 1st
```

```
14  00008010  1081   STORE   MOVE.B  D1,(A0)      ;done!
15  00008012  4E4E           TRAP    #14
16
17  00009000                 ORG     DATA
18  00009000  19     BYTE1   DC.B    25
19  00009001  23     BYTE2   DC.B    35
20  00009002  00     RESULT  DC.B    0
21  00009003                 END     LARGER
```

**Discussion:** The compare instruction in line 11 performs the operation D1–D0. The condition code bits are set accordingly. If D1 is higher than D0, the *branch-if-higher* (BHI) test in line 12 passes and the program skips ahead to line 14 to store D1 in RESULT. If the branch test fails, the BHI instruction falls through to line 13. The value in D1 is replaced with the value in D0 (which is higher) before writing D1 to RESULT.

Since the data are bytes, it is important to append .B to the CMP and MOVE instructions. (Recall that .W is assumed if the suffix is omitted.) The .S appended to BHI forces the short form of relative addressing, with the relative offset ($02) inserted in the low-byte of the instruction word (line 12). If .S were omitted, the assembler would use the long form because the branch destination is a forward-referenced symbol. The method shown shortens the code by one word.  ■

### Example 5-3: Add a List of Numbers

**Problem:** Write a 68000 program called ADD to compute the sum of three 16-bit words of data. The data are stored in memory starting at address $9000, identified by the label NUMBERS. Store the result immediately after the data, in SUM at memory location $9006.

Sample Conditions:

Before:

| Address | Contents |
|---------|----------|
| 009000  | 1234 |
| 009002  | 5678 |
| 009004  | 9ABC |
| 009006  | 0000 |

After:

| Address | Contents |
|---------|----------|
| 009000  | 1234 |
| 009002  | 5678 |
| 009004  | 9ABC |
| 009006  | 0368  Note: |

$1234 + $5678 + $9ABC = $0368

This problem provides a good opportunity to explore a few simple programming techniques. These are presented incrementally, through three separate solutions.

**Solution 1:** See below.

```
 1            ***********************************************************
 2            * ADD.SRC                                              *
 3            ***********************************************************
 4  00008000         CODE    EQU    $8000        ;program starts at $8000
 5  00009000         DATA    EQU    $9000        ;data starts at $9000
 6
 7  00008000                 ORG    CODE         ;program at $8000
 8  00008000  30390000 ADD   MOVE.W >NUMBERS,D0  ;get 1st word
    00008004  9000
 9  00008006  D0790000       ADD.W  >NUMBERS+2,D0 ;add 2nd word to 1st
    0000800A  9002
10  0000800C  D0790000       ADD.W  >NUMBERS+4,D0 ;add 3rd word
    00008010  9004
11  00008012  33C00000       MOVE.W D0,>SUM       ;store result
    00008016  9006
12  00008018  4E4E           TRAP   #14
13                   *
14                   * Use DC directives to initialize RAM
15                   *
16  00009000                 ORG    DATA         ;data at $9000
17  00009000  1234   NUMBERS DC.W   $1234        ;1st word
18  00009002  5678           DC.W   $5678        ;2nd word
19  00009004  9ABC           DC.W   $9ABC        ;3rd word
20  00009006  0000   SUM     DC.W   0            ;result
21  00009008                 END    ADD
```

Figure B.

```
 1                    ************************************************
 2                    * ADD2.SRC                                   *
 3                    ************************************************
 4 00008000          CODE     EQU      $8000
 5 00009000          DATA     EQU      $9000
 6
 7 00008000                   ORG      CODE
 8 00008000 207C0000 ADD2     MOVEA.L  #NUMBERS,A0  ;use A0 as pointer
   00008004 9000
 9 00008006 3018              MOVE.W   (A0)+,D0
10 00008008 D058              ADD.W    (A0)+,D0
11 0000800A D058              ADD.W    (A0)+,D0
12 0000800C 3080              MOVE.W   D0,(A0)
13 0000800E 4E4E              TRAP     #14
14
15 00009000                   ORG      DATA
16 00009000 1234     NUMBERS  DC.W     $1234
17 00009002 5678              DC.W     $5678
18 00009004 9ABC              DC.W     $9ABC
19 00009006 0000     SUM      DC.W     0
20 00009008                   END      ADD2
```

**Discussion:** This solution is very simple. The first word of data is moved into data register D0 in line 8. The second word is added to the first in line 9, and then the third word is added to the *accumulated* sum in line 10. Note that the second and third words are identified by the labels NUMBERS+2 ($9002) and NUMBERS+4 ($9004). In line 11, the result is stored in memory location $9006. The program ends in line 12 with TRAP #14, which returns to the monitor program.

A point mentioned earlier deserves repeating. The ">" preceding NUMBERS and SUM forces the assembler to use absolute long addressing. This operator may not be necessary with some assemblers (particularly three-pass assemblers), depending on the default handling of forward-referenced symbols. The mechanism to force absolute long or short addressing varies from one assembler to the next (see Chapter 2).

Note the use of labels to make the source code more readable. No addresses appear in the source-program statements in lines 8–11, although they are seen in the second and third hexadecimal words of each instruction in the listing (third column).

Solution 1 works, but it is not a good program.

Knowledge of the 68000's addressing modes suggests another approach that exploits *address register indirect with postincrement* addressing:

**Solution 2:** See Figure B.

**Discussion:** The instruction MOVEA initializes A0 with the starting address of the data in line 8. (A0 is a *pointer* to the data.) Using address register indirect with postincrement addressing in line 9, the first word of data is moved into D0. The address register is incremented after moving data; therefore, the following instruction (line 10), which uses the same addressing mode, adds the second word to the first, and so on.

Solution 2 is shorter than solution 1 (8 words vs. 13 words; lines 8–13). There are obvious advantages to keeping programs short; but solution 2 is also better because it executes faster.

Although solution 2 is better than solution 1, it can be improved. If we consider adding 30 words rather than three, then both approaches are poor. Solution 3 demonstrates how to construct a loop around a single add instruction to perform the same task:

**Solution 3:** See below.

```
 1                    ************************************************
 2                    * ADD3.SRC                                   *
 3                    ************************************************
 4 00008000          CODE     EQU      $8000
 5 00009000          DATA     EQU      $9000
 6
 7 00008000                   ORG      CODE
 8 00008000 207C0000 ADD3     MOVEA.L  #NUMBERS,A0 ;use A0 as pointer
   00008004 9000
 9 00008006 323C0003          MOVE.W   #COUNT,D1   ;use D1 as counter
10 0000800A 4240              CLR.W    D0          ;init D0 = 0
11 0000800C D058     LOOP     ADD.W    (A0)+,D0
```

```
12   0000800E 5341              SUBQ     #1,D1
13   00008010 66FA              BNE      LOOP
14   00008012 3080              MOVE.W   D0,(A0)
15   00008014 4E4E              TRAP     #14
16
17   00009000                   ORG      DATA
18   00009000 1234     NUMBERS  DC.W     $1234
19   00009002 5678              DC.W     $5678
20   00009004 9ABC              DC.W     $9ABC
21   00000003         COUNT     EQU      (*-NUMBERS)/2
22   00009006 0000     SUM      DC.W     0
23   00009008                   END      ADD3
```

**Discussion:** Although solution 3 is longer than solution 2 (11 words vs. 8 words), the length is the same regardless of the number of entries in the list. This is due to the looping structure of the program. Loops are one of the most fundamental structures in assembly language programming. The idea of enclosing a primitive operation in a loop and using a count to terminate the loop is featured in the flowchart in Figure 5-1.

The block labeled *Do something* will contain one or more instructions performing the operation desired (adding, counting, shifting, etc.) It is easy to see that solution 3 conforms to the flowchart in Figure 5-1.

Flowcharting is a bit of a chicken-and-egg problem. That is, it is common to teach flowcharting as a good program-design technique; but when it gets down to the gritty task of getting the job done, flowcharting is often a last resort. The act of constructing a flowchart often follows programming, as a form of documentation. Flowcharts are useful primarily when the weave of conditional branching is so complex that maintaining a mental image of the flow of a program is too difficult. Although flowcharting may help, it is often the case that the problem should be decomposed into subroutines small enough to understand on their own, without the need for a flowchart.

Solution 3 begins by initializing A0 as a pointer and D1 as a counter. The loop begins in line 11. After each add, the count is decremented by 1 (line 12). Note that SUBQ is only 1 word; the immediate data are embedded in a field within the instruction word (see Chapter 3).

If the count does not equal 0 (line 13), the loop is repeated and another add operation occurs. It is extremely important to understand the relationship between the SUBQ and the BNE (branch if not equal zero) instructions. SUBQ not only decrements the count in D0, it sets or clears bits in the 68000's condition code register according to the result of the subtraction. In particular, the Z-bit is set if the result is zero, or is cleared if the result is not zero. BNE is a conditional branch instruction. It tests the Z-bit in the CCR, as affected by the preceding instruction. If $Z = 0$, the branch occurs; if $Z = 1$, the branch does not occur and execution continues with the next instruction.

The combination of SUBQ and BNE in lines 12 and 13 could be replaced with a single DBRA instruction. This is illustrated in the next example program.

Note that address register indirect addressing is essential in this approach. An absolute address (as in Example 5-1) cannot be used because there is no way to increment the address within the loop.

An interesting feature of this program lies in the label COUNT. The fact that three words are added is not explicitly coded anywhere in the program. To change the number of words, the source program is edited and extra words are

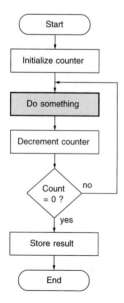

**Figure 5-1.** Loop structure using a count.

**Figure C.**    Before:

```
Address     Contents
9000        00000000
9004        00000000
9008        12345678
900C        9ABCDEF0
9010        23456789
9014        ABCDEF01
9018        3456789A
901C        BCDEF012
```

After:

```
Address     Contents
9000        69D0369D    (Result, upper-bytes)
9004        0369BE03    (Result, lower-bytes)
9008        12345678
900C        9ABCDEF0
9010        23456789
9014        ABCDEF01
9018        3456789A
901C        BCDEF012
```

```
Note:
 123456789ABCDEF0
+23456789ABCDEF01
+3456789ABCDEF012
-----------------
 69D0369D0369BE03
```

inserted after line 20. Note in line 21, COUNT is automatically computed when the program is assembled. The computation uses a powerful feature of assembly-language programming known as *assemble-time expressions* (see Chapter 4). The asterisk is a special symbol equal to the current value of the assembler's location counter. The expression $*-DATA$ is equivalent to $\$9006 - \$9000 = 6$, which is the number of bytes of data. Division-by-two converts this to the number of words.  ■

### Example 5-4: 64-bit Addition

**Problem:** Write a 68000 program called ADD64 to add three 64-bit numbers stored in memory starting at address $9008. Store the result in byte addresses $9000 through $9007. The numbers are formatted with the high-byte in the first byte-address and the low-byte in the last byte-address.

Sample Conditions: See Figure C.

**Solution:** See below.

```
 1                       ************************************************
 2                       * ADD64.SRC                                   *
 3                       ************************************************
 4 00008000             CODE    EQU     $8000       ;program starts at $8000
 5 00009000             DATA    EQU     $9000       ;data starts at $9000
 6 00000003             COUNT   EQU     3           ;add 3 64-bit numbers
 7
 8 00008000             ORG     CODE                ;program at $8000
 9 00008000 303C0002     ADD64  MOVE.W  #COUNT-1,D0 ;use D0 as counter
10 00008004 207C0000            MOVEA.L #NUM64,A0   ;A0 points to numbers
   00008008 9008
11 0000800A 4281                CLR.L   D1          ;use D1 for high-bytes
12 0000800C 4282                CLR.L   D2          ;use D2 for low-bytes
13 0000800E D4A80004     LOOP   ADD.L   4(A0),D2    ;add low-bytes to D2
14 00008012 2610                MOVE.L  (A0),D3     ;get high-bytes
15 00008014 D383                ADDX.L  D3,D1       ;add high-bytes to D1
16 00008016 41E80008            LEA     8(A0),A0    ;adjust address pointer
17 0000801A 51C8FFF2            DBRA    D0,LOOP     ;if count != -1, repeat
18 0000801E 23C10000            MOVE.L  D1,>RESULT  ;otherwise, store result
   00008022 9000
19 00008024 23C20000            MOVE.L  D2,>RESULT+4
   00008028 9004
20 0000802A 4E4E                TRAP    #14
21               *
```

```
22                              * Use DC directives to initialize RAM
23                              *
24 00009000                        ORG     DATA
25 00009000 00000000 RESULT    DC.L    0,0
   00009004 00000000
26 00009008 12345678 NUM64     DC.L    $12345678,$9ABCDEF0 ;1st number
   0000900C 9ABCDEF0
27 00009010 23456789           DC.L    $23456789,$ABCDEF01 ;2nd number
   00009014 ABCDEF01
28 00009018 3456789A           DC.L    $3456789A,$BCDEF012 ;3rd number
   0000901C BCDEF012
29 00009020                        END     ADD64
```

**Discussion:** This program uses a slightly different approach to looping. The instruction DBRA in line 17 is equivalent to *decrement and branch if not −1*. This replaces two instructions: SUBQ following by BNE (see Example 5-3). Since the branch test fails only when the count reaches −1 (rather than zero), the initialization requires a slight adjustment. In line 9, D0 is initialized with COUNT−1, thus ensuring the loop executes *count* times. Note that DBRA performs a word-size decrement only; so it is important that D0 is initialized using MOVE.W, even if the count is small.

Since the operands are 64 bits, addition is performed in two stages. First the low-order longwords are added (line 13), then the high-order longwords are added (lines 14−15). The low-order longwords must be added first in case a carry occurs. To propagate carries from the low to high longwords, ADDX is used for the second addition. Since ADDX is restricted in the addressing modes available (see Appendix B), the high-order source word is loaded into D3 (line 14) before the addition.

The address pointer, A0, is used in an interesting way in this program. After each addition, A0 is incremented by eight using LEA 8(A0),A0 in line 16. LEA (load effective address) is used anytime an address pointer must be adjusted using an offset or index. The value loaded is the effective address, rather than the data referenced by the effective address. ■

### Example 5-5: Move a Block of Memory

**Problem:** Write a 68000 program called BMOVE to move a block of 16-bit data. The length of the block as a 16-bit word is stored in COUNT ($9000) and the block address is stored in START ($9002). The destination of the block moved is stored in DEST ($9006).

Sample Conditions:

Before:

| Address | Contents |
| --- | --- |
| 009000 | 0003 |
| 009002 | 00009020 |
| 009006 | 00009040 |
| 009020 | 1234 |
| 009022 | 5678 |
| 009024 | 9ABC |
| 009040 | 0000 |
| 009042 | 0000 |
| 009044 | 0000 |

After:

| Address | Contents |
| --- | --- |
| 009000 | 0003 |
| 009002 | 00009020 |
| 009006 | 00009040 |
| 009020 | 1234 |
| 009022 | 5678 |
| 009024 | 9ABC |
| 009040 | 1234 |
| 009042 | 5678 |
| 009044 | 9ABC |

**Solution 1:** See below.

```
1           *****************************************************
2           * BMOVE.SRC                                        *
3           *****************************************************
4 00008000          CODE    EQU     $8000       ;program starts at $8000
5 00009000          DATA    EQU     $9000       ;data starts at $9000
6
7 00008000                  ORG     CODE        ;program at $8000
8 00008000 20790000 BMOVE   MOVEA.L >START,A0   ;A0 points to start
  00008004 9002
9 00008006 22790000         MOVEA.L >DEST,A1    ;A1 point to destination
  0000800A 9006
10 0000800C 3E390000        MOVE.W  >COUNT,D7   ;use D7 as counter
   00008010 9000
11 00008012 32D8    LOOP    MOVE.W  (A0)+,(A1)+ ;move data
```

```
12 00008014 5347              SUBQ.W   #1,D7       ;last word moved?
13 00008016 66FA              BNE      LOOP        ;no: move another
14 00008018 4E4E              TRAP     #14         ;yes: return to monitor
15
16 00009000              ORG      DATA
17 00009000 0003     COUNT DC.W     3
18 00009002 00009020 START DC.L     $9020
19 00009006 00009040 DEST  DC.L     $9040
20
21 00009020                   ORG      $9020
22 00009020 12345678          DC.W     $1234,$5678,$9ABC
   00009024 9ABC
23
24 00009040                   ORG      $9040
25 00009040 00000000          DC.W     0,0,0
   00009044 0000
26 00009046              END      BMOVE
```

**Discussion:** The first three instructions (lines 8–10) initialize A0 as the source pointer, A1 as the destination pointer, and D7 as a counter. The block move is performed in a three-instruction loop (lines 11–13).

Note in this program that even though the suffix .S was omitted from the BNE instruction (line 13), the short form of relative addressing was used. This occurred because a forward reference was not used.

The solution to this problem includes a small potential bug: If the count = 0, the program fails. This occurs because COUNT is decremented (line 12) before it is tested (line 13). The same problem exists in ADD3.SRC in Example 5-3 and ADD64.SRC in Example 5-4. The following modified solution is an easy fix to this problem.

**Solution 2:** See Figure D.

**Discussion:** The addition of BEQ.S in line 11 ensures that no data are moved if the count is zero. The fact that D7 is initialized immediately before the BEQ.S instruction is critical. MOVE.W in line 10 affects the Z-bit in the CCR according to COUNT; so, BEQ.S, which immediately follows, is effectively testing the condition COUNT=0. ∎

### Example 5-6: Count Negative Entries in a List

**Problem:** Write a program called NEG that counts the number of negative entries in a list of 8-bit numbers. The length of the list is in the 8-bit variable LENGTH at address $9000 and the starting address of the list is in the 32-bit variable START at $9002. Store the answer in the 8-bit variable RESULT at $9001.

**Figure D.**

```
 1                    ************************************************
 2                    * BMOVE2.SRC                                   *
 3                    ************************************************
 4 00008000           CODE   EQU    $8000         ;program starts at $8000
 5 00009000           DATA   EQU    $9000         ;data starts at $9000
 6
 7 00008000                  ORG    CODE          ;program at $8000
 8 00008000 20790000 BMOVE2  MOVEA.L >START,A0    ;A0 points to start
   00008004 9002
 9 00008006 22790000         MOVEA.L >DEST,A1     ;A1 point to destination
   0000800A 9006
10 0000800C 3E390000         MOVE.W >COUNT,D7     ;use D7 as counter
   00008010 9000
11 00008012 6706             BEQ.S  EXIT          ;if count = 0, exit now
12 00008014 32D8     LOOP    MOVE.W (A0)+,(A1)+   ;move data
13 00008016 5347             SUBQ.W #1,D7         ;last word moved?
14 00008018 66FA             BNE    LOOP          ;no:  move another
15 0000801A 4E4E     EXIT    TRAP   #14           ;yes: return to monitor
16
17 00009000                  ORG    DATA
18 00009000 0000     COUNT   DC.W   0
19 00009002 00009020 START   DC.L   $9020
20 00009006 00009040 DEST    DC.L   $9040
21 0000900A                  END    BMOVE2
```

Sample Conditions:

Before:

```
Address   Contents
009000    04
009001    00
009002    00009040
009040    25
009041    80
009042    7F
009043    55
```

After:

```
Address   Contents
009000    04
009001    01           (only 1 entry is negative)
009002    00009040
009040    25
009041    80
009042    7F
009043    55
```

Solution 1:

```
 1                       ************************************************
 2                       * NEG.SRC                                     *
 3                       ************************************************
 4  00008000             CODE    EQU     $8000       ;program starts at $8000
 5  00009000             DATA    EQU     $9000       ;data starts at $9000
 6
 7  00008000                     ORG     CODE        ;program at $8000
 8  00008000 10390000 NEG        MOVE.B  >LENGTH,D0  ;use D0 as counter
    00008004 9000
 9  00008006 42390000            CLR.B   >RESULT     ;clear RESULT
    0000800A 9001
10  0000800C 22790000            MOVEA.L >START,A1   ;A1 points to numbers
    00008010 9002
11  00008012 4A19     LOOP       TST.B   (A1)+       ;test number
12  00008014 6A06                BPL.S   SKIP        ;negative?
13  00008016 52390000            ADDQ.B  #1,>RESULT  ;yes: increment RESULT
    0000801A 9001
14  0000801C 5300     SKIP       SUBQ.B  #1,D0       ;no:  decrement counter
15  0000801E 66F2                BNE     LOOP        ;repeat until count = 0
16  00008020 4E4E                TRAP    #14
17                       *
18                       * Use DC directives to initialize RAM
19                       *
20  00009000                     ORG     DATA        ;data at $9000
21  00009000 04       LENGTH     DC.B    4
22  00009001 00       RESULT     DC.B    0
23  00009002 00009040 START      DC.L    $9040
24
25  00009040                     ORG     $9040
26  00009040 25807F55            DC.B    $25,$80,$7F,$55
27  00009044                     END     NEG
```

**Figure E.**

```
 1                              ***************************************************
 2                              * NEG2.SRC                                       *
 3                              ***************************************************
 4  00008000        CODE     EQU     $8000        ;program starts at $8000
 5  00009000        DATA     EQU     $9000        ;data starts at $9000
 6
 7  00008000                 ORG     CODE         ;program at $8000
 8  00008000 207C0000 NEG2    MOVEA.L #DATA,A0
    00008004 9000
 9  00008006 1018            MOVE.B  (A0)+,D0     ;use D0 as counter
10  00008008 4218            CLR.B   (A0)+        ;clear RESULT
11  0000800A 2250            MOVEA.L (A0),A1      ;A1 points to numbers
12  0000800C 4A19    LOOP    TST.B   (A1)+        ;test number
13  0000800E 6A04            BPL.S   SKIP         ;negative?
14  00008010 5228FFFF        ADDQ.B  #1,-1(A0)    ;yes: increment RESULT
15  00008014 5300    SKIP    SUBQ.B #1,D0         ;no: decrement counter
16  00008016 66F4            BNE     LOOP         ;repeat until count = 0
17  00008018 4E4E            TRAP    #14
18                  *
19                  * Use DC directives to initialize RAM
20                  *
21  00009000                 ORG     DATA         ;data at $9000
22  00009000 04      LENGTH  DC.B    4
23  00009001 00      RESULT  DC.B    0
24  00009002 00009040 START  DC.L    $9040
25
26  00009040                 ORG     $9040
27  00009040 25807F55        DC.B    $25,$80,$7F,$55
28  00009044                 END     NEG2
```

**Discussion:** This program contains two conditional branch instructions. A loop is used, as before; however, within the loop a second conditional branch is required. Data are tested in line 11 using TST.B. Note that TST.B (A1)+ is the same as CMP.B #0,(A1)+. If the data byte pointed at by A1 is negative, then the N-bit in the CCR is set following the test. A *branch-if-plus* (BPL) instruction in line 12 skips over the *increment count* operation in line 13 if the byte is *not* negative.

The result is incremented directly in memory in line 13, so a *store result* operation is not necessary when the loop terminates.

**Solution 2:** See Figure E.

**Discussion:** In solution 2, we illustrate how to use address register indirect addressing to reduce the size of the program from 17 words (solution 1) to 13 words. A0 is set up as a pointer to the data area in line 8. Subsequent accesses to the variables LENGTH, RESULT, and START use variations of address register indirect addressing (lines 9–11, and 14) to reduce the size of the program. ∎

**Example 5-7: Add a Series of BCD Bytes**

**Problem:** Write a 68000 program called ADDBCD to add a series of BCD bytes. The length of the series is stored in the 16-bit variable called COUNT at address $9000. The sum should be placed in the 16-bit variable SUM at address $9002. The starting address of the series is stored in the 32-bit variable NUMBERS at address $9004. A 4-digit (16-bit) sum should be computed in case the sum is greater than $99_{10}$.

Sample Conditions:

Before:

| Address | Contents |
|---|---|
| 9000 | 0003 |
| 9002 | 0000 |
| 9004 | 00009040 |
| 9040 | 99 |
| 9041 | 99 |
| 9042 | 25 |

After:

| Address | Contents |
|---|---|
| 9000 | 0003 |
| 9002 | 0223 |

(Note: $99_{10} + 99_{10} + 25_{10} = 223_{10}$)

| | |
|---|---|
| 9004 | 00009040 |
| 9040 | 99 |
| 9041 | 99 |
| 9042 | 25 |

**Solution:** See below.

```
 1                         *************************************************
 2                         *  ADDBCD.SRC                                   *
 3                         *************************************************
 4 00008000               CODE    EQU     $8000      ;program starts at $8000
 5 00009000               DATA    EQU     $9000      ;data starts at $9000
 6
 7 00008000               ORG     CODE               ;program at $8000
 8 00008000 207C0000 ADDBCD MOVEA.L #COUNT,A0        ;A0 -> COUNT
   00008004 9000
 9 00008006 3018          MOVE.W  (A0)+,D0           ;use D0 as counter
10 00008008 4201          CLR.B   D1                 ;use D1 for low-byte
11 0000800A 4202          CLR.B   D2                 ;use D2 for high-byte
12 0000800C 4204          CLR.B   D4
13 0000800E 22680002      MOVEA.L 2(A0),A1           ;A1 -> numbers
14 00008012 600A          BRA.S   SKIP
15 00008014 023C00EF LOOP ANDI.B  #$EF,CCR           ;clear X-bit
16 00008018 1619          MOVE.B  (A1)+,D3           ;get BCD byte
17 0000801A C503          ABCD    D3,D2              ;accumulate sum
18 0000801C C304          ABCD    D4,D1              ;add X-bit (D4 = 0)
19 0000801E 51C8FFF4 SKIP DBRA    D0,LOOP            ;no: decrement count, repeat
20 00008022 10C1          MOVE.B  D1,(A0)+           ;store high-byte
21 00008024 1082          MOVE.B  D2,(A0)            ;store low-byte
22 00008026 4E4E          TRAP    #14
23                  *
24                  * Use DC directives to initialize RAM
25                  *
26 00009000               ORG     DATA    ;data at $9000
27 00009000 0003   COUNT   DC.W    3
28 00009002 0000   SUM     DC.W    0
29 00009004 00009040 NUMBERS DC.L  $9040
30
31 00009040               ORG     $9040
32 00009040 999925        DC.B    $99,$99,$25
33 00009043               END     ADDBCD
```

**Discussion:** The ABCD instruction has two forms, one with both operands in data registers, and one using predecrement address register indirect addressing (see Appendix B). The solution above uses the former. Note the style of loop control in the program. The loop is entered in line 14 by branching unconditionally to the terminating DBRA instruction. The fact that DBRA causes the loop to repeat until the count is −1 works well with this structure. No *adjustment* is needed when the counter is initialized. More importantly, the *zero count* problem is avoided, because if the count is 0, it is decremented to −1 right away and the program terminates as it should.

Carries for sums greater than $99_{10}$ are handled by including a second ABCD instruction that adds D4, which is always zero, to D1. Each time a carry occurs, X = 1 and D1 increases by 1.  ∎

### Example 5-8: Add a Series of BCD Words

**Problem:** Write a program called ADDBCD2 that adds a series of BCD words. The length of the series is three, as defined through the equated symbol COUNT. The series starts in memory at $9000. The 4-digit sum is stored just after the last BCD word. Assume the sum does not exceed 4 digits.

Sample Condition:

Before:

```
Address   Contents
9000      0199
9002      0301
9004      0023
9006      0000
```

After:

```
Address   Contents
9000      0199
9002      0301
9004      0023
9006      0523        (Note: 199₁₀ + 301₁₀ + 23₁₀ = 523₁₀)
```

(Note: $199_{10} + 301_{10} + 23_{10} = 523_{10}$)

**Solution:**

```
 1                         ************************************************
 2                         *  ADDBCD2.SRC                                 *
 3                         ************************************************
 4 00008000        CODE    EQU     $8000       ;program starts at $8000
 5 00009000        DATA    EQU     $9000       ;data starts at $9000
 6 00000003        COUNT   EQU     3           ;three BCD words to add
 7
 8 00008000                ORG     CODE        ;program at $8000
 9 00008000 303C0003 ADDBCD2 MOVE.W #COUNT,D0  ;use D0 as counter
10 00008004 207C0000        MOVEA.L #NUMBERS+COUNT*2,A0 ;A0 -> past data
   00008008 9006
11 0000800A 43E80002        LEA     2(A0),A1            ;A1 -> past sum
12 0000800E 600C            BRA.S   SKIP
13 00008010 023C00EF LOOP   ANDI.B  #$EF,CCR    ;clear X-bit
14 00008014 C308            ABCD    -(A0),-(A1);add low-bytes
15 00008016 C308            ABCD    -(A0),-(A1);add high-bytes
16 00008018 43E90002        LEA     2(A1),A1   ;adjust pointer to sum
17 0000801C 51C8FFF2 SKIP   DBRA    D0,LOOP     ;no: decrement count, repeat
18 00008020 4E4E            TRAP    #14
19                      *
20                      * Use DC directives to initialize RAM
21                      *
22 00009000                ORG     DATA        ;data at $9000
23 00009000 01990301 NUMBERS DC.W   $199,$301,$19,0
   00009004 00190000
24 00009008                END     ADDBCD2
```

**Discussion:** This BCD addition program uses *predecrement address register indirect* addressing for ABCD. A0 points to the list of BCD words, and A1 points to the memory location which accumulates the sum. Since *predecrement* addressing is used, both address registers must point just past the source and destination operands when the ABCD takes place. Initially A0 is loaded with NUMBERS+COUNT*2 (line 10), so it points just past the last word in the list. The *2 adjustment converts the word count to a byte count. Initially A1 is loaded with A0+2 using load effective address (LEA) in line 11. Since ABCD only operates on byte operands, each word addition requires two consecutive ABCD instructions (lines 14–15). After every second add, A1 is adjusted to undo the effect of the two predecrement memory references (line 16). ■

### Example 5-9: Convert ASCII Digits to Binary

**Problem:** Write a program to convert a null-terminated string of ASCII digits to a 16-bit binary value. The ASCII string begins at STRING in memory location $9002. Place the result in the 16-bit variable RESULT at location $9000. Assume the ASCII string represents an unsigned integer between 0 and 65,535.

Sample Conditions:

|        | Before:  |          |        | After:   |          |                        |
|--------|----------|----------|--------|----------|----------|------------------------|
|        | Address  | Contents |        | Address  | Contents |                        |
|        | 9000     | 0000     |        | 9000     | 1E03     | $(1E03_{16} = 7683_{10})$ |
|        | 9002     | 30  '0'  |        | 9002     | 30       |                        |
|        | 9003     | 30  '0'  |        | 9003     | 30       |                        |
|        | 9004     | 30  '0'  |        | 9004     | 30       |                        |
|        | 9005     | 37  '7'  |        | 9005     | 37       |                        |
|        | 9006     | 36  '6'  |        | 9006     | 36       |                        |
|        | 9007     | 38  '8'  |        | 9007     | 38       |                        |
|        | 9008     | 33  '3'  |        | 9008     | 33       |                        |
|        | 9009     | 00       |        | 9009     | 00       |                        |

**Solution:**

```
 1                      ***********************************************************
 2                      * ASCBIN.SRC                                             *
 3                      ***********************************************************
 4  00008000            CODE   EQU    $8000           ;program at $8000
 5  00009000            DATA   EQU    $9000           ;data starts at $9000
 6
 7  00008000                   ORG    CODE            ;program at $8000
 8  00008000 207C0000          MOVEA.L #STRING,A0
    00008004 9002
 9  00008006 4246              CLR.W  D6              ;D6 accumulates answer
10  00008008 4284              CLR.L  D4              ;D4 holds ASCII character
11  0000800A 3A3C000A          MOVE.W #10,D5          ;D5 = 10 (always)
12  0000800E 1818     LOOP     MOVE.B (A0)+,D4        ;get character
13  00008010 670A              BEQ.S  DONE            ;if null, done
14  00008012 CCC5              MULU   D5,D6           ;if not, old X 10
15  00008014 0204000F          ANDI.B #$0F,D4         ;reduce new to BCD
16  00008018 DC84              ADD.L  D4,D6           ;add new to old
17  0000801A 60F2              BRA    LOOP            ;repeat
18  0000801C 33C60000 DONE     MOVE.W D6,>RESULT      ;save result
    00008020 9000
19  00008022 4E4E              TRAP   #14
20                    *
21                    * Use DC directives to initialize RAM
22                    *
23  00009000                   ORG    DATA            ;data at $9000
24  00009000 0000     RESULT   DC.W   0
25  00009002 30303037 STRING   DC.B   '0007683',0
    00009006 36383300
26  0000900A                   END    ASCBIN
```

**Discussion:** This program uses the 68000's unsigned multiply (MULU) instruction to continually adjust each digit by a factor of ten. Although the program only uses one conditional branch instruction, organizing the loop is tricky. The flowchart in Figure 5-2 illustrates the sequence of operations.

D6, which accumulates the binary result, is cleared initially (line 9). If the first character read is a null byte, the program terminates immediately (lines 12 and 13) and the result is stored in memory. If a non-zero byte is read, we assume it is an ASCII digit and proceed. The old value in D6 is adjusted by a factor of ten (line 14), then the ASCII digit is reduced to four bits by masking-off the upper nibble (line 15), as described in Chapter 0. The result is added to D6 to update the binary result (line 16). These steps are repeated until a null byte is read from the string.

The type of conversion illustrated in this example is extremely useful for software that interfaces with a console. A *calculator* program, for example, must input decimal numbers from a keyboard, perform operations on the decimal numbers, and output decimal results to a CRT display. Numbers received from the keyboard are input as a series of ASCII characters corresponding to digits. A routine such as ASCBIN is required to convert the incoming stream of characters to binary before the operations are performed. ■

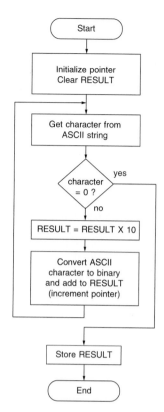

**Figure 5-2.** Flowchart for ASCBIN example.

## Example 5-10: Sort a List of Bytes

**Problem:** Write a subroutine called SORT that sorts a list of signed 8-bit numbers in ascending order. Pass two parameters to the subroutine: A0 = the starting address of the list, and D7 = the number of bytes in the list.

Sample Conditions:

Before:

| Register | Contents |
|---|---|
| A0 | 00009000 |
| D7 | 00000005 |

| Address | Contents |
|---|---|
| 9000 | 05 |
| 9001 | 08 |
| 9002 | 02 |
| 9003 | FF |
| 9004 | 07 |

After:

| Address | Contents |
|---|---|
| 9000 | FF (FF = -1 = lowest number) |
| 9001 | 02 |
| 9002 | 05 |
| 9003 | 07 |
| 9004 | 08 (08 = highest number) |

**Solution:**

```
 1                  * * * * * * * * * * * * * * * * * * * * * * * * * * * * * * * * * * * * * * *
 2                  * SORT.SRC                                                                *
 3                  * * * * * * * * * * * * * * * * * * * * * * * * * * * * * * * * * * * * * * *
 4 00008000        CODE    EQU     $8000           ;program starts at $8000
 5 00009000        DATA    EQU     $9000           ;data starts at $9000
 6
 7 00008000                ORG     CODE            ;program at $8000
 8 00008000 207C0000       MOVEA.L #BYTES,A0
   00008004 9000
 9 00008006 3E3C0004       MOVE.W  #COUNT-1,D7
10 0000800A 6102           BSR.S   SORT
11 0000800C 4E4E           TRAP    #14
12
13                  * * * * * * * * * * * * * * * * * * * * * * * * * * * * * * * * * * * * * * *
14                  * SORT   ascending SORT of 8-bit signed bytes        *
15                  *                                                     *
16                  *       ENTER  A0 = address of list                   *
17                  *              D7 = length of list                     *
18                  * * * * * * * * * * * * * * * * * * * * * * * * * * * * * * * * * * * * * * *
19 0000800E 2248   SORT    MOVEA.L A0,A1           ;save pointer
20 00008010 2049   LOOP2   MOVEA.L A1,A0           ;reset pointer
21 00008012 4245           CLR.W   D5             ;use D5 as SWAP flag
22 00008014 5347           SUB.W   #1,D7          ;number of comparisons
23 00008016 3C07           MOVE.W  D7,D6          ;use D6 within loop
24 00008018 1818   LOOP    MOVE.B  (A0)+,D4       ;get first byte
25 0000801A B810           CMP.B   (A0),D4        ;compare with next
26 0000801C 6F08           BLE.S   SKIP           ;if 1st bigger, swap
27 0000801E 1150FFFF       MOVE.B  (A0),-1(A0)    ;...put 2nd into 1st
28 00008022 1084           MOVE.B  D4,(A0)        ;...put 1st into 2nd
29 00008024 5245           ADDQ.W  #1,D5          ;set SWAP flag
30 00008026 51CEFFF0 SKIP  DBRA    D6,LOOP        ;if last comparison,
31 0000802A 4A45           TST.W   D5             ;any bytes swapped?
```

```
32 0000802C 66E2            BNE.S   LOOP2      ;yes: repeat
33 0000802E 4E75    DONE    RTS                ;no: done
34                  *
35                  * Use DC directives to initialize RAM
36                  *
37 00009000                 ORG     DATA       ;data at $9000
38 00009000 050802FF BYTES  DC.B    5,8,2,-1,7
   00009004 07
39 00000005          COUNT  EQU     *-BYTES
40 00009005                 END     SORT
```

**Discussion:** The solution to this problem is placed in a subroutine. A small *main program* is included (lines 8–11) to set up the parameters for the sample data and call the subroutine.

Since sorting data, like sorting a deck of cards, is a tedious and repetitive process, it is a task well-suited to computing. This example uses a well-known technique called **bubble sort**. During a bubble sort of a list of *n* data items, the list is scanned up to *n −1* times. On the first pass through the list, the first comparison is

between the 1st and 2nd bytes in the list. If the 2nd byte is smaller than the 1st, the two are swapped. The next comparison is between the 2nd and 3rd bytes, and so on. After one pass through the data in this manner, the sort is partially complete because the largest byte has *bubbled-up* to the top (end) of the list. The next pass begins again at the bottom of the list, but requires one less comparison than the first pass. Figure 5-3a illustrates the data comparisons and swaps for each pass through the sample data.

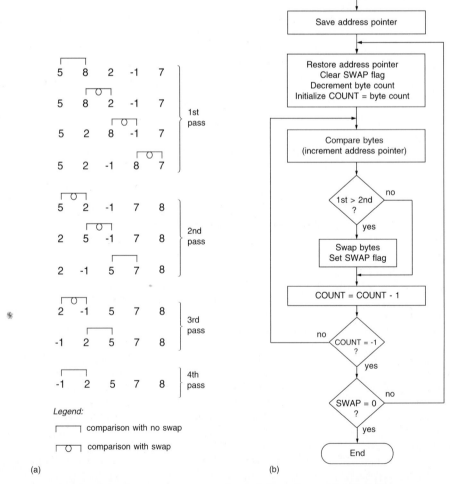

**Figure 5-3.** Sorting example. (a) data flow, (b) flowchart.

The SORT subroutine contains 15 instructions, including three conditional branch instructions. It is, of course, the conditional branch instructions that control the overall flow of the routine, as illustrated in the flowchart in Figure 5-3b.

The program contains an outer loop (lines 20–32) controlling the passes through the data, and an inner loop (lines 24-30) controlling the data comparisons during each pass. D5 is used as a *swap* flag. If at least one swap takes place during a pass, SWAP is incremented (line 29). At the end of each pass, SWAP is tested (line 31) and if no swap took place (SWAP = 0), the data are sorted, and the routine terminates.

The bubble sort routine is efficient for two reasons. First, on each pass through the list, one less comparison is performed than on the previous pass. This is possible because of the bubble-up effect. After the first pass, the last item in the list is definitely the largest; so, it is not tested again. After the second pass, the second-from-last item is not tested again, and so on. The second performance benefit follows from the variable SWAP. Once a complete pass has occurred without a swap, it is not necessary to perform

another pass. At most, $n-1$ passes are required, where $n$ is the number of items to sort. Still, other sorting algorithms are faster. We'll leave this for the reader to explore.  ■

### Example 5-11: Square Root of a 32-bit Integer

**Problem:**   Write a subroutine called SQRT to calculate the square root of a 32-bit integer. Pass the integer to the subroutine in D0 and return the result in D1 as a 16-bit integer.

Sample Conditions:

Before:

| Register | Contents |
| --- | --- |
| D0 | 000002BC |
| D1 | 00000000 |

After:

| Register | Contents |
| --- | --- |
| D0 | 000002BC |
| D1 | 0000001A     ( $\sqrt{2BC_{16}} = 1A_{16}$ ) |

**Solution:**

```
1               *************************************************
2               *  SQRT.SRC                                    *
3               *************************************************
4  00008000                ORG     $8000        ;program at $8000
5  00008000 203C0000       MOVE.L  #700,D0      ;find square root of 700
   00008004 02BC
6  00008006 6102           BSR.S   SQRT         ;do it!
7  00008008 4E4E           TRAP    #14          ;return to monitor
8
9               *************************************************
10              *  SQRT calculate SQuare RooT of a 32-bit number  *
11              *                                               *
12              *       ENTER  D0 = 32-bit integer (N)          *
13              *       EXIT   D1 = 16-bit square root          *
14              *************************************************
15 0000800A 48E73000 SQRT  MOVEM.L D2/D3,-(SP)  ;save D2 and D3
16 0000800E 2200           MOVE.L  D0,D1        ;put copy of N in D1
17 00008010 E249           LSR.W   #1,D1        ;1st estimate = N/2
18 00008012 2400     NEXT  MOVE.L  D0,D2        ;put N in D2
19 00008014 84C1           DIVU    D1,D2        ;divide N by estimate
20 00008016 3602           MOVE.W  D2,D3        ;new estimate in D3
21 00008018 9641           SUB.W   D1,D3        ;last two equal?
22 0000801A 6712           BEQ.S   EXIT         ;yes: finished
23 0000801C 0C43FFFF       CMPI.W  #-1,D3       ;differ by -1?
24 00008020 670C           BEQ.S   EXIT         ;yes: good enough
25 00008022 0C430001       CMPI.W  #1,D3        ;differ by +1?
26 00008026 6706           BEQ.S   EXIT         ;yes: good enough
27 00008028 D242           ADD.W   D2,D1        ;average last two
28 0000802A E249           LSR.W   #1,D1        ;D1 = (D1 + D2) / 2
29 0000802C 60E4           BRA     NEXT
30 0000802E 4CDF000C EXIT  MOVEM.L (SP)+,D2/D3  ;restore registers
31 00008032 4E75           RTS
32 00008034                END     SQRT
```

**Discussion:** Square roots, and other complex mathematical functions, can be calculated using a series of approximations, with each improving on the preceding. The approximations terminate once a reasonable degree of accuracy—in this case 1 bit—is reached. Consider a number $N$, and its square root $a$. The following illustrate the relationship between $N$ and $a$:

$$N = a \times a$$

or

$$\frac{N}{a} = a$$

The equation above uses a division operator on the left. Since the 68000 has a DIVU instruction, this is a good place to begin. If we guess a value for $a$, and plug it into the left side above, then the following result occurs:

$$\frac{N}{a} = b$$

If the guess was correct, $a = b$, but this is not likely. If the guess was too high, then $a > b$, or if the guess was too low, $a < b$. Either way, a better guess is the average of $a$ and $b$, so we reassign $a$ as follows:

$$a = \frac{a + b}{2}$$

and try again. Each time, the difference between $a$ and $b$ is smaller and the answer gets closer. To terminate the process, the difference between $a$ and $b$ is checked after each division. If $a = b$, or if $a$ and $b$ differ only by ±1, the answer is as close as possible and the calculation stops.

The algorithm described above is implemented in the solution to this programming problem. The first estimate is $N/2$ (line 17). Recall that division-by-2 is implemented quickly by a right shift. Throughout the program loop, D0 holds $N$. A new estimate is calculated by making a temporary copy of $N$ in D2 (line 18), then dividing this by the old estimate in D1 (lines 19) and placing a temporary copy of the result in D3 (line 20). The new estimate is compared against the old estimate by subtraction (line 21). If the difference is 0 or ±1 (lines 22–26), the answer in D1 is close enough and the loop terminates. Otherwise, the old and new estimates are averaged (lines 27–28) and the loop is repeated (line 29). ■

## 5.3.  SUMMARY

This chapter has presented eleven examples of problems solved in 68000 assembly language.

There is no substitute for experience, however. The reader is advised to solve a few of the problems that follow using a laboratory computer. The experience gained through hands-on debugging will strengthen the skills necessary to begin advanced programming in 68000 assembly language.

## 5.4.  QUESTIONS

1. Write a program called SUB to subtract the 16-bit integer in memory location $9000 from the 16-bit integer in $9002. Store the result in memory location $9004.

2. Write a program called REVERSE that reads a byte of data from memory location $9000 and stores the same byte, except with the nibbles reversed, in memory location $9001.

3. Write a program called COMBINE that combines the low-order nibbles of the four bytes in memory locations $9000 to $9003 into a single 16-bit word. The nibbles should be ordered low-to-high in the result beginning with the data from location $9000. Store the result as 16-bits in memory location $9004.

4. Write a program called FIND to find the larger of two signed bytes. Assume the two bytes are in memory location $9000 and $9001. Store the larger of the two in memory location $9002.

5. Perform the following timing analyses on the program ADD3 in Example 5-3.
   (a) How long does the program take to execution on a 10-MHz system?
   (b) How long does the program take to execution on a 16-MHz 68000 with slow RAM requiring two wait states?
   (c) What is the formula for the execution time ($t_{EXE}$), given the CPU clock period ($t_C$), and COUNT (the number of entries to add)? (Assume a memory interface with zero wait states.)
   (d) Use the formula in (c) to compute the time to add 1,000 words on an 8-MHz 68000 operating with zero wait states?

6. Write a program called LSHIFT to shift logically the 16-bit contents of memory location $9000 left according to the 8-bit shift count stored in memory location $9002.

7. Write a program called FIND2 to find the largest unsigned 16-bit word in a list. The list begins at address $9004. The length of the list is stored in a 16-bit variable at address $9002. Store the largest entry in memory location $9000.

8. Write a program called SCAN to scan a list of unsigned bytes and find the smallest and largest entries in the list. The length of the list is stored in a 16-bit variable at address $9002. The list begins at address $9004. Store the smallest byte at address $9000 and the largest byte at address $9001.

9. Write a program called COUNT to count the number of characters in a null-terminate ASCII string that are equal to a KEY. The KEY is stored in memory location $9001. The string is stored in memory beginning at address $9002. Store the 8-bit count in memory location $9000.

10. Write a program called ONES to determine the number of bits equal to one in a 32-bit variable. The 32-bit variable is in memory location $9002. Store the 8-bit count in memory location $9000.

11. Write a subroutine called STRLEN that determines the length of a null-terminated ASCII string. Pass the address of the string to the subroutine in address register A0. Return the

length, excluding the null byte, in data register D0. All registers (except D0) should return to the calling program intact.

12. Write a subroutine called REPLACE that processes a null-terminated string of decimal characters and replaces leading zeros with null bytes. Pass the address of the string to the subroutine in address register A0. Return from the subroutine with all registers intact.

13. Write a program called UNPACK to convert the 16-bit BCD variable in memory location $9000 to four ASCII characters, each representing a digit. Store the ASCII characters with the high-order digit first, beginning in memory location $9002.

14. Consider the SORT subroutine in Example 5-10. How can SORT be modified such that
    (a) all registers remain intact when the subroutine returns to the main program?
    (b) the data are sorted in descending order?
    (c) the data are treated as unsigned integers rather than signed integers?

# 6. Privilege States, Exceptions, Reset

## 6.1. INTRODUCTION

There are several important distinctions between the 68000 microprocessor and its 8-bit predecessor (the 6800). One is the classification of the processor's execution modes into two **privilege states,** known as **user mode** and **supervisor mode.** A related difference is the organization of a variety of special conditions into **exceptions.** Although privilege states and exceptions represent a new challenge for the student, they are quite simple. The first hurdle is the word *exception.* This is a bit misleading, since in many instances the occurrence of an exception is a perfectly normal event in the execution of a user program. An example is the TRAP instruction which initiates exception processing. In many instances, TRAP is similar to a *branch-to-subroutine* (BSR) in the traditional, 8-bit way of thinking, so there is nothing particularly exceptional at all. For other exceptions, such as *divide-by-zero,* the event really is abnormal or exceptional. A system reset—also an exception—is the most *final* of all exceptions. Reset occurs when the system is powered-up or manually reset following a system hang condition. By organizing these and other *special* conditions into a common scheme, the 68000 architecture becomes clean and consistent in handling a variety of conditions.

## 6.2. PRIVILEGE STATES

To protect the system from potentially catastrophic errors in user programs, the 68000 architecture specifies two states of privilege: user and supervisor. Protection is achieved by designating some system resources as supervisor-only. Table 6-1 identifies the differences between user mode and supervisor mode.

Changing from user mode to supervisor mode may occur only through exception processing, such as executing a TRAP instruction or through interrupts (see Figure 6-1). Changing from supervisor mode to user mode is accomplished by any of

four instructions that can alter the system byte of the SR. These include MOVE to SR, ANDI to SR, exclusive OR to SR, and RTE. RTE (return from exception) restores the SR to its previous value at the end of an exception. If the previous mode was user, it is restored to user.

A variety of instructions are privileged and any attempt to execute them while in user mode causes a *privilege violation* exception. The primary mechanism for user programs to access system resources is the TRAP instruction. Usually, a variety of operations such as input/output routines are packaged in traps (as opposed to subroutines). A specification of the call sequence is published so that users may incorporate traps in their programs. Through traps, a user program may enter supervisor mode cleanly to perform a system-level operation and then return to user mode. These operations are often referred to as *system calls.*

## 6.3. EXCEPTIONS

Exceptions are generated either by internal or external causes. Figure 6-2 places all exceptions in a tree structure to facilitate the discussions that follow.

The externally generated exceptions are interrupts, bus errors, and reset. Interrupts are requests from peripheral devices for processor action (see Chapter 7). A bus error occurs when the control bus signal $\overline{\text{BERR}}$ is asserted to terminate a bus cycle. Reset occurs when the control bus signal $\overline{\text{RESET}}$ is asserted.

The internal exceptions are generated by instructions, tracing, or execution errors. The TRAP instruction always causes an exception, whereas, TRAPV (trap on overflow), CHK (check register against bounds), and DIV (divide) generate exceptions conditionally. Illegal instructions, unimplemented instructions, and privilege violations also cause exceptions. Tracing is similar to a very high-priority, internally generated interrupt following each instruction.

Table 6-1.   User Mode vs. Supervisor Mode.

|  | User Mode | Supervisor Mode |
|---|---|---|
| Entered by | Clearing S-bit in SR | Exception processing |
| FC2 = | 0 | 1 |
| Active stack pointer | USP | SSP |
| Other stacks using | A0-A6 | USP, A0-A6 |
| Status Register access | | |
| Read: | Entire SR | Entire SR |
| Write: | CCR bits only | Entire SR |
| Instructions available | All except | All |
| | AND       #data,SR | |
| | EOR       #data,SR | |
| | MOVE      <ea>,SR | |
| | MOVE      USP,An | |
| | MOVE      An,USP | |
| | OR        #data,SR | |
| | RESET | |
| | RTE | |
| | STOP | |

Except for reset (discussed later in this chapter), every exception will cause the 68000 processor to take the following five steps:

1. save the 16-bit status register (SR) in an internal register

2. set the supervisor (S) bit and clear the trace (T) bit in the SR. (If the exception is due to an interrupt, the interrupt mask bits in the SR are updated according to the level of the interrupt.)

3. determine the *vector number* of the exception, then multiply this number by four to obtain the *vector address*

4. save the PC and the internally saved SR on the system stack. (An additional four words are saved if the exception is a bus error or an address error.)

5. load the PC with a new value read from the vector address computed in step 3

These steps are featured in Figure 6-3.

The information saved on the stack is known as the **stack frame.** The stack frame is the same for all exceptions except for a bus error or address error (discussed later in this chapter). In Figure 6-4, the stack frame is shown as a memory map with low-memory at the bottom and high-memory at the top.

### 6.3.1.   Exception Vectors

An exception vector is a memory location from which the processor fetches the address of a routine to handle an exception. Each exception type requires a unique handler routine and a unique vector. All exception vectors are two words in length, except the reset vector which is four words.

Except for user interrupt vectors, exception vectors are generated internally by the 68000. There are 255 different vector numbers: 0, 2, 3, etc., up to 255. (Vector "1" is missing; see Table 6-2.) The 8-bit vector number is multiplied by four to obtain the vector address. This is illustrated in Figure 6-5.

The vector address is the *address of the address.* That is, the vector address is the address of the memory location that contains the address of the exception handler. This address is read during step 5 of the exception processing sequence described earlier.

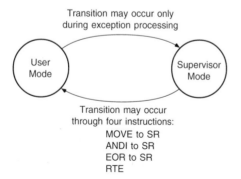

Figure 6-1.   Change between user mode and supervisor mode.

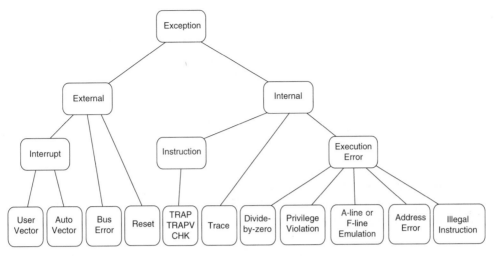

Figure 6-2.   Exception tree.

**Example 6-1:** An exception occurs for which the vector number is $65_{10}$. From what address is the address of the exception routine read?

**Solution:** $000104_{16}$

**Discussion:** The vector number is multiplied by four to obtain the vector address. The vector number $65_{10} = 1000001_2$. Shifting this left two positions (i.e., multiply by four) yields $100000100_2$. The vector address is found by padding to the left with zeros and converting to hexadecimal: $0000000000000000100000100_2 = 000104_{16}$. ■

Of the 68000's 16-megabyte memory space, the bottom 1K—from address $000000 to $0003FF—is reserved for exception vectors (see Table 6-2). Note that many of the vector numbers are reserved by Motorola for future enhancements.

## 6.3.2.   Multiple Exceptions

It is important that the 68000 architecture organize exceptions such that any possible anomalous condition is treated in a consistent, predictable manner. One of the most common, for example, is the occurrence of an exception condition while a previous exception is still being processed. To coordinate this and other possibilities, exceptions are grouped by their occurrence and priority. There are three groups: 0, 1, and 2. Group 0 exceptions will be processed before those in groups 1 or 2, and group 1 exceptions will be processed before group 2 exceptions. The grouping and priority of exceptions are summarized in Table 6-3.

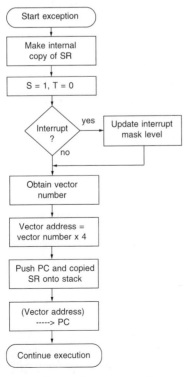

Figure 6-3.   Exception processing sequence.

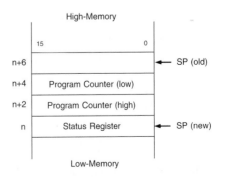

Figure 6-4.   Stack frame for exceptions (except bus error and address error).

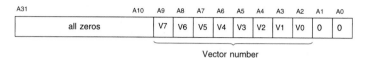

**Figure 6-5.   Exception vector address.**

Group 0 exceptions are reset, bus error, and address error. These exceptions cause the instruction currently executing to abort and exception processing to commence within two CPU cycles. The group 1 exceptions are trace, interrupt, illegal instructions, and privilege violations. Trace and interrupt exceptions allow the current instruction to complete but preempt the execution of the next instruction by forcing exception processing to commence. A privilege violating instruction or an illegal instruction is detected when it is the next instruction to execute. Group 2 exceptions occur as part of the normal instruction-execution sequence of a program. These include TRAP, TRAPV, CHK, DIVU, and DIVS.

Table 6-3 indicates not only the grouping of exceptions, but the priority within groups. Within group 0, reset has the highest priority, followed by address error, and then by bus error. Within group 1, trace has priority over external interrupts, which in turn takes priority over illegal instructions and privilege violations. Since only one instruction can execute at a time, no priority relationship exists in group 2.

The priority relationship between two exceptions determines which is taken, or taken first, if the condition for both arises simultaneously. For example, if an interrupt occurs during the execution of an instruction while the T-bit is set, the trace exception has priority and is processed first. Before instruction execution resumes, however, the interrupt exception is also processed, and instruction execution finally resumes *in the interrupt handler.* From the preceding sentence, the reader may notice that, as a general rule, the *lower* the priority of an exception, the sooner the routine for that exception executes. This rule does not apply to the reset exception because the reset operation clears all other exceptions.

### 6.3.3.   *Processing of Specific Exceptions*

This section describes the processing of each of the 68000's exception conditions. Since the reset exception is distinctly different, it is discussed in a

**Table 6-2.   Reset and Exception Vector Assignments.**

| Vector Number | Hexadecimal Address | Assignment |
|---|---|---|
| 0 | 000 | Reset SSP[†] |
| – | 004 | Reset PC[†] |
| 2 | 008 | Bus Error |
| 3 | 00C | Address Error |
| 4 | 010 | Illegal instruction |
| 5 | 014 | Divide-by-zero |
| 6 | 018 | CHK instruction |
| 7 | 01C | TRAPV instruction |
| 8 | 020 | Privilege violation |
| 9 | 024 | Trace |
| 10 | 028 | Line 1010 emulator |
| 11 | 02C | Line 1111 emulator |
| 12 | 030 | (reserved) |
| 13 | 034 | (reserved) |
| 14 | 038 | Format error (68010) |
| 15 | 03C | Uninitialized interrupt vector |
| 16-23 | 040-05C | (reserved) |
| 24 | 060 | Spurious interrupt[††] |
| 25 | 064 | Level 1 interrupt autovector |
| 26 | 068 | Level 2 interrupt autovector |
| 27 | 06C | Level 3 interrupt autovector |
| 28 | 070 | Level 4 interrupt autovector |
| 29 | 074 | Level 5 interrupt autovector |
| 30 | 078 | Level 6 interrupt autovector |
| 31 | 07C | Level 7 interrupt autovector |
| 32-47 | 080-0BC | TRAP instruction vectors[†††] |
| 48-63 | 0C0-0FC | (reserved) |
| 64-255 | 100-3FC | User interrupt vectors |

[†] The reset vector is four words and resides in the supervisor program (SP) space. All other vectors reside in the supervisor data (SD) space.
[††] The spurious interrupt vector is taken when there is a bus error during an interrupt acknowledge cycle.
[†††] Trap #*n* uses vector number 32 + *n*. See Table 6-5.

**Table 6-3.   Exception Grouping and Priority.**

| Group | Exception | Processing |
|---|---|---|
| 0 | Reset<br>Address Error<br>Bus Error | Exception processing begins within two CPU cycles |
| 1 | Trace<br>Interrupt<br>Illegal Instruction<br>Privilege Violation | Exception processing begins before the next instruction |
| 2 | TRAP, TRAPV<br>CHK<br>Zero Divide | Exception processing is started by normal instruction execution |

dedicated section later in this chapter. The interrupt exception (except for the uninitialized and spurious interrupt) is presented in detail in Chapter 7 where input/output topics are presented.

***Uninitialized Interrupt*** During an interrupt-acknowledge cycle, an interrupting device provides an interrupt vector number and asserts data transfer acknowledge ($\overline{\text{DTACK}}$), valid peripheral address ($\overline{\text{VPA}}$), or bus error ($\overline{\text{BERR}}$). Motorola's peripheral interface ICs (or others conforming to the same standard) contain a vector register that is initialized with the desired vector number. If this register is not initialized, it will contain, by default, the value 15 corresponding to the uninitialized interrupt vector. Providing this vector number, in the absence of a software initialization of the interrupt vector register, provides a uniform way to recover from a programming error.

***Spurious Interrupt*** During the interrupt-acknowledge cycle, if no device responds by asserting $\overline{\text{DTACK}}$ or $\overline{\text{VPA}}$ the bus logic should assert $\overline{\text{BERR}}$ to terminate the vector acquisition. The processor separates this type of bus error from the usual bus error (discussed below) by fetching the spurious interrupt vector number, 24. The processor then proceeds with the usual exception-processing sequence. Note that only the PC and the SR are saved on the stack during a spurious-interrupt exception.

***Instruction Traps*** Traps are exceptions caused by either the TRAP, TRAPV, CHK, DIVS, or DIVU instructions. TRAP is one of the most common 68000 instructions for input/output operations. As noted at the beginning of this chapter, the TRAP instruction often functions similar to BSR or JSR. There are, however, important distinctions, and these are featured in Table 6-4. First, trap instructions always initiate exception processing, switching the CPU's privilege state to supervisor; whereas BSR or JSR has no effect on the CPU's privilege state. Subroutines may execute in either supervi-

Table 6-5. Vector Assignments for TRAP Instructions.

| Instruction | Vector Number | Vector Address |
|---|---|---|
| TRAP #0 | 32 | $000080 |
| TRAP #1 | 33 | $000084 |
| TRAP #2 | 34 | $000088 |
| TRAP #3 | 35 | $00008C |
| TRAP #4 | 36 | $000090 |
| TRAP #5 | 37 | $000094 |
| TRAP #6 | 38 | $000098 |
| TRAP #7 | 39 | $00009C |
| TRAP #8 | 40 | $0000A0 |
| TRAP #9 | 41 | $0000A4 |
| TRAP #10 | 42 | $0000A8 |
| TRAP #11 | 43 | $0000AC |
| TRAP #12 | 44 | $0000B0 |
| TRAP #13 | 45 | $0000B4 |
| TRAP #14 | 46 | $0000B8 |
| TRAP #15 | 47 | $0000BC |

sor mode or user mode. Second, the TRAP instruction saves the PC and the SR on the system stack. BSR or JSR saves only the PC, and it is saved on the active state, which may be user or system depending on the current execution mode. Finally, exception routines end with return-from-exception (RTE), which restores the PC and the SR from the system stack and returns the privilege state to its previous mode. Subroutines end with return-from-subroutine (RTS) which simply restores the PC from the active stack.

The vector number for TRAP is partially generated from the instruction through an immediate data constant. TRAP #$n$ generates the vector number $32 + n$, where $n$ is from 0 to 15. When a TRAP instruction executes, the value of the PC saved on the stack is the address of the instruction following TRAP. The vector number for each trap is illustrated in Table 6-5, which expands the single row in Table 6-2 for the trap exception.

Although at first it might seem that the 68000 is limited to 16 trap operations, it is common to implement multiple routines through a single trap by passing an integer to the trap in a data register.

Table 6-4. Traps vs. Subroutines.

| | Trap | Subroutine |
|---|---|---|
| Initiated from | user mode or supervisor mode | user mode or supervisor mode |
| Routine executes in | supervisor mode | user mode or supervisor mode |
| Registers saved | PC and SR | PC |
| Register saved on | system stack | user stack or system stack |
| Routine ends with | RTE | RTS |
| Privilege state after is | user mode or supervisor mode | user mode or supervisor mode |

Within the trap routine, the integer is used as an index into a jump table leading to the desired routine. One nice feature about traps is that they transfer control to a routine whose address is not known to the calling program. This form of *dynamic linkage* is important for operating systems since they must upgrade frequently but maintain a fixed set of call sequences for system services.

A detailed before/after example of a trap instruction is found in Chapter 3.

> **Example 6-2:** A PRINT_STRING routine is implemented on a 68000 system using TRAP #7. At what address must the address of the PRINT_STRING routine be stored?
>
> **Solution:** $00009C_{16}$
>
> **Discussion:** TRAP #7 generates the vector number $32 + 7 = 39$. The vector address is $39 \times 4 = 156_{10} = 00009C_{16}$. ∎

TRAPV (trap on overflow) will cause an exception through vector address $00001C if the V-bit in the CCR is set. This provides a convenient, consistent mechanism to handle overflows at the operating system level.

CHK (check register against bounds) is used to verify that a data access is within a designated storage space. Applications include limit-checking for arrays, matrices, strings, user stacks, and so on. CHK takes two operands, as follows:

```
CHK  <ea>,Dn
```

If the word-size index in the data register is $\geq 0$ or $\leq$ the integer specified by the effective address, then no exception takes place and execution proceeds with the following instruction. If the index in Dn is negative or exceeds the upper bound at the effective address, exception processing commences through vector address $000018. The index specified by the effective address is treated as a signed integer; thus, the maximum size of the index is $2^{15} - 1 = 32,767$.

> **Example 6-3:** Write a subroutine called SQUARE to compute the square of an integer between 0 and 9. Use a table-look-up method, passing the integer to the subroutine in D0. Return with its square in D0. Within the subroutine, use a CHK instruction to ensure the parameter is within the limits of the look-up table.
>
> **Solution:** See Figure A.
>
> **Discussion:** The solution is in three parts: a main section to set up some parameters and call the subroutine (lines 5–9), the SQUARE subroutine (lines 11–13), and the look-up table (line 14). First the square of 5 is computed (lines 5 & 6) without an error. In line 7, D0 is loaded with a new value, 15, which exceeds the limits of the subroutine. The subroutine is called for the second time in line 8. The CHK instruction checks the index in D0 against the bounds $0 \leq D0 \leq 9$. Since D0 = $15_{10}$, exception processing commences using the CHK vector number. Note that this example is simplistic since it does not include a graceful recovery from the error. ∎

DIVS (signed divide) and DIVU (unsigned divide) are the most conditional of the trap instructions because they initiate exception processing only for one specific case—division-by-zero. The vector number is 5.

Figure A.

```
 1        ********************************************************
 2        * SQUARE.SRC                                          *
 3        ********************************************************
 4 00008000                 ORG      $8000
 5 00008000 7005    ENTER   MOVE.L   #5,D0             ;5X5 = 25
 6 00008002 6106            BSR.S    SQUARE
 7 00008004 700F            MOVE.L   #15,D0            ;15 is too big!
 8 00008006 6102            BSR.S    SQUARE
 9 00008008 4E4E            TRAP     #14               ;return to monitor
10
11 0000800A 41BC0009 SQUARE CHK     #9,D0             ;9 = maximum size of D0
12 0000800E 103B0004        MOVE.B   TABLE(PC,D0),D0
13 00008012 4E75            RTS
14 00008014 00010409 TABLE  DC.B     0,1,4,9,16,25,36,49,64,81
   00008018 10192431
   0000801C 4051
15 0000801E                 END      ENTER
```

**Example 6-4:** Illustrate an instruction sequence that will force a divide-by-zero exception to occur.

**Solution:**

```
DIVS  #0,D5
```

**Discussion:** The source operand is the divisor and the destination operand is the dividend. The operation attempted by this instruction is (D5)/0. This will force exception processing to commence through vector address $000014. ∎

*Illegal Instruction* *Illegal instruction* is the term used to refer to any of the 16-bit patterns that do not match the bit pattern of the first word of a legal 68000 instruction. If such an instruction is fetched, an illegal instruction exception occurs. Illegal instructions are also called *undefined* instructions.

Three bit patterns are guaranteed to force an illegal exception on all Motorola 68000-compatible CPUs. The patterns are $4AFA, $4AFB, and $4AFC. The first two are reserved for Motorola system products, while the third is reserved for user purposes. The ILLEGAL instruction mnemonic represents the third pattern ($4AFC) and always initiates exception processing. Many other instruction bit patterns are also illegal (and initiate exception processing); however, their use is discouraged since many of the patterns appear as legal instructions on newer processors of the 68000 family. The illegal instruction vector number is 4.

*Unimplemented Instructions* Word patterns with bits 15–12 equal to 1010 or 1111 are distinguished as *unimplemented* instructions (as opposed to illegal or undefined instructions). Instructions beginning with these patterns are commonly known as *A-line instructions* (1010) or *F-line instructions* (1111). Separate exception vectors are assigned to each of these to permit custom emulation of extended instructions. For example, the 68000 does not include floating-point instructions. These can be emulated through machine-language routines by using a DC.W directive to encode a floating-point instruction beginning with 1010 or 1111. The remaining 12 bits in the instruction word can encode the type of operation, source and destination data registers, and so on.

Opcodes beginning with 1111 (line F) are implemented on the 68020 processor as coprocessor instructions. If the coprocessor is not present, the extended instruction can be emulated through a jump table in the exception handler.

The A-line exception vector number is 10. The F-line exception vector number is 11.

*Privilege Violations* To provide system security, various instructions are privileged. An attempt to execute a privileged instruction while the CPU is in user mode causes a privilege violation exception. The privileged instructions are

```
AND     #data,SR
EOR     #data,SR
MOVE    <ea>,SR
MOVE    An,USP
MOVE    USP,An
OR      #data,SR
RESET
RTE
STOP
```

The privilege violation exception vector number is 8.

*Tracing* To aid in program development, the 68000 includes a facility to allow tracing following each instruction. When tracing is enabled, an exception is forced after each instruction. Thus, a debugging program can monitor the execution of a program under test.

The trace facility is controlled by the T-bit in the SR. If T = 0, tracing is disabled and instructions execute one after another in the usual manner. If T = 1, a trace exception is generated after each instruction is completed. Since the T-bit is cleared as part of the exception-initiation sequence, tracing does not occur within the trace-exception routine. However, upon completion of the routine, the T-bit is restored. This causes the CPU to initiate another trace exception after the next instruction executes.

The trace-exception vector number is 9.

*Bus Error* A bus error exception occurs when the external logic requests that a bus error be processed by an exception. This occurs by asserting the control bus signal $\overline{BERR}$ instead of $\overline{DTACK}$ or $\overline{VPA}$ to terminate a bus cycle. The current bus cycle is aborted. The current processor activity, whether instruction or exception processing, is terminated and the processor immediately begins exception processing. The bus error vector number is 2.

As noted earlier, the information saved on the stack—the stack frame—is more extensive for a bus error or address error than for the other exceptions. The stack frame consists of seven words, as illustrated in Figure 6-6a. The PC and SR are saved, as with the other exceptions. Note that the PC-value saved will be offset from the address of

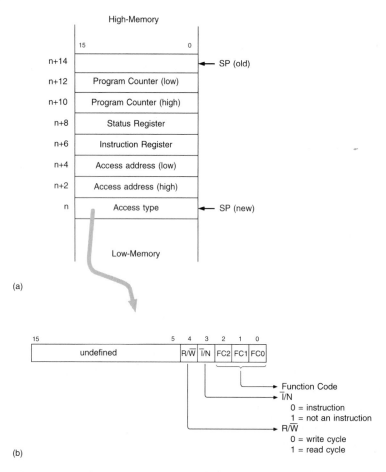

Figure 6-6.    Stack frame for bus error and address error. (a) Stacking order, (b) Access type.

the instruction executing by 2, 4, 6, 8, or 10, depending on the length of the instruction and where the error occurred within the instruction. Recall that the PC is automatically incremented as each instruction word is fetched.

Four additional words are saved, including the first word of the instruction currently executing, the access address, and access type. The access address is the address of the memory location that was being accessed when $\overline{\text{BERR}}$ was asserted. As shown in Figure 6-6b, specific information about the type of access is also saved, including direction of access (read vs. write), processor activity, and the function code output when the error occurred. The processor is considered processing an instruction if it is in the normal state or processing a group 2 exception. The processor is not processing an instruction if it is processing a group 0 or group 1 exception.

If a bus error occurs during exception processing for a bus error, an address error, or a reset, the processor halts and all processing ceases. This halt simplifies the detection of a catastrophic system failure, and the processor removes itself from the system to protect memory contents from erro-

neous accesses. Only an external reset operation can restart a halted processor.

A common implementation of bus error is through a watchdog timer, as described in Chapter 2. If a program inadvertently accesses a memory address for which no memory is present, the usual acknowledgment on $\overline{\text{DTACK}}$ will not occur. After a lengthy wait, say 40 CPU cycles, the watchdog timer asserts $\overline{\text{BERR}}$ and a bus-error exception is initiated.

*Address Error*    An address error occurs any time the processor attempts to access a word or longword operand at an odd address. (Only byte-size operands may reside at odd addresses.) An address error is similar to an internally generated bus error. The bus cycle is aborted and the processor ceases current processing and begins exception-processing. The exception-processing sequence is the same as that for a bus error, including the information saved on the system stack. The vector number for an address error is 3.

An address error is usually a sign of improper manipulation of a pointer. Consider the following instruction sequence:

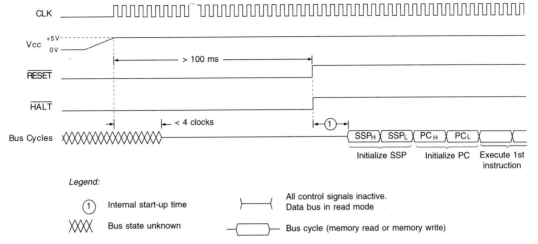

**Figure 6-7. Power-on reset timing.**

```
MOVEA.L    #$60000,A0
MOVE.W     D7,(A0)
LEA        5(A0),A0
MOVE.W     D6,(A0)
```

The last instruction above causes an address error. Since both MOVE instructions write a word operand to memory, the address of the destination location must be even. This is the case for the first MOVE, which writes the low-word in D7 to address $60000. However, after adjusting the address register in the third instruction, A0 contains $60005—an odd address. The fourth instruction is attempting to copy the low-word in D6 to an odd address, and this causes an address error.

## 6.4.   RESET

When a microprocessor-based system is turned on, a sequence of events occurs to start up the system gracefully and begin execution of a program. If during the subsequent execution of a program, the system *hangs* due to an unrecoverable hardware or software error, it is necessary to reset the system externally and begin a new start-up sequence. The CPU can also reset external devices if an unrecoverable error is detected in an interface. All these activities are variations of the **reset operation.** The 68000 supports three forms of reset:

- power-on reset
- external reset
- RESET instruction

### 6.4.1.   *Power-On Reset*

When the on/off switch is moved from off to on, the system undergoes a **power-on reset.** Since

we are interested in examining the 68000 microprocessor from the lowest level possible, a detailed understanding of the power-on reset is important. Imagine the following: We have designed and built a prototype 68000-based system and wish to test it for proper operation. After attaching a power supply to the prototype, we turn it on. What happens next? Within the first second of powering-on the system, a great deal has happened. If there is a design or construction flaw in the prototype, chances are the system cannot successfully complete its power-on reset. (It will hang in some crazy loop fetching and executing meaningless instructions.) If, for example, a RAM address line is open, the system cannot correctly read memory, let alone execute a program. Debugging requires monitoring bus activity during the reset operation, probably with an oscilloscope or logic analyzer.

The timing and bus activity for a power-on reset are shown in Figure 6-7. As power is turned on, the power supply voltage rises toward +5 volts. RESET and HALT must remain low during power-up and for at least 100 ms afterward. This allows the internal state of the 68000 CPU to stabilize.

After RESET and HALT reach the inactive state, the CPU buses are idle for a brief internal start-up time.[1] Then, the CPU initializes the system stack pointer (SSP) and program counter (PC). This is accomplished by reading a longword from address $000000 and placing it in the SSP, and then by reading a longword from address $000004 and placing it in the PC. Four memory-read cycles provide, in sequence, the high-word of the SSP, the low-word of the SSP, the high-word of the PC, and the low-word of the PC. All the timings and re-

---

[1]Motorola's literature for the 68000 CPU does not specify the duration of the internal start-up time.

**Figure B.**

| Upper-byte EPROM: | | | Lower-byte EPROM: | |
|---|---|---|---|---|
| Address | Contents | | Address | Contents |
| 000000 | 00 | | 000000 | 00 |
| 000001 | 00 | | 000001 | 00 |
| 000002 | 00 | | 000002 | 00 |
| 000003 | 00 | | 000003 | 08 |
| 000004 | 60 | | 000004 | FE |

quirements of the memory-read cycle described in Chapter 2 apply (such as the need for the memory interface to terminate the cycles with $\overline{\text{DTACK}}$).

After initializing the SSP and PC, the CPU initializes the status register with $2700. This has the following effect:

- turns off trace mode (SR[15] = 0)
- puts the CPU in supervisor state (SR[13] = 1)
- sets the interrupt mask level to seven (SR[10:8] = $111_2$)

With an interrupt mask of seven, interrupts on levels 1 through 6 are inhibited (masked). Interrupt 7 is non-maskable.

After initializing the SSP, PC, and SR, the system executes the first instruction. This is the 5th bus cycle in Figure 6-7. It is an opcode fetch at the address contained in the PC. Thus, the longword in memory location $000004 must be the address of the first instruction to execute following a system reset.

Since the reset values for the SSP and PC must exist in memory upon power-up, the bottom of the 68000's memory space is usually configured to contain ROM or EPROM. If, for example, the first longword in the memory space contains $0000C000 and the second longword contains $00000400, then after a power-on reset, the SSP is initialized to $0000C000, and the 24-bit program counter is initialized to $000400. With a PC value of $000400, the CPU begins execution just above the reset and exception vector space. The initial value for the SSP is normally just above an area of RAM used as the supervisor stack. (Remember, the stack grows *down* as items are written to it.)

**Example 6-5:** Imagine you have just designed and built a prototype 68000-based single-board computer. To verify that the system buses are functioning correctly, the first program installed in EPROM consists of a single BRA instruction that branches to itself. What hexadecimal bytes

must be burned into EPROMs at the bottom of memory to achieve this? Give the hexadecimal bytes separately for the upper-byte EPROM and lower-byte EPROM.

**Solution:** See Figure B.

**Discussion:** The solution consists of two longwords loaded into the system SP and PC immediately after reset, and a single word for the BRA instruction. The listing in Figure C illustrates how the data above were obtained. For convenience, the upper-byte EPROM data are in boldface type. ■

With this simple program the operation of the system buses is easily verified using an oscilloscope or logic analyzer. All bus cycles are memory-read cycles, and should conform to the timing given in Chapter 2. Immediately following reset, the system SP is initialized with zero and the PC is initialized with $00000008—the address of the BRA instruction. Zero is a reasonable value for the SSP since no stack accesses take place. Although the BRA instruction resides in the bus-error vector address, this is of no consequence for a quick test of the system buses, as shown above. Incremental testing of the system would require follow-up programs to test read/write operations to the system RAM, and so on.

## 6.4.2. *External Reset*

If the system experiences an unrecoverable hardware or software error, it is necessary to reset the system externally and begin a new start-up sequence. This is called an **external reset.** Figure 6-8 illustrates the timing and bus activity. Note that power is not lost during an external reset. Most commonly, an external reset is accomplished by a human operator pressing a momentary reset switch on the chassis of the system.

Both $\overline{\text{RESET}}$ and $\overline{\text{HALT}}$ must be asserted for an external reset, and they must be asserted for at least ten CPU clock cycles. The start-up sequence

**Figure C.**

```
1 00000000                    ORG   $0
2 00000000 00000000           DC.L  0      ;SSP reset value
3 00000004 00000008           DC.L  TEST   ;PC reset value
4 00000008 ·60FE      TEST    BRA.S TEST
```

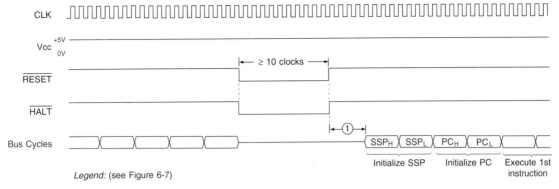

**Figure 6-8.   External reset timing.**

after $\overline{RESET}$ and $\overline{HALT}$ return to the inactive state is identical to the power-on reset just described.

### 6.4.3.   RESET *Instruction*

The RESET instruction causes the processor to assert $\overline{RESET}$ for 124 clock periods to reset the external devices of the system. This is called an internal reset operation. The internal state of the processor is not affected. Neither the status register nor any of the internal registers of the 68000 is affected by an internal reset. All external devices in the system should be reset upon completion of the RESET instruction. The $\overline{HALT}$ line is not affected. Figure 6-9 illustrates the timing and bus activity.

### 6.4.4.   *Reset Circuitry*

A circuit is required to supply a power-on reset and external reset to the 68000 CPU. Figure 6-10 is an example. The power-on circuit consists of an RC (resistor-capacitor) network with R1 = 10 kΩ and C1 = 22 μF. Power-on reset is achieved as follows: At the moment the system's power supply is turned on and +5 volts arrives at the system's ICs, the capacitor is discharged and 0 volts is maintained at the 7414 input and, consequently, on

$\overline{RESET}$ and $\overline{HALT}$. Even though the devices in the system (including the CPU) are powered-up, the system is held in a reset state because of the RC network. The capacitor begins to charge (through R1) and eventually reaches +5 volts. The double inversion in Figure 6-10 provides isolation and noise immunity. A logic 1 is presented to $\overline{RESET}$ and $\overline{HALT}$ when the input to the 7414 reaches +2.4 volts—the minimum voltage interpreted as a logic 1. Open-collector inverters are used since $\overline{RESET}$ and $\overline{HALT}$ are bidirectional and are occasionally driven by the CPU.

Let's verify that the input to the 7414 is below +2.4 volts for at least 100 ms after power-up. The voltage at the plus (+) terminal of the capacitor ($V_{CAP}$) rises from 0 volts after power-up according to the following formula:

$$V_{CAP} = V_{CC}(1 - e^{-t/RC})$$

where

$$
\begin{array}{ll}
V_{CC} & = +5 \text{ volts} \\
e & = 2.7183 \\
R = R1 & = 10 \times 10^3 \text{ Ohms} \\
C = C1 & = 22 \times 10^{-6} \text{ Farads} \\
t & = ?
\end{array}
$$

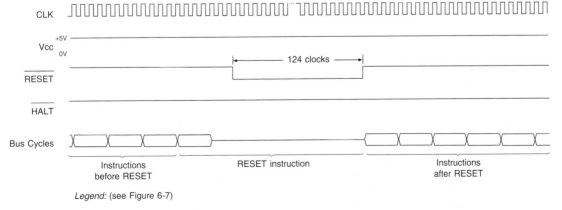

**Figure 6-9.   RESET instruction timing.**

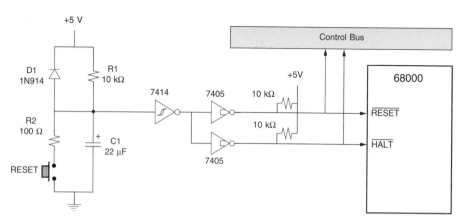

Figure 6-10.   Reset circuitry.

Solving for $t$ using $V_{CAP} = +2.4$ V, the minimum voltage for a logic 1 at the input to the 7414, yields

$$t = 143 \text{ ms}$$

The waveforms are illustrated in Figure 6-11.

An external reset is implemented with a push-button switch, labeled RESET in Figure 6-10. When the switch is depressed, a logic 0 is presented to the 7414 input and C1 is discharged to 0 volts. When the switch is released, C1 is charged as in Figure 6-11 and after 143 ms the system begins the start-up sequence.

## 6.5.   CONCLUSIONS

This chapter has introduced some advanced topics in the architecture of the 68000 microprocessor. However, the last word on exceptions, privilege states, and so on lies with Motorola's literature. For more thorough and specific details, consult Motorola's *M68000 8-/16-/32-Bit Microprocessor's User's Manual.* (M68000UM/AD).

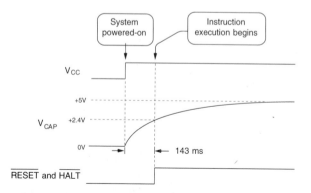

Figure 6-11.   Power-on reset waveforms.

Interrupts were omitted in our treatment of exceptions in this chapter. Since interrupts are usually associated with input/output operations, we have deferred discussing this important topic until after introductory topics in I/O are presented. Chapter 7 begins with simple I/O and advances to complex interrupt-driven and direct-memory-access-driven operations.

## 6.6.   QUESTIONS

1. Assume a 68000-based system is currently executing in supervisor mode. Illustrate how user mode may be started using an EOR instruction.

2. Assume a 68000-based system is currently executing in supervisor mode. Illustrate how user mode may be started using an AND instruction.

3. Assume a 68000-based system is currently executing in supervisor mode. Illustrate how user mode may be started using a MOVE instruction.

4. Assume a 68000-based system is currently executing in supervisor mode. Illustrate how a user program at address $4000 can be started in trace mode with an interrupt mask level of 5.

5. Assume an RTE instruction appears in a 68000 program which is executing in user mode. Describe what happens.

6. What is the vector number and the vector address for a trap-on-overflow exception?

7. What is the vector address for TRAP #5?

8. (a) What exception condition initiates exception processing at the address found in location $00000C?

   (b) What causes this exception?

9. Consider the SQUARE subroutine in Example 6-3. Modify the subroutine such that the value in D0 is returned intact if an out-of-bounds exception occurs. To answer this question, assume the CHK exception routine—if it executes—returns with D7 = −1.

10. Identify the exceptions, the vector numbers, and the starting addresses for the exceptions associated with the following memory assignments:

| Address | Contents |
|---------|----------|
| 000010  | 0012     |
| 000012  | 0F00     |
| 000014  | 0000     |
| 000016  | 80D0     |
| 000018  | 0001     |
| 00001A  | 0000     |
| 00001C  | 0000     |
| 00001E  | 4008     |

11. Assume the following conditions exist immediately prior to TRAP #5 executing.

| Memory Address | Memory Contents | Register | Register Contents |
|----------------|-----------------|----------|-------------------|
| 000094         | 0005F           | PC       | 008040            |
| 000096         | 1F00            | SSP      | 00BFF0            |
|                |                 | SR       | 0503              |

(a) Determine the *after* conditions.

(b) Illustrate the stack frame.

12. The memory map in Figure D illustrates the stack frame for an exception routine currently executing.

(a) What is the address of the first instruction to execute after the exception routine terminates?

(b) What privilege state is the CPU returned to upon completion of the exception routine?

(c) What is the interrupt mask level of the CPU upon completion of the exception routine?

13. The instruction in line 5 below causes an address error.

```
1 00008000              ORG    $8000
2 00008000  46FC271F    MOVE.W #$271F,SR
3 00008004  2E7C0000    MOVEA.L #$00B800,A7
  00008008  B800
4 0000800A  207C0000    MOVEA.L #$009001,A0
  0000800E  9001
5 00008010  3080        MOVE.W D0,(A0)
```

Illustrate the stack frame that is created upon initiating exception processing. (Assume the undefined bits of the access type equal zero.)

14. Propose an instruction format for A-line emulation of four floating-point instructions: FPADD, FPSUB, FPDIV, and FPMUL. The instructions should include a specification for a source and destination data register. Give examples of instruction words for the following operations:

(a) FPADD D5,D7

(b) FPSUB D0,D1

(c) FPMUL D4,D3

15. What value of resistor (R1) could be used in the circuit in Figure 6-10 to achieve a power-on reset duration of 250 ms?

**Figure D.**

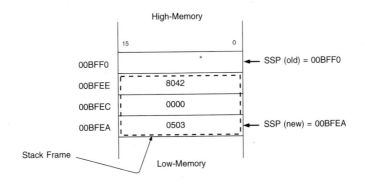

# 7. Input/Output

## 7.1. INTRODUCTION

*Input/output* is the transfer of data between external devices and the CPU. The terms *input* and *output* are, by convention, used with respect to the CPU. Input is the transfer of data from an external device into the CPU. Output is the transfer of data from the CPU out to an external device.

There are numerous examples of input devices and output devices, and their complexity covers just about every possibility imaginable, from a simple switch to a high-speed magnetic disk drive. Examples of input devices include:

| | |
|---|---|
| keyboard | switch |
| microphone | mouse |
| analog-to-digital converter | trackball |
| optical character reader | image scanner |
| thermistor | CD-ROM drive |
| video camera | |

Examples of output devices include:

| | |
|---|---|
| cathode-ray tube (CRT) | printer |
| light-emitting diode (LED) | speaker |
| digital-to-analog converter | solenoid |
| relay | buzzer |

The devices listed above range from components to complex subsystems. This illustrates the vast territory this topic covers. Some devices are bidirectional, implying a capability of receiving data from the CPU (output) or of providing data to the CPU (input). Examples of bidirectional devices include:

| | |
|---|---|
| disk drive | tape drive |
| modem | video display terminal |

We begin with examples of very simple input/output and progress to advanced forms of I/O.

## 7.2. UNCONDITIONAL I/O

The simplest type of input/output is called **unconditional I/O.** This applies to very trivial devices that do not require any special synchronization for input or output transfers. The device is always *ready* and a transfer of data can occur at any time at the discretion of the program.

The idea of unconditional I/O is best developed by considering interfaces to the simplest devices possible: the switch for input and the LED for output. A switch is a 1-bit input device with two states, OPEN and CLOSED. It is easy to configure a switch in a circuit such that OPEN is a logical "1" and CLOSED is a logical "0." The idea is to have the computer sense these two conditions and respond accordingly. Similarly, it is easy to configure an LED to be controlled by the switch, with *switch-OPEN* leaving the LED off and *switch-CLOSED* turning the LED on. This is shown in Figure 7-1.

The switch controls the LED in Figure 7-1a using a wire connection. When the switch is open, current does not flow and the LED is off. When the switch is closed, current flows from the +5V terminal of the power supply, through the resistor, through the LED (turning it on), and through the switch to the ground terminal of the power supply.

In Figure 7-1b, a computer replaces the wire as the interconnection. At this point, because of the power of software, the possibilities are virtually limitless as to the relationship between the switch and the LED. Once we have the interface circuitry in place to read the state of the switch and to write to the LED, it is possible to conjure up powerful relationships between input devices and output devices. This is one of the most exciting aspects of learning about computer hardware; and it is a topic we will dwell on in detail in this chapter as we examine a variety of topics in input/output.

### 7.2.1. Interface to Switches as Input

To complete the picture in Figure 7-1b, we must design an interface between the 68000 buses and the switch and LED. The interface requires

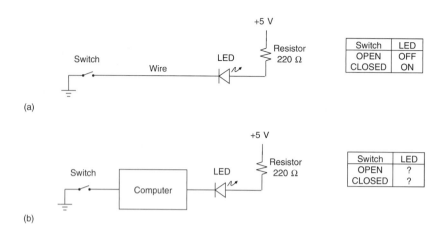

Figure 7-1.   A switch as an input device and an LED as an output device.

- address decode circuitry
- three-state buffers to sense state of switches
- type-D latches to store output data for LEDs

An interface to the 68000 is shown in Figure 7-2. The interface circuitry is overly complex, but it will serve to introduce important topics in input/output.

In Figure 7-2, eight switches and eight LEDs are

connected to the 68000's data bus. The switches are connected through three-state buffers, and the LEDs are connected through type-D latches. The connections are to the upper-byte of the 68000's data bus (D8–D15), therefore both the switches and the LEDs are positioned at *even* addresses in the memory map.

For the switches, the three-state buffers are *off* most of the time. The active-low enable input of

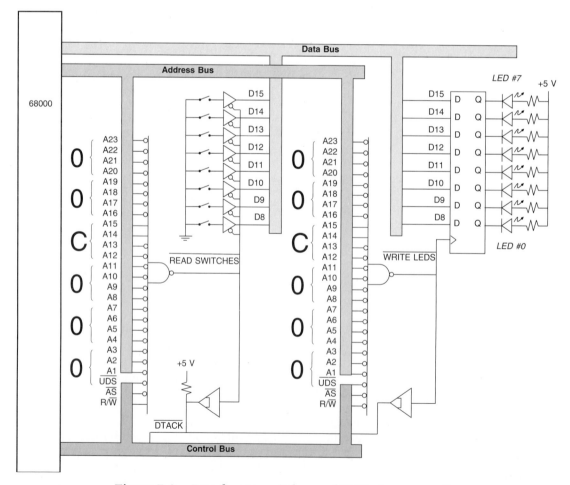

Figure 7-2.   Interface to switches and LEDs (conceptual).

the buffers is driven by a very large NAND gate. (The bubbles at some of the inputs are a convenient way of showing inverters.) This is the address decode circuitry. Very specific conditions must occur for the NAND gate's output to go low and turn on the three-state buffers. Reading directly from the figure, these conditions from the top of the NAND gate to the bottom are:

- a low on A23
- a low on A22
- a low on A21
- etc.
- a high on A15
- a high on A14
- a low on A13, etc.
- a high on R/$\overline{\text{W}}$

The upper 23 lines are from the 68000's address bus; the lower three signals are from the control bus. Recall from Chapter 2 that A0 is not present externally on the 68000. Rather, it is implicitly encoded in the control bus signals $\overline{\text{UDS}}$ (upper data strobe) and $\overline{\text{LDS}}$ (lower data strobe). With $\overline{\text{UDS}}$ connected as shown, it implies that A0 = 0 (i.e., the address is even) and transfers occur on the high-byte of the data bus. The complete address of the interface, then, is $00C000, as indicated on the left of the signals connected to the NAND gate. Of course, this address must be available on the 68000 target system. All RAM, ROM, and so on, must reside at other addresses.

Besides the 23 address lines and $\overline{\text{UDS}}$, the address decode circuitry includes two other signals. Address strobe ($\overline{\text{AS}}$) synchronizes the decode circuitry and prevents spurious selections when the address changes between cycles. Read/write (R/$\overline{\text{W}}$) connects to the NAND gate without a bubble, therefore it must be high to contribute to fulfilling the NAND function.

If we combine the pieces above, it is evident that the NAND gate's output only goes low when the following conditions exist:

- the address bus contains $00C000
- a valid cycle is taking place ($\overline{\text{AS}}$ = 0, $\overline{\text{UDS}}$ = 0)
- the cycle is a read cycle (R/$\overline{\text{W}}$ = 1)

These conditions are met in software by executing any instruction that reads memory location $00C000, such as

```
MOVE.B  $00C000,D0
```

This instruction reads a byte value from memory location $00C000 and places the byte in data register D0, bits 0–7. Of course, memory location $00C000 does not contain *memory* in the usual sense; it contains data from an input device, selected through address decode circuitry to reside at that address. This point is so important it deserves special emphasis:

> *Memory location $00C000 does not contain memory in the usual sense; it contains data from an input device, selected through address decode circuitry to reside at that address.*

The MOVE.B instruction above takes 16 machine cycles (see Appendix D). These consist of 4 memory-read cycles of 4 machine cycles each ($4 \times 4 = 16$). The first three memory-read cycles read the three instruction words (the opcode and the two-word absolute address).[1] The fourth memory read is the *execute* phase of the instruction. At this time, the CPU reads memory location $00C000 and the following take place:

- the address bus contains $00C000
- $\overline{\text{AS}}$ = 0
- R/$\overline{\text{W}}$ = 1
- the output of the NAND gate goes low
- the three-state buffers turn on
- the state of the switches passes through the buffers
- the buffers *drive* D8–D15 high or low according to the state of the switches
- the data are latched into the low-byte of data register D0
- $\overline{\text{DTACK}}$ goes low
- the cycle is terminated

Recall from Chapter 2 that $\overline{\text{DTACK}}$ must pulse low as acknowledgement to the CPU that the cycle can be terminated. The timing for MOVE.B is illustrated in Figure 7-3. The switches are read during the fourth memory-read cycle. Note that the timing conforms to the same restrictions as any memory-read cycle, as presented in Chapter 2. The difference is that switches are read rather than a RAM location.

And there we have it! We have just illustrated the union of software and hardware in designing interfaces to I/O devices. From here the possibilities are limitless.

---

[1] Note: The MOVE.B instruction must use absolute long addressing because the I/O address has A15 = 1. If absolute short addressing were used, the address $C000 would sign-extend to $FFC000 upon execution.

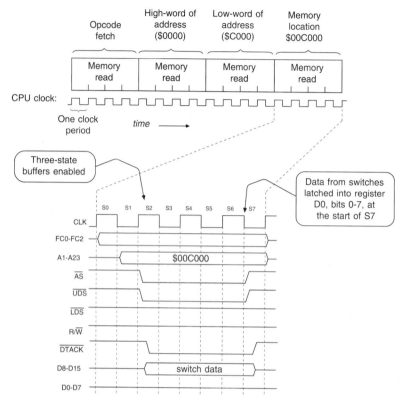

**Figure 7-3.**    Timing for MOVE.B $00C000,D0.

## 7.2.2.    *Interface to LEDs as Output*

Output to the LEDs is straightforward and very similar to the input interface described in Figure 7-2. For output, data travel out on the CPU's data bus and are grabbed (latched) by the output device. The D-inputs of the latch sense the state of data bus lines D8–D15. The clock input to the latch is driven by the address decode circuit. The decode circuit is identical to that for the switches, except R/$\overline{W}$ is inverted. Although the same address is used, the cycle must be a write cycle for the NAND output to pulse low. Since a read cycle and a write cycle cannot take place simultaneously, there is no problem using the same address for the LEDs and switches. The following instruction writes data from the low-byte of D0 to the LEDs:

```
MOVE.B  D0,$00C000
```

For example, the following instruction turns on the two least-significant LEDs and turns off the others:

```
MOVE.B  #%11111100,$00C000
```

At this point, we can write software to establish a link between the switches and the LEDs. The simplest program to consider is a *wire* program. For each switch we want a *virtual* connection to the corresponding LED, such that the LED turns on if the switch is closed or turns off if the switch is open. The program is shown in Figure A.

**Example 7-1:** For the program in Figure A, what is the time delay ($t_D$) between a switch changing and the update to the corresponding LED? (Assume a 68000 operating at 4 MHz.)

**Solution:** $t_D$ is from 5 µs (best case) to 14.5 µs (worst case)

**Discussion:** Consider the linear representation of our program in Figure 7-4. Each MOVE.B instruction takes 16 machine cycles, as looked up in Appendix D. These consist of memory-read cycles and memory-write cycles that require 4 machine cycles each. The first instruction requires 3 read cycles to fetch the instruction words and a single read cycle to read address $00C000 (the switches), for a total of 16 machine cycles. The second instruction requires 3 read cycles to read the instruction and a single

**Figure A.**
```
2 00001000 10390000 WIRE    MOVE.B  $C000,D0  ;read switches
  00001004 C000
3 00001006 13C00000         MOVE.B  D0,$C000  ;update LEDs
  0000100A C000
4 0000100C 60F2             BRA     WIRE      ;repeat
```

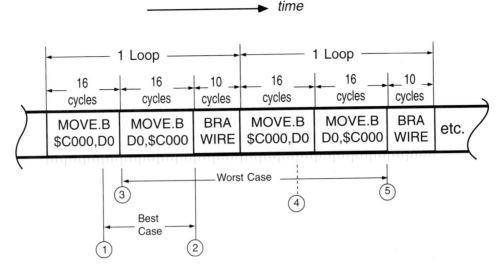

Figure 7-4.   Instruction sequence for *wire* program.

write cycle to output data from D0 to address $00C000 (the LEDs). The BRA instruction requires 10 clock cycles.

The *best case* calculation proceeds as follows. If a switch changes state just *before* the read cycle that senses this change ("1" in Figure 7-4), the change is reflected in the next update to the LEDs, at the end of the write cycle in the next instruction ("2"). This is the fastest update possible with this program. The delay is the number of machine cycles ($n$) multiplied by the cycle time of the CPU clock ($t_C$). Machine cycles are shown as small ticks below the instructions in Figure 7-4. Counting the ticks from "1" to "2," $n = 20$. With a CPU clock of 4 MHz, $t_C = 1/4 = 0.25$ μs, therefore

$$\begin{aligned} t_D &= n \times t_C \\ &= 20 \times 0.25 \\ &= 5 \text{ μs} \end{aligned}$$

The *worst case* calculation proceeds as follows. If the switch changes state just *after* the read cycle that senses this change ("3"), then the change is not detected until the next read of address $00C000 ("4"). The update is delayed until the subsequent write to $00C000 ("5"). The number of machine cycles ($n$) between "3" and "5" is 58, therefore

$$\begin{aligned} t_D &= n \times t_C \\ &= 58 \times 0.25 \\ &= 14.5 \text{ μs} \end{aligned} \quad \blacksquare$$

Example 7-1 has important implications for the design of control systems using microprocessors such as the 68000. The switch-to-LED connection in Fig. 7-1a is extremely fast. The time delay is limited only by the speed of electrons along a wire and by the turn-on time of the LED. When a computer is introduced as an intermediary, the relationships between inputs and output can be very flexible and powerful; however, the time delays are substantial in comparison to *direct* connections not under software control.

In most human interface situations, the delays are inconsequential. For example, in an automobile dashboard display indicating *low gas*, it makes no difference whether the display lights in 10 μs vs. 10 ms after sensing the gas tank level. However, in control systems such as those for antilock braking, delays on the order of a few hundred microseconds may be extremely important in overall system performance. (See also, Question 1 at the end of this chapter.)

**Example 7-2:** With reference to Figure 7-2, write a program that turns on LED #0 and then rotates the position of the LED that is on left at a rate of 1 Hz. After LED #7 is on, turn on LED #0 again, and repeat continually.

**Solution:** See below (continued on page 164).

```
2 0003640E        COUNT   EQU     222222
3 0000C000        PORT    EQU     $C000
4                 *
5                 * Initialize
6                 *
7 00001000 207C0000        MOVEA.L #PORT,A0      ;A0 points to LEDs
  00001004 C000
8 00001006 103C00FE        MOVE.B  #%11111110,D0 ;light LED #0
9                 *
```

*Continued.*

```
10                              * Main Loop
11                              *
12 0000100A 1080    LOOP    MOVE.B   D0,(A0)      ;write to LEDs
13 0000100C 2E3C0003         MOVE.L   #COUNT,D7    ;initialize delay count
   00001010 640E
14 00001012 6104            BSR.S    DELAY        ;delay 1 sec.
15 00001014 E318            ROL.B    #1,D0        ;rotate LED data
16 00001016 60F2            BRA      LOOP         ;repeat
17                          *
18                          * Delay Subroutine
19                          *
20 00001018 5387    DELAY   SUBQ.L   #1,D7        ;decrement count
21 0000101A 66FC            BNE      DELAY        ;    until zero,
22 0000101C 4E75            RTS                   ;    then return
```

**Discussion:** The program contains three sections: initialize, main loop, and a delay subroutine. In the initialize section, A0 is set up as a pointer to the LED output port (line 7), and D0 is set up with the correct pattern of 1s and 0s to light LED #0 (line 8). In the main loop, the LEDs are updated by writing the content of data register D0 to address $00C000 (line 12). Then, the appropriate count is placed in D7 and a delay subroutine is called. After returning, the LED data in D0 undergo a left circular rotate (ROL). This shifts the *zero-bit* left one position so the next update turns on LED #1, and so on.

The delay subroutine implements a time delay by repeatedly decrementing a count until it reaches zero. The subroutine receives COUNT in D7 from the main program. The SUBQ and BNE instructions each execute COUNT times. SUBQ takes 8 machine cycles (see Appendix D). BNE takes 10 machine cycles when the branch is taken and 8 machine cycles when the branch is not taken. The branch is taken COUNT $-1$ times. When the count reaches zero, the branch

test fails and the program falls through to the RTS instruction. RTS, which executes only once, takes 16 machine cycles. The exact time delay of the subroutine is

$$t_D = (8 \times COUNT + 10 \times (COUNT-1) + 8 + 16) \times t_C$$

where $t_C$ is the machine cycle period (0.25 μs @ 4 MHz). For large counts, the delay is approximately

$$t_D = 18 \times COUNT \times t_C$$

A one-second delay is obtained using

$$COUNT = 1,000,000 / (18 \times 0.25) = 222,222 \quad \blacksquare$$

## 7.3. FULL DECODING VS. PARTIAL DECODING

The circuit in Figure 7-2 uses **full decoding.** All the 68000's address lines were used in decoding

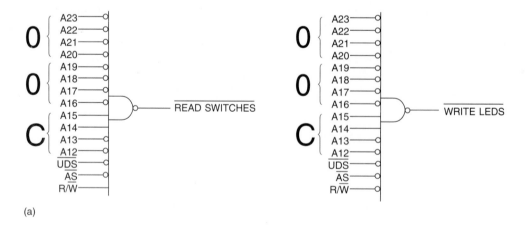

(a)

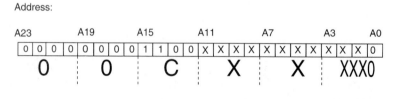

(b)

Figure 7-5.   Example of partial decoding. (a) Logic, (b) Addressing.

the I/O address. Although this is reasonable to illustrate the concept of address decoding, it is impractical for many microprocessor-based systems. The logic can be simplified by using **partial decoding.** Since the 68000 has a very large address space, it is practical to reserve a large block of addresses for I/O. For example, if we reserve the entire 16K block at $00C000 for the LEDs and switches in Figure 7-2, then the decoding can be simplified as shown in Figure 7-5.

The circuits in Figure 7-5a do not use address lines A1–A11, so the decoded address is only a partial address (Figure 7-5b). For simplicity, the circuit to generate $\overline{DTACK}$ is missing in the figure, but it is still needed.

Partial decoding is also called **reflected decoding** because the address of the I/O device *reflects* itself to other locations. Switches selected with the decode circuitry in Figure 7-5a are read just as easily through address $00C0F0 as with address $00C000.

**Example 7-3:** Through how many addresses does the decoding circuit in Figure 7-5a reflect itself?

**Solution:** 2048

**Discussion** Eleven address lines (A1–A11) are unused: $2^{11} = 2048$. Remember, there is an implicit assumption of A0 = 0, since the three-state buffers connect to the upper-byte of the 68000's data bus (see Figure 7-2). ∎

The interface in Figure 7-5a is still too awkward. To build it would require too many gates. In many designs, it is critical to minimize the gate and chip

count. This means the reflected decoding idea must be taken to the extreme.

Note also that the partial decoding idea applies to memory ICs as well as to I/O devices. Figure 7-6 shows a minimal decoding interface for a complete small-scale 68000 system with

- two 16K ROMs
- one 16K RAM
- eight switches
- eight LEDs

The circuit in Figure 7-6a is simple and economical. If the memory and I/O requirements of the intended system are fixed as described above, the circuit in Figure 7-6a is a perfectly reasonable approach to address decoding. (Limited expansion is possible with minor changes.)

**Example 7-4:** Through how many addresses does the switch decoding in Figure 7-6a reflect itself?

**Solution:** $2^{21} = 2,097,152$

**Discussion:** Twenty-one address lines are not used. These consist of A1-A13 and A16-A23. There is an implicit A0 = 0, as noted earlier. ∎

**Example 7-5:** Is the RAM in Figure 7-6a also selected using partial decoding?

**Solution:** Yes

**Discussion:** The RAM occupies addresses $008000 through $00BFFF. More generally, it appears in every 16K block with A15 = 1 and A14 = 0. That is, it reflects itself to the 16K blocks starting at $018000, $028000, $038000, and so on, up to $FF8000. The 16K RAM

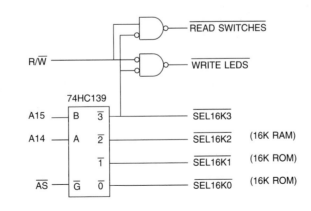

(a)

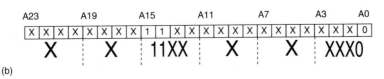

(b)

Figure 7-6.  Partial decoding for a complete 68000 system. (a) Circuit, (b) Addressing.

appears in a total of 256 16K blocks (all combinations for A16 through A23). ■

## 7.4. PROGRAM-CONDITIONAL I/O

The I/O discussed thus far pertains to very trivial devices, such as switches for input or LEDs for output. Many I/O devices are considerably more complex. For example, a printer is an output device for which interfaces can be designed similar to those just discussed. However, a printer is much slower than a typical CPU. If the CPU attempts to send a text file to a printer, the timing of the transfers must be carefully coordinated so as not to lose data. In particular, the CPU will spend a considerable amount of time waiting for the printer to finish with the data previously sent.

To facilitate data transfers, interfaces to devices such as printers, keyboards, and so on, include a status flag to indicate when they can be read or written. The CPU interrogates the **status flag** continually until a *device ready* condition is indicated. Then the CPU reads or writes data. The status flag is reset after the transfer so the next test correctly indicates *device not ready*.

As an analogy, think of a status flag like a *flag* on the side of a rural mailbox. Instead of going outdoors and looking inside the mailbox to see if mail has arrived, a protocol exists between the letter carrier and the residents of each house. A resident simply looks at the mailbox (through the living-room window). If the flag is down, no mail is waiting. Subsequently, the letter carrier places mail in the mailbox and raises the flag. The next time the resident looks, the flag position indicates *mail has arrived*. When the resident retrieves the mail, the flag is turned downward indicating *no mail* until the next time the letter carrier arrives.

When a device interface includes a status flag that is checked through software prior to a data transfer, the method of I/O is called **program-conditional I/O.** The process of checking the status flags prior to a data transfer is depicted using flowcharts in Figure 7-7 for input and output devices with status flags.

We now develop the idea of program-conditional I/O through a hypothetical example. Figure 7-8 shows a keyboard interface with an 8-bit data input port and a 1-bit status input port.

The keyboard operates as follows: Each time a key is hit, the logic circuitry within the keyboard places the ASCII code for the key on the KBD DATA lines and pulses the KEYHIT line (see Figure

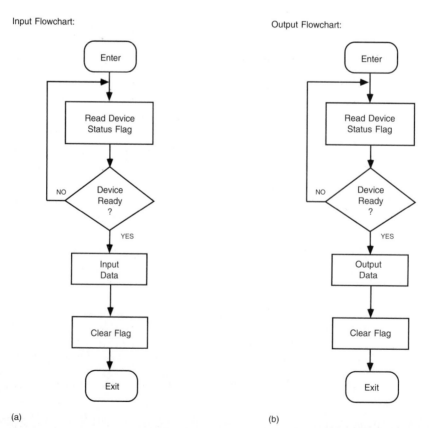

Figure 7-7.   Flowcharts for program-conditional I/O. (a) Input, (b) Output.

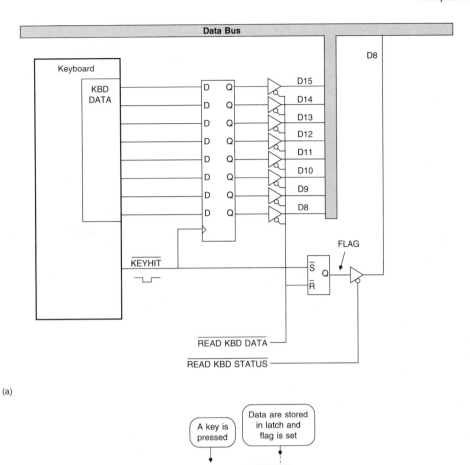

Figure 7-8.  Keyboard interface. (a) Schematic, (b) timing.

7-8b). The pulse on $\overline{\text{KEYHIT}}$ stores the data in an 8-bit latch and sets the keyboard status flag.

The interface to the keyboard consists of eight three-state buffers for keyboard data and one three-state buffer for the keyboard status flag. The signals $\overline{\text{READ KBD DATA}}$ and $\overline{\text{READ KBD STATUS}}$ are generated from address decode circuitry, as described earlier. For the purpose of this example, we assume address decoding is present as follows:

| Address | Function |
| --- | --- |
| $00C000 | Read Keyboard Data (on D8–D15) |
| $00C002 | Read Keyboard Status (on D8) |

The fact that the interface uses the upper-byte of the 68000's data bus means that even addresses are used for the keyboard interface. Regardless, bytes read from these addresses are stored in the bits 0–7 of the destination register.

The flowchart in Figure 7-7a serves as a guide to write the interface software. Note that an explicit clear of the keyboard status flag is not necessary since the $\overline{\text{READ KBD DATA}}$ strobe connects to the $\overline{\text{RESET}}$ line of the status flag latch *and* to the enable input of the three-state data buffers. Below is a READKBD subroutine:

```
 2   0000C000              KEYBOARD  EQU     $00C000     ;keyboard interface address
 3   00000000              DATA      EQU     0           ;offset for data register
 4   00000002              STATUS    EQU     2           ;offset for status register
 5   00001000   207C0000   READKBD   MOVEA.L #KEYBOARD,A0 ;use A0 as pointer
     00001004   C000
 6   00001006   10280002   AGAIN     MOVE.B  STATUS(A0),D0  ;read status flag
 7   0000100A   02000001             ANDI.B  #1,D0          ;clear other bits
 8   0000100E   67F6                 BEQ     AGAIN          ;if clear, check again
 9   00001010   10280000             MOVE.B  DATA(A0),D0    ;read keyboard data
10   00001014   4E75                 RTS                    ;done
```

The testing of the keyboard status flag occurs in lines 6–8. The first MOVE.B reads the keyboard status flag and places it in bit 0 of D0. Since the status flag is only one bit, the other seven bits read into D0 are indeterminate following the status read. The ANDI.B instruction clears bits 1–7 of D0; thus, the entire low-order byte of D0 is zero if the flag is clear or non-zero if the flag is set. The appropriate test is therefore BEQ (branch if equal zero). The branch returns to the MOVE.B instruction to read the keyboard status flag again. These three instructions repeat until the status flag is set causing the branch test to fail. When this occurs, the program continues through to the final MOVE.B instruction (line 9) which reads the keyboard data into bits 0–7 of data register D0. Reading the keyboard data also clears the status flag.

**Example 7-6:** Illustrate a shorter version of the READKBD subroutine.

**Solution:** See Figure B.

**Discussion:** The subroutine in Example 7-5 was 22 bytes. There are numerous ways to rework the subroutine. The version in Figure B is only 18 bytes long. The ANDI instruction (4 bytes) has been replaced with ROR (2 bytes). This places the keyboard status flag in the CCR's carry flag; so, the correct test is BCC in the following instruction. The last MOVE instruction removes the DATA offset which is zero and therefore unnecessary. This saves a further 2 bytes (but makes the routine slightly less readable). ∎

**Example 7-7:** Illustrate how to rework READKBD so that it does not destroy A0. Include an appropriate comment header stating:
- the name and operation of the subroutine
- entry conditions
- exit conditions
- subroutines used

**Solution:** See Figure C.

**Discussion:** The only change introduced is saving A0 on the stack at the beginning of the subroutine (line 12), and restoring it from the stack at the end (line 18). Note the clarity introduced by the comment block. It is easy to

**Figure B.**

```
2 0000C000                 KEYBOARD EQU     $00C000
3 00000002                 STATUS   EQU     2
4 00001000 207C0000 READKBD MOVEA.L #KEYBOARD,A0
  00001004 C000
5 00001006 10280002 AGAIN   MOVE.B  STATUS(A0),D0
6 0000100A E218             ROR.B   #1,D0
7 0000100C 64F8             BCC     AGAIN
8 0000100E 1010             MOVE.B  (A0),D0
9 00001010 4E75             RTS
```

**Figure C.**

```
 1              ***************************************************
 2              * READKBD - READ KeyBoarD data                   *
 3              *                                                 *
 4              * Entry: no conditions                           *
 5              * Exit:  data in D0[0:7]; D0[8:31] intact        *
 6              *        all other registers intact              *
 7              * Uses:  no subroutines used                     *
 8              ***************************************************
 9 00001000               ORG      $1000
10 0000C000     KEYBOARD  EQU      $00C000
11 00000002     STATUS    EQU      2
12 00001000 2F08 READKBD  MOVE.L   A0,-(A7) ;save A0 on stack
13 00001002 207C0000      MOVEA.L  #KEYBOARD,A0
   00001006 C000
14 00001008 10280002 AGAIN MOVE.B  STATUS(A0),D0
15 0000100C E218         ROR.B    #1,D0
16 0000100E 64F8         BCC      AGAIN
17 00001010 1010         MOVE.B   (A0),D0
18 00001012 205F         MOVE.L   (A7)+,A0 ;restore A0
19 00001014 4E75         RTS
```

**Figure D.**

```
*********************************************************
*  INLINE - INput a LINE of characters from the keyboard  *
*                                                        *
*        Entry:      A0 points to line buffer            *
*        Exit:       data in buffer; null byte at end;   *
*                    all registers intact                *
*        Uses:       READKBD                             *
*********************************************************
```

gain a good sense of the operation of the subroutine just by examining the comments. ■

**Example 7-8:** Figure D contains comment header for an INLINE subroutine. Write the subroutine.

**Solution:** See Figure E.

**Discussion:** Before calling INLINE from a main program, A0 is initialized with the starting address of a buffer where the characters are stored. For example, the following instructions input a line of characters from the keyboard and place them in RAM starting at address $009000:

```
        MOVEA.L  #$009000,A0
        BSR      INLINE
```

There are several shortcomings of the INLINE subroutine shown in Figure E. First, the subroutine does not permit editing (backing up) as characters are entered from the keyboard. Also, there is no indication of the maximum length of the buffer and no checking for an input line that is too long. We'll leave it for the reader to add these improvements. ■

**Example 7-9:** A fast typist enters characters at about five keystrokes per second. At this rate, how many times (approximately) is the keyboard status checked using the software in Figure C for each entry? (Assume a 68000 with a 4 MHz clock.)

**Solution:** 26,667

**Discussion:** At five keystrokes per second, a key is hit every 1/5 second, or every 200,000 μs. The loop to check the status flag consists of the following three instructions:

```
AGAIN MOVE.B STATUS(A0),D0 ;12 cycles
      ROR.B  #1,D0          ;8 cycles
      BCC    AGAIN          ;10/8 cycles
```

The number of CPU cycles in each instruction is indicated above. BCC takes 10 cycles if the branch is taken, 8 if the branch is not taken.

Most of the time, the branch is taken. Summing these, each test of the status flag takes 30 machine cycles, or $30 \times 0.25$ μs = 7.5 μs on a 4 MHz 68000. The number of status checks per character typed is about

$$200,000 / 7.5 \approx 26,667$$

Obviously, the software is largely busy checking the keyboard status. ■

## 7.5. MEMORY-MAPPED I/O VS. I/O-MAPPED I/O

The I/O examples above use **memory-mapped I/O.** This is because the device registers occupy memory addresses. Accessing devices is the same as accessing memory locations. As noted, the interface to devices is similar to the interface to RAM or ROM.

Some CPU architectures provide a separate I/O space for interfacing to I/O devices. This is called **I/O-mapped I/O** or **isolated I/O.** Most Intel microprocessors, such as the 8085 or 80386, use I/O-mapped I/O; whereas Motorola microprocessors, such as the 6809 or 68000, use memory-mapped I/O. In either case, the same physical address lines are used.

On Intel microprocessors using I/O-mapped I/O, a control bus signal called $\overline{IO}/M$ distinguishes between a memory reference ($\overline{IO}/M = 1$) and an I/O reference ($\overline{IO}/M = 0$). I/O operations are limited to *IN port* and *OUT port* instructions. Table 7-1 summarizes the differences between memory-mapped I/O and I/O-mapped I/O. Note that systems supporting I/O-mapped I/O do not preclude the possibility of using memory-mapped I/O.

**Figure E.**

```
 2 0000000D           CR       EQU      $0D
 3 00001000 48E78080   INLINE   MOVEM.L  D0/A0,-(A7)   ;save D0 & A0
 4 00001004 61000014   INLINE2  BSR      READKBD       ;get character
 5 00001008 10C0                MOVE.B   D0,(A0)+      ;store; increment A0
 6 0000100A 0C00000D            CMPI.B   #CR,D0        ;char. = CR?
 7 0000100E 6702                BEQ.S    DONE          ;yes: end of line
 8 00001010 60F2                BRA      INLINE2       ;no: get another
 9 00001012 4210       DONE     CLR.B    (A0)          ;null byte at end
10 00001014 4CDF0101            MOVEM.L  (A7)+,D0/A0   ;restore D0 & A0
11 00001018 4E75                RTS                    ;return
12 0000101A 4E75       READKBD  RTS                    ;put READKBD here
```

Table 7-1.  Memory-mapped I/O vs. I/O-mapped I/O.

|  | Memory-mapped I/O | I/O-mapped I/O |
|---|---|---|
| Advantages | • any instruction that can access memory can access I/O devices<br>• control bus requires one less signal | • full memory space available for RAMs, etc.<br>• separate I/O space is conceptually simple |
| Disadvantages | • memory space divided between memory ICs and I/O devices | • only accessible through IN and OUT instructions<br>• extra control bus signal required |

## 7.6.  PERIPHERAL INTERFACE ICS

By way of introduction, the interfaces shown thus far used standard logic devices, such as registers, gates, and three-state buffers. In practice, many interfaces to peripheral devices utilize a single custom-purpose interface IC, with a minimum of additional components. Such ICs come in many forms and are usually known by their acronyms. Table 7-2 gives examples of peripheral interface ICs from the 68000 family.

Although we defer specific examples until Chapter 10, Figure 7-9 shows the general idea of interfacing a peripheral interface IC to a CPU's buses.

The concept of address decoding applies precisely as before. There are two distinctions to note: (1) the peripheral interface is both *readable* and *writable,* and (2) there are multiple registers within the IC. The example shows a peripheral IC with eight internal registers, consisting of four read-only registers and four write-only registers. Two address lines in conjunction with the R/$\overline{\text{W}}$ control signal provide access to each register.

Although the purpose of the internal registers depends on the type of device, most peripheral interface ICs include a control or command register and a status register. The control register is a write-only register initialized through software to select modes of operation, and so forth. The status register

Table 7-2.    Examples of 68000-Compatible Peripheral Interface ICs.

| Device | Acronym | Full Name | Features |
|---|---|---|---|
| 68450 | DMAC | Direct Memory Access Controller | • four DMA channels<br>• 4 Mbytes/second transfer rate |
| 68681 | DUART | Dual Asynchronous Receiver/Transmitter | • two asyncronous receiver/transmitter channels<br>• 1 Mbits/second maximum transfer rate<br>• quadruple-buffered receiver<br>• double-buffered transmitter<br>• multi-function 6-bit input port<br>• multi-function 8-bit output port<br>• 16-bit programmable counter/timer |
| 68605 | XPC | X.25 Protocol Controller | • implements X.25 protocol<br>• DMA transfer of information frames<br>• programmable time-out and re-try<br>• 16- or 32-bit CRC generation and checking |
| 68230 | PI/T | Parallel Interface/Timer | • two 8-bit fully programmable I/O ports<br>• programmable handshake options<br>• 24-bit programmable timer<br>• separate port and interrupt service requests<br>• five separate interrupt vectors |
| 68901 | MFP | Multifunction Peripheral | • eight programmable I/O pins<br>• 16-source interrupt controller<br>• four timers<br>• single-channel full-duplex synchronous/asynchronous receiver/transmitter |

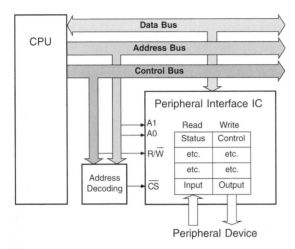

Figure 7-9. Interface using a peripheral interface IC.

is a read-only register interrogated through software to check conditions in the interface (e.g., a character has been received). Figure 7-9 also shows a read-only input port and a write-only output port. The ports (registers) are in fact a direct link to pins on the peripheral ICs. When software writes to the output register, the data are written to latches that drive output pins on the device. Several registers are labeled *etc.* to emphasize the general-purpose and programmable qualities of peripheral interface ICs.

If the CPU in Figure 7-9 is a 68000, then the connection to the peripheral interface IC's lines A1 and A0 uses the 68000's address bus lines A2 and A1 respectively. (There is no A0 on the 68000.) This means that the internal registers are accessible through consecutive even or odd addresses. If the data lines of the peripheral interface IC connect to the upper-byte of the 68000's data bus (D8–D15), the internal registers are accessible through consecutive even addresses. If the data lines of the peripheral interface IC connect to the lower-byte of the 68000's data bus (D0–D7), the internal registers are accessible through consecutive odd addresses.

**Example 7-10.** Suppose the peripheral interface IC in Figure 7-9 interfaces to a 68000 using partial decoding at odd addresses using the 64K block starting at address $080001. Illustrate an address decoding circuit.

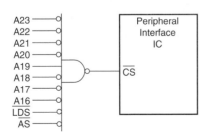

Figure 7-10. Address decoding for peripheral interface IC.

**Solution:** The address decode circuit is shown in Figure 7-10.

**Discussion:** Address decoding for 64K blocks requires the upper 8 address lines only (A16–A23). Since the peripheral interface IC's internal registers are accessed at odd addresses, lower data strobe ($\overline{\text{LDS}}$) is also required. Address strobe ($\overline{\text{AS}}$) is required (as always) to prevent spurious selections during address transitions. Note that an acknowledgement on $\overline{\text{DTACK}}$ is also required (as in Figure 7-2) to properly terminate read or write cycles to the IC. Finally, we should emphasize that the circuit in Figure 7-10 is only an example. In practice, the address decode circuitry is designed in consideration of the entire memory and I/O requirements of the system (as in Figure 7-6). ■

## 7.7.    INTERRUPT-INITIATED I/O

An interrupt is the occurrence of an event that causes temporary suspension of a program while the condition that caused the event is serviced by another program. The system responds asynchronously to an event and deals with it. Interrupts are hardware-initiated and asynchronous. *Hardware-initiated* means they are generated by an external signal driving a control bus line on the CPU. The external signal is asserted by a device (e.g., keyboard, printer, disk drive) when it needs the CPU's attention, usually for a transfer of data. *Asynchronous* means interrupts occur at any time (e.g., a human presses a key on a keyboard).

Using interrupts, a system gives the illusion of doing many things simultaneously. Of course, the CPU can only execute one instruction at a time; however, interrupts can effectively *time-slice* the CPU's instruction sequencing among several resources.

The routine, or program, that services the interrupt is called an **interrupt service routine (ISR)** or **interrupt handler.** The main program executes at **base-level,** and the interrupts execute at **interrupt-level.** The terms *foreground* (base-level) and *background* (interrupt-level) are also used. This is illustrated in Figure 7-11.

### 7.7.1.    *Implementation on the* 68000

Most CPUs support several interrupt sources, and the 68000 is no different. There are seven distinct interrupt sources on the 68000. Instead of providing seven separate pins on the CPU device for each, interrupts are encoded and presented to the CPU on three inputs pins, $\overline{\text{IPL2}}$, $\overline{\text{IPL1}}$, and $\overline{\text{IPL0}}$. Although the encoding requires a separate external IC, the savings in pins makes this approach

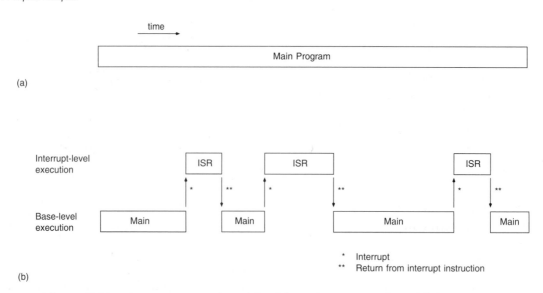

Figure 7-11.    Program execution: (a) without interrupts, (b) with interrupts.

worthwhile. The number associated with each interrupt source (1 through 7) serves not only to distinguish between interrupts, but to create a priority scheme among interrupts. Interrupt 7 is the highest priority, whereas interrupt 1 is the lowest. The possibilities for $\overline{IPL2}$, $\overline{IPL1}$, and $\overline{IPL0}$ are given in Table 7-3.

Normally $\overline{IPL2}$, $\overline{IPL1}$, and $\overline{IPL0}$ are high, signaling no interrupt. If any of these lines is driven low, an interrupt request occurs. The interrupt is serviced at the end of the current instruction if the priority is higher than the current processor priority (and no higher-level exception condition exists). The current processor priority is reflected in the status register in the interrupt mask bits (I2, I1, and I0). If, for example, the mask bits contain "4," then interrupt requests on levels 1, 2, 3, and 4 are *masked*—ignored.

**Example 7-11:** The 68000's status register contains $2515. What interrupts are enabled?

**Solution:** Interrupts 7 and 6

**Discussion:** The interrupt mask bits in the status register (bits 10–8) indicate a current processor priority of "5," as shown below.

I2    I1    I0

1    0    1

Either the CPU is currently responding to a level-5 interrupt, or the interrupt mask bits were explicitly set through software to mask subsequent interrupts below level 6. Regardless, the CPU will only respond to interrupts at level 7 or 6 (i.e., higher than the current processor priority). It should be emphasized that the interrupt input signals ($\overline{IPL2}$, $\overline{IPL1}$, $\overline{IPL0}$) do not necessarily correspond to the interrupt mask bits in the SR (I2, I1, and I0).    ■

Interrupt 7 is *non-maskable* and is always serviced at the end of the current instruction. Even if the interrupt bits are set to $111_2$, the appearance of a level-7 interrupt generates an interrupt that is responded to by the CPU.

Interrupt processing on the 68000 is one type of exception. Regardless of the level of the interrupt request, the acceptance of the interrupt initiates a

Table 7-3.    Interrupt Priority Conditions on $\overline{IPL2}$, $\overline{IPL1}$, and $\overline{IPL0}$.

| Signal | | | | | | |
|---|---|---|---|---|---|---|
| IPL2 | IPL1 | IPL0 | Interrupt | Condition | Maskable | Priority |
| 1 | 1 | 1 | 0 | No interrupt | - | - |
| 1 | 1 | 0 | 1 | Interrupt | Yes | Lowest |
| 1 | 0 | 1 | 2 | Interrupt | Yes | (etc.) |
| 1 | 0 | 0 | 3 | Interrupt | Yes | (etc.) |
| 0 | 1 | 1 | 4 | Interrupt | Yes | (etc.) |
| 0 | 1 | 0 | 5 | Interrupt | Yes | (etc.) |
| 0 | 0 | 1 | 6 | Interrupt | Yes | (etc.) |
| 0 | 0 | 0 | 7 | Interrupt | No | Highest |

strict sequence of events known as the Exception Processing Sequence. There are four steps:

1. Update the status register.
   (a) Make an internal copy of the current SR contents.
   (b) Set the S bit (privilege mode is set to *supervisor*).
   (c) Clear the T bit (tracing is suppressed).
   (d) Set the interrupt mask bits (I2, I1, & I0) to the level of the interrupt.
2. Determine the vector number of the exception (interrupt).
   (a) Execute an interrupt acknowledge (IACK) cycle.
3. Save the current CPU status.
   (a) Save program counter on stack.
   (b) Save status register (from step 1a) on stack.
4. Fetch the new value of program counter.
   (a) Use vector number (from step 2) to read new value for PC (address of ISR).

Then, the ISR executes. At the end of the ISR, the RTE (return from exception) instruction is executed to return to the main program. RTE restores the PC and SR from the stack. The saving and restoring of the PC and SR allows for a smooth transition back to the interrupted program. The next instruction to execute is the one that would have executed had the interrupt not occurred.

It is perfectly reasonable for *interrupts to interrupt interrupts*. That is, if the interrupt mask bits are set to $000_2$, and then a level-4 interrupt request occurs, the interrupt is accepted and the steps outlined above take place. If during the level-4 ISR, a level-6 interrupt request occurs, it is accepted and responded to immediately (at the end of the current instruction). After the level-6 ISR completes with an RTE instruction, the CPU's state is restored accordingly and the level-4 ISR continues. When the level-4 ISR completes (with an RTE instruction), the CPU returns to normal (level-0) processing.

## 7.7.2. Interrupt Vectoring

Interrupt service routines can be located anywhere in the 68000's memory space. The address of the ISR is placed in the exception vector table near the bottom of the 68000's memory space (as presented in Chapter 6; see Table 6-2, Reset and Exception

Table 7-4. Autovectors for Automatic IACK Cycles.

| Interrupt | Vector Address (Autovector) |
|---|---|
| 0 | - |
| 1 | $000064 |
| 2 | $000068 |
| 3 | $00006C |
| 4 | $000070 |
| 5 | $000074 |
| 6 | $000078 |
| 7 | $00007C |

Vector Assignments). During the interrupt acknowledge (IACK) cycle (step 2 of the Exception Processing Sequence), the CPU fetches the address (from the vector table) and places it in the PC (step 4) to begin execution of the ISR.

*Autovectors*  There are two types of IACK cycles: automatic and user. For an automatic IACK cycle, the vector number (called an **autovector**) is predetermined. The vector number, or vector address, is given in Table 7-4 for each of the seven possible interrupts.

The distinction between automatic and user IACK cycles lies in the control bus signal that terminates the cycle. If the interrupting device asserts $\overline{VPA}$ (valid peripheral address) during the cycle (rather than $\overline{DTACK}$), then the CPU assumes an automatic cycle and fetches the address of the ISR from the address given in Table 7-4. The hardware mechanism for providing a $\overline{VPA}$ acknowledgement is identical to that for $\overline{DTACK}$ acknowledgements, as shown earlier in Figure 7-2.

*User Vectors*  For a user IACK cycle, the device provides an interrupt vector number on data bus lines D0–D7 during the IACK cycle and asserts $\overline{DTACK}$. The processor reads the interrupt vector (address of the ISR) from the address formed by multiplying the vector number by four, as given in Table 7-5.

Table 7-5. Vector Addresses for User IACK Cycles.

| Vector Number | Vector Address |
|---|---|
| 0 | $000000 |
| 1 | $000004 |
| 2 | $000008 |
| etc. | etc. |
| 255 | $0003FC |

**Figure F.**

| $\overline{INT7}$ | $\overline{INT6}$ | $\overline{INT5}$ | $\overline{INT4}$ | $\overline{INT3}$ | $\overline{INT2}$ | $\overline{INT1}$ |
|---|---|---|---|---|---|---|
| 1 | 1 | 1 | 0 | 1 | 0 | 0 |

Although there are 256 possible vector numbers, only 192 are specifically reserved for user interrupt vectors. These are vector numbers 64–255, as given in Chapter 6. Vector numbers 0–63 can still be used if the intent is to use the same routine as another exception. This possibility is most likely for a trap exception. That is, it is possible to use the same routine for a TRAP #n instruction and for a hardware interrupt. (See Question 6 at the end of this chapter.)

Although the *user* interrupt acknowledge cycle offers the greatest flexibility, autovector acknowledgement is easier to implement and is sufficient for most interrupt-driven configurations.

### 7.7.3. Interface Hardware for Interrupts

A typical hardware configuration to support interrupts on the 68000 is shown in Figure 7-12. The figure shows seven interrupt sources. $\overline{INT7}$ (NMI) is driven by a switch and uses autovectoring. The other interrupt sources can provide a user vector or an autovector.

The left side of the circuit in Figure 7-12 operates as follows: The interrupt inputs to the 68000 ($\overline{IPL2}$, $\overline{IPL1}$ and $\overline{IPL0}$) signal both an interrupt request and the priority level of the request, as noted earlier. The 74HC148, which drives these inputs, is a priority encoder with eight active-low inputs and three active-low outputs. The output code equals the highest active input signal. External sources (devices) connect to any of the seven interrupt inputs ($\overline{INT1}$ to $\overline{INT7}$) in configuring a complete interrupt-driven system. When a device drives an interrupt input low, the corresponding code appears on $\overline{IPL2}$, $\overline{IPL1}$, and $\overline{IPL0}$ (if no higher input is active) and an interrupt request is made pending.

**Example 7-12:** Assume the interrupt inputs in Figure 7-12 are in the state shown in Figure F.

(a) What devices are requesting interrupts?

(b) What signal levels are present on the 68000's inputs $\overline{IPL2}$, $\overline{IPL1}$, and $\overline{IPL0}$?

**Solution:** (a) devices 4, 2, and 1, (b) $\overline{IPL2} = 0$, $\overline{IPL1} = 1$, $\overline{IPL2} = 1$

**Discussion:** (a) The *active state* of the interrupt inputs is low. Since lines $\overline{INT4}$, $\overline{INT2}$, and $\overline{INT1}$ are low and the others are high, the devices driving lines 4, 2, and 1 are requesting interrupts; (b) since the highest active input to the 74HC148 is #4 ($\overline{INT4}$), the output code from the 74HC148 is *four*. The outputs are active low, so the signal levels are $011_2$. (Complement this binary number and the result is $100_2 = 4_{10}$.) Device #4's interrupt is serviced first. ∎

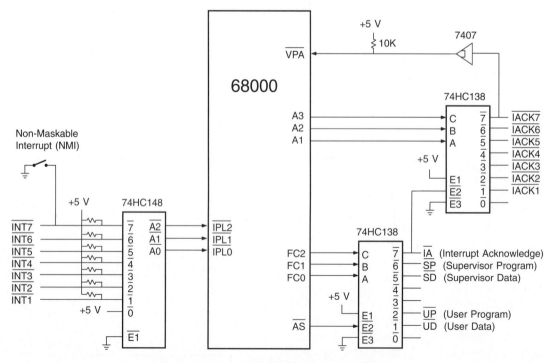

**Figure 7-12.   68000 interrupt circuitry.**

### 7.7.4. Interrupt Acknowledge Cycle

The second step in the exception processing sequence given earlier is the interrupt-acknowledge (IACK) cycle. If we think of the IACK cycle as a variation of a memory-read cycle, then its mystique vanishes. The following conditions occur during an IACK cycle:

- A4–A23 are high
- A1–A3 contain the level of the interrupt begin responded to
- FC0–FC2 contain $111_2$ indicating *interrupt-acknowledge cycle*
- $\overline{AS}$ is low
- R/$\overline{W}$ is high

The signals above are all outputs. They connect to two 74HC138 3-line to 8-line decoders in Figure 7-12, with the following effect: The function code lines plus $\overline{AS}$ drive the first 74HC138 in the figure. The code $111_2$ will appear since the 68000 is performing an IACK cycle. The $\overline{7}$ output, $\overline{IA}$ (interrupt acknowedge), goes active (low). $\overline{IA}$ along with A1–A3 drive the second 74HC138. If the interrupt being responded to is #4 (as in Example 7-12), then A3 = 1, A2 = 0, and A1 = 0. The 74HC138 output $\overline{IACK4}$ goes active (low). At this point, it is the responsibility of the interface circuitry for device #4 to detect the acknowledgement of its interrupt and respond in one of two ways:

User vector:  place a vector number on D0–D7 & activate $\overline{DTACK}$

or

Autovector:  activate $\overline{VPA}$

In Figure 7-12, a simple mechanism is illustrated for $\overline{INT7}$ to generate a $\overline{VPA}$ acknowledgement to an interrupt-acknowledge cycle. Although many devices are sophisticated and fully capable of providing a vector number for a user IACK cycle, many devices (e.g., a switch) include no such provision. The non-maskable interrupt in Figure 7-12 is an example. $\overline{INT7}$ is generated by depressing a switch. When $\overline{IACK7}$ goes low during the interrupt-acknowledge cycle, the cycle is terminated directly with an acknowledgement on $\overline{VPA}$ through a 7407 open-collector buffer with a 10K pull-up resistor. An open collector buffer is used since $\overline{VPA}$ is a bus signal. Other devices can respond similarly using wired-OR connections to $\overline{VPA}$.

**Example 7-13:** Assume the interrupt circuitry in Figure 7-10 is installed on a 68000 system with 32K of ROM (or EPROM) starting at address $000000 and 16K of RAM starting at address $008000. Assume further that the system contains 8 LEDs as output at address $00C000. Write a complete (ROMable) program to do the following:

1. Upon reset, turn off the LEDs to indicate a count of zero.

2. Each time INT7 occurs, increment an 8-bit count and update the LEDs accordingly.

**Solution:** See below.

```
 1 0000C000              LEDS   EQU    $C000
 2 00009000              STACK  EQU    $9000    ;top of RAM + 1
 3 00000000              ORG    0               ;EPROM begins at 0
 4 00000000 00009000     DC.L   STACK           ;SSP reset value
 5 00000004 00000400     DC.L   START           ;PC reset value
 6 0000007C              ORG    $00007C         ;INT 7 autovector
 7 0000007C 0000040E     DC.L   ISR
 8 00000400              ORG    $000400         ;Above vector space
 9                  *
10                  * Main Program
11                  *
12 00000400 4200    START  CLR.B  D0            ;clear count
13 00000402 1200    LOOP   MOVE.B D0,D1          ;copy count to D1
14 00000404 4601           NOT.B  D1            ;complement for LED interface
15 00000406 13C10000       MOVE.B D1,$C000;update LEDs
   0000040A C000
16 0000040C 60F4           BRA    LOOP          ;repeat
17                  *
18                  * Interrupt Service Routine
19                  *
20 0000040E 5200    ISR    ADDQ.B #1,D0          ;increment count
21 00000410 4E73           RTE                   ;return to main program
```

**Discussion:** This program contains only seven instructions, yet it includes several complex and challenging details. The requirement that the solution to this example should represent a *complete (ROMable) program* is extremely important in learning about interrupts. This way, we make no assumptions about features present on a laboratory computer. We are working at the lowest level possible — with the defined architecture of the 68000 CPU (rather than with features of an implementation).

The program above could be burned into an EPROM and exist as the only software on a complete 68000 system. So long as the memory space is configured as stated (ROM, RAM, I/O), the LEDs will light as specified. To understand the program we begin by assuming the 68000 has just been reset. After the reset line reaches a logic 1 level, the CPU begins its start-up sequence. The CPU reads two longwords from memory. First, it reads a longword from address $000000 and places it in the system stack pointer (SSP, A7); then it reads a longword from address $000004 and places it in the program counter (PC). The two DC.L directives immediately after ORG $0 determine these values (lines 4 and 5): the SSP is initialized with $009000 and the PC is initialized with $000400. The first write to the stack will be in RAM at word address $008FFE. The first instruction to execute is at address $000400. The reset operation will leave $2700 in the status register, so the CPU is in supervisor state with all interrupts masked except INT7, the non-maskable interrupt.

The main program contains five instructions (lines 12–16). Data register D0 holds the count of the number of pulses detected on the switch. It is initialized to zero. Next, the count is moved to D1, which is then complemented and sent to the LEDs. (Remember, a zero turns an LED on; see Figure 7-2.) And that's it. The main programs just sit in a loop performing these simple operations.

When the switch is pressed, $\overline{INT7}$ goes low and the encoded interrupt priority lines are all driven low, signaling a non-maskable interrupt request. The 68000 will finish the current instruction (whatever it happens to be) and process the interrupt. An interrupt acknowledge cycle is executed and the PC and SR are saved on the stack. The cycle uses an autovector because the acknowledgement to the IACK bus cycle is on $\overline{VPA}$ (see Figure 7-12). The $\overline{INT7}$ autovector is at address $00007C (see Table 7-4). The DC.L following the ORG $7C statement ensures that the address of the interrupt service routine is in this address (line 7). The CPU reads this address and places the value read in the PC. The ISR executes. D0 is incremented (line 20) and the ISR terminates with RTE (line 21). Return from exception restores the PC and SR from the stack causing program execution to continue where it left off. The next time the main loop writes to the LEDs, the count is one greater than the previous write. ■

The description above is quite lengthy. However, it should be reviewed until the idea and process are clear. Example 7-13 represents, arguably, the simplest possible implementation of interrupts on the 68000. Our goal is to take a very simple example and understand it in as much detail as possible.

### 7.7.5.    Let the ISRs Do the Work

There are numerous ways to alter the solution to Example 7-13 to illustrate different ways to implement interrupts. First of all, note that most of the *work* is done in the main program, not in the ISR. This is not desirable in larger systems that must accommodate numerous interrupt sources. We can rearrange the code as shown in Figure G to make the ISR do the work:

**Figure G.**

```
 1  00000400                      ORG      $000400
 2                          *
 3                          *  Main Program
 4                          *
 5  00000400 4200    START   CLR.B    D0          ;clear count
 6  00000402 1200            MOVE.B   D0,D1       ;copy count to D1
 7  00000404 4601            NOT.B    D1          ;complement for LED interface
 8  00000406 13C10000        MOVE.B   D1,$C000    ;clear LEDs (once only)
    0000040A C000
 9  0000040C 60FE            BRA      *           ;do nothing!
10                          *
11                          *  Interrupt Service Routine
12                          *
13  0000040E 5200    ISR     ADDQ.B   #1,D0       ;increment count
14  00000410 1200            MOVE.B   D0,D1       ;copy count to D1
15  00000412 4601            NOT.B    D1          ;complement for LED interface
16  00000414 13C10000        MOVE.B   D1,$C000    ;clear LEDs (once only)
    00000418 C000
17  0000041A 4E73            RTE                  ;return to main program
```

The main program in Figure G clears the count in D0, turns off the LEDs, and then sits in a loop doing nothing. As interrupts occur, the work is done in the background—in the ISR. D0 is incremented (line 13) and the complement of the count is sent to the LEDs (lines 14–16). Thinking ahead, the fact that the main program is doing nothing means that once the necessary work is done to prepare for interrupts, the main program can expand to do other things. This is one of the tricks used in the successful implementation of multiple interrupts.

### 7.7.6.  *Parameter Passing and Use of the Stack*

Using a register to hold the count is a poor strategy in practice because the registers are usually needed in the main program. Alternatively, a RAM byte could be reserved using a DS.B directive, similar to a global variable in a high-level language. This is illustrated in Figure H.

COUNT represents the address of a byte of RAM, as defined in line 24. The label COUNT is used as an absolute long address in lines 5, 6, 14, and 15.

A second change appears in the example above. Although we have effectively avoided using D0 as a counter, the ISR still uses D1 to hold the comple-

ment of the count sent to the LEDs. This is potentially a problem, since the value of D1 from the main program is lost. In practice, this must be avoided. A simple solution is shown above. D1 is saved on the stack in the first instruction of the ISR (line 13), and is restored just before RTE (line 18). This way, the ISR executes (in the background) without altering any of the 68000's internal registers. This is critical for most implementations of interrupts.

**Example 7-14.** If the 68000 is operating from a 10 MHz clock, what is the duration of the interrupt service routine in Figure H?

**Solution:** 9.2 µs

**Discussion:** The duration of each instruction (in machine cycles) is found in Appendix D. For example, first instruction in the ISR is MOVE.W D1,-(A7) which takes 8 machine cycles. The total for the ISR is

$$8 + 20 + 16 + 4 + 16 + 8 + 20 = 92 \text{ machine cycles}$$

Operating at 10 MHz, the duration of a machine cycle is 1/10 = 0.1 µs, so the entire ISR takes

$$0.1 \times 92 = 9.2 \text{ µs} \quad \blacksquare$$

**Figure H.**

```
 1 00000400                        ORG      $000400
 2                       *
 3                       * Main Program
 4                       *
 5 00000400 42390000 START CLR.B   >COUNT       ;clear count
   00000404 8000
 6 00000406 12390000       MOVE.B  >COUNT,D1 ;copy count to D1
   0000040A 8000
 7 0000040C 4601           NOT.B   D1           ;complement for LED interface
 8 0000040E 13C10000       MOVE.B  D1,$C000  ;clear LEDs (once only)
   00000412 C000
 9 00000414 60FE           BRA     *            ;do nothing!
10                       *
11                       * Interrupt Service Routine
12                       *
13 00000416 3F01     ISR   MOVE.W  D1,-(A7)  ;save D1 on stack
14 00000418 52390000       ADDQ.B  #1,>COUNT ;increment count
   0000041C 8000
15 0000041E 12390000       MOVE.B  >COUNT,D1 ;copy count to D1
   00000422 8000
16 00000424 4601           NOT.B   D1           ;complement for LED interface
17 00000426 13C10000       MOVE.B  D1,$C000  ;update LEDs
   0000042A C000
18 0000042C 321F           MOVE.W  (A7)+,D1  ;restore D1
19 0000042E 4E73           RTE                  ;return to main program
20                       *
21                       * RAM Declarations
22                       *
23 00008000                        ORG      $008000    ;RAM byte
24 00008000     COUNT DS.B   1                 ;store count here
```

**Figure I.**

```
 2 00002000                SEND    EQU      $002000   ;example address
 3 00F00000                PORT    EQU      $F00000   ;output port address
 4 000003E8                COUNT   EQU      1000      ;example count
 5 00001000 207C0000               MOVEA.L  #SEND,A0  ;A0 as data address
   00001004 2000
 6 00001006 227C00F0               MOVEA.L  #PORT,A1  ;A1 as port address
   0000100A 0000
 7 0000100C 203C0000               MOVE.L   #COUNT,D0 ;use D0 as counter
   00001010 03E8
 8                         *
 9                         * Transfer routine
10                         *
11 00001012 3298           LOOP    MOVE.W   (A0)+,(A1);12 cycles
12 00001014 51C8FFFC               DBRA     D0,LOOP   ;10 cycles
```

The duration of ISRs is extremely important is many instances. ISRs of high priority that execute frequently must be very short. An example is an ISR to update cursor position based on mouse movement. The mouse position is sampled frequently; however, the routine to do so (the ISR) must be short; otherwise, foreground execution is impaired. Often the duration of an ISR is important in setting its priority level. It may also be necessary to block subsequent interrupts by changing the interrupt mask bits in the SR within an ISR.

## 7.8.  DIRECT MEMORY ACCESS

**Direct memory access** (DMA) is the transfer of data between a peripheral device and RAM *directly*—without using the CPU.

### 7.8.1.  Why DMA Is Needed

DMA is necessary when a very fast rate of transfer is required. *Very fast* means a rate that is too high for direct CPU control. When data transfers are controlled by the CPU through software, there is an upper limit on the transfer rate achievable. This is set by the clock speed of the CPU. Furthermore, if the CPU is busy performing I/O operations, overall system performance may degrade. With DMA, input/output operations can occur concurrently with other CPU operations, thus greatly boosting overall system performance.

Before presenting the structure of direct memory access, the following four examples illustrate the limits of a CPU in performing I/O operations.

Example 7-15. A device connected to a hypothetical output port at address $F00000 is capable of receiving words of data as fast as the 68000 can send them. If we wish to send a block of COUNT words starting at address SEND, what is the fastest possible transfer rate (in bytes/second) for a 10-MHz 68000 CPU?

Solution: 909,090 bytes per second

Discussion: The answer is based on the transfer routine in Figure I. The routine (lines 11–12) sends a word of data every 22 machine cycles. At 10 MHz, a machine cycle takes 0.1 µs, so a word is sent every 2.2 µs. This is equivalent to sending a byte every 1.1 µs. The transfer rate is the reciprocal of this, or $1/1.1 = 0.90909$ million bytes per second = 909,090 bytes per second. ∎

Notwithstanding the overhead of setting up initial conditions or adding error-handling software, the example is a simple illustration of the finite capabilities of a CPU in terms of its data transfer rate, or **bandwidth.** The bottleneck is not the speed of memory, but rather the speed of the CPU. In order to achieve higher bandwidths, DMA techniques must be used.

Example 7-16. In the transfer routine in Figure I, what percentage of time is the CPU performing bus cycles that transfer data?

Solution: 18.2%

Discussion: The transfer routine takes 22 machine cycles per transfer. However, the actual transfer occurs during the single memory-write cycle at the end of the MOVE.W instruction (line 11). This takes 4 machine cycles; so, the percentage of time in data transfers is $4/22 \times 100\% = 18.2\%$. ∎

Thus, not only is the bandwidth of the CPU limited by its clock speed, the software routines that perform I/O are very inefficient. Looping control, incrementing address pointers, and fetching instruction words are all necessary parts of the I/O software; but they represent a software overhead that keeps the CPU busy and limits I/O bandwidth.

Example 7-17. What is the potential bandwidth of a 10-MHz 68000 CPU if the software overhead from the transfer routine is eliminated?

**Solution:** 5 Mbytes/second

**Discussion:** By eliminating the software overhead in the transfer routine, all CPU cycles are eliminated except the memory-write cycle. The highest bandwidth occurs with a continuous stream of write (or read) cycles. The potential bandwidth, therefore, is the reciprocal of the memory-write cycle time. A memory-write cycle takes four CPU clock cycles, or $4 \times 0.1$ μs = 0.4 μs. The potential bandwidth is $1/0.4 = 2.5$ megawords/second = 5 Mbytes/second. ■

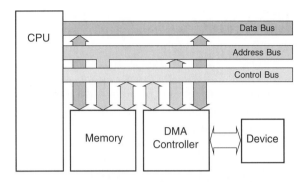

**Figure 7-13. Bus connections for DMA interface.**

Not only is a high bandwidth desirable, it is often essential. We'll illustrate this by considering a typical disk drive interface.

**Example 7-18.** A typical high-speed disk drive has a magnetic platter that rotates at 2400 revolutions per minute. Data are stored serially on magnetic circles, or *tracks,* with a density of 2200 bits per inch. For the purpose of this example, assume a nominal track radius of two inches. What is the *required* transfer rate when reading data from or writing data to this disk drive?

**Solution:** 138,600 bytes/second

**Discussion:** The three numbers quoted in the example set the transfer rate for read or write operations. With $r = 2$ inches, the track circumference is $2\pi r = 12.6$ inches. With a bit density of 2200 bits per inch, there are $12.6 \times 2200 = 27,720$ bits per track. With a rotational speed of 2400 rpm, bits must be transferred at a rate of $27,720 \times 2400 = 66,528,000$ bits per minute = 1,108,800 bits per second = 138,600 bytes per second. ■

We should emphasize that data transfers to or from disk drives must occur at a precise rate, set by (a) the bit density of the magnetic medium, (b) the rotational speed of the platter, and (c) the nominal radius of data tracks. In complex interrupt-driven systems with multiple I/O devices and, perhaps, multiple users, the immediate and high-bandwidth service needed by disk drives necessitates a fast and direct path to memory. Direct memory access is the answer.

## 7.8.2.  DMA Bus Interface

With this introduction, we present the general idea of a DMA interface in Figure 7-13. The interface between a DMA controller (DMAC) and the system buses is similar to the interface for any other peripheral interface IC. The interface between the DMA controller and a device may be quite complex, depending on the device and its interface requirements.

A DMAC differs from other peripheral interface ICs in that it is also capable of taking control of the

system buses and becoming a **bus master.** As the bus master, it generates addresses (like a CPU) and generates control signals to coordinate bus timings (like a CPU). Internally, the DMAC has numerous registers setting modes of operations, and so on. Most importantly, the DMAC has an *address register,* a *count register,* and a *command register.* The address register is the starting address in memory for a transfer. The count register indicates the number of bytes to transfer. The command register sets the direction of transfer and other details of the operation.

Figure 7-13 is greatly simplified. In practice, substantial additional circuitry is often present, such as a peripheral interface IC allowing direct CPU-to-device communication. If the device is a disk drive, for example, the CPU usually specifies the disk location (track and sector) for the transfer by writing to registers in the peripheral interface IC. After the disk subsystem finds the data, it signals the DMAC which in turn signals the CPU and takes control of the system buses. The transfer then takes place under DMA control.

Figure 7-14 illustrates bus activity during DMA transfers. The CPU is missing from the figure, since it has relinquished control of the bus to the DMAC. Although not evident in the figure, DMA

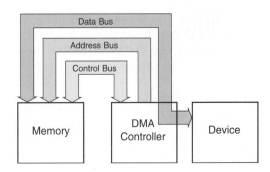

**Figure 7-14.  Device-to-memory transfer using DMA.**

controllers usually support memory-to-memory transfers as well. This is important in large systems that must perform sophisticated memory management tasks, such as relocating user programs within the CPU's memory space. Memory-to-memory transfers are considered **dual-channel transfers,** since each transfer requires two distinct accesses to memory.

The interface between the DMAC and the device may include a large buffer. Transfers, in this case, occur in two stages: between the memory and the buffer, and between the buffer and the device. The DMA transfers are those between the system memory and the buffer. Transfers between the buffer and the device occur in the background, without involving the CPU or system buses.

DMA transfers between system memory and a device buffer are often performed in a single high-speed sequence of transfers. This is called **burst mode.** Burst mode transfers usually occur at a high rate, determined by the bandwidth of the system buses (see Example 7-17). If the transfer is between memory and the device without buffering, usually one byte (or word) is transferred at a time, at a rate dependent on the device. This is called **cycle steal mode.** (Each transfer steals one cycle from the CPU.) In either case, when a DMA transfer begins, the DMAC takes control of the system buses and initiates the transfer. When a DMA request occurs, the CPU halts all bus activity immediately (perhaps in the middle of an instruction!) and places its address, data, and control signal outputs in the high-impedance state. The transfer takes place. If the mode is cycle steal, a single transfer occurs and bus control is returned to the CPU. If the mode is burst, a large number of transfers occur in rapid succession before bus control is returned to the CPU.

During cycle steal mode, DMA cycles are interspersed with CPU cycles. CPU operation is slowed, but still continues. Interrupt requests are still processed, but their execution time is longer. In burst mode, CPU operation is suspended—no instructions execute and no interrupts are serviced. Obviously, a number of very complex issues surface in the design of systems supporting multiple interrupt sources and DMA transfers.

**Example 7-19.** Consider the disk in Example 7-18 which transfers data at a rate of 138,600 bytes/second. If the disk is formatted with 1K-byte sectors, how long does a DMA transfer take for each sector using (a) unbuffered cycle steal mode, or (b) buffered burst mode? Assume a 10-MHz 68000 CPU and DMAC.

**Solution:** (a) 7388 µs (b) 205 µs

**Discussion:** (a) In cycle steal mode, a transfer occurs each time a word is read from or written to the disk. The time for a 1024-byte transfer is $1/(138,600/1024) = 7388$ µs. (b) In burst mode, a 16-bit transfer occurs every 4 CPU clocks, or every 0.4 µs. The time to transfer 1024 bytes, or 512 words, is $512 \times 0.4 = 205$ µs. Note that for cycle steal mode, the rate of transfer depends on the device, whereas for burst mode it depends on the bus bandwidth. ■

**Example 7-20.** What is the percentage reduction in the CPU's normal processing during the cycle steal transfers in Example 7-19? Ignore the DMA overhead of acquiring and relinquishing the system buses.

**Solution:** 2.8%

**Discussion:** At 138,600 bytes/second, or 69,300 words/second, the disk is ready for a transfer every $1/69,300 = 14.4$ µs. However, the transfer only takes 4 CPU clock cycles, or 0.4 µs. So, every 14.4 µs, the DMAC *steals* 0.4 µs of the CPU's execution time. The reduction in normal processing is $0.4/14.4 \times 100\% = 2.8\%$. ■

### 7.8.3.   DMA *on the* 68000

A detailed presentation of the 68000's implementation of direct memory access is beyond the scope of this text. In this section, the most important points are presented without venturing into the full hardware and software details of implemetation. Motorola's user manual for the 68000 is the primary reference for further details.

The 68000 includes three bus arbitration control signals to coordinate DMA transfers. These are $\overline{BR}$ (Bus Request), $\overline{BG}$ (Bus Grant), and $\overline{BGACK}$ (Bus Grant Acknowledge). The connections and direction for these signals are illustrated in Figure 7-15.

A DMA controller takes control of the system buses through **bus arbitration.** Once it has control of the buses, read or write cycles take place under DMA control, and then bus control is returned to the CPU. The steps are presented in Figure 7-16.

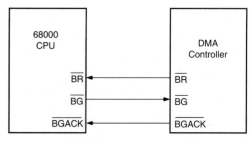

**Figure 7-15. 68000 bus arbitration control signals.**

68000 CPU                    DMA Controller

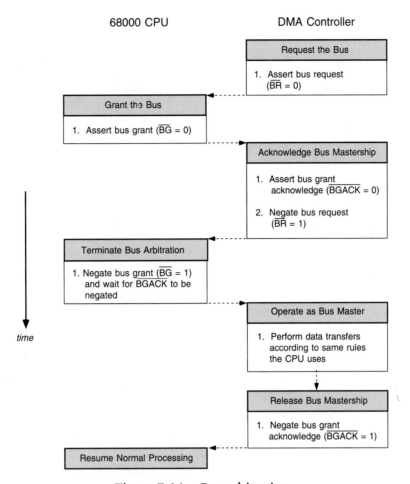

Figure 7-16.   Bus arbitration.

The steps in Figure 7-16 are simplified somewhat. If the system includes several DMACs, the step *Acknowledge Bus Mastership* is more complicated. External arbitration is required for the DMACs to sort out among themselves which is the next bus master.

To emphasize the timing of bus arbitration, the events in Figure 7-16 are redrawn in Figure 7-17 as a timing diagram.

Although bus requests and acknowledgements are *asynchronous,* and occur at any time, the CPU's response on $\overline{\text{BG}}$ is sychronized with the CPU clock to grant bus mastership at the end of the current memory-read or memory-write cycle. This is not necessarily at the end of an instruction. It is perfectly common for the CPU to relinquish bus control in the middle of an instruction. When bus mastership is returned to the CPU, the suspended instruction continues.

## 7.9.   SUMMARY

This chapter has introduced the mechanism for computer systems to communicate with the outside world. The topic of input/output is much larger than presented here. In particular, the use of peripheral interface ICs to simplify connections to I/O devices is increasingly common. These devices have their own characteristics that must be fully understood before they enter into a design. In Chapters 8 and 9, we will meet an example of a multi-purpose peripheral interface IC—the 68681 Dual Asynchronous Receiver/Transmitter (DUART). We'll examine it in detail and illustrate a variety of possible interfaces to external devices.

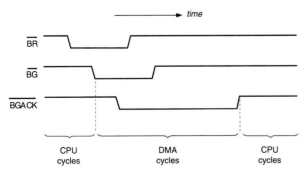

Figure 7-17.   Timing for bus arbitration.

## 7.10.   QUESTIONS

1. With reference to Figure 7-2, the following *wire* program provides a faster update of the LEDs when a switch changes state:

```
          MOVE.L      #$C000,A0
LOOP      MOVE.B      (A0),(A0)
          BRA         LOOP
```

What is the best-case and worst-case time delay between a switch changing and an update to the corresponding LED, given

(a) a 68000 system operating at 6 MHz with no wait states, or

(b) a 68000 system operating at 12 MHz with 1 wait state per memory access (including accesses to I/O devices).

2. With reference to Figure 7-2, write a *wire* program with a reverse relationship between the switches and LEDs. The program should turn on an LED if the corresponding switch is open (rather than closed). For the new program, what is the best-case and worst-case delay between a switch changing and an update to the LEDs? Assume the CPU is operating at 12 MHz with no wait states.

3. Construct a memory map for a 68000 system that uses the address decoding shown in Figure 7-6a.

4. An interface to four switches and a 7-segment LED is shown in Figure 7-18. (For simplicity, the address decode circuitry is omitted.) Write a program that continually reads the switches and writes to the LED to display the hexadecimal character corresponding to the binary code read. For example, if $0011_2$ is read, display "3" on the LED. Switch A is the LSB. The LED is a common anode type; therefore, a 0 presented at an input turns on the corresponding segment.

5. Design a minimal address decoding circuit for a 68000-based system with a single 32K-word EPROM, two 32K-word RAMs, and a single peripheral interface adapter (PIA). The EPROM must reside at the bottom of the 68000's memory space (to provide reset and exception vectors); however, the RAMs and PIA can reside anywhere in the 68000's memory space.

6. Suppose that TRAP #9 is used in a program to force an update of a visual display. Suppose further that external interrupt 6 uses the same code to force an update of the display. If the device generating Interrupt 6 provides a user interrupt vector during the interrupt acknowledge cycle, what vector number is required? Where is the starting address of the update routine stored?

7. An EPROM at the bottom of the 68000's memory space contains the following data:

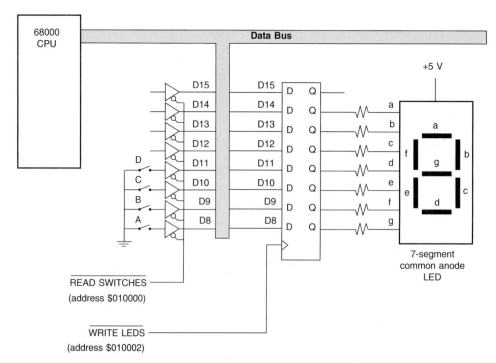

Figure 7-18.   7-segment LED example.

```
Address        Contents
00006C         0000
00006E         0F40
000070         0200
000072         0146
000074         0000
000076         F900
```

If we assume interrupts are implemented using autovectors, then

(a) At what address does the ISR for a level-4 interrupt begin?

(b) At what address does the ISR for a level-6 interrupt begin?

8. The 68000's status register contains $221A_{16}$. What is the lowest-level interrupt to which the CPU will respond?

9. Illustrate in software how to set the 68000's status register's interrupt mask bits to $011_2$. The other bits in the SR should remain as is.

10. Under what circumstances is external arbitration required for a DMAC to become a bus master?

11. Illustrate a circuit that could be added to Figure 7-12 to provide a user vector in response to a level-4 interrupt. The circuit should be able to provide any vector number, but use vector #64 in your schematic.

# 8. *The* 68KMB

## 8.1. INTRODUCTION

Many of the 68000's hardware features are now brought together in a case study of a complete 68000-based single-board computer. It is called the 68KMB. The goal in designing the 68KMB was to provide a powerful tool to study the 68000 microprocessor as well as interfacing to input/output devices. The latter subject is the focus of Chapter 7. A parallel goal was to design a 68000-based system with a minimum number of ICs that could be prototyped and manufactured as cheaply as possible. The design uses 13 ICs that can be purchased for less than $33. The following features are supported:

- 68000 microprocessor
- 16K bytes EPROM
- 16K bytes RAM
- two RS232C serial ports
- 16-bit timer
- 8-bit parallel output port
- 6-bit parallel input port
- seven levels of interrupts
- easy expansion to 6800 peripheral ICs
- easy expansion for RAM, EPROM, or I/O devices

A monitor program in EPROM is required before a single-board computer is *up-and-running*. Basic system functions must be supported, such as loading and executing user programs, or examining and changing CPU registers or memory locations. A small monitor program, called MON68K, has been written to meet these requirements. MON68K is described in detail in Appendix E and is included on the diskette accompanying this text. Although detailed discussions are deferred to Appendix E, MON68K is occasionally mentioned in this chapter to help explain subtle hardware features of the 68KMB.

The reader can approach this chapter from several viewpoints. Initially, the 68KMB can be studied as an example of a 68000-based system. Perhaps the reader will extend the design for a custom application with a different memory configuration or with different I/O features. Also, since the 68KMB is small and inexpensive, it is relatively easy to construct a prototype and gain hands-on experience through the monitor program and the interfacing examples in Chapter 9. Wire wrapping is the most practical method of construction. Figure 8-1 shows the original prototype 68KMB; it was wire wrapped on a Vector 3682 prototype board.

Since many readers may wish to avoid the labors of prototyping, the 68KMB is also available as a fully assembled and tested printed-circuit board from the following source:

> URDA, Inc.
> 1811 Jancey St., Suite 200
> Pittsburgh, PA
> USA 15206
> Phone: 1-800-338-0517

The PC-board version is shown in Figure 8-2. Several enhancements are included to facilitate expansion or substituting different memory ICs. These are discussed in the literature provided by URDA.

## 8.2. SYSTEM SUMMARY

This section will summarize the design of the 68KMB. We begin with Table 8-1, listing the ICs along with their purpose and price. Absent in the table are the discrete components, IC sockets, switches, connectors, and prototyping board, so the total cost is somewhat higher than indicated. Nevertheless, with 13 ICs, the 68KMB represents about the smallest possible configuration for a complete 68000-based system. As we shall see, a powerful set of features is supported.

The 68KMB comprises nine distinct blocks, as shown in Figure 8-3. These include the following:

- 68000 CPU
- system clock
- reset circuit
- interrupt circuit

185

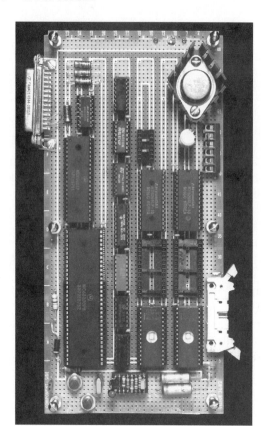

Figure 8-1.   Wire wrap version of the 68KMB.

- address decode circuit
- monitor EPROM
- user EPROM
- RAM
- 68681 DUART

## 8.3.   CPU SIGNALS

We'll now walk through the design, describing each block in Figure 8-3. Signals, pin connections,

Figure 8-2.   Printed-circuit-board version of 68KMB (Courtesy URDA, Inc.).

and all additional components will be shown as well. Portions of the following descriptions will be familiar to readers who have followed this text from the beginning. Nevertheless, we have many subtle implementation details to present and explain. The 68000 CPU is shown in Figure 8-4, complete with signal names and pin numbers. The signals are grouped by function as address bus, data bus, or control bus.

Bear in mind that the 23 address lines are outputs and the 16 data lines are bidirectional. Of the control bus signals, ten are outputs, nine are inputs, and two are bidirectional. Pull-up resistors appear on the control bus signals with multiple sources. These signals will originate from open collector buffers in a wired-OR configuration, as explained in Types of Outputs in Chapter 0.

Pull-up resistors are so common in microprocessor-based designs that they are conveniently offered in dual-inline packages (DIPs). Since one side

Table 8-1.   Integrated Circuits in the 68KMB.

| PN | Name | Purpose | Qty. | Unit | Total* |
|---|---|---|---|---|---|
| 68000 | CPU | CPU | 1 | – | 6.95 |
| 68681 | DUART | serial I/O, parallel I/O, timer | 1 | – | 3.95 |
| 74HC14 | Schmitt trigger | clock, reset | 1 | – | .35 |
| 7407 | open collector buffer | reset, bus control | 1 | – | .45 |
| 74HC138 | decoder | interrupts | 2 | .45 | .90 |
| 74HC148 | priority encoder | interrupts | 1 | – | .79 |
| 16L8 | PAL | address decoding | 1 | – | 1.95 |
| MAX232 | RS232C transceiver | serial interface | 1 | – | 2.75 |
| 2764A | EPROM | MON68K | 2 | 3.45 | 6.90 |
| 6264 | RAM | system/user RAM | 2 | 3.79 | 7.58 |
| | | Total: | 13 | – | $32.57 |

* Prices are from the 1994 catalog of JDR Microdevices, 2233 Samaritan Dr., San Jose, CA, USA 95124.

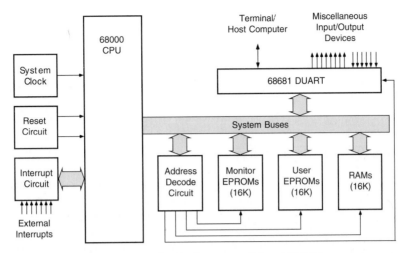

Figure 8-3.   Block diagram of the 68KMB.

of each pull-up resistor connects to +5V, a DIP with 16 pins can accommodate 15 pull-up resistors, as shown in Figure 8-5. This is the preferred packaging for prototyping. An example of a 16-pin 10K arrangement is the 4116R-002-103 by Bourns, Inc.

## 8.4.   SYSTEM CLOCK

One of the most critical circuits in any microcomputer is the system clock. The 68KMB clock circuit in Figure 8-6 uses a 3.6864 MHz quartz crystal oscillator made from a 74HC14 hex Schmitt trigger

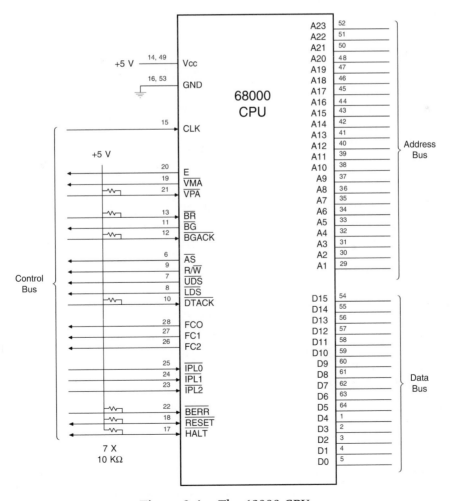

Figure 8-4.   The 68000 CPU.

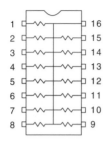

**Figure 8-5. Pull-up resistors in a dual-inline package.**

and a few additional components. The 74HC14 provides noise immunity and buffering to maintain a clean, stable clock source. The frequency 3.6864 MHz was chosen since it is the ideal frequency for the 68681 serial port clock, as described later in this chapter. It allows both the 68000 and the 68681 to operate from the same crystal, thus reducing costs. This frequency is quite low for the 68000 CPU; however, it is more than adequate for the intended purpose of the 68KMB. It also permits use of the slowest (and cheapest) EPROMs and RAMs available.

## 8.5.   RESET CIRCUIT

The 68KMB's reset circuit is shown in Figure 8-7. The circuit asserts both $\overline{\text{RESET}}$ and $\overline{\text{HALT}}$ to the 68000 CPU upon power-up or when the RESET switch is depressed (closed). The combination of the 74HC14 and the 7407 provides a clean 0–1 transition to the 68000 device when the input voltage to the first inverter rises above 2.4 volts. This will occur at a fixed time interval following power-up or the release of the RESET switch. The time interval is set by the RC network connecting to pin 9 of the first inverter, as explained in Reset Circuitry in Chapter 6.

7407 open collector buffers are used since $\overline{\text{RESET}}$ and $\overline{\text{HALT}}$ are bidirectional signals that are also driven by the 68000 CPU. Pull-up resistors on $\overline{\text{RESET}}$ and $\overline{\text{HALT}}$ are not shown since they appeared earlier in Figure 8-4.

## 8.6.   INTERRUPT CIRCUIT

An important design decision for the 68KMB was to implement the full complement of 68000 interrupts. Although this increases the IC count by three, the advantages are significant. Not the least of these is the educational benefit in learning about the architecture of the 68000 microprocessor and software implementation of interrupt-driven applications.

As shown in Figure 8-8, a 74HC148 priority encoder receives an interrupt input and encodes the level on three outputs driving the $\overline{\text{IPL2}}$, $\overline{\text{IPL1}}$, and $\overline{\text{IPL0}}$ lines on the 68000. Two 74HC138s are required to implement interrupt acknowledge (IACK) cycles when the 68000 responds to an interrupt.

Of the seven interrupt levels, four are committed and three are available to the user. These are briefly presented here. Details on the software implementation of interrupts on the 68KMB are given in Appendix E.

Interrupt 7 is generated by a momentary switch labeled MONITOR in Figure 8-8. When this switch is pressed it generates a level-7, non-maskable interrupt to the 68000 CPU. The user program is terminated and control returns to MON68K. The user environment is saved and can be examined as a debugging feature.

Interrupts 6, 5, and 4 are available to the user.

Interrupt 3 is reserved for I/O expansion to 6800 peripherals, as described later in this chapter.

Interrupt 2 is reserved for the 68681 DUART, as described later in this chapter.

Interrupt 1 is generated by a jumper labeled X16 in Figure 8-8. If this jumper is installed upon power-up or manual reset, MON68K begins executing from the user EPROMs. The importance of this feature is that a terminal or host computer is not needed to initiate the user program. If X16 is installed, execution following a reset operation *immediately* passes to the user EPROMs. To ensure that the level-0 interrupt is serviced, it is important that other interrupt signals are not asserted during the reset operation.

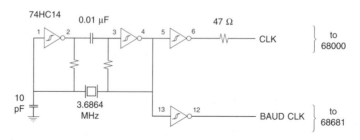

**Figure 8-6.   68KMB clock circuit.**

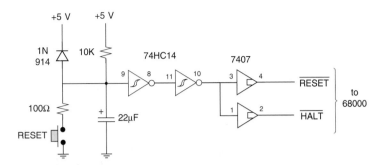

Figure 8-7.   68KMB reset circuit.

Interrupts 7, 3, and 1 use autovectors, so the IACK cycle terminates by asserting $\overline{VPA}$. The 7407 open collector buffers in Figure 8-8 provide this function. The 68681 supports *user* IACK cycles, and provides the necessary assertion on $\overline{DTACK}$ during a level-2 IACK cycle (hence, an open collector driver is not present on $\overline{IACK2}$). The distinction between user and autovector IACK cycles was presented in detail in Chapter 7.

## 8.7.   ADDRESS DECODING

All the address decoding for the 68KMB is implemented in a single IC, a 16L8 PAL. If a PAL programmer is not available to the reader, an equivalent combinational circuit is easily substituted, as described in Appendix F. The 16L8 in Figure 8-9 is configured with ten inputs and eight outputs. The ten inputs are address lines A14 through A20, upper data strobe ($\overline{UDS}$), lower data strobe ($\overline{LDS}$), and address strobe ($\overline{AS}$). Seven outputs provide the chip select signals to the system's RAMs, EPROMs, and the 68681 DUART. The eighth output is the all-important data transfer acknowledge ($\overline{DTACK}$) signal that connects back to the CPU to terminate all bus cycles (except autovector IACK cycles). Since $\overline{DTACK}$ is a control input to the 68000, it is driven by an open collector device, as shown in the figure.

Since address lines A1–A13 are not present, the decoding is on 8K word boundaries ($2^{13} = 8K$). Each 8K word block, starting at $000000, is used for RAM, EPROM, or I/O. Since the upper three address lines (A21–A23) are not present, the decoding is reflected eight times ($2^3 = 8$) throughout

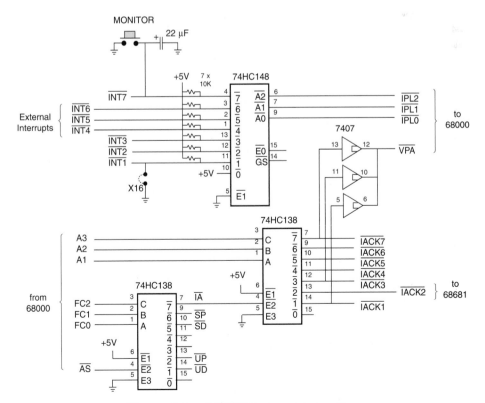

Figure 8-8.   68KMB interrupt circuit.

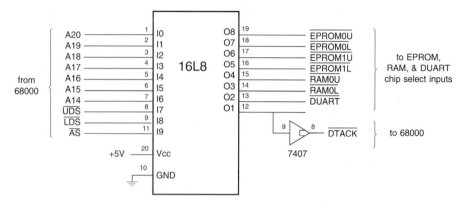

Figure 8-9.   68KMB address decoding.

the 68000's 8M word address space. (Reflected decoding was presented in Chapter 7.)

The effect of the address decoding is shown in the memory map in Figure 8-10. The decoding is *full* within the bottom 1M words of memory. The area labeled *expansion* in the figure is available for additional off-board RAM, EPROM, or I/O, as discussed later in this chapter.

A word view is shown in the memory map to distinguish the upper and lower bytes of the RAMs and EPROMs. The 68681 DUART is an 8-bit peripheral IC residing at odd addresses starting at $00C001. The even (upper-byte) addresses starting at $00C000 are unused.

Although awkward, it is easy to design decode circuitry using standard 7400-series ICs to conform

to the memory map in Figure 8-10 (see Appendix F). By using a 16L8 PAL, the job is reduced to a single IC. PAL programmers, once expensive and specialized tools, are now available as inexpensive, PC-hosted plug-in cards.[1] Furthermore, they are packaged with software to enter and minimize logic designs for combinational or sequential circuits. The program to burn the 16L8 in the 68KMB is given in Figure 8-11.

While discussing the 68KMB's address decoding and memory map, it is worthwhile to dwell briefly

---

[1]The PAL for the SBC68K was programmed using Modular Circuit Technology's MOD-PAL and the CUPL Starter Kit  available from JDR Microdevices, 2233 Samaritan Dr., San Jose, CA, USA 95124.

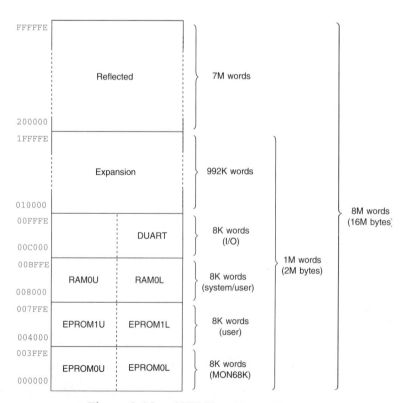

Figure 8-10.   68KMB memory map.

```
name          sbc68k;
partno        000000;
revision      none  ;
date          26/05/93;
designer      Scott MacKenzie;
company       University of Guelph;
location      none ;
assembly      none ;

pin  1 = a20              ;
pin  2 = a19              ;
pin  3 = a18              ;
pin  4 = a17              ;
pin  5 = a16              ;
pin  6 = a15              ;
pin  7 = a14              ;
pin  8 = uds              ;
pin  9 = lds              ;
pin 11 = as               ;
pin 12 = !dtack           ;
pin 13 = !duart           ;
pin 14 = !ram0l           ;
pin 15 = !ram0u           ;
pin 16 = !eprom1l         ;
pin 17 = !eprom1u         ;
pin 18 = !eprom0l         ;
pin 19 = !eprom0u         ;

eprom0u  = !a20 & !a19 & !a18 & !a17 & !a16 & !a15 & !a14 & !uds & !as ;
eprom0l  = !a20 & !a19 & !a18 & !a17 & !a16 & !a15 & !a14 & !lds & !as ;
eprom1u  = !a20 & !a19 & !a18 & !a17 & !a16 & !a15 &  a14 & !uds & !as ;
eprom1l  = !a20 & !a19 & !a18 & !a17 & !a16 & !a15 &  a14 & !lds & !as ;
ram0u    = !a20 & !a19 & !a18 & !a17 & !a16 &  a15 & !a14 & !uds & !as ;
ram0l    = !a20 & !a19 & !a18 & !a17 & !a16 &  a15 & !a14 & !lds & !as ;
duart    = !a20 & !a19 & !a18 & !a17 & !a16 &  a15 &  a14 & !lds & !as ;
dtack    = !a20 & !a19 & !a18 & !a17 & !a16 & !a15 & !a14 & !uds & !as
         # !a20 & !a19 & !a18 & !a17 & !a16 & !a15 & !a14 & !lds & !as
         # !a20 & !a19 & !a18 & !a17 & !a16 & !a15 &  a14 & !uds & !as
         # !a20 & !a19 & !a18 & !a17 & !a16 & !a15 &  a14 & !lds & !as
         # !a20 & !a19 & !a18 & !a17 & !a16 &  a15 & !a14 & !uds & !as
         # !a20 & !a19 & !a18 & !a17 & !a16 &  a15 & !a14 & !lds & !as
         # !a20 & !a19 & !a18 & !a17 & !a16 &  a15 &  a14 & !uds & !as ;
```

Figure 8-11.   Program for 16L8 address decoder.

on a subtle but important implementation detail. Consider the following question: What will happen if a memory access occurs to an address in the expansion area of the 68KMB's memory map? This is an interesting question with several implications for the 68KMB and other 68000-based systems. The answer: The system will hang. The problem is that $\overline{DTACK}$ is not generated to terminate the cycle. The 68000 CPU is stuck at state 4 in a bus cycle waiting for $\overline{DTACK}$ to be asserted (see Data Transfer Timings in Chapter 2). Normally, this situation will not occur; however, it is possible that a user program or a monitor command will inadvertently access this region. This small design quirk remains in the 68KMB for two reasons: (a) to keep the chip count down, and (b) to inspire exploration of alternative approaches in student lab exercises.

There are a couple of possible solutions to the problem above. One is to modify the 16L8 decoder such that $\overline{DTACK}$ is asserted whenever $\overline{AS}$ is asserted. This will cause every memory reference to be terminated even if no memory or I/O is present. This is the *cheap-and-dirty* solution. It works, but it is not how the 68000 architecutre was intended to work. Although fine for minimal implementations such as the 68KMB, this is a bad approach for large 68000-based systems that require graceful recovery from error conditions.

A more elegant approach is to build a watchdog circuit to generate $\overline{BERR}$ if $\overline{DTACK}$ is not asserted within a few clock periods after State 4 is entered (see Bus Error in Chapter 2). This is the intended purpose of $\overline{BERR}$, and on large 68000-based systems this is the usual approach. A bus-error exception routine should be written to generate an appropriate error message and recover in some manner.

The following two points are also relevant: (a) a byte access to an even address in the range $00C000 to $00FFFE will also hang the system, and (b) the seven 1M word blocks starting at address $200000 behave the same as the 1M block starting at $000000.

## 8.8.  MONITOR EPROMS

At the bottom of the 68000's memory space reside two 2764A 8K byte EPROMs. These contain the monitor program, MON68K. This area of memory *must* contain EPROM, since, upon reset, the 68000 reads the initial values for the SSP and PC from addresses $000000 and $000004, respectively. The monitor EPROMs are shown in Figure 8-12.

The only differences in the connections to the two EPROMs in Figure 8-12 are the signals driving the chip select ($\overline{CS}$) inputs and the connections to the 68000's data bus. The upper EPROM in the figure is selected by $\overline{EPROM0U}$ to reside at even addresses; so, the data lines connect to the upper byte of the 68000's data bus (D8–D15). Conversely, the lower EPROM in the figure is selected by $\overline{EPROM0L}$ to reside at odd addresses; so, the data lines connect to the lower byte of the 68000's data bus (D0–D7).

With 8K bytes each, the two 2764A EPROMs in Figure 8-12 comprise 8K words of memory. The address decode circuit places these EPROMs in the 68000's memory space from word addresses $000000 to $003FFE.

Recall from Chapter 2 that the 68000 does not have an address line called A0. The A0 function is covered by the $\overline{UDS}$ and $\overline{LDS}$ control bus signals. For this reason, A0 on the 2764A (pin 10) is driven by A1 from the 68000 CPU, and so on. The $\overline{UDS}$ and $\overline{LDS}$ signals, although not shown in Figure 8-12, participate in the decode circuit generating the chip select signals (see Figure 8-9).

## 8.9.  USER EPROMS

To facilitate placing user programs in EPROM and installing them on the 68KMB, the address decode circuit generates chip select signals for two more 2764A EPROMs. These reside from addresses $004000 to $007FFE. Since they are not needed for the normal operation of the system or to execute user programs in RAM, these devices are not included in the 13-chip count for the 68KMB. The empty 28-pin sockets visible in Figure 8-1 are available for user EPROMs. The ability to add user

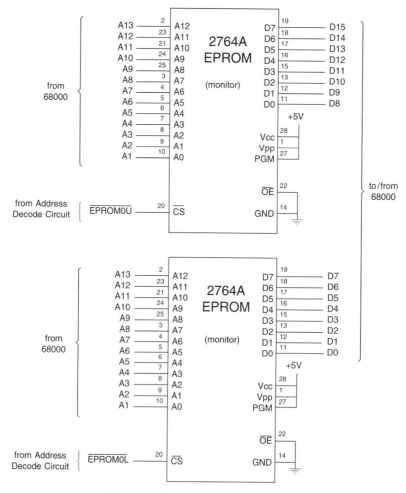

Figure 8-12.   Monitor EPROMs.

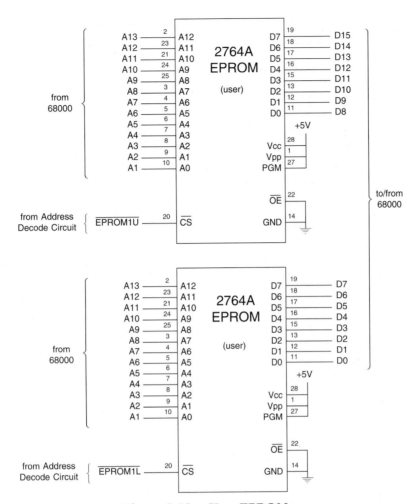

Figure 8-13.    User EPROMs.

programs in EPROM separate from the monitor program is a useful (and inexpensive) feature. The signal connections for the user EPROM sockets are shown in Figure 8-13. The only signals that differ from the monitor EPROMs are the chip select inputs driven from the address decode circuit.

stack and the command line buffer. User programs can start at the beginning of RAM, at address $008000, but should not venture above $00B7FF. Interrupts and user-defined traps are available to user programs, through a jump table in RAM (see Appendix E).

## 8.10.  SYSTEM/USER RAM

The system/user RAM lies just above the user EPROMs in the 68KMB's memory map, at addresses $008000 to $00BFFE. As shown in Figure 8-14, two 6264 8K byte static RAMs are used for a total of 8K words. The pin connections for the 6264s are very similar to the 2764A EPROMs. The main difference is that pin 27, instead of connecting to +5V as on the 2764A, is an input driven by the system's R/$\overline{\text{W}}$ signal.

If MON68K is used as the 68KMB's monitor program, then portions of the RAM are reserved for system use. The upper 1024 words, from $00B800 to $00BFFE, are used for the system

## 8.11.  DUART

All of the 68KMB's on-board I/O features are provided through the 68681 dual universal asynchronous receiver/transmitter (DUART). The 68681 was chosen since it is inexpensive, easily obtained, and includes the most fundamental I/O features needed for a single-board computer. These features include the following:

- two fully programmable asynchronous serial ports
- 16-bit programmable timer
- 6-bit programmable input port
- 8-bit programmable output port

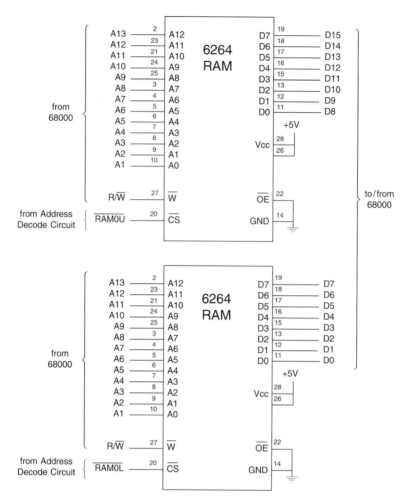

**Figure 8-14.    System/User RAM.**

The word *programmable* above hints at the many powerful and flexible operating modes of the 68681. In this chapter we limit discussion to the hardware interface to the 68681. A subset of the 68681's programming features is presented in Chapter 9 and the data sheet is given in Appendix H. The 68681's pin connections and signals are shown in Figure 8-15.

Since the 68681 was designed specifically as a 68000 peripheral, the interface is very simple. The device is selected by the signal $\overline{\text{DUART}}$ from the address decode circuit. $\overline{\text{DUART}}$ is active any time the 68000 accesses an odd address in the 8K word section of memory beginning at $00C000. With four register select lines (RS1–RS4) driven by the 68000's address lines A1–A4, the 68681 registers are accessed at addresses $00C001, $00C003, and so on, up to $00C01F. These 16 addresses are reflected throughout this 8K word block. The internal registers accessible at these addresses are examined in detail in Chapter 9. Connections are provided for a level-2 interrupt, if desired. The serial port clock is driven by the signal BAUD CLK

originating from the system clock circuit (see Figure 8-6).

The 68681 can interface to any RS232C device, such as a dumb terminal or a host computer with an RS232C communications port. The MAX232 device greatly simplifies the interface. In a single IC, this versatile device provides dc/dc voltage conversion, two RS232C transmitters, and two RS232C receivers. The RS232C side of the MAX232 (on the right in Figure 8-15) transmits and receives ±12 volt signals compatible with the RS232C standard. The CPU side of the MAX232 transmits and receives TTL signals compatible with the 68681. The connector labeled J3 is a 25-pin DB25S, typical of RS232C interfaces. (It is seen at the top left of Figure 8-1.) A second, optional connector can be added if an additional port is needed. It was not implemented on the prototype 68KMB.

The connector J1 is provided on the 68KMB to simplify interfacing to the 68681's parallel and serial ports. These signals will be used extensively in the examples in Chapter 9.

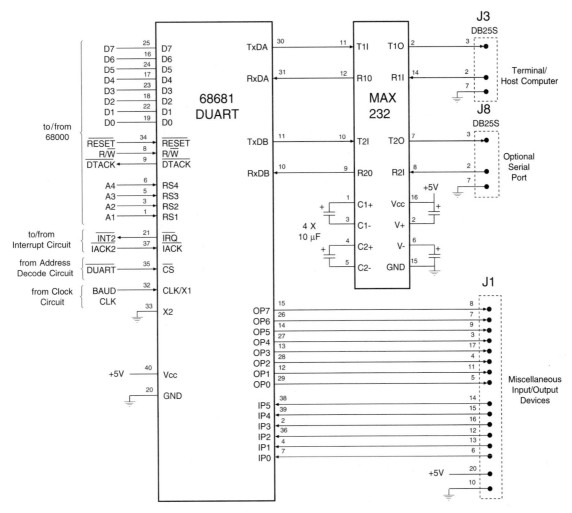

Figure 8-15.    68681 DUART.

## 8.12.  EXPANSION TO 6800 PERIPHERALS

Although the 68681 is a versatile and inexpensive peripheral interface IC, it is important to provide the capability to interface to other peripherals as well. In particular, there are several common and popular peripheral interface ICs that have persisted since the days of the 6800 microprocessor—the 68000's 8-bit predecessor. These include the following:

- 6821 parallel interface adapter IC
- 6850 universal asynchronous receiver/transmitter
- 6840 timer

The J2 connector on the 68KMB (bottom right in Figure 8-1) provides a simple interface to such peripheral ICs. The signal connections are given in Figure 8-16.

The control signals E (enable) and $\overline{VPA}$ (valid peripheral address) are used instead of $\overline{AS}$ and $\overline{DTACK}$ when accessing a 6800 peripheral. When the 68000 detects $\overline{VPA}$ (instead of $\overline{DTACK}$), it will stretch the current bus cycle and synchronize the data transfer with E, as required by 6800 peripherals (see Appendix G).

Address decoding is provided through A16 and (supervisor data). Using A16 as an active-high chip select input, the following binary address should be used for the peripheral IC:

```
0000 0001 0000 0000 0000 xxx1
```

The three x's represent the eight locations addressed by A1–A3, also provided on J2. In hexadecimal, the peripheral addresses are $010001, $010003, $010005, and so on, up to $01000F. These addresses will be the internal registers of the 6800 peripheral interface IC. The addresses are odd since data transfers occur on the low-order byte of the 68000's data bus (D0–D7).

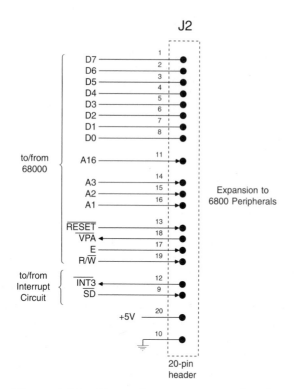

J2

Figure 8-16.    Expansion to 6800 peripherals.

peripheral IC from being inadvertently selected during IACK cycles (when A16 is also high). Note that user programs execute in supervisor mode with MON68K; therefore, the signal $\overline{SD}$ is asserted (low) during any data read or write cycle (see Data Transfer Timings in Chapter 2). Interface examples using the J2 connector are given in Chapter 9.

The J2 connector provides access to level-2 interrupts for the peripheral device. Autovectoring is used since a level-2 IACK cycle forces activation of $\overline{VPA}$ (see Figure 8-8).

## 8.13.    EXPANSION FOR RAM, EPROM, AND I/O

With 8K words each of RAM and user EPROM, the 68KMB provides ample room to develop large, complex applications. Nevertheless, in some instances it may be important to expand memory or I/O further. For example, if an application program is written in C and compiled to 68000 machine language, more than 8K words of RAM may be needed. The overhead of compiled C code is substantial, and if numerous functions are included, the machine-language program will be large. If a data acquisition or signal processing application is developed, a large sampling buffer in RAM may be needed.

The signal $\overline{SD}$ (supervisor data) originates from the 74HC138 driven by the CPU's function code outputs (see Figure 8-8). $\overline{SD}$ operates as an additional active-low chip select signal to prevent the

J6

| Pin | Signal | Pin | Signal |
|-----|--------|-----|--------|
| 1 | D5 | 26 | D4 |
| 2 | D5 | 27 | D3 |
| 3 | D7 | 28 | D2 |
| 4 | D8 | 29 | D1 |
| 5 | D9 | 30 | D0 |
| 6 | D10 | 31 | $\overline{AS}$ |
| 7 | D11 | 32 | $\overline{UDS}$ |
| 8 | D12 | 33 | $\overline{LDS}$ |
| 9 | D13 | 34 | R/$\overline{W}$ |
| 10 | D14 | 35 | $\overline{DTACK}$ |
| 11 | D15 | 36 | $\overline{BG}$ |
| 12 | A23 | 37 | $\overline{BGACK}$ |
| 13 | A22 | 38 | $\overline{BR}$ |
| 14 | A21 | 39 | VCC |
| 15 | VCC | 40 | CLK |
| 16 | 16L8-1 | 41 | GND |
| 17 | A20 | 42 | $\overline{HALT}$ |
| 18 | A19 | 43 | $\overline{RESET}$ |
| 19 | A18 | 44 | $\overline{VMA}$ |
| 20 | A17 | 45 | $\overline{E}$ |
| 21 | A16 | 46 | $\overline{VPA}$ |
| 22 | A15 | 47 | $\overline{BERR}$ |
| 23 | A14 | 48 | IPL2 |
| 24 | A13 | 49 | ILP1 |
| 25 | A12 | 50 | ILP0 |

J7

| Pin | Signal | Pin | Signal |
|-----|--------|-----|--------|
| 1 | FC2 | 26 | A10 |
| 2 | A11 | 27 | A9 |
| 3 | FC0 | 28 | A8 |
| 4 | FC1 | 29 | A1 |
| 5 | A7 | 30 | A2 |
| 6 | A6 | 31 | A3 |
| 7 | A5 | 32 | BAUDCLK |
| 8 | - | 33 | A4 |
| 9 | - | 34 | - |
| 10 | GND | 35 | GND |
| 11 | VCC | 36 | VCC |
| 12 | - | 37 | - |
| 13 | $\overline{I4}$ | 38 | $\overline{I5}$ |
| 14 | $\overline{I6}$ | 39 | $\overline{I7}$ |
| 15 | $\overline{I3}$ | 40 | $\overline{I2}$ |
| 16 | $\overline{I1}$ | 41 | - |
| 17 | - | 42 | - |
| 18 | - | 43 | - |
| 19 | - | 44 | - |
| 20 | $\overline{IACK5}$ | 45 | $\overline{IACK6}$ |
| 21 | - | 46 | $\overline{IACK7}$ |
| 22 | - | 47 | - |
| 23 | - | 48 | - |
| 24 | - | 49 | - |
| 25 | - | 50 | - |

Figure 8-17.    Expansion for RAM, EPROM, and I/O.

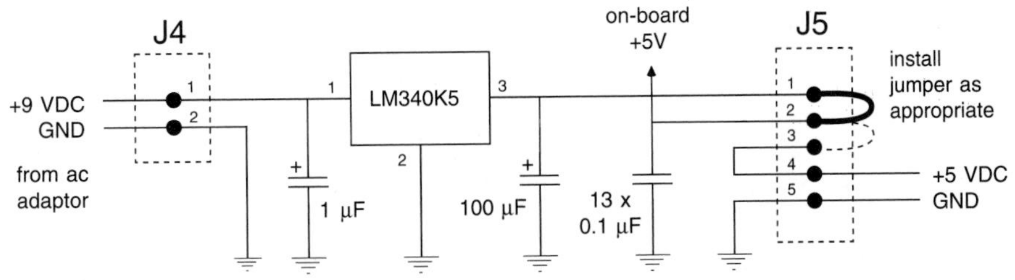

Figure 8-18.   DC power for the 68KMB.

Regardless of the reason, the potential to expand the 68KMB for addition resources is an important feature. The PC-board version includes two connectors, J6 and J7, with most of the 68000's address, data, and control bus signals. These are shown in Figure 8-17.

J6 and J7 are 50-pin headers. With the signals shown in Figure 8-17, full decoding is possible within the 68KMB's 992K word *expansion* space. This is from addresses $010000 to $1FFFFE. Interrupts 4–6 are available and may be implemented with user or autovector IACK cycles, as necessary. Since all control bus signals are present, a variety of RAMs, EPROMs, or peripheral interface ICs can be added. Note that bus signals are not buffered on the 68KMB. It may be necessary to add buffers on an expansion board if bus loading is significant.

## 8.14.  DC POWER

To complete our documentation of the 68KMB, we present the power supply connections. The board requires about 750 mA at 5 volts DC. Figure 8-18 shows the J4 and J5 connectors that bring power onto the prototype board. There are two possibilities for providing DC power. If a conventional +5 VDC power supply is used, +5 volts and ground are brought in through connector J5 on pins 4 and 5. An inexpensive and convenient alternative is to use an AC adapter connected to J4. Any model providing 9 VDC at 1 amp will do the job.[2] A jumper on J5 selects between the two possibilities. If pins 1 and 2 on J5 are shorted, as shown in Figure 8-18, the AC adapter is selected and power enters from J4. If pins 2 and 3 are shorted, the +5 VDC power supply is selected and power enters from J5, pins 4 and 5.

If an AC adapter is used, a LM340K5 voltage regulator reduces the supply to +5 volts. Con-

nectors J4 and J5 and the LM340K5 regulator are seen in the top right of Figure 8-1.

Figure 8-18 also identifies 13 decoupling capacitors of 0.1 μF each. These capacitors are distributed throughout the board, with one situated next to each IC. They are visible in Figure 8-1. In electronic circuits, small inductive effects can accumulate in the wiring and create glitches in the power supply voltages arriving at ICs. (It is actually the flow of current that is inhibited; but the effect is usually witnessed as voltage glitches.) These capacitors compensate for this by providing an alternate and *immediate* source of current to the ICs.

To summarize, Table 8-2 lists the ICs in the 68KMB and the pin connections for +5 volts and ground.

## 8.15.  SUMMARY

This chapter presented the hardware design of a 68000 single-board computer—the 68KMB. Before the 68KMB is of much use, a monitor program is needed to provide a primitive interface for basic system functions. MON68K, described in Appendix E, has been written for this purpose. Its operation should be studied to gain a full understanding of the characteristics and potential of the 68KMB.

Table 8-2.  Power Connections for 68KMB ICs.

| Device | +5V | GND |
|---|---|---|
| 68000 | 14,49 | 16,53 |
| 68681 | 40 | 20 |
| 74HC14 | 14 | 7 |
| 74HC138 | 16 | 8 |
| 74HC148 | 16 | 8 |
| 16L8 | 20 | 10 |
| MAX232 | 16 | 15 |
| 2764A | 28 | 14 |
| 6264 | 28 | 14 |

[2]The AC adapter used with the 68KMB is an AD901A from LRZ Electronics, Inc.

## 8.16.   QUESTIONS

1. What will happen if the following instruction is executed within a user program executing in RAM on the 68KMB? Why?

   ```
   MOVE.B    $00C0000,D0
   ```

2. Since the 68KMB uses reflected decoding, all memory addresses have other addresses which are the same. Thus, if memory location X is read, it is the same as reading memory location Y, and so on. Consider an address such as $000040. Through what other addresses does this address reflect itself?

3. How could the 16L8 program in Figure 8-11 be modified to cause $\overline{DTACK}$ to be asserted whenever $\overline{AS}$ is asserted?

# 9. Interface Examples

## 9.1.  INTRODUCTION

Think of this chapter with an alternative title: The Joy of Interfacing. Readers who have followed this text from the beginning have invested substantial effort to reach this point. Now, we are ready to have fun interfacing a 68000 microprocessor to input and output devices. Much of the pleasure lies in the control one feels (finally!) in writing software to sense inputs, control outputs, and establish relationships between inputs and outputs. In this chapter, we work through numerous *case studies* of interfaces to I/O devices. We'll start with very simple I/O and advance to complex interfaces with interrupt-driven software.

Central to each example is a peripheral interface IC. The interface components connect to a peripheral interface IC, which in turn connects to the 68000 CPU through address decoding, and so on. Peripheral interface ICs were discussed in general terms in Chapter 7; but now we'll examine specific devices. The opening examples use the 68681 DUART and the last several examples use the 6821 PIA. The data sheets for these devices are found in Appendix H (68681) and Appendix I (6821).

Table 9-1 is a summary of the interface examples in this chapter.

## 9.2.  THE 68681 DUART

The 68681 dual universal asynchronous receiver/transmitter (DUART) is a 40-pin peripheral interface IC that greatly simplifies interfaces be-

tween a variety of I/O devices and the 68000 microprocessor. It is inexpensive (less than $10) and available through many electronics parts outlets. As noted in Chapter 8, the 68681 is quite powerful and, unfortunately, quite complex. We'll avoid much of the complexity of the 68681 by focusing on a subset of its features. These are explained in detail, but we'll not attempt to fully explore the 68681's potential. Appendix H contains the 68681 data sheet, and should be consulted for more information on other interfacing schemes.

The hardware interface between the 68681 and the 68000 microprocessor was presented in Chapter 8 in the context of the 68KMB (see Figure 8-15). In this chapter we are concerned primarily with (a) the hardware interface to the *other side* of the 68681—the I/O devices, and (b) writing programs to read and write the 68681's internal registers to set and control its modes of operation and perform I/O to interface circuits.

Since the 68681 has four register select lines (RS1–RS4), it occupies 16 addresses in the memory space of the host system. Each address can be read or written; so, it includes 16 read addresses and 16 write addresses. These are summarized in Table 9-2.

The address decoding on the 68KMB places the 68681 at $00C001, $00C003, and so on, up to $00C01F, and these are the addresses we'll use in this chapter. The addresses are odd since the interface is on the low-order byte of the 68000's data bus. Within a program the easiest way to access the 68681 is through equated symbols for each register, as illustrated below.

```
DUART   EQU   $00C001   ;68681 DUART base address
MR1A    EQU   0*2       ;Mode Register 1A
MR2A    EQU   0*2       ;Mode Register 2A
SRA     EQU   1*2       ;Status Register A
CSRA    EQU   1*2       ;Clock Select Register A
CRA     EQU   2*2       ;Command Register A
RBA     EQU   3*2       ;Receive Buffer A
TBA     EQU   3*2       ;Transmit Buffer A
* etc.
```

Table 9-1.   Summary of Interface Examples.

| Example | Description | 68681 Serial Port | 68681 Parallel Ports | Timer | 6821 | Interrupts |
|---------|-------------|:---:|:---:|:---:|:---:|:---:|
| 9-1 | Initialize the 68681 serial port | • | | | | |
| 9-2 | Output messages to the console | • | | | | |
| 9-3 | Read switches and write to LEDs | | • | | | |
| 9-4 | Rotating bit program using LEDs and input switches | | • | | | |
| 9-5 | Generate a 2 Hz square using the 68681 Timer | | • | • | | |
| 9-6 | Send characters to the console, timed by interrupts | • | | • | | • |
| 9-7 | Read four input switches and output code to 7-segment LED | | • | | | |
| 9-8 | Counting using one 7-segment LED | | • | | | |
| 9-9 | Counting using four 7-segment LEDs driven by MC14499 | | • | • | | |
| 9-10 | Time-of-day clock using interrupts and 7-segment LEDs driven by MC14499 | | • | • | | • |
| 9-11 | Input expansion using 74LS165 shift registers | • | • | | | |
| 9-12 | Hexadecimal keypad interface | • | | | • | |
| 9-13 | Sawtooth wave using MC1408L8 DAC | | | | • | |
| 9-14 | Digital sine wave generator using MC1408L8 DAC | | | | • | |
| 9-15 | Musical scale using keyboard, DAC, filter, amplifier, speaker, and interrupts | • | | • | • | • |
| 9-16 | Analog input using trimpot connected to ADC0804 | • | | | • | |
| 9-17 | Speech digitizing/playback using DAC & ADC | | | • | • | • |

This looks a bit strange at first, but it is an efficient way to set up the software. The base address of the DUART appears only once, in the first equate. If the address changes, only the first line needs updating. Each register is assigned its mnemonic symbol, and is equated to *two times* the address given in Table 9-2. We multiply by two because every second address is used—the odd addresses. To access the 68681's registers, we use address register indirect addressing. An address

Table 9-2.   68681 Internal Registers.

| RS4 | RS3 | RS2 | RS1 | Read Operation Mnemonic | Read Operation Full Name | Write Operation Mnemonic | Write Operation Full Name |
|-----|-----|-----|-----|----------|-----------|----------|-----------|
| 0 | 0 | 0 | 0 | MR1A, MR2A | Mode Register A | MR1A, MR2A | Mode Register A |
| 0 | 0 | 0 | 1 | SRA | Status Registrar A | CSRA | Clock-Select Register A |
| 0 | 0 | 1 | 0 | - | (do not access) | CRA | Command Register A |
| 0 | 0 | 1 | 1 | RBA | Receive Buffer A | TBA | Transmit Buffer A |
| 0 | 1 | 0 | 0 | IPCR | Input Port Change Register | ACR | Auxiliary Control Register |
| 0 | 1 | 0 | 1 | ISR | Interrupt Status Register | IMR | Interrupt Mask Register |
| 0 | 1 | 1 | 0 | CUR | Counter Upper Register | CTUR | Counter/Timer Upper Reg. |
| 0 | 1 | 1 | 1 | CLR | Counter Lower Register | CTLR | Counter/Timer Lower Reg. |
| 1 | 0 | 0 | 0 | MR1B, MR2B | Mode Register B | MR1B, MR2B | Mode Register B |
| 1 | 0 | 0 | 1 | SRB | Status Register B | CSRB | Clock-Select Register B |
| 1 | 0 | 1 | 0 | - | (do not access) | CRB | Command Register B |
| 1 | 0 | 1 | 1 | RBB | Receive Buffer B | TBB | Transmit Buffer B |
| 1 | 1 | 0 | 0 | IVR | Interrupt-Vector Register | IVR | Interrupt-Vector Register |
| 1 | 1 | 0 | 1 | IP | Input Port (unlatched) | OPCR | Output Port Config. Reg. |
| 1 | 1 | 1 | 0 | START | Start Counter Command[†] | OPRSET | Output Port Reg. Bit Set |
| 1 | 1 | 1 | 1 | STOP | Stop Counter Command[†] | OPRCLR | Output Port Reg. Bit Clear |

[†] Address triggered commands

**Figure A.**

```
MOVEA.L  #DUART,A0    ;A0 points to 68681
MOVE.B   #$55,CRA(A0) ;put $55 in Command Register A
```

register is initialized with the 68681's base address and the register mnemonic is used as an offset. For example, the value $55 is written to the 68681's command register A as shown in Figure A.

A single instruction with absolute long addressing would also work, but if the software accesses many 68681 registers, then the approach above is much better because of the reduced size and execution time of the MOVE.B instructions. The mechanism for MR1A and MR2A to share the same address is explained later in this chapter.

## 9.3.  RS232C SERIAL INTERFACE

The 68681 includes two asynchronous serial ports, called *channel A* and *channel B*. Typically, these connect to terminals, computers, or modems through RS232C drivers and receivers. The hardware interface presented in Chapter 8 will suffice for the present discussion; that is, channel A is interfaced to an RS232C terminal or host computer running terminal emulation software (see Figure 8-15 in Chapter 8).

We begin with a brief introduction to RS232C and asynchronous communications. When a character is sent over an RS232C interface, it is framed with a *start bit* at the beginning and one or more *stop bits* at the end. The start bit is low, the stop bit(s) is high. If a continuous stream of characters is transmitted, the next start bit immediately follows the stop bit(s). If there are gaps between characters, an *idle state*, also high, is maintained. This form of communication channel, in which the receiver must resynchronize with each character, is called *asynchronous*.

A *parity bit* is sometimes added between the last data bit and the stop bit. Either *even parity* or *odd*

parity is used. For example, if odd parity is used, then the parity bit is set to 1 or 0 such that the total number of 1-bits, including the data bits and the parity bit, is odd.

The number of data bits depends on the coding scheme. ASCII codes are seven bits, so this is a common configuration. Figure 9-1 illustrates asynchronous transmission of the letter *a* framed by a start bit, a stop bit, and an odd parity bit.

The reciprocal of the transmission time for each bit is called the *baud rate*. Note that, although baud rate is often quoted in *bits per second*, the figure does not represent the transmission rate of the original data because of the overhead in the start bit, party bit, and stop bit(s).

One final point: The logic levels "1" and "0" in Figure 9-1 represent TTL signal levels transmitted or received by the 68681 IC. RS232C signal levels are different, so special translation buffers are needed. A TTL logic 0 is in the range 0 volts to 0.8 volts. The equivalent RS232C condition is called a SPACE, which is between +3 volts and +25 volts. A TTL logic 1 is in the range 2.4 volts to 5.0 volts. The equivalent RS232C condition is a MARK, which is between −3 volts and −25 volts (see Table 9-3).

Translation is performed by special ICs, such as the MC1488 RS232C line driver and the MC1489 RS232C line receiver. Recent devices combine the driver and receiver in a single package along with dc/dc voltage conversion. An example is the MAX232 (Maxim Integrated Products, Inc.) used in the 68KMB (see Chapter 8, Figure 8-15).

Back to the 68681. To prepare the 68681 for receiving and transmitting ASCII characters, several registers must be initialized to set the mode of operation.

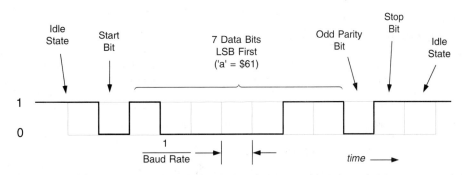

**Figure 9-1.   Asynchronous character transmission.**

## Table 9-3.   RS232C-to-TTL Signal Conversion.

| TTL | | | RS232C | |
|---|---|---|---|---|
| Logic | Voltage | | Logic | Voltage |
| high (1) | 2.4 to 5 volts | = | MARK | −3 to −25 volts |
| low (0) | 0 to 0.8 volts | = | SPACE | +3 to +25 volts |

**Example 9-1:** Write an instruction sequence to initialize the 68681's channel A to operate at 9600 baud with 1 start bit, 7 data bits, odd parity, and 2 stop bits.

**Solution:** See Figure B.

**Discussion:** There are five instructions in the initialize sequence. The first sets up address register A0 as a pointer to the DUART (line 26). The second through fifth instructions write the appropriate bit patterns into four DUART registers. These patterns and their effect are summarized in Figure 9-2.

In line 27, mode register 1A is initialized with $06 to set the character size to 7 bits and to enable odd parity. For clarity, the offset "MR1A" is included in the instruction; however, since the offset for this register is zero (see line 19), it could be omitted. If omitted, the addressing mode in line 27 becomes address register indirect (with no offset) and one word is saved. To fully appreciate the programmable potential of the 68681, Appendix H should be consulted to learn about other features enabled by writing different bit patterns to 68681 registers.

In line 28, mode register 2A is initialized with $0F to set the number of stop bits to two. This pertains to the transmitter only. When characters are transmitted out of the 68681, two stop bits are appended at the end of the character (after the parity bit). This is a safety precaution only, to avoid the potential loss of characters at the receiving end of the connection. The 68681 only needs one stop bit for incoming characters.

A subtle feature of MR1A and MR2A needs explaining: They occupy the same address in the 68681. This is a common trait of many peripheral interface ICs, and we'll meet it again

## Figure B.

```
 1                     ***********************************************************
 2                     * INIT681.SRC                                            *
 3                     *                                                        *
 4                     * The following instructions initialize serial port     *
 5                     * A of the 68681 DUART to operate at 9600 baud with      *
 6                     * the following character format:                        *
 7                     *                                                        *
 8                     *       1 start bit (by definition)                      *
 9                     *       7 data bits                                      *
10                     *       odd parity                                       *
11                     *       2 stop bits (transmit only)                      *
12                     *                                                        *
13                     * Note: These instructions must execute immediately      *
14                     * after a reset operation and before the 68681           *
15                     * serial port A is used for character reception/          *
16                     * transmission.                                          *
17                     ***********************************************************
18 0000C001            DUART  EQU     $C001           ;68681 base address
19 00000000            MR1A   EQU     0*2             ;mode register 1A
20 00000000            MR2A   EQU     0*2             ;mode register 2A
21 00000002            CSRA   EQU     1*2             ;clock select register A
22 00000004            CRA    EQU     2*2             ;command register A
23 000000BB            B9600  EQU     $BB             ;9600 baud init value
24
25 00008000                   ORG     $8000
26 00008000 207C0000  INIT681 MOVEA.L #DUART,A0       ;A0 points to DUART
   00008004 C001
27 00008006 117C0006          MOVE.B  #$06,MR1A(A0)   ;7 data, odd parity
   0000800A 0000
28 0000800C 117C000F          MOVE.B  #$0F,MR2A(A0)   ;2 stop bits
   00008010 0000
29 00008012 117C00BB          MOVE.B  #B9600,CSRA(A0) ;set baud rate
   00008016 0002
30 00008018 117C0005          MOVE.B  #$05,CRA(A0)    ;Tx/Rx enabled
   0000801C 0004
31 0000801E                   END     INIT681
```

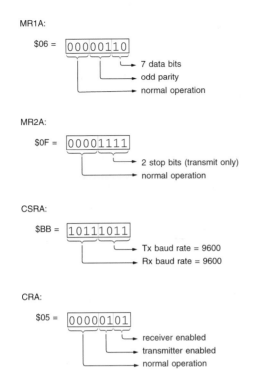

MR1A:

$06 = `00000110`
→ 7 data bits
→ odd parity
→ normal operation

MR2A:

$0F = `00001111`
→ 2 stop bits (transmit only)
→ normal operation

CSRA:

$BB = `10111011`
→ Tx baud rate = 9600
→ Rx baud rate = 9600

CRA:

$05 = `00000101`
→ receiver enabled
→ transmitter enabled
→ normal operation

**Figure 9-2.  Initializing the 68681 DUART.**

with the 6821 PIA. After reset, the first write to register zero in the 68681 writes to MR1A. The second and subsequent writes to the same address are directed to MR2A. Note that the instructions in lines 27 and 28 both write to address 0 inside the 68681. Since the first write follows a system reset (in which the 68681 is also reset), it writes to MR1A. The second write is directed to MR2A. Although this seems peculiar at first, it saves one address and helps keep the number of register select lines low. There is a mechanism to switch back to MR1A on-the-fly if necessary (through CRA bits 4–6; see Table 6, in Appendix H).

In line 29, clock select register A is initialized with $BB to set the receive and transmit baud rates to 9600. A variety of other baud rates may be selected, as given in Table 6 in Appendix H. Note that the rates in Appendix H assume the 68681's X1/CLK pin is driven at 3.6864 MHz.

In line 30, command register A is initialized with $05 to enable the receiver and transmitter for channel A.  ∎

**Example 9-2:** Write a program called MESSAGE that displays *Assembly-language programming is fun* on the terminal attached to the 68681's serial port A. Display the message ten times on ten separate lines. Assume the 68681 has been initialized as shown earlier. Provide two solutions: The first should be self-contained and include the necessary subroutines. The second should use subroutines or traps from MON68K, as appropriate (see Appendix E).

**1st Solution:** See below.

```
1                    *********************************************************
2                    * MESSAGE.SRC                                          *
3                    *                                                      *
4                    * This program sends a message to the console ten      *
5                    * times on ten separate lines.  The program includes  *
6                    * OUTSTR and OUTCHR subroutines.                       *
7                    *********************************************************
8    0000C001        DUART    EQU    $C001            ;68681 base address
9    00000002        SRA      EQU    1*2              ;status register A
10   00000006        TBA      EQU    3*2              ;Tx buffer A
11   0000000D        CR       EQU    $0D              ;ASCII carriage return
12   0000000A        LF       EQU    $0A              ;ASCII line feed
13
14   00008000                 ORG    $8000
15   00008000 3E3C0009 MESSAGE MOVE.W #9,D7           ;use D7 as counter
16   00008004 227C0000 LOOP    MOVEA.L #MESSAGE,A1    ;A1 --> message
     00008008 803E
17   0000800A 6124             BSR.S  OUTSTR          ;send it
18   0000800C 51CFFFF6         DBRA   D7,LOOP         ;repeat until done
19   00008010 60FE             BRA    *               ;infinite loop
20
21                    *********************************************************
22                    * OUTCHR - OUTput CHaRacter in D0 to serial port      *
23                    *                                                      *
24                    *          ENTER:  D0[0:8] contains ASCII character    *
25                    *          EXIT:   D0[0:8] unchanged                   *
26                    *                  D0[8:31] cleared                    *
27                    *          USES:   no subroutines                      *
28                    *********************************************************
```

*Continued.*

```
29    00008012 2F08       OUTCHR    MOVE.L    A0,-(A7)          ;save A0
30    00008014 3F07                 MOVE.W    D7,-(A7)          ;save D7
31    00008016 207C0000             MOVEA.L   #DUART,A0         ;A0 points to 68681
      0000801A C001
32    0000801C 1E280002   OUTCHR2   MOVE.B    SRA(A0),D7        ;get port A status
33    00008020 02070004             ANDI.B    #4,D7             ;buffer empty?
34    00008024 67F6                 BEQ.S     OUTCHR2           ;no:  check again
35    00008026 11400006             MOVE.B    D0,TBA(A0)        ;yes: send character
36    0000802A 3E1F                 MOVE.W    (A7)+,D7          ;restore D7
37    0000802C 205F                 MOVE.L    (A7)+,A0          ;restore A0
38    0000802E 4E75                 RTS
39
40                       ********************************************************
41                       * OUTSTR - OUTput null-terminated STRing              *
42                       *                                                     *
43                       *         ENTER:   A1 points to string               *
44                       *         EXIT:    A1 points to null-terminator       *
45                       *         USES:    OUTCHR                             *
46                       ********************************************************
47    00008030 2F00       OUTSTR    MOVE.L    D0,-(A7)          ;save D0 on stack
48    00008032 1019       OUTSTR2   MOVE.B    (A1)+,D0          ;get character
49    00008034 6704                 BEQ.S     EXIT              ;if null byte, done
50    00008036 61DA                 BSR.S     OUTCHR            ;send it
51    00008038 60F8                 BRA.S     OUTSTR2           ;repeat
52    0000803A 201F       EXIT      MOVE.L    (A7)+,D0          ;restore D0
53    0000803C 4E75                 RTS
54
55    0000803E 0D0A4173   MESSAGE   DC.B      CR,LF,'Assembly language programming'
      00008042 73656D62
      00008046 6C79206C
      0000804A 616E6775
      0000804E 61676520
      00008052 70726F67
      00008056 72616D6D
      0000805A 696E67
56    0000805D 20697320             DC.B      ' is fun',0
      00008061 66756E00
57    00008065                      END       MESSAGE
```

**Discussion:** The solution above contains a main program loop, two subroutines, and a null-terminated ASCII string. The main loop is very straightforward. In line 15, D7 is initialized as a counter prior to entering the loop. The loop contains three instructions: line 16 initializes A1 to point to the message string, line 17 sends the message to the console using the OUTSTR subroutine, and line 18 decrements the counter and branches back until the counter equals −1. The program ends with an infinite *branch-to-itself* instruction in line 19.

All the work is done in the subroutines. The entry and exit conditions of the subroutines are well documented, making them very easy to understand. OUTSTR calls OUTCHR for individual character output to the console. The process is repeated until a null character is found. Note that the output message is followed by a null byte (line 56). Within OUTCHR, two 68681 registers are accessed: SRA (status register, channel A) and TBA (transmit buffer, channel A). The status register contains eight bits that signal various conditions for channel A, such as parity error, overrun error, or receiver ready (see Appendix H, Table 6). Bit 2 is the TxRDY flag that is set when the 68681 is ready to accept a new character for transmission. A zero in TxRDY indicates the 68681 is still transmitting a previous character and its buffer is full. In the event TxRDY = 0, the software must sit in a loop waiting for TxRDY = 1. All this takes place in lines 32–34. Once the 68681 transmitter is ready, a character is loaded into the transmit buffer by writing to TBA (line 35).

**Figure C.**

```
 1                          *************************************************
 2                          *  MESSAGE2.SRC                                 *
 3                          *                                               *
 4                          *  This program sends a message to the console ten  *
 5                          *  times on ten separate lines.  The program uses two *
 6                          *  traps from MON68K: TRAP #2 (OUTSTR) and TRAP #14   *
 7                          *  (return to monitor).                         *
 8                          *************************************************
 9  0000000D     CR       EQU     $0D             ;ASCII carriage return
10  0000000A     LF       EQU     $0A             ;ASCII line feed
11
12  00008000              ORG     $8000
13  00008000 3E3C0009  MESSAGE2 MOVE.W  #9,D7           ;use D7 as counter
14  00008004 227C0000  LOOP     MOVEA.L #MESSAGE,A1  ;A1 --> message
    00008008 8012
15  0000800A 4E42               TRAP    #2              ;OUTSTR trap
16  0000800C 51CFFFF6           DBRA    D7,LOOP         ;repeat until done
17  00008010 4E4E               TRAP    #14             ;return to MON68K
18
19  00008012 0D0A4173  MESSAGE  DC.B    CR,LF,'Assembly language programming'
    00008016 73656D62
    0000801A 6C79206C
    0000801E 616E6775
    00008022 61676520
    00008026 70726F67
    0000802A 72616D6D
    0000802E 696E67
20  00008031 20697320           DC.B    ' is fun',0
    00008035 66756E00
21  00008039              END     MESSAGE2
```

**2nd Solution:** See Figure C above.

**Discussion:** By using the resources in MON68K, the second solution to this problem is much more compact. The OUTSTR subroutine is packaged in MON68K as a trap. It is exactly the same as OUTSTR in solution #1, except the final instruction is RTE (return from exception) rather than RTS (return from subroutine). Within OUTSTR a trap accesses OUTCHR; but this is local to MON68K, so an additional trap is not needed in our solution. The listings for OUTSTR and OUTCHR are found in Appendix E in IO.LST. OUTSTR is assigned trap #2 so its address must exist in the monitor EPROM at address $000088—the vector address for trap #2. This assignment is found in MON68K.LST, also in Appendix E.

Solution #2 terminates smoothly with trap #14, which branches to the correct entry point in MON68K to display the monitor prompt and prepare for the next command. One nice point about traps is that we need not concern ourselves with the absolute address of the subroutines or the absolute address of the MON68K entry point. This will become more evident later as we use more MON68K resources, some through traps, some through subroutine calls. ■

## 9.4.  SWITCHES AND LEDS

Our next interface is simple input from switches and output to LEDs. For this, we use the parallel input and output ports of the 68681. The input port is only 6 bits, while the output port is 8 bits. As evident in Figure 9-3, the interface is quite simple. Connections are shown on the J1 connector of the 68KMB for reference.

The LEDs are driven from OP0–OP7 at the 68681. Since the 68681 is an MOS device, and can only drive slightly more than one TTL load ($I_{OL} = 2.4$ mA, see Appendix H, DC Electrical Characteristics), buffers are added. The 74LS244 provides sufficient current for the LEDs. Series resistors set the operating current to about 15 mA. With the LEDs connected as shown, a low (0) turns them on, and a high (1) turns them off.

The switches are connected to IP0–IP5 at the 68681. For any switch that is closed, 0 volts or logic 0 is read at the corresponding input pin. For any switch that is open a pull-up resistor ensures that the corresponding pin is read as a logic 1.

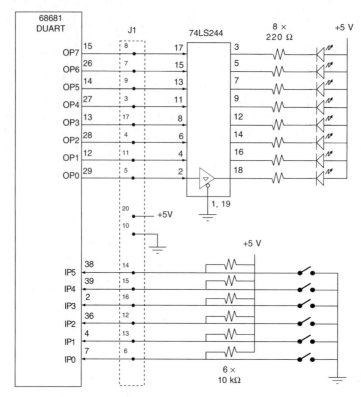

Figure 9-3.   68681 interface to LEDs and switches.

**Example 9-3:** Write a *wire* program using the switch/LED interface in Figure 9-3. The program should continually read the switches at IP0–IP5 and turn on/off the corresponding LED at OP0–OP5 for any switch that is closed/open.

**Solution:** See Figure D.

**Discussion:** The solution above uses three of the 68681's registers: IPR, OPR_SET, and OPR_CLR. The input port is easily accessed by reading IPR

**Figure D.**

```
 1     ****************************************************************
 2                     * WIRE681.SRC                                    *
 3                     *                                                *
 4                     * This is a "wire" program.  It reads the 68681  *
 5                     * input port and updates the output port, simulating *
 6                     * wire connections, as follows:                  *
 7                     *                                                *
 8                     *       IP0 ——> OP0                              *
 9                     *       IP1 ——> OP1                              *
10                     *       IP2 ——> OP2                              *
11                     *       IP3 ——> OP3                              *
12                     *       IP4 ——> OP4                              *
13                     *       IP5 ——> OP5                              *
14                     ****************************************************************
15  0000C001           DUART   EQU     $00C001         ;base address of 68681
16  0000001A           IPR     EQU     13*2            ;input port register
17  0000001C           OPR_SET EQU     14*2            ;set bit command reg.
18  0000001E           OPR_CLR EQU     15*2            ;clear bit cmd. reg.
19
20  00008000                   ORG     $8000
21  00008000 207C0000 WIRE681  MOVEA.L #DUART,A0       ;A0 points to 68681
    00008004 C001
22  00008006 1028001A LOOP     MOVE.B  IPR(A0),D0      ;read input port
23  0000800A 020000FF          ANDI.B  #$FF,D0         ;(mask if desired)
24  0000800E 6102              BSR.S   OUT681          ;update output port
25  00008010 60F4              BRA     LOOP            ;repeat
26
```

*Continued.*

```
27                         **************************************************
28                         * OUT681 - OUTput data to 68681 output port      *
29                         *                                                *
30                         *        ENTER:   D0[0:7] contains data to output *
31                         *                 A0 points to 68681 DUART       *
32                         *        EXIT:    all registers intact           *
33                         *        USES:    no subroutines                 *
34                         **************************************************
35   00008012 1140001E     OUT681  MOVE.B   D0,OPR_CLR(A0) ;clr. bits, set pins
36   00008016 4600                 NOT.B    D0
37   00008018 1140001C             MOVE.B   D0,OPR_SET(A0) ;set bits, clr. pins
38   0000801C 4600                 NOT.B    D0             ;restore D0
39   0000801E 4E75                 RTS
40   00008020                      END      WIRE681
```

**Table 9-4.   Function of Input Switches for Example 9-4.**

| Input Switches | | | LED Rotation | |
|---|---|---|---|---|
| IP2 | IP1 | IP0 | Direction | Frequency |
| 0 | 0 | 0 | left | 1 Hz |
| 0 | 0 | 1 | left | 2 Hz |
| 0 | 1 | 0 | left | 4 Hz |
| 0 | 1 | 1 | left | 8 Hz |
| 1 | 0 | 0 | right | 1 Hz |
| 1 | 0 | 1 | right | 2 Hz |
| 1 | 1 | 0 | right | 4 Hz |
| 1 | 1 | 1 | right | 8 Hz |

at address $13_{10}$ inside the 68681. Writing data to the output pins is tricky, so the instructions are packaged in a subroutine called OUT681 (discussed below). The main loop has four instructions. Data are read from IP0–IP5 in line 22 and placed into D0. Line 24 calls the OUT681 subroutine to write data to the output port. The last instruction (line 25) completes the loop by branching back to line 22.

OUT681 works as follows: First, data are written to OPR_CLR (line 35). Where there are 1s in the data, the corresponding register bit is cleared. The output pins are the complement of the register bits, so writing 1s to OPR_CLR sets the corresponding output pin. Then, data are complemented (line 36) and written to OPR_SET (line 37). Where there are 0s in the original data, the corresponding output pins are cleared. The combined effect of writing to OPR_CLR and OPR_SET, as just described, is to copy the original data in D0 to the output port. The data are restored to the original value in line 38 just prior to returning in line 39.

The operation the 68681's output port may seem odd, but there is a good reason for it to work as it does. First, note that the output port is not *readable* (see Table 9-2). Second, consider that the outputs might be divided among two or more interfaces. If the software driver for one interface needs to set or clear a few bits in the output port while leaving the others as is, there is no easy way to do so (since the output port is write-only). The 68681 implementation, as evident in the OUT681 subroutine, is a simple solution to this, allowing output pins to be set or cleared independent of other pins. ∎

Our next design example is purely for fun. It illustrates the sort of software play that is possible once input and output ports are available.

**Example 9-4:** Write a *rotating bit* program to operate with the switches and LEDs in Figure 9-3. The program should light one LED and then rotate its position according to the input switches as specified in Table 9-4.

**Solution:** See below.

```
1                          **************************************************
2                          * ROTATE.SRC                                     *
3                          *                                                *
4                          * This program performs a few simple operations with *
5                          * the switches and LEDs attached to the 68681 ports. *
6                          * The program turns on one LED and then rotates its   *
7                          * position left or right at a variable frequency.    *
8                          * Input switches control the program as follows:     *
9                          *                                                *
10                         *        IP1   IP0    Frequency of Rotation      *
11                         *        ====================================    *
12                         *        0     0         1 Hz                    *
13                         *        0     1         2 Hz                    *
```

*Continued.*

```
14                          *         1         0          4 Hz                    *
15                          *         1         1          8 Hz                    *
16                          *                                                      *
17                          *         IP2              Direction of Rotation       *
18                          *         ===================================          *
19                          *         0                   left                     *
20                          *         1                   right                    *
21                          *************************************************************
22  0000C001       DUART    EQU     $00C001         ;68681 base address
23  0000001A       IPR      EQU     13*2            ;input port reg.
24  0000001C       OPR_SET  EQU     14*2            ;set bit command reg.
25  0000001E       OPR_CLR  EQU     15*2            ;clear bit cmd. reg.
26  00032000       ONE_SEC  EQU     204800          ;1 sec. delay count
27                 * NOTE: 3686400 / 18 / 204800 = 1 Hz
28
29  00008000                ORG     $8000
30  00008000 207C0000 ROTATE MOVEA.L #DUART,A0                ;point to 68681
    00008004 C001
31  00008006 103C00FE       MOVE.B   #$FE,D0                  ;begin at LED #0
32  0000800A 6138    LOOP9  BSR.S    OUT681                   ;update LEDs
33  0000800C 1228001A       MOVE.B   IPR(A0),D1               ;read switches
34  00008010 02410003       ANDI.W   #3,D1                    ;check IP0/IP1 1st
35  00008014 E519           ROL.B    #2,D1                    ;long word align
36  00008016 2E3B1016       MOVE.L   COUNT(PC,D1.W),D7 ;get delay count
37  0000801A 6122           BSR.S    DELAY                    ;delay
38  0000801C 1228001A       MOVE.B   IPR(A0),D1               ;read switches
39  00008020 08010002       BTST.B   #2,D1                    ;test bit #2 (IP2)
40  00008024 6704           BEQ.S    LEFT                     ;IP2 = 1?
41  00008026 E218    RIGHT  ROR.B    #1,D0                    ;no:  rotate right
42  00008028 60E0           BRA      LOOP9
43  0000802A E318    LEFT   ROL.B    #1,D0                    ;yes: rotate left
44  0000802C 60DC           BRA      LOOP9
45
46                 * Create look-up table for counts
47  0000802E 00032000 COUNT DC.L    ONE_SEC         ;1 Hz (1 sec. delay)
48  00008032 00019000       DC.L     ONE_SEC/2      ;2 Hz
49  00008036 0000C800       DC.L     ONE_SEC/4      ;4 Hz
50  0000803A 00006400       DC.L     ONE_SEC/8      ;8 Hz
51
52                 *************************************************************
53                 * DELAY - create a software DELAY using D7 as count  *
54                 *                                                      *
55                 *         ENTER:   D7[0:31] = count                    *
56                 *         EXIT:    D7[0:31] = 0                         *
57                 *                  all other registers intact          *
58                 *         USES:    no subroutines                      *
59                 *                                                      *
60                 * NOTE: If the 68000 is operating from a 3.6864 MHz  *
61                 * crystal, the delay equals COUNT x 18/3686400 sec.   *
62                 *************************************************************
63  0000803E 5387    DELAY  SUBQ.L   #1,D7   ;8 cycles
64  00008040 66FC           BNE      DELAY   ;10 cycles (branch taken)
65  00008042 4E75           RTS
66
67                 *************************************************************
75  00008044 1140001E OUT681 MOVE.B  D0,OPR_CLR(A0) ;clr. bits, set pins
76  00008048 4600           NOT.B    D0
77  0000804A 1140001C       MOVE.B   D0,OPR_SET(A0) ;set bits, clr. pins
78  0000804E 4600           NOT.B    D0              ;restore D0
```

*Continued.*

```
79  00008050 4E75        RTS
80  00008052             END    ROTATE
```

**Discussion:** The program contains a main loop (lines 30–44), a look-up table (lines 47–50), and two subroutines (lines 52–79). No new features of the 68681 are introduced, so our discussion focuses on programming techniques. D0 is initialized in line 31 with $FE. When this value is written to the output port (line 32), LED #0 turns on and LEDs #1–7 turn off.

Lines 33–37 control the frequency of rotation using a software delay. The switches are read into D1 in line 33. The two least-significant bits control the frequency. These bits are isolated in line 34, then multiplied by four in line 35. This adjustment is necessary since each count is 32-bits or four bytes. The look-up occurs in line 36 using PC-relative addressing with an index and offset. D1 is the index. The offset is COUNT which identifies the beginning of the table. The assembler converts COUNT to the appropriate PC-relative offset. The offset is $16 which is embedded in the low-byte of the extension word in line 36. The 32-bit count is read from the look-up table and placed in D7 (line 36), and then the delay subroutine is called.

After returning from the delay subroutine, the direction of rotation is determined in lines 38–44. The switches are read again in line 38, then bit 2 (IP2) is tested. If IP2 = 0 the rotation is left, so a branch occurs (line 40) to a rotate left instruction, operating on D0. If IP2 = 1, the branch test in line 40 fails and the rotate right in line 41 occurs. Either way, the program branches back to line 32 to repeat the process.

The delay subroutine (lines 63–65) is very straightforward. The count in D7 is repeatedly decremented until it equals zero. The main trick is *tuning* the count to achieve the correct delay. The delay ($t_D$) is controlled by three parameters: COUNT, the number of clock cycles in the delay loop ($n$), and the CPU clock period ($t_C$):

$$t_D = COUNT \times n \times t_C$$

With COUNT = 204,800 (lines 26 & 47), $t_C = 1/(3.6864 \text{ MHz})$, and $n = 18$ (lines 63–64),

$$t_D = 204,800 \times 18 \times (1/3,686,400)$$
$$= 1 \text{ second}$$

So, a count of 204,800 yields a 1-second delay (line 47) for a rotate frequency of 1 Hz. A count of half of that yields a 0.5-second delay for a frequency of 2 Hz (line 48), and so on. The exact frequencies are slightly less than desired because of the extra instruction cycles outside the delay loop.

Since the OUT681 subroutine is the same as in Example 9-3, the comment header is deleted to keep the listing short. ■

## 9.5.  68681 TIMER

Software delays are the poor man's solution to timed input/output. The main disadvantage is that the CPU is stuck in a loop and *cannot go out and do other things* while the delay is ongoing. The solution is a timer. The 68681 includes a 16-bit timer/counter that can be programmed to give the same effect as a software delay. The timing occurs in the background, in the 68681's internal hardware. Furthermore, it is possible to set up the 68681 to interrupt the CPU when a timeout occurs. This relieves the CPU from the burden of decrementing a register in software or checking the timer status. The CPU is free to service other devices or execute other programs.

Before we advance to interrupt-driven programs (let's walk before we run!), we'll present a simple example using the 68681's timer. As with the serial port example earlier, we limit ourselves to one mode of operation. The 68681 timer can also operate as a counter. In this mode, it counts *events* arriving as pulses on an input port pin. See Appendix H for details.

**Example 9-5:** Write a program using the 68681's timer to create a 2 Hz square wave on OP3.

**Solution:** See below.

```
1   ************************************************************
2   *  TWOHZ.SRC                                              *
3   *                                                         *
4   *  This program uses the 68681 timer to create a 2 Hz     *
5   *  square wave on OP3.  If the 68681 X1 input is          *
6   *  driven at 3.6864 MHz, then the frequency on OP3        *
7   *  equals                                                 *
8   *                                                         *
9   *       3686400 / 2 / 16 / COUNT                          *
```

*Continued.*

```
10                              *                                                           *
11                              * where COUNT is the 16-bit integer in the timer            *
12                              * registers CTUR and CTLR.  CTUR holds the upper             *
13                              * byte, CTLR holds the lower byte.                           *
14                              * * * * * * * * * * * * * * * * * * * * * * * * * * * * * * * * * * * * * * * * * * * * *
15   0000C001             DUART     EQU     $00C001          ;68681 base address
16   00000008             ACR       EQU     4*2              ;auxiliary control reg.
17   0000000C             CTUR      EQU     6*2              ;counter/timer upper reg
18   0000000E             CTLR      EQU     7*2              ;counter/timer lower reg.
19   0000001A             OPCR      EQU     13*2             ;output port config. reg.
20   0000E100             COUNT     EQU     57600            ;2 Hz count (see above)
21
22   00008000                       ORG     $8000
23   00008000 207C0000    TWOHZ     MOVEA.L #DUART,A0
     00008004 C001
24   00008006 303CE100              MOVE.W  #COUNT,D0
25   0000800A 0188000C              MOVEP.W D0,CTUR(A0)
26   0000800E 117C0070              MOVE.B  #$70,ACR(A0)     ;crystal clock / 16
     00008012 0008
27   00008014 117C0004              MOVE.B  #$04,OPCR(A0)    ;timer output to OP3
     00008018 001A
28   0000801A 60FE                  BRA     *                ;now relax a bit
29   0000801C                       END     TWOHZ
```

**Discussion:** If this program is run with the interface in Figure 9-3, then LED #2 will flash at 2 Hz. The entire program is only six instructions. Furthermore, the last instruction (line 28) is a *branch-to-itself* loop which could expand into another program while the LED continues to flash. Let's walk through the program.

A0 is initialized with the base address of the 68681 in line 23. The 16-bit timer/counter is initialized in line 25 using a MOVEP instruction. This instruction moves a word of data to two consecutive odd-byte addresses (see Appendix B). The timer/counter counts down from this value and is reloaded with the same value after reaching zero. The square wave generated by the timer has a frequency equal to the "clock source" frequency divided by two, divided by the preload integer. There are several possible clock sources. The 3-bit pattern written to bits 4–6 of the auxiliary control register determines which is used. The value $70 (line 26) selects timer mode with the X1/CLK input divided by 16 as the clock source. (Table 6 in Appendix H describes the other possible clock sources.) So, with COUNT = 57,600 (line 20) and X1/CLK driven from the system clock at 3.6864 MHz, the frequency of the timer output is

```
3686400 / 16 / 2 / 57600 = 2 Hz
```

The instruction in line 27 writes $04 into the output port configuration register, which directs the timer output to OP3. ■

## 9.6.   68681 TIMER WITH INTERRUPTS

Our next example will be slightly larger than the previous one. We'll add interrupts to the recipe, so we must proceed with caution. Several details emerge that must be understood thoroughly. The choice of which interrupt level to use is determined by the hardware connection to pin 21 on the 68681. This is the 68681's $\overline{\text{IRQ}}$ output. In Chapter 8 we showed $\overline{\text{IRQ}}$ connecting to the 68KMB's level-2 interrupt input, so we'll use level-2 interrupts here. The 68681 can be programmed to provide any interrupt vector during an IACK cycle. We'll program it to provide the usual level-2 autovector. This is 26, as given in Chapter 6 (see Table 6-2), which will cause the PC to be loaded with the vector in location $4 \times 26 = 104_{10} = \$000068$. We can't load address $000068 with anything, however, since it lies within the monitor EPROM. MON68K provides user access to interrupts through a jump table (see Appendix E, MON68K Resources). The jump table begins at address $008000 as the entry point for user programs, followed by $008006 as the entry point for the level-2 ISR, $00800C as the entry point for the level-3 ISR, and so on. These entry points are spaced 6 bytes apart, just enough for a jump instruction to the appropriate routine.

**Example 9-6:** Write an interrupt-driven program using the 68681 timer to display an asterisk on the console upon each interrupt. Use $FFFF as the timer reload value.

**Solution:** See below.

```
 1            ***********************************************************
 2            * STAR.SRC                                                *
 3            *                                                         *
 4            * This is a simple interrupt-driven program using the     *
 5            * 68681 timer.  The timer is initialized with $FFFF        *
 6            * and interrupts are enabled using level-2                 *
 7            * autovectors.  Upon each interrupt, an asterisk is        *
 8            * sent to the console.                                     *
 9            *                                                         *
10            * Note: The entry point for a level-2 interrupt is        *
11            * $008006, as programmed in the MON68K EPROM.             *
12            ***********************************************************
13 0000C001          DUART   EQU     $00C001 ;68681 base address
14 00000008          ACR     EQU     4*2     ;auxiliary control register
15 0000000C          CTUR    EQU     6*2     ;counter/timer upper register
16 0000000E          CTLR    EQU     7*2     ;counter/timer lower register
17 0000000A          IMR     EQU     5*2     ;interrupt mask register
18 00000018          IVR     EQU     12*2    ;interrupt vector register
19 0000001E          STOP    EQU     15*2    ;timer stop command address
20 0000001A          I2VECTOR EQU    26      ;I2 autovector number
21
22 00008000                  ORG     $8000                ;MON68K jump table
23 00008000 4EF90000 STAR    JMP     >INIT    ;user prog. at $8000
   00008004 800C
24 00008006 4EF90000         JMP     >L2ISR   ;INT2 entry at $8006
   0000800A 803A
25 0000800C 207C0000 INIT    MOVEA.L #DUART,A0        ;A0 -> 68681 DUART
   00008010 C001
26 00008012 117C0008         MOVE.B  #$08,IMR(A0)
   00008016 000A
27 00008018 117C001A         MOVE.B  #I2VECTOR,IVR(A0)
   0000801C 0018
28 0000801E 117C00FF         MOVE.B  #$FF,CTUR(A0)
   00008022 000C
29 00008024 117C00FF         MOVE.B  #$FF,CTLR(A0)
   00008028 000E
30 0000802A 117C0070         MOVE.B  #$70,ACR(A0)
   0000802E 0008
31 00008030 007C0700         ORI.W   #$0700,SR    ;mask all interrupts
32 00008034 027CF9FF         ANDI.W  #$F9FF,SR    ;mask level 1 only
33 00008038 60FE             BRA     *            ;sit on this awhile
34
35            ***********************************************************
36            * L2ISR - Level 2 Interrupt Service Routine               *
37            *                                                         *
38            *         - read 68681 STOP_COUNTER_COMMAND register       *
39            *            to clear the timer interrupt flag             *
40            *         - send an asterisk to the serial port            *
41            ***********************************************************
42 0000803A 4A28001E L2ISR   TST.B   STOP(A0)  ;stop cmd, clr interrupt
43 0000803E 103C002A         MOVE.B  #'*',D0   ;send an asterisk
44 00008042 4E41             TRAP    #1        ; upon each interrupt
45 00008044 4E73             RTE
46 00008046          END     STAR
```

**Discussion:** This program has only fifteen instructions; however, it contains several subtle and complex details. Our previous programs began at $8000 without consideration of the jump table. This is fine if interrupts are not used. If interrupts are used, then $8000 is the entry point for the user program, $8006 is the entry point for level-2 ISRs, and so on (see Appendix E). Our program, therefore, begins at $8000 with a jump instruction (line 23) that skips over the level-2 interrupt entry point. The instruction JMP >INIT is exactly 6 bytes long; so the following jump instruction (line 24) lands in address $8006, the correct entry point for a level-2 ISR.[1] The instruction JMP >L2ISR only executes when a level-2 interrupt occurs.

The main program begins in line 25 with six instructions that initialize the 68681. The interrupt mask register is loaded with $08 in line 26. Bit 3 in the mask is set to enable timer interrupts. The interrupt vector register is loaded with $26_{10}$ in line 27. When the 68681 responds to an IACK cycle, it puts this value on the data bus. The 68000 CPU uses this value to retrieve the level-2 interrupt vector and begin execution of the ISR. In lines 28 and 29, the reload value $FFFF ($65,535_{10}$) is placed in the timer/counter registers. Based on the equation given earlier, the timer output frequency—the frequency of interrupts—is

```
3686400 / 16 / 2 / 65535 = 1.76 Hz
```

---

[1]Recall that the assembler for these examples uses ">" to force absolute long addressing.

Because $70 is written to the auxiliary control register (line 30), the formula uses the same clock source as in the previous example.

The instructions in lines 31 and 32 have the combined effect of setting the 68000's interrupt mask level to 1. This blocks level-1 interrupts, but enables interrupts on levels 2 through 7.

The timer/counter generates an interrupt every $1/1.76 = 571$ ms. In the level-2 ISR, two things happen. First, the interrupt source is cleared in line 42 by reading the STOP command register in the 68681. This register is *address triggered* (see Table 9-2), which means that reading the register triggers some action within the 68681. The action is to clear the interrupt request. This is necessary, otherwise another level-2 interrupt is generated immediately upon returning from the ISR. The second action performed in the ISR is to send an asterisk to the console (lines 43–44). This is a simple action that is useful for debugging or observing the program. The ISR terminates with RTE in line 45, which returns to the main routine—the *do nothing* loop in line 33. ■

---

## 9.7. 7-SEGMENT LED INTERFACE

One of the most useful interfaces is output to a 7-segment display. Whether a clock radio or a microwave oven, driving inexpensive output displays is one of the most common interfaces for microprocessors. We'll develop several such interfaces, beginning with a very simple one-digit display and advancing to a complex interrupt-driven time-of-day clock.

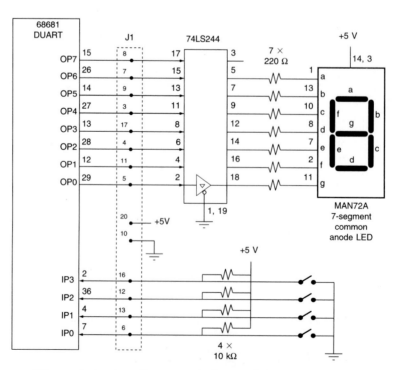

Figure 9-4.   Interface to switches and 7-segment LED.

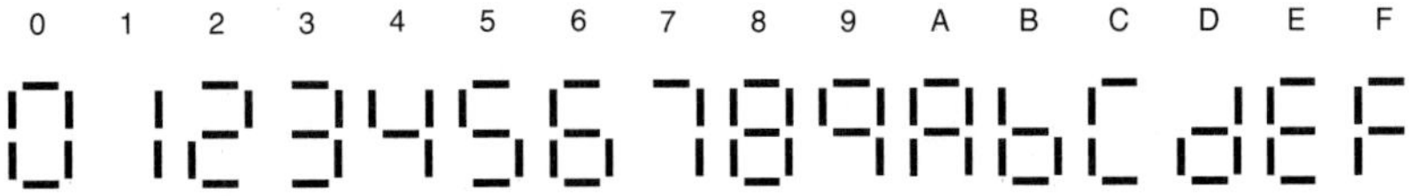

Figure 9-5.    7-segment LED patterns.

A simple interface between the 68681's parallel output port and a 7-segment LED display is shown in Figure 9-4. Four input switches are also shown connected to the input port.

As with the interface shown earlier to single LEDs, buffers are needed because the 68681 is an MOS device and has very limited drive capability. The 74LS244 includes eight three-state buffers, each capable of sinking 24 mA of current. The 220 Ω series resistors set the operating current of each LED to about 15 mA. The 7-segment display is a common anode type. Internally, the anodes of all seven LEDs are connected together; they appear on pins 14 and 3 for connection to +5 volts. The cathode of each LED appears on a separate pin for connection to the interface drivers. A low (logic 0) is required at the buffer output to turn a segment on.

Seven-segment displays are standardized in the labeling of the segments. The labeling starts with segment a at the top and proceeds clockwise around the character, finishing with segment g in the middle. Note in Figure 9-4 that segment g is driven by OP0 on the 68681, segment f is driven by OP1, and so on. Given this, the data pattern for each character is easily determined. Figure 9-5 shows the required pattern for the characters 0-9, and A-F.

So, the character "0" requires segment a on, segment b on, and so on, through to segment g which must be off. The pattern at the 68681's output port is $0000001_2 = \$01$.

Switches are added in Figure 9-4 to permit some interesting programming challenges, such as the following example.

**Example 9-7:** Write a program loop for the interface in Figure 9-4 that reads a hexadecimal code from the input switches and displays the equivalent 7-segment pattern on the output display.

**Solution:** See below.

```
 1                     *****************************************************
 2                     * LED7.SRC                                         *
 3                     *                                                   *
 4                     * This program performs hexadecimal-to-7-segment   *
 5                     * conversion.  A 4-bit code is read from IP0-IP3 and *
 6                     * converted to a 7-segment code to drive a 7-segment *
 7                     * LED connected to OP0-OP6.                         *
 8                     *****************************************************
 9  0000C001          DUART    EQU    $00C001      ;68681 base address
10  0000001A          IPR      EQU    13*2         ;input port register
11  0000001C          OPR_SET  EQU    14*2         ;set bit command reg.
12  0000001E          OPR_CLR  EQU    15*2         ;clear bit command reg.
13
14  00008000                   ORG    $8000
15  00008000 207C0000 LED7     MOVEA.L #DUART,A0   ;A0 points to 68681
    00008004 C001
16  00008006 1028001A LOOP     MOVE.B  IPR(A0),D0  ;read input port
17  0000800A 0240000F          ANDI.W  #$F,D0      ;clear bits 4-15
18  0000800E 6104              BSR.S   CONVERT     ;convert to 7-seg code
19  00008010 6118              BSR.S   OUT681      ;update LEDs
20  00008012 60F2              BRA     LOOP        ;repeat
21
22                     *****************************************************
23                     * CONVERT - CONVERT a 4-bit code to a 7-segment code *
24                     *                                                   *
25                     *          ENTRY   D0[0:3] contains 4-bit code      *
26                     *                  D0[4-15] cleared                 *
27                     *          ENTRY   D0[0:6] contains 7-segment code  *
28                     *          USES    no subroutines                   *
29                     *****************************************************
30  00008014 103B0004 CONVERT  MOVE.B  TABLE(PC,D0.W),D0 ;table look-up
```

*Continued.*

```
31   00008018 4E75                    RTS
32   0000801A 014F1206  TABLE  DC.B   $01,$4F,$12,$06   ;7-segment LED
33   0000801E 4C24200F         DC.B   $4C,$24,$20,$0F   ;  patterns
34   00008022 000C0860         DC.B   $00,$0C,$08,$60
35   00008026 31423038         DC.B   $31,$42,$30,$38
36
37                   * * * * * * * * * * * * * * * * * * * * * * * * * * * * * * * * * * * * * * * *
45   0000802A 1140001E  OUT681 MOVE.B D0,OPR_CLR(A0) ;clr. bits, set pins
46   0000802E 4600             NOT.B  D0
47   00008030 1140001C         MOVE.B D0,OPR_SET(A0) ;set bits, clr. pins
48   00008034 4600             NOT.B  D0              ;restore D0
49   00008036 4E75             RTS
50   00008038                  END    LED7
```

**Discussion:** The main loop of the program contains five instructions. The input code is read in line 16, reduced to four bits in line 17, converted to a 7-segment pattern in line 18, and written to the output display in line 19. Line 20 branches back to repeat the process.

The conversion from a 4-bit hexadecimal code to a 7-segment pattern is packaged in the CONVERT subroutine in lines 30–35. All the work is done in one MOVE.B instruction in line 30. The source addressing mode is PC-relative with index and offset. D0—the 4-bit code—is the index, and TABLE is the offset. The assembler converts TABLE to the appropriate 8-bit offset ($04) that is inserted as the low-byte of the extension word. The table immediately follows the RTS instruction. The first code in the table is $01, the correct 7-segment pattern for the character "0," as explained earlier. The other codes are easily determined from Figure 9-4 and Figure 9-5.

The subroutine OUT681 is the same as in Example 9-3, so the comment header is deleted. ∎

**Example 9-8:** Write a program using the 7-segment LED interface in Figure 9-4 that counts from *0* to *F* repeatedly at a rate of 5 Hz.

**Solution:** See below.

```
1                   * * * * * * * * * * * * * * * * * * * * * * * * * * * * * * * * * * * * * * * *
2                   * LED5HZ.SRC                                              *
3                   *                                                         *
4                   * This is a count program.  It repeatedly counts         *
5                   * from 0 through F and outputs the count to the           *
6                   * 7-segment LED connected to OP0-OP6.  The rate of        *
7                   * counting is 5 Hz.                                       *
8                   * * * * * * * * * * * * * * * * * * * * * * * * * * * * * * * * * * * * * * * *
9    0000C001       DUART  EQU   $00C001         ;68681 base address
10   0000001C       OPR_SET EQU  14*2            ;set bit command reg.
11   0000001E       OPR_CLR EQU  15*2            ;clear bit command reg.
12   00032000       ONE_SEC EQU  204800          ;1 second delay count
13
14   00008000              ORG   $8000
15   00008000 207C0000 LED5HZ MOVEA.L #DUART,A0  ;A0 points to 68681
     00008004 C001
16   00008006 4201          CLR.B  D1            ;use D1 as counter
17   00008008 1001   LOOP   MOVE.B D1,D0         ;use D0 for look-up
18   0000800A 0240000F      ANDI.W #$F,D0        ;clear bits 4-15
19   0000800E 610E          BSR.S  CONVERT       ;convert to 7-seg code
20   00008010 6122          BSR.S  OUT681        ;update LEDs
21   00008012 2E3C0000      MOVE.L #ONE_SEC/5,D7
     00008016 A000
22   00008018 6128          BSR.S  DELAY         ;rest here awhile
23   0000801A 5241          ADDQ   #1,D1         ;increment counter
24   0000801C 60EA          BRA    LOOP          ;repeat
25
26                   * * * * * * * * * * * * * * * * * * * * * * * * * * * * * * * * * * * * * * * *
34   0000801E 103B0004 CONVERT MOVE.B TABLE(PC,D0.W),D0 ;table look-up
35   00008022 4E75          RTS
36   00008024 014F1206 TABLE DC.B   $01,$4F,$12,$06   ;7-segment LED
37   00008028 4C24200F      DC.B    $4C,$24,$20,$0F   ;  patterns
```

*Continued.*

```
38  0000802C 000C0860          DC.B    $00,$0C,$08,$60
39  00008030 31423038          DC.B    $31,$42,$30,$38
40
41                             *******************************************************
49  00008034 1140001E  OUT681  MOVE.B  D0,OPR_CLR(A0) ;clr. bits, set pins
50  00008038 4600              NOT.B   D0
51  0000803A 1140001C          MOVE.B  D0,OPR_SET(A0) ;set bits, clr. pins
52  0000803E 4600              NOT.B   D0             ;restore D0
53  00008040 4E75              RTS
54
55                             *******************************************************
66  00008042 5387      DELAY   SUBQ.L  #1,D7          ;8 cycles
67  00008044 66FC              BNE     DELAY          ;10 cycles (branch taken)
68  00008046 4E75              RTS
69  00008048              END   LED5HZ
```

**Discussion:** This is a simple program that uses subroutines presented earlier. Register D1 is cleared in line 16 and is used as a binary counter throughout the program. The count is copied to D0 (line 17) and then reduced to 4-bits (line 18) before conversion to a 7-segment pattern (line 19). The usual delay subroutine is called in line 22 with ONE_SEC/5 as the delay count. With a 1/5th second delay, the count rate is 5 Hz. The count is incremented in line 23 just prior to branching back to repeat the loop. ∎

## 9.8. 4-DIGIT 7-SEGMENT DISPLAY

A major drawback of the interface in Figure 9-4 is that is consumes seven output lines on the 68681's output port. Not only that, a single digit of output is not of much use. There is a variety of multiplexing schemes to expand the interface to more digits without adding too many more lines to the interface. However, we can do better with a completely new strategy.

The Motorola MC14499 is a CMOS, 4-digit, 7-segment display driver that requires only three interface lines. The device is inexpensive (less than $5) and available from many electronics parts outlets. Furthermore, it is cascadable, allowing any number of output digits to be driven from the same three interface signals. We'll demonstrate the latter point shortly in an example of a time-of-day clock; but, first, we'll examine the interface schematic and timing requirements (see Figure 9-6).

The MC14499 includes internal logic to accept serial data, shift it along a series of flip flops, perform BCD-to-7-segment conversion, and multiplex

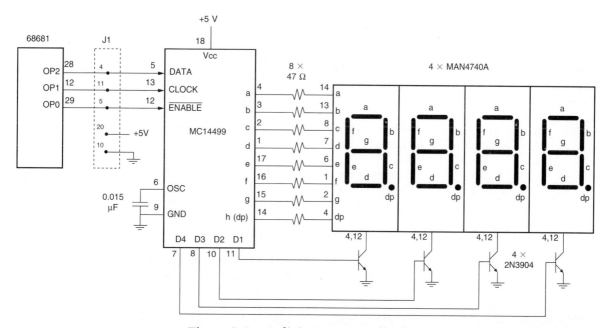

Figure 9-6.   4-digit 7-segment display.

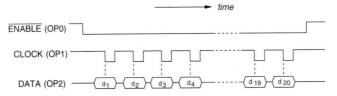

**Figure 7-7.   MC14499 timing.**

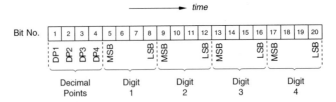

**Figure 9-8.   MC14499 digit and bit sequence.**

output data onto four 7-segment displays. The internal multiplex clock is generated through a single 0.015 μF capacitor. The common-cathode displays are individually turned on by a *digit* output signal (D1–D4) driving the base of an NPN transistor. The segment lines are driven through 47 Ω resistors that set the operating current of each LED to about 40 mA. The LEDs are pulsed with a duty cycle of 25%, so the average current is 10 mA.

With four digits driven from three output lines, the MC14499 is an economical choice for multi-digit displays. Three signals are required:

$\overline{\text{ENABLE}}$  active-low input that enables the MC14499 to receive new data

DATA  serial data in

CLOCK  a clock input that stores DATA in the internal shift register

The MC14499 accepts 20 bits of serial input, consisting of four 1-bit decimal-point codes and four 4-bit digit codes. The timing requirements are illustrated in Figure 9-7.

The software requirements are summarized as follows:

1. Ensure $\overline{\text{ENABLE}}$ and CLOCK are high.
2. Assert $\overline{\text{ENABLE}}$ (drive it low).
3. Put a valid data bit on the DATA line.
4. Toggle the CLOCK line (2 μs minimum low-time).
5. Go to step 3 and repeat 20 times.
6. De-assert $\overline{\text{ENABLE}}$ (drive it high).

The order that DATA bits are sent is, of course, critical. Figure 9-8 illustrates the sequencing of the decimal points and digit data.

The first bit transmitted is the decimal point for digit #1. Note that digit #1 is on the left in Figure 9-6. A "1" will light a decimal point; a "0" will leave it off. Following the decimal point bits, the four digit codes are sent. Digit #1 is sent first, beginning with the most-significant bit. The last bit transmitted is the least-significant bit for digit #4.

**Example 9-9:** Write a program that displays a 4-digit count on the LED interface in Figure 9-6. The count should increment at a rate of 10 Hz.

**Solution:** See below.

```
 1    ***********************************************************
 2    * COUNT4.SRC                                             *
 3    *                                                        *
 4    * This program copies BCD data to four 7-segment         *
 5    * displays driven by a MC14499 serial display            *
 6    * driver.  A 4-digit count is copied at a rate of        *
 7    * 10 Hz.  The interface uses the 68681 DUART to          *
 8    * drive the MC14499 as follows:                          *
 9    *                                                        *
10    *     68681              14499                           *
11    *     =====    ==============================            *
12    *     OP0      ENABLE (active low)                       *
13    *     OP1      CLOCK (negative edge-triggered)           *
14    *     OP2      DATA                                      *
15    ***********************************************************
```

*Continued.*

```
16    0000C001                DUART    EQU      $00C001        ;base address of 68681
17    0000001C                OPR_SET  EQU      14*2           ;set bit command reg.
18    0000001E                OPR_CLR  EQU      15*2           ;clear bit cmd. reg.
19    00032000                ONE_SEC  EQU      204800         ;count for 1 sec. delay
20
21    00008000                         ORG      $8000
22    00008000 207C0000       COUNT4   MOVEA.L  #DUART,A0      ;A0 points to 68681
      00008004 C001
23    00008006 117C0007                MOVE.B   #7,OPR_CLR(A0) ;MC14499 inputs high
      0000800A 001E
24    0000800C 227C0000                MOVEA.L  #DIGITS,A1     ;A1 points to digits
      00008010 A000
25    00008012 247C0000                MOVEA.L  #INC,A2        ;A2 points to inc.
      00008016 80A6
26    00008018 32BC0000                MOVE.W   #0,(A1)        ;init BCD digits
27    0000801C 137C0000                MOVE.B   #0,2(A1)       ;init decimal points
      00008020 0002
28    00008022 611A           LOOP     BSR.S    UPDATE         ;update LED display
29    00008024 43E90002                LEA      2(A1),A1       ;A1 -> past digits
30    00008028 45EA0002                LEA      2(A2),A2       ;A2 -> past increment
31    0000802C 023C00EF                ANDI.B   #$EF,CCR       ;clear X-bit in CCR
32    00008030 C30A                    ABCD     -(A2),-(A1)    ;increment BCD digits
33    00008032 C30A                    ABCD     -(A2),-(A1)
34    00008034 2E3C0000                MOVE.L   #ONE_SEC/10,D7 ;delay for 10 Hz
      00008038 5000
35    0000803A 6164                    BSR.S    DELAY
36    0000803C 60E4                    BRA      LOOP
37
38                            *********************************************************
39                            * UPDATE - send 4 BCD digits to MC14499               *
40                            *                                                     *
41                            * Clear OP0 (MC14499 ENABLE), send four decimal       *
42                            * points = 0 followed by four digits, then set OP0.   *
43                            * The most significant digit (bits 12-15) is sent     *
44                            * first.                                              *
45                            *                                                     *
46                            *       ENTER - A0 points to 68681                    *
47                            *             - A1 points to digits                   *
48                            *       EXIT  - display updated, all reg. intact      *
49                            *       USES  - OUT4                                  *
50                            *********************************************************
51    0000803E 48A7C000       UPDATE   MOVEM.W  D0-D1,-(SP)    ;save registers
52    00008042 117C0001                MOVE.B   #1,OPR_SET(A0) ;assert ENABLE line
      00008046 001C
53    00008048 4200                    CLR.B    D0             ;clear decimal points
54    0000804A 611A                    BSR.S    OUT4           ;send DPs first
55    0000804C 3011                    MOVE.W   (A1),D0        ;get BCD digits
56    0000804E 123C0004                MOVE.B   #4,D1          ;use D1 as counter
57    00008052 E958           UPDATE2  ROL.W    #4,D0          ;align bits (0-3 1st)
58    00008054 6110                    BSR.S    OUT4           ;send them
59    00008056 5341                    SUBQ     #1,D1          ;last digit?
60    00008058 66F8                    BNE      UPDATE2        ;no: send again
61    0000805A 117C0001                MOVE.B   #1,OPR_CLR(A0) ;yes: deassert ENABLE
      0000805E 001E
62    00008060 4C9F0003                MOVEM.W  (SP)+,D0-D1    ;restore registers
63    00008064 4E75                    RTS
64
65                            *********************************************************
66                            * OUT4 - OUTput 4 bits to the MC14499                 *
67                            *                                                     *
68                            * Place data bit on OP2 (MC14499 DATA), then toggle   *
```

*Continued.*

```
69                                 * OP1 (MC14499 CLOCK).  Repeat four times.  Bit 3 is *
70                                 * sent first.  Serial data is output on OP2.         *
71                                 *                                                     *
72                                 *          ENTER:   D0[0:3] contains bits to output   *
73                                 *          EXIT:    data bits sent, all reg. intact   *
74                                 *          USES:    no subroutines                    *
75                                 * * * * * * * * * * * * * * * * * * * * * * * * * * * * * * * * * * * * * * * * * *
76   00008066 48A7F800   OUT4      MOVEM.W   D0-D4,-(SP)
77   0000806A E418                 ROR.B     #2,D0              ;align as D0[1,0,7,6]
78   0000806C 163C0004             MOVE.B    #4,D3              ;use D3 as counter
79   00008070 E318       LOOP2     ROL.B     #1,D0              ;put bit in D0 bit 2
80   00008072 1400                 MOVE.B    D0,D2              ;save data
81   00008074 02000004             ANDI.B    #$04,D0            ;mask other bits
82   00008078 1140001E             MOVE.B    D0,OPR_CLR(A0)     ;if bit set, set pin
83   0000807C 0A000004             EORI.B    #$04,D0            ;complement data bit
84   00008080 1140001C             MOVE.B    D0,OPR_SET(A0)     ;if bit clr, clr pin
85   00008084 183C0002             MOVE.B    #$02,D4            ;create CLK pulse
86   00008088 1144001C             MOVE.B    D4,OPR_SET(A0)     ;clear CLK pin
87   0000808C 4E71                 NOP                          ;stretch (MC14499
88   0000808E 4E71                 NOP                          ; needs 2 us pulse)
89   00008090 1144001E             MOVE.B    D4,OPR_CLR(A0)     ;set CLK pin
90   00008094 1002                 MOVE.B    D2,D0              ;restore data
91   00008096 5343                 SUBQ      #1,D3              ;last of 4 bits?
92   00008098 66D6                 BNE       LOOP2              ;no:  do again
93   0000809A 4C9F001F             MOVEM.W   (SP)+,D0-D4        ;yes: done
94   0000809E 4E75                 RTS
95
96                                 * * * * * * * * * * * * * * * * * * * * * * * * * * * * * * * * * * * * * * * * * *
107  000080A0 5387       DELAY     SUBQ.L    #1,D7        ;8 cycles
108  000080A2 66FC                 BNE       DELAY        ;10 cycles (branch taken)
109  000080A4 4E75                 RTS
110
111  000080A6 0001       INC       DC.W      1            ;inc. = 1 (code segment)
112
113  0000A000                      ORG       $A000        ;data segment at $A000
114  0000A000            DIGITS    DS.W      1            ;digits in data segment
115  0000A002                      END       COUNT4
```

**Discussion:** This is our most substantial program yet. There are 50 instructions spanning 115 lines of source code. The code section includes initialization instructions (lines 22–27), a main loop (lines 28–36), three subroutines (lines 38–109), and one constant (line 111). The data section contains one RAM word to store the count (line 114).

The program is well documented, so our discussion is brief. The main loop does the following: update the LED display (line 28), increment the count (lines 29–33), delay 1/10th second (line 34–35), and branch back (line 36). Incrementing the count is tricky because it is decimal and requires ABCD (add binary-coded decimal) instructions. The main limitation is the addressing modes available to ABCD. The program places the digits in the *data segment* (line 114) and the increment in the *code segment* (line 111). The distinction between code and data is not overly important in this example; however, if we imagine installing the program in EPROM or ROM in an embedded control system, then the program, including the

increment, is read-only and the digit codes are read/write. The instruction preceding the two ABCDs (line 31) explicitly clears the X-bit in the CCR just in case it is set. This is necessary because ABCD performs an *add with carry* operation with X as the BCD carry.

Data are output to the MC14499 in two subroutines. UPDATE asserts ENABLE (OP0), then calls OUT4 five times, each time passing the appropriate 4-bit code. OUT4 performs the low-level task of putting a data bit on DATA (OP2) and toggling CLOCK (OP1). Two NOP instructions are inserted in OUT4 to stretch the CLOCK pulse applied to the MC14499. After five calls to OUT4, UPDATE de-asserts ENABLE and returns to the main loop.  ■

---

## 9.9.  8-DIGIT 7-SEGMENT DISPLAY

Although four output digits are better than one, this is not enough for many readouts. Any number

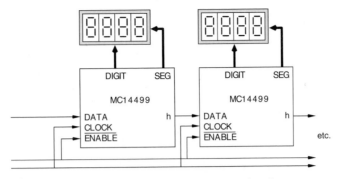

Figure 9-9.    8-digit 7-segment display.

of MC14499s may be cascaded to drive any number of output digits. A circuit with two MC14499s driving an 8-digit display is shown in Figure 9-9.

Most connections from Figure 9-6 are the same, and are therefore omitted in the figure. The CLOCK and $\overline{\text{ENABLE}}$ lines connect to both MC14499s. Serial data propagate from one MC14499 to the next on the decimal point line—$h$. Cascading requires $1111_2$ as the decimal point data. This pattern causes data to pass through the MC14499 and exit on $h$ during clocking. This scheme precludes decimal points in the output display.

The following steps are required to send data to cascaded MC14499s:

1. Ensure $\overline{\text{ENABLE}}$ and CLOCK are high.
2. Assert $\overline{\text{ENABLE}}$ (drive it low).
3. Put a valid data bit on the DATA line.
4. Toggle the CLOCK line (2 µs minimum low-time).

5. Go to step 3 and repeat $20 \times n$ times, where $n$ is the number of MC14499s.
6. De-assert $\overline{\text{ENABLE}}$ (drive it high).

These steps are the same as those given earlier, except (a) the first four bits in each group of 20 must be $1111_2$, and (b) steps 3 and 4 are repeated $20 \times n$ times, where $n$ is the number of MC14499s.

With eight output digits, more interesting and complex applications are possible, such as the following:

**Example 9-10.** Write a time-of-day program to display the time using the circuit in Figure 9-9. The program should be interrupt-driven with updates occurring in the background. Store the time in RAM locations that can be initialized on-the-fly from the monitor program.

**Solution:** See below.

```
 1   ************************************************************
 2   * TIME.SRC - time-of-day clock                           *
 3   *                                                        *
 4   * This program implements a time-of-day clock using      *
 5   * two cascaded MC14499 serial 7-segment display          *
 6   * drivers.  The two MC14499s drive 8 displays, as        *
 7   * follows:                                               *
 8   *                                                        *
 9   *        DISPLAY   PURPOSE                               *
10   *        1 & 2     hours                                 *
11   *        3 & 4     minutes                               *
12   *        5 & 6     seconds                               *
13   *        7 & 8     not used (always blank)               *
14   *                                                        *
15   * The program is interrupt-driven and returns to         *
16   * MON68K after the initialize sequence.  The time is     *
17   * set using MON68K's memory modify command at the        *
18   * following RAM addresses:                               *
19   *                                                        *
20   *        ADDRESS   CONTENTS                              *
21   *        00A000    hours                                 *
22   *        00A001    minutes                               *
23   *        00A002    seconds                               *
24   ************************************************************
```

*Continued.*

```
25   0000C001              DUART    EQU      $00C001     ;68681 base address
26   0000001C              OPR_SET  EQU      14*2        ;set bit reg. (clear pin)
27   0000001E              OPR_CLR  EQU      15*2        ;clear bit reg. (set pin)
28   00000008              ACR      EQU      4*2         ;auxiliary control reg.
29   0000000C              CTUR     EQU      6*2         ;counter/timer upper reg.
30   0000000E              CTLR     EQU      7*2         ;counter/timer lower reg.
31   0000000A              IMR      EQU      5*2         ;interrupt mask register
32   00000018              IVR      EQU      12*2        ;interrupt vector register
33   0000001E              STOP     EQU      15*2        ;stop timer command
34   0000E100              COUNT    EQU      57600       ;0.5 second timeout
35   F10000FF              TIME     EQU      $F10000FF   ;initial time for clock
36   0000001A              I2VECTOR EQU      26          ;level 2 interrupt vector
37
38   00008000                       ORG      $8000
39   00008000 4EF90000     TIME     JMP      >INIT       ;user program entry point
     00008004 800C
40   00008006 4EF90000              JMP      >L2ISR      ;INT2 entry point
     0000800A 8054
41                         * initialize pointers
42   0000800C 207C0000     INIT     MOVEA.L  #DUART,A0      ;A0 points to 68681
     00008010 C001
43   00008012 227C0000              MOVEA.L  #DIGITS,A1     ;A1 points to digits
     00008016 A000
44                         * initialize MC14499 and BCD codes
45   00008018 117C0007              MOVE.B   #7,OPR_CLR(A0) ;MC14499 inputs high
     0000801C 001E
46   0000801E 22BCF100              MOVE.L   #TIME,(A1)     ;init BCD digits
     00008022 00FF
47   00008024 137C00FF              MOVE.B   #$FF,4(A1)     ;init decimal points
     00008028 0004
48   0000802A 137C0002              MOVE.B   #2,5(A1)       ;init timeout counter
     0000802E 0005
49                         * initialize interrupts
50   00008030 117C0008              MOVE.B   #$08,IMR(A0)
     00008034 000A
51   00008036 117C001A              MOVE.B   #I2VECTOR,IVR(A0)
     0000803A 0018
52   0000803C 303CE100              MOVE.W   #COUNT,D0
53   00008040 0188000C              MOVEP.W  D0,CTUR(A0)
54   00008044 117C0070              MOVE.B   #$70,ACR(A0)
     00008048 0008
55   0000804A 007C0700              ORI.W    #$0700,SR      ;mask all interrupts
56   0000804E 027CF9FF              ANDI.W   #$F9FF,SR      ;mask level 1 only
57   00008052 4E4E                  TRAP     #14            ;return to MON68K
58
59                         *****************************************************
60                         * L2ISR - Level-2 Interrupt Service Routine        *
61                         *                                                  *
62                         *          - clear interrupt source                *
63                         *          - increment time                        *
64                         *          - output time                           *
65                         *****************************************************
66   00008054 48E700E0     L2ISR    MOVEM.L  A0-A2,-(SP)
67   00008058 207C0000              MOVEA.L  #DUART,A0      ;A0 -> DUART
     0000805C C001
68   0000805E 227C0000              MOVEA.L  #DIGITS,A1     ;A1 -> BCD digits
     00008062 A000
69   00008064 4A28001E              TST.B    STOP(A0)       ;clr interrupt source
70   00008068 53290005              SUBQ.B   #1,5(A1)       ;second time here?
71   0000806C 6652                  BNE.S    SKIP           ;no:  do nothing
72   0000806E 137C0002              MOVE.B   #2,5(A1)       ;yes: re-init count &
     00008072 0005
```

*Continued.*

```
73   00008074 61000050              BSR      UPDATE2          ;      update display
74   00008078 227C0000              MOVEA.L  #DIGITS+3,A1     ;A1 -> past digits
     0000807C A003
75   0000807E 247C0000              MOVEA.L  #INC+1,A2        ;A2 -> past increment
     00008082 8139
76   00008084 44FC0004              MOVE.W   #$04,CCR         ;clear X, set Z
77   00008088 C30A                  ABCD     -(A2),-(A1)      ;increment SECONDS
78   0000808A 0C110060              CMP.B    #$60,(A1)        ;SECONDS > 59?
79   0000808E 6D30                  BLT.S    SKIP             ;no:  done
80   00008090 4211                  CLR.B    (A1)             ;yes: reset to 0
81   00008092 45EA0001              LEA      1(A2),A2         ;
82   00008096 023C00EF              ANDI.B   #$EF,CCR         ;clear X in CCR
83   0000809A C30A                  ABCD     -(A2),-(A1)      ;increment MINUTES
84   0000809C 0C110060              CMP.B    #$60,(A1)        ;MINUTES > 59?
85   000080A0 6D1E                  BLT.S    SKIP             ;no:  done
86   000080A2 4211                  CLR.B    (A1)             ;yes: reset to 0
87   000080A4 45EA0001              LEA      1(A2),A2         ;
88   000080A8 5221                  ADD.B    #1,-(A1)         ;increment HOURS
89   000080AA 0C1100FA              CMP.B    #$FA,(A1)        ;HOURS > 12?
90   000080AE 6606                  BNE.S    SKIP2            ;no:  done
91   000080B0 12BC0010              MOVE.B   #$10,(A1)
92   000080B4 600A                  BRA.S    SKIP
93   000080B6 0C110013  SKIP2       CMP.B    #$13,(A1)
94   000080BA 6604                  BNE.S    SKIP
95   000080BC 12BC00F1              MOVE.B   #$F1,(A1)        ;yes: reset to 1
96   000080C0 4CDF0700  SKIP        MOVEM.L  (SP)+,A0-A2
97   000080C4 4E73                  RTE
98
99                     ************************************************************
100                    * UPDATE2 - send 8 BCD digits to two MC14499s             *
101                    *                                                         *
102                    * Clear OP0 (MC14499 ENABLE), send the decimal            *
103                    * points and the four digits, then set OP0.  Repeat.      *
104                    * Note: The most significant digit (bits 12-15) is        *
105                    * sent first.                                             *
106                    *                                                         *
107                    *       ENTER - A0 points to 68681                        *
108                    *             - A1 points to digits                       *
109                    *             - 4(A1) points to decimal points            *
110                    *       EXIT  - display updated, all reg. intact           *
111                    *       USES  - OUT4                                       *
112                    ************************************************************
113  000080C6 48A7FC20  UPDATE2     MOVEM.W  D0-D5/A2,-(SP)
114  000080CA 45E90004              LEA      4(A1),A2         ;A2 points to DPs
115  000080CE 3A3C0004              MOVE.W   #4,D5            ;2xD5 counts MC14499s
116  000080D2 117C0001  LOOP3       MOVE.B   #1,OPR_SET(A0)   ;assert ENABLE line
     000080D6 001C
117  000080D8 1012                  MOVE.B   (A2),D0          ;get DPs in D0[0:3]
118  000080DA 6122                  BSR.S    OUT4             ;send them
119  000080DC 5545                  SUBQ.W   #2,D5
120  000080DE 30315000              MOVE.W   0(A1,D5.W),D0    ;get digits
121  000080E2 163C0004              MOVE.B   #4,D3            ;D3 counts digits
122  000080E6 E958      LOOP4       ROL.W    #4,D0            ;align bits (0-3 1st)
123  000080E8 6114                  BSR.S    OUT4             ;send them
124  000080EA 5343                  SUBQ     #1,D3            ;last digit?
125  000080EC 66F8                  BNE      LOOP4            ;no:  send again
126  000080EE 4A45                  TST.W    D5               ;last MC14499?
127  000080F0 66E0                  BNE      LOOP3            ;no:  send again
128  000080F2 117C0001              MOVE.B   #1,OPR_CLR(A0)   ;yes: done
     000080F6 001E
129  000080F8 4C9F043F              MOVEM.W  (SP)+,D0-D5/A2
130  000080FC 4E75                  RTS
```

*Continued.*

```
131
132                             ***********************************************
143  000080FE  48A7F800  OUT4    MOVEM.W  D0-D4,-(SP)
144  00008102  E418              ROR.B    #2,D0              ;align as D0[1,0,7,6]
145  00008104  163C0004          MOVE.B   #4,D3              ;use D3 as counter
146  00008108  E318      LOOP2   ROL.B    #1,D0              ;put bit in D0 bit 2
147  0000810A  1400              MOVE.B   D0,D2              ;save data
148  0000810C  02000004          ANDI.B   #$04,D0            ;mask other bits
149  00008110  1140001E          MOVE.B   D0,OPR_CLR(A0)     ;if bit set, set pin
150  00008114  0A000004          EORI.B   #$04,D0            ;complement data bit
151  00008118  1140001C          MOVE.B   D0,OPR_SET(A0)     ;if bit clr, clr pin
152  0000811C  183C0002          MOVE.B   #$02,D4            ;create CLK pulse
153  00008120  1144001C          MOVE.B   D4,OPR_SET(A0)     ;clear CLK pin
154  00008124  4E71              NOP                         ;stretch (MC14499
155  00008126  4E71              NOP                         ; needs 2 us pulse)
156  00008128  1144001E          MOVE.B   D4,OPR_CLR(A0)     ;set CLK pin
157  0000812C  1002              MOVE.B   D2,D0              ;restore data
158  0000812E  5343              SUBQ     #1,D3              ;last of 4 bits?
159  00008130  66D6              BNE      LOOP2              ;no:  do again
160  00008132  4C9F001F          MOVEM.W  (SP)+,D0-D4        ;yes: done
161  00008136  4E75              RTS
162
163  00008138  01        INC     DC.B     1                  ;increment for BCD add
164
165  0000A000                    ORG      $A000              ;data segment (digits)
166  0000A000          DIGITS    DS.B     4                  ;4 bytes, 8 digits
167  0000A004          DP        DS.B     1                  ;decimal points
168  0000A005          TIMEOUT   DS.B     1                  ;counter for timeouts
169  0000A006                    END      TIME
```

This is a very ambitious program, with 85 instructions in 169 lines of source code. After the program is started, the time 1:00:00 appears on the output display and the monitor prompt appears. The monitor program executes *normally*, while interrupts occur in the background to update the display. Every second, the display increments. To set the time, the monitor's memory modify command is used to change byte locations $A000 (hours), $A001 (minutes), and $A002 (seconds).

Accuracy is limited only by the system's crystal. After several days of running on the prototype 68KMB, about one minute was lost. Accuracy is improved by substituting a trimming capacitor for the 10 pF capacitor in the system clock (see Figure 8-6 in Chapter 8) and tuning the output with a precision frequency counter.

Although bigger, there is little in the solution above that is new from our previous examples. Setting up the 68681's timer for interrupts (lines 50–56) is exactly the same as in Example 9-6, except that a count of 57,600 is used. This will cause an interrupt to be generated every 0.5 seconds. (Every second interrupt is ignored; see lines 70–71.) Incrementing the time is messier than incrementing a decimal count, since overflows occur on 59 (seconds), 59 (minutes), and 12 (hours). Incrementing occurs in the ISR in lines 74–95. UPDATE2 is modified to accommodate multiple MC14499s. OUT4 is the same as in the previous example. ∎

## 9.10.   68681 INPUT EXPANSION

With only six parallel inputs, the 68681 is limited in its ability to receive parallel data from external devices. As an example, a security system may sample a large number of *points*. Each point may indicate a status condition such as *door open* or *window broken*. A simple mechanism to expand the number of inputs on the 68681 is shown in Figure 9-10 using multiple 74LS165 shift registers.

Sixteen external inputs are shown in Figure 9-10; but the interface easily expands to any number of 74LS165s. The following steps are required to read the external inputs:

1. Ensure $\overline{LOAD}$ (OP1) and CLK (OP0) are high.
2. Pulse $\overline{LOAD}$ low for 1 μs.
3. Read data bit on IP0.
4. Pulse CLK low for 1 μs.
5. Go to step 3 and repeat $8 \times n$ times, where $n$ is the number of 74LS165s.

Step 2 is the critical *sampling window*. The state of the inputs when $\overline{LOAD}$ returns high is latched into

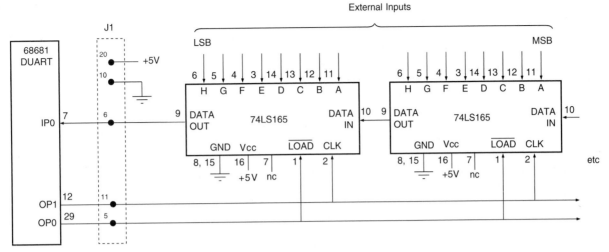

Figure 9-10.    68681 input expansion using 74LS165s.

the shift registers. Subsequent changes on the inputs are not sensed until the next pulse on $\overline{LOAD}$.

Since step 3 and step 4 occur in a loop, reading a data bit also requires a rotate operation to *build* a word of data. This is illustrated through the following example.

**Example 9-11.** Write a subroutine called RD165 to read the inputs in Figure 9-10 and save the data in locations $A000 and $A001. Place the subroutine within a program called LS165 that also outputs the data on the console as two hexadecimal bytes.

**Solution:** See below.

```
1           ***********************************************************
2           * LS165.SRC                                               *
3           *                                                         *
4           * This program reads two 74LS165s connected to the        *
5           * 68681.  The 16-bits read appear in RAM locations        *
6           * $00A000 and $0A001.                                     *
7           ***********************************************************
8  0000C001          DUART    EQU    $00C001  ;68681 base address
9  0000001A          IPR      EQU    13*2     ;input port register
10 0000001C          OPR_SET  EQU    14*2     ;set bit command register
11 0000001E          OPR_CLR  EQU    15*2     ;clear bit command register
12 0000000D          CR       EQU    $0D      ;ASCII carriage return code
13 0000000A          LF       EQU    $0A      ;ASCII line feed code
14 00000B14          OUT2HX   EQU    $000B14  ;address of OUT2HX subroutine
15 00000002          CHIPS    EQU    2        ;number of 74LS165s
16 00000002          CLOCK    EQU    $02      ;bit 1 on output port
17 00000001          LOAD     EQU    $01      ;bit 0 on output port
18 00032000          ONE_SEC  EQU    204800   ;count for 1 sec. delay
19
20 00008000                   ORG    $8000
21 00008000 207C0000 LS165     MOVEA.L #DUART,A0      ;A0 points to 68681
   00008004 C001
22 00008006 117C0003           MOVE.B  #3,OPR_CLR(A0) ;set interface lines
   0000800A 001E
23 0000800C 227C0000           MOVEA.L #BANNER,A1     ;send banner message
   00008010 8094
24 00008012 4E42               TRAP    #2            ; using OUTSTR trap
25
26           *********************************************************
27           * The main loop reads the 74LS165 inputs, outputs the   *
28           * ASCII hexadecimal code to the console, delays 1/5      *
29           * second, and repeats.                                  *
30           *********************************************************
```

*Continued.*

```
31   00008014 6112        LOOP     BSR.S    RD165            ;read 74LS165 data
32   00008016 6158                 BSR.S    REPORT           ;report result
33   00008018 2E3C0000             MOVE.L   #ONE_SEC/5,D7    ;delay 1/5 second
     0000801C A000
34   0000801E 6102                 BSR.S    DELAY
35   00008020 60F2                 BRA      LOOP             ;repeat
36
37                        ***********************************************************
38   00008022 5387        DELAY    SUBQ.L   #1,D7
39   00008024 66FC                 BNE      DELAY
40   00008026 4E75                 RTS
41
42                        ***********************************************************
43                        * RD165 - ReaD inputs from multiple 74LS165s            *
44                        *                                                        *
45                        * The interface between the 74LS165s and the 68681      *
46                        * uses the following lines:                             *
47                        *                                                        *
48                        *     74LS165  68681                                    *
49                        *     =====================                             *
50                        *     IP0      DATA IN                                  *
51                        *     OP1      CLOCK                                    *
52                        *     OP0      SHIFT/-LOAD                              *
53                        *                                                        *
54                        *     ENTER:  no conditions                            *
55                        *     EXIT:   data in RAM at $A000 & $A001              *
56                        *             all registers intact                     *
57                        *     USES:   no subroutines                           *
58                        ***********************************************************
59   00008028 48E7F0C0    RD165    MOVEM.L  D0-D3/A0-A1,-(SP) ;save reg. on stack
60   0000802C 207C0000             MOVEA.L  #DUART,A0         ;A0 points to 68681
     00008030 C001
61                        * a single pulse on LOAD latches data into the 74LS165s
62   00008032 117C0001             MOVE.B   #LOAD,OPR_SET(A0) ;pulse for 1 us
     00008036 001C
63   00008038 117C0001             MOVE.B   #LOAD,OPR_CLR(A0) ;——_____——
     0000803C 001E
64   0000803E 163C0002             MOVE.B   #CHIPS,D3        ;number of LS165s
65   00008042 227C0000             MOVEA.L  #LINES+CHIPS,A1  ;just past buffer
     00008046 A002
66                        * multiple pulses on CLOCK shift data out the 74LS165s
67   00008048 103C0008    BACK2    MOVE.B   #8,D0            ;8 lines per LS165
68   0000804C 1228001A    BACK     MOVE.B   IPR(A0),D1       ;read LS165
69   00008050 E211                 ROXR.B   #1,D1            ;put bit in C bit
70   00008052 E212                 ROXR.B   #1,D2            ;data byte in D2
71   00008054 117C0002             MOVE.B   #CLOCK,OPR_SET(A0) ;pulse for 1 us
     00008058 001C
72   0000805A 117C0002             MOVE.B   #CLOCK,OPR_CLR(A0)  ;——_____——-
     0000805E 001E
73   00008060 5300                 SUBQ.B   #1,D0            ;last bit read?
74   00008062 66E8                 BNE      BACK             ;no:  get next bit
75   00008064 1302                 MOVE.B   D2,-(A1)         ;yes: store byte
76   00008066 5303                 SUBQ.B   #1,D3            ;last LS165 read?
77   00008068 66DE                 BNE      BACK2            ;no:  read next
78   0000806A 4CDF030F             MOVEM.L  (SP)+,D0-D3/A0-A1 ;yes: restore &
79   0000806E 4E75                 RTS                       ;       return
80
81                        ***********************************************************
82                        * Report results on console (debugging aid)            *
83                        ***********************************************************
84   00008070 48E7C040    REPORT   MOVEM.L  D0-D1/A1,-(SP)   ;save reg. on stack
```

*Continued.*

```
85  00008074  103C000D           MOVE.B   #CR,D0            ;send CR using
86  00008078  4E41               TRAP     #1                ; OUTCHR trap
87  0000807A  227C0000           MOVEA.L  #LINES,A1         ;A1 points to data
    0000807E  A000
88  00008080  323C0001           MOVE.W   #CHIPS-1,D1       ;D1 counts LS165s
89  00008084  1019       REPORT2 MOVE.B   (A1)+,D0          ;get data
90  00008086  4EB80B14           JSR      OUT2HX            ;send it
91  0000808A  51C9FFF8           DBRA     D1,REPORT2        ;do next LS165
92  0000808E  4CDF0203           MOVEM.L  (SP)+,D0-D1/A1    ;yes: restore &
93  00008092  4E75               RTS                        ;    return
94
95  00008094  0D0A2A2A   BANNER  DC.B     CR,LF,'*** TEST 74LS165s ***',CR,LF,0
    00008098  2A205445
    0000809C  53542037
    000080A0  344C5331
    000080A4  36357320
    000080A8  2A2A2A0D
    000080AC  0A00
96
97  0000A000                     ORG      $A000             ;data segment
98  0000A000   LINES     DS.B     CHIPS             ;1 byte per LS165
99  0000A002                     END      LS165
```

**Discussion:** When this program executes, the following message is displayed on the console:

```
     *** TEST 74LS165s ***
     FFFF
```

The value FFFF is continually updated. A simple way to test the interface is with a test probe connected to ground. As inputs change to zero, the hexadecimal value displayed on the console changes accordingly.

The program looks messy, but it is really quite simple. The main loop reads the 74LS165s (line 31), reports the results on the console (line 32), delays for 200 ms (lines 33–34), and then repeats. The bulk of the work is done in the RD165 subroutine (lines 59–79) which follows the steps given earlier. The $\overline{\text{LOAD}}$ line is pulsed low in lines 62–63 to grab the input data. The subroutine is designed to work with any number of 74LS165s through the constant CHIPS, defined in line 15. Before data are read, D3 is initialized to count the number of 74LS165s (line 64), and A0 is initialized to point just past a RAM buffer where data are stored (line 65). Data are read in lines 67–77, eight bits per chip, with a series of rotate instructions interleaved with pulses on CLK.

The REPORT subroutine is purely to facilitate demonstrating the interface. Note, however, the effective use of a MON68K subroutine within REPORT. OUT2HX is called in line 90 to output a byte of data as two hexadecimal characters. This is a common subroutine from MON68K, so it is used here. The address of OUT2HX (line 14) is read from MON68K's link map, MON68K.MAP, found in Appendix E. The listing for OUT2HX is found in IO.LST, also in Appendix E. ■

## 9.11  6821 PERIPHERAL INTERFACE ADAPTER

While the 68681 is a powerful and inexpensive peripheral interface IC, there are many similar devices we could study. One of the most popular is the 6821 peripheral interface adapter (PIA), originally introduced with the 8-bit 6800 microprocessor. It has seen widespread use ever since, including many designs with advanced processors in the 68000 family. The 6821 is a parallel interface chip. It includes two 8-bit parallel ports each with two handshake signals to facilitate interfaces with devices that include write strobes, status signals, and so on. Each line in each port is programmable to function as an input or output. The data sheet for the 6821 is given in Appendix I.

Since the 6821 is a 6800-family peripheral, the interface to the 68000 microprocessor is slightly different than for the 68681. Data transfers are synchronized to the control bus signal E (enable) and acknowledgment is returned on $\overline{\text{VPA}}$. The timing for 6800 peripheral bus cycles is described in Appendix G. The PIA interface for the next several examples is shown in Figure 9-11. The J2 connections to the 68KMB are shown for reference. All J2 signals connect directly to the 68000 CPU except $\overline{\text{SD}}$ and $\overline{\text{INT3}}$, which appear in the interrupt circuitry in Figure 8-8 in Chapter 8.

Note in Figure 9-11 that data travel over the low-byte of the 68000's data bus, so only odd addresses are used. Address decoding uses A16 and $\overline{\text{SD}}$ to select the PIA, and A2 and A1 to select regis-

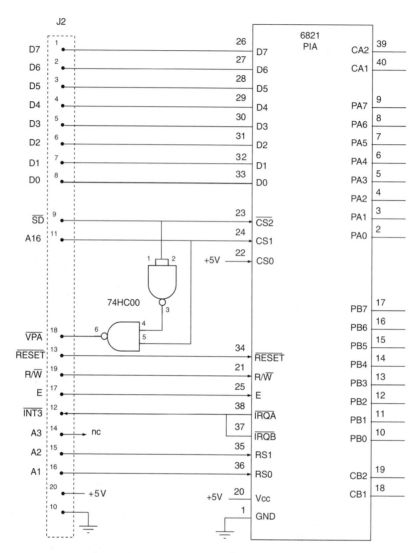

Figure 9-11.   6821 interface to the 68000.

ters within the PIA. Since A16 connects to the PIA's active-high chip select input, CS1, the following addresses are selected:

```
0000 0001 0000 0000 0000 0xx1
```

The zeros are really *don't cares,* but they are coded as zeros to avoid conflict with other devices or memories. In hexadecimal, the 6821 addresses are $010001, $010003, $010005, and $010007.

The $\overline{SD}$ (supervisor data) signal connects to 6821's $\overline{CS2}$ input; so it also contributes to the address decoding. $\overline{SD}$ could be omitted, except for one problem. During IACK cycles, the 68000 drives all address lines high except A1–A3, which contain the level of the interrupt. If A16 were the only chip select input, the 6821 would be selected during an IACK cycle, and this is definitely to be avoided. So, we include $\overline{SD}$ which is driven by the

68000's function code outputs (see Figure 8-8 in Chapter 8). During an IACK cycle $\overline{SD} = 1$, preventing the 6821 from being selected. Selection requires A16 = 1 *and* $\overline{SD} = 0$. The latter occurs during any supervisor data read or data write operation, precisely the type of operation used to read or write the 6821.

When A16 = 1 and $\overline{SD} = 0$, the 6821 is selected. This condition also asserts $\overline{VPA}$ through the two NAND gates in Figure 9-11. Bus cycles that terminate with $\overline{VPA}$ (instead of $\overline{DTACK}$) signal that a 6800 peripheral is being accessed. This is a very special condition. The 68000 stretches the bus cycle and synchronizes the data transfer with E (enable). In fact, E is a control bus signal included on the 68000 CPU specifically to interface to 6800 peripherals, such as the 6821 PIA.

The 6821 can interrupt the CPU through two outputs called interrupt request A and B ($\overline{IRQA}$

Table 9-5.  6821 Internal Registers.

| RS1 | RS0 | Decoded Address | Mnemonic | Name |
|-----|-----|-----------------|----------|------|
| 0 | 0 | $010001 | Port A | Peripheral Register A |
| 0 | 0 | $010001 | DDRA | Data Direction Register A |
| 0 | 1 | $010003 | CRA | Control Register A |
| 1 | 0 | $010005 | Port B | Peripheral Register B |
| 1 | 0 | $010005 | DDRB | Data Direction Register B |
| 1 | 1 | $010007 | CRB | Control Register B |

and $\overline{IRQB}$). These are open drain outputs and can be tied together as shown in Figure 9-11.[2] They connect to the $\overline{INT3}$ interrupt line. The 68KMB configures level-3 IACK cycles to terminate with $\overline{VPA}$. Recall that this initiates generation of the level-3 autovector. This setup, which was illustrated in Figure 8-8 in Chapter 8, is used here as well.

The four PIA addresses provide access to the six internal registers in Table 9-5.

Note that addresses $010001 and $010005 each contain two registers. Bit 2 in each control register determines which is active. Consider port A. If CRA[2] = 0, then reading or writing address $010001 accesses the data direction register. If CRA[2] = 1, then reading or writing address $010001 accesses the peripheral register. Since all 6821 registers are cleared following a system reset, initial access is to the data direction registers.

Each data direction register (DDR) bit controls the direction of the corresponding port pin. A zero in a DDR bit, configures the correspond port pin as

an input. A one in a DDR bit configures the corresponding port pin as an output. After a system reset, all bits in the DDRs are cleared; therefore, both ports default to input.

The description above is very sketchy. For instance, we have not discussed the operation of the handshake signals CA1, CA2, CB1, and CB2, or the generation of interrupts on $\overline{IRQA}$ or $\overline{IRQB}$. Consult Appendix I for more details on the operation of the 6821.

## 9.12  HEXADECIMAL KEYPAD INTERFACE

Our first 6821 interface example is a hexadecimal keypad connected to port A (see Figure 9-12). Four column lines are driven by PA0–PA3 and four row lines are read on PA4–PA7.

Since a keypad is a collection of switches, the keys *bounce* when pressed and released. This is a mechanical phenomenon that creates electrical glitches when the switches are configured as inputs to logic circuits. *Debouncing* is the process of eliminating this problem. It is accomplished in software in the following example.

---

[2]"Open Drain" outputs are similar to "open collector" outputs, discussed in Chapter 0, except the type of transistor in the device is MOS (metal-oxide semiconductor).

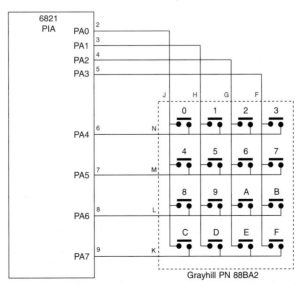

Figure 9-12.  Keypad interface to the 6821.

**Example 9-12.** Write a program called KEYPAD to read the keypad in Figure 9-12. Include software debouncing to detect smooth down-up keystrokes. When a key is detected, send the correspond ASCII character to the console.

**Solution:** See below.

```
 1                        ********************************************************
 2                        * KEYPAD.SRC                                           *
 3                        *                                                      *
 4                        * This program reads a hex codes from a keypad         *
 5                        * attached to the 6821, Port A.  The code is           *
 6                        * converted to ASCII and sent to the console.          *
 7                        ********************************************************
 8   00010001     PIA      EQU      $010001      ;6821 PIA base address
 9   00000002     CRA      EQU      1*2          ;Control Register A
10   0000099E     HTOA     EQU      $00099E      ;MON68K hex -> ASCII sub.
11
12   00008000              ORG      $8000
13   00008000 207C0001  KEYPAD  MOVEA.L  #PIA,A0      ;A0 points to DDRA
     00008004 0001
14   00008006 10BC000F          MOVE.B   #$0F,(A0)    ;bits PA0-PA3 = outputs
15   0000800A 117C0004          MOVE.B   #$04,CRA(A0) ;A0 points to Port A
     0000800E 0002
16   00008010 227C0000          MOVEA.L  #BANNER,A1   ;send test message to
     00008014 8090
17   00008016 4E42              TRAP     #2           ;   console
18   00008018 6108      LOOP    BSR.S    IN_HEX       ;get a code from keypad
19   0000801A 61008982          BSR.L    HTOA         ;convert to ASCII
20   0000801E 4E41              TRAP     #1           ;send to console
21   00008020 60F6              BRA      LOOP         ;repeat
22
23                        ********************************************************
24                        * IN_HEX - INput a HEXadecimal code from keypad        *
25                        *                                                      *
26                        * This routine includes debouncing.  It calls GET_KEY  *
27                        * continually until 50 consecutive calls return with   *
28                        * C = 1, indicating a key is pressed.  It then calls    *
29                        * GET_KEY continually until 50 consecutive calls        *
30                        * return with C = 0, indicating the key is released.    *
31                        *                                                      *
32                        *        ENTER:  A0 points to PIA, Port A               *
33                        *        EXIT:   D0[0:3] contains hexadecimal code      *
34                        *                D0[4:31] cleared                       *
35                        *                all other registers intact            *
36                        *        USES:   GET_KEY                                *
37                        ********************************************************
38   00008022 48A76000  IN_HEX  MOVEM.W  D1-D2,-(SP)
39   00008026 323C0031  OVER    MOVE.W   #49,D1       ;use D1 as counter
40   0000802A 611C      AGAIN   BSR.S    GET_KEY      ;key pressed?
41   0000802C 64F8              BCC      OVER         ;no:  start over again
42   0000802E 51C9FFFA          DBRA     D1,AGAIN     ;yes: check again
43   00008032 1400              MOVE.B   D0,D2        ;save code in D2
44   00008034 323C0031  OVER2   MOVE.W   #49,D1       ;wait for key release
45   00008038 610E      AGAIN2  BSR.S    GET_KEY      ;key released?
46   0000803A 65F8              BCS      OVER2        ;no:  start over again
47   0000803C 51C9FFFA          DBRA     D1,AGAIN2    ;yes: check again
48   00008040 1002              MOVE.B   D2,D0        ;restore code
49   00008042 4C9F0006          MOVEM.W  (SP)+,D1-D2
50   00008046 4E75              RTS
51
52                        ********************************************************
53                        * GET_KEY - GET a scanned code from KEYpad             *
54                        *                                                      *
```

*Continued.*

```
55              *           ENTER:   A0 points to PIA, Port A              *
56              *           EXIT:    C = 0 if no key hit                   *
57              *                    C = 1 if key hit and                  *
58              *                    D0[0:3] contains hex code             *
59              *                    D0[4:31] cleared                      *
60              *           USES:    no subroutines                        *
61              ************************************************************
62  00008048 48A77000  GET_KEY  MOVEM.W  D1-D3,-(SP)
63  0000804C 4240               CLR.W    D0           ;build hex. code in D0
64  0000804E 123C00FE           MOVE.B   #$FE,D1      ;start with column 0
65  00008052 343C0003           MOVE.W   #3,D2        ;use D2 as counter
66  00008056 1081      NEXT     MOVE.B   D1,(A0)      ;activate column line
67  00008058 1010               MOVE.B   (A0),D0      ;read PIA Port A
68  0000805A 020000F0           ANDI.B   #$F0,D0      ;isolate row lines
69  0000805E B03C00F0           CMP.B    #$F0,D0      ;any row line active?
70  00008062 660C               BNE.S    KEY_HIT      ;yes: check it out
71  00008064 E319               ROL.B    #1,D1        ;no:  rotate col. code
72  00008066 51CAFFEE           DBRA     D2,NEXT      ;     and check next
73  0000806A 027CFFFE           ANDI.W   #$FFFE,SR    ;if reached here, no
74  0000806E 601A               BRA.S    EXIT         ;    key hit, clear C
75  00008070 4203      KEY_HIT  CLR.B    D3           ;build code in D3
76  00008072 E219      KEY2     ROR.B    #1,D1        ;rotate column code
77  00008074 6404               BCC.S    SKIP         ;found active column?
78  00008076 5203               ADDQ.B   #1,D3        ;no:  add weight of 1 &
79  00008078 60F8               BRA      KEY2         ;     check again
80  0000807A E818      SKIP     ROR.B    #4,D0        ;yes: align row code
81  0000807C E218      KEY3     ROR.B    #1,D0        ;rotate row code
82  0000807E 6404               BCC.S    SKIP2        ;found active code?
83  00008080 5803               ADDQ.B   #4,D3        ;no:  add weight of 4 &
84  00008082 60F8               BRA      KEY3         ;     check again
85  00008084 1003      SKIP2    MOVE.B   D3,D0        ;yes: put code in D0
86  00008086 007C0001           ORI.W    #1,SR        ;set C-bit in CCR
87  0000808A 4C9F000E  EXIT     MOVEM.W  (SP)+,D1-D3  ;restore registers &
88  0000808E 4E75               RTS                   ;return
89  00008090 0D0A2A2A  BANNER   DC.B     $0D,$0A,'*** TEST KEYPAD ***'
    00008094 2A205445
    00008098 5354204B
    0000809C 45595041
    000080A0 44202A2A
    000080A4 2A
90  000080A5 0D0A00             DC.B     $0D,$0A,0
91  000080A8             END    KEYPAD
```

**Discussion:** The 6821 is initialized in lines 14 and 15. Using A0 = $010001 as a pointer, the instruction in line 14 initializes the data direction register of port A to $0F. This configures port A bits 0–3 as outputs and bits 4–7 as inputs. Control register A is initialized in line 15 with $04. The only bit set in $04 is bit 2, the *DDR access bit*. By setting this bit, subsequent reads or writes to address $010001 access the port pins, rather than DDRA. See Appendix I for a detailed discussion of each bit in the 6821's control registers.

Lines 16–17 send a banner message to the console to facilitate debugging and observing program execution. The main loop which follows contains four instructions. A character is read from the keypad in line 18 (see below), converted to ASCII in line 19, then sent to the console in line 20. Line 21 branches back to repeat the process. Note that the conversion of the 4-bit binary code to ASCII in line 19 uses the HTOA (hex-to-ASCII) subroutine from MON68K. The subroutine's address is defined in line 10. This address is obtained from the link map, MON68K.MAP, found in Appendix E. The listing for HTOA is found in CONVERT.LST, also in Appendix E.

The subroutines IN_HEX and GET_KEY do most of the work. They are well documented so our discussion is brief. IN_HEX does not return until a key is pressed and released on the keypad. GET_KEY checks the keypad to see if a key is pressed. If so, it returns with C = 1 and the 4-bit code in D0[0:3]; otherwise, it returns with C = 0.

A crude form of software debouncing is included in IN_HEX. It calls GET_KEY continually until 50 consecutive calls return with C = 1, indicating a *smooth* key closure. It then calls GET_KEY continually until 50 consecutive calls return with C = 0, indicating a *smooth* key release.

The dirty work is performed in GET_KEY. It begins by writing $1110_2$ to the column lines, PA0–PA3 (line 64), and then reading the row lines, PA4–PA7 (lines 67–68). If no key is closed on column #0, $1111_2$ is read back on the row lines. This process is repeated by sending $1101_2$, $1011_2$, then $0111_2$ to the column lines. If a key is pressed, a zero is read back on the corresponding row line. The combined column and row pattern is the *scan code*, which is converted to a 4-bit binary code in D0 before returning with C = 1. If no key was closed for the entire keypad, GET_KEY returns with C = 0. All this is pretty messy, but it gets the job done (see lines 62–88).

Since interrupts are not used, the software in this example is of limited practical use. A better approach is to place GET_KEY in an ISR that executes, say, 20 times per second. Debouncing would require about five consecutive calls each for a smooth key closure and a smooth key release. We'll leave it to the reader to explore this possibility. ∎

## 9.13   ANALOG OUTPUT

Interfacing to the real world often requires generating or sensing analog conditions. Analog output requires a digital-to-analog converter (DAC) and analog input requires an analog-to-digital converter (ADC). These are *linear* devices, usually ICs, that are very different from digital devices. We have a few interesting examples to present; but our treatment of these devices is by no means exhaustive. Readers interested in learning more about DACs and ADCs should consult the data books and application notes from the

device manufacturers, such as Motorola, National Semiconductor, or Analog Devices. See the design notes at the end of this chapter for the references used for this and other interface designs presented here.

Analog output is shown in Figure 9-13. Port A of the 6821 drives an MC1408L8, 8-bit DAC. The MC1408L8 is inexpensive (less than $2) and easily obtained. The output of the DAC (pin 4) is a current, so a current-to-voltage circuit using an LM301 operational amplifier, or op amp, is added. The output of the op amp (pin 6) is the analog output signal, $V_O$. Note that the op amp is powered from +12 volts and −12 volts. The MC1408L8 operates from +5 volts and −12 volts.

After building the circuit, it should be calibrated by adjusting the 1 kΩ trimpot and measuring $V_O$ with a voltmeter or oscilloscope. Calibration does not require software. The monitor's memory modify command is used to write data to the 6821's port A. This requires four steps:

1. Reset the system. (This clears all 6821 registers.)
2. Write $FF to DDRA at address $010001. (This configures port A as an output.)
3. Write $04 to CRA at address $010003. (This provides access to port A.)
4. Write test data to port A at address $010001.

Test data are written to port A while measuring $V_O$. Adjust the trimpot to get 0 volts with port A = $00 and about 10 volts with port A = $FF. Now we are ready to have fun with interface software.

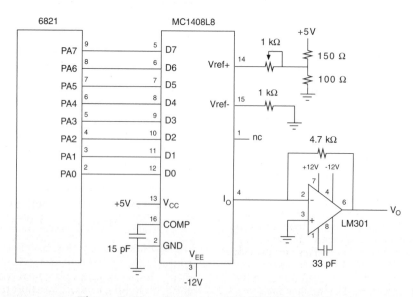

**Figure 9-13.   Output to a MC1408L8 DAC.**

Figure E.

```
 1                              *****************************************************
 2                              *  SAWTOOTH.SRC                                    *
 3                              *                                                  *
 4                              *  This is a test program for the MC1408L8 digital-to- *
 5                              *  analog converter interface to the 6821 PIA.  The *
 6                              *  program creates a sawtooth wave by continually   *
 7                              *  incrementing a count and sending it to the MC1408L8.*
 8                              *  The constants STEP and COUNT control the frequency *
 9                              *  and the number of conversions per cycle.         *
10                              *****************************************************
11   00010001         PIA        EQU        $10001          ;base address of 6821
12   00000002         CRA        EQU        1*2             ;Control Register A
13   00000010         STEP       EQU        16              ;increment for data out
14   00000032         COUNT      EQU        50              ;count for delay loop
15
16   00008000                    ORG        $8000
17   00008000 207C0001 SAWTOOTH MOVEA.L    #PIA,A0          ;A0 -> DDRA
     00008004 0001
18   00008006 10BC00FF            MOVE.B    #$FF,(A0)        ;Port A = output
19   0000800A 117C0004            MOVE.B    #$04,CRA(A0)     ;A0 -> Port A
     0000800E 0002
20   00008010 4200                CLR.B     D0               ;init D0 = 0
21   00008012 1080      LOOP      MOVE.B    D0,(A0)          ;send to MC1408L8
22   00008014 D03C0010            ADD.B     #STEP,D0         ;inc D0 by STEP
23   00008018 323C0032            MOVE.W    #COUNT,D1        ;create cheap-and-dirty
24   0000801C 51C9FFFE            DBRA      D1,*             ;   software delay
25   00008020 60F0                BRA       LOOP             ;do it again!
26   00008022                     END       SAWTOOTH
```

**Example 9-13.** Write a program for the interface in Figure 9-13 to generate a ramp, or sawtooth, waveform at $V_O$.

**Solution:** See Figure E.

**Discussion:** The program above uses only nine instructions. An oscilloscope is required to observe the output. Port A of the 6821 is configured as an output by writing $FF to DDRA (line 18). Then CRA[2] is set in line 19 to provide access to the port A output pins. The main body of program does the following: send the contents of register D0 to port A (line 21), increment D0 by STEP (line 22), delay (lines 23–24), repeat (line 25).

As D0 increases, the output voltage increases. Once incremented beyond $FF, D0 wraps around to $00 and the ramp starts over. The frequency is controlled by STEP and COUNT. These are changed by modifying memory locations $8016/17 (STEP, line 22) and $801A/1B (COUNT, line 23). By default, STEP = 16 (line 13), so D0 is incremented 256/16 = 16 times for each waveform period. By default, COUNT = 50, so the DBRA instruction in line 24 consumes $10 \times 50 + 14 = 514$ CPU cycles (see Appendix D). The additional instructions in the loop consume 34 cycles, for a total of 548 CPU cycles. The number of CPU cycles per waveform period is $16 \times 548 = 8768$. With a 3.6864 MHz system clock, the waveform period is 8768 × (1/3686400) = 2.36 milliseconds, and the waveform frequency is 1/2.36 = 420 Hz. ∎

## 9.14 DIGITAL SINE-WAVE GENERATOR

Generating a sawtooth wave with a DAC is a good interfacing and programming exercise; however, we can generate other more interesting waveforms. Consider the challenge of generating a sine wave with the interface in Figure 9-13. This is a tough task because there is no easy way to generate the output data stream. The assembly-language algorithm for a sine function is messy, so we adopt another approach. The easiest method uses a look-up table where each entry is one point along a sine wave. With 8-bit entries, the table must start around 127, increase to 255, then decrease through 127 to 0, and rise back up to 127. This is roughly the pattern for one cycle of a sine wave.[3]

A reasonable rendition of a sine wave requires a large table. The question arises, How do we generate the table? Manual methods are impractical. The easiest approach is to write a program in a

---

[3]It is also possible to design the look-up table to store only the first quarter of a sine wave. The rest of the samples can be obtained through mirror-image mapping.

```
/**************************************************/
/* table.c - program to generate a sine wave table  */
/*                                                */
/* The table consists of 1024 entries between 0      */
/* and 255.  Each entry is preceded by " DC.B " for */
/* inclusion in a 68000 source program.  The table   */
/* is written to the file s_table.src                */
/**************************************************/

#include <stdio.h>
#include <math.h>

#define PI    3.1415927
#define MAX   1024
#define BYTE 255

main()
{
   FILE *fp, *fopen();
   double x, y;

   fp = fopen("s_table.src", "w");
   for(x = 0; x < MAX; ++x) {
     y = ((sin((x / MAX) * (2 * PI)) + 1) / 2) * BYTE;
     fprintf(fp," DC.B %3d\n", (int)y);
   }
}
```

**Figure 9-14.**    C program to generate a sine-wave table.

high-level language to create the table and save the entries in a file. The table is then imported into a 68000 source program. Figure 9-14 is a simple C program, called *table.c,* that does the job. The program generates a 1024-entry sine-wave table with values constrained between 0 and 255. The entire table, which is written to a file called s_table.src, represents one cycle of a sine wave. Each entry is

preceded with " DC.B " for compatibility with 68000 source code.

**Example 9-14.** Write a program called SINEWAVE to generate a sine wave using the MC1408L8 interface in Figure 9-13.

**Solution:** See Figure F.

**Discussion:** The source code for this program contains 1066 lines. Of course, most of it is the

```
Figure F.  1        **********************************************************
           2        * SINEWAVE.SRC                                          *
           3        *                                                       *
           4        * This program generates a sine wave with a MC1408L8    *
           5        * digital-to-analog converter attached to Port A of     *
           6        * the 6821 PIA.  Each value output to the PIA is read  *
           7        * from a look-up table containing 1024 8-bit entries.  *
           8        * The entire table represents one period of a sine      *
           9        * wave.  The frequency is controlled by the constant    *
          10        * STEP which is used as the increment for the index     *
          11        * into the table.                                       *
          12        **********************************************************
          13  00010001          PIA      EQU      $10001          ;PIA base address
          14  00000002          CRA      EQU      1*2             ;Control Register A
          15  0000000D          STEP     EQU      13              ;index into the table
          16
          17  00008000                   ORG      $8000
          18  00008000 227C0000 SINEWAVE MOVEA.L  #TABLE,A1       ;A1 -> sine wave table
              00008004 8028
          19  00008006 207C0001          MOVEA.L  #PIA,A0         ;A0 -> DDRA
              0000800A 0001
          20  0000800C 10BC00FF          MOVE.B   #$FF,(A0)       ;Port A = output
```

*Continued.*

```
21   00008010 117C0004              MOVE.B   #$04,CRA(A0)  ;A0 -> Port A
     00008014 0002
22   00008016 4241                  CLR.W    D1
23   00008018 10311000  LOOP        MOVE.B   0(A1,D1.W),D0 ;14 cycles +
24   0000801C 1080                  MOVE.B   D0,(A0)       ;8 cycles  +
25   0000801E 0641000D              ADDI.W   #STEP,D1      ;8 cycles  +
26   00008022 024103FF              ANDI.W   #$3FF,D1      ;8 cycles  +
27   00008026 60F0                  BRA      LOOP          ;10 cycles = 48 cycles
28
29                           ***********************************************
30                           * Frequency calculation:                     *
31                           *     F = 3686400 / 48 / (1024 / STEP)        *
32                           *       = 975 Hz                              *
33                           ***********************************************
34                           * The following sine wave table contains 1024 entries *
35                           * of integers between 0 and 255.                      *
36                           ***********************************************
37   00008028 7F   TABLE           DC.B 127
38   00008029 80                   DC.B 128
39   0000802A 81                   DC.B 129
40   0000802B 81                   DC.B 129
41   0000802C 82                   DC.B 130
42                           * Turn listing off after first five entries
1059                         *_____
1060                         * Turn listing on for last five entries
1061 00008423 7B                   DC.B 123
1062 00008424 7C                   DC.B 124
1063 00008425 7D                   DC.B 125
1064 00008426 7D                   DC.B 125
1065 00008427 7E                   DC.B 126
1066 00008428         END  SINEWAVE
```

sine-wave table (lines 37–1065). To keep the listing file short, listing output was turned off in line 43 and turned back on in line 1058.[4]

The program requires only ten instructions (lines 18–27). The base address of the table is put in A1 in line 18, and the base address of the PIA is put in A0 in line 19. The PIA is initialized with port A as an output port in line 20 by writing $FF to DDRA. Access to port A is enabled by setting CRA[2] in line 21. D1 is cleared in line 22 to prepare for the main loop that follows in lines 23–27. In line 23, a byte is read from the table using A1 as a pointer and D1 as an index. The value read is placed in D0 and sent to port A of the 6821 in line 24. Then the constant STEP is added to D1 to prepare for the next read operation. The index is limited to 10 bits by masking D1 with $3FF in line 26, just prior to branching back in line 27.

The frequency of the sine wave is determined by frequency of the system clock (3,686,400 Hz), the number of CPU cycles in the program loop (48), the number of entries in the sine-wave table (1024), and the size of STEP (default = 13, see line 15). As calculated in lines 30–32 of the listing, the frequency of the sine wave is 975 Hz. This is easily verified with an oscilloscope. ∎

## 9.15 MUSIC OUTPUT FROM A DIGITAL-TO-ANALOG CONVERTER

The digital sine-wave generator in Example 9-14 can be tuned to generate frequencies of a musical scale. In addition, the console keyboard can control the frequency, thus acting as a primitive musical instrument. The circuit of Figure 9-15 facilitates music generation by adding a low-pass filter and an audio amplifier to the $V_o$ signal in Figure 9-13.

The first LM301 in Figure 9-15 is configured as a low-pass filter with a cut-off frequency around 4 kHz and a roll-off of 20 dB per decade above 4 kHz. The second LM301 is a voltage follower driving a loudspeaker. The audio quality is reasonable; but, it can be improved using a dedicated speaker/amplification system connected to the auxiliary jack shown in the figure.

As a prelude to the next example, we present some music theory. The frequency of each note in an "A major" musical scale is given in Table 9-6. The mapping to keys on the console keyboard is also given to prepare for the next example.

---

[4] The assembler directive LSTOUT- turns listing output off, and the directive LSTOUT+ turns listing output on. These directives vary from one assembler to the next.

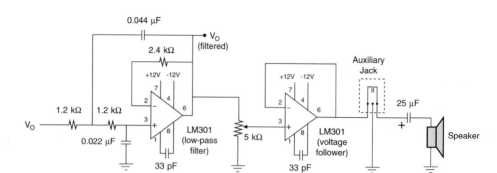

Figure 9-15.   Low-pass filter and audio output.

Table 9-6.   "A Major" Musical Scale.

| Musical Note | Frequency (Hz) | Console Key |
|---|---|---|
| A | 440.00 | 1 |
| B | 493.88 | 2 |
| C# | 554.37 | 3 |
| D | 587.33 | 4 |
| E | 659.26 | 5 |
| F# | 739.99 | 6 |
| G# | 830.61 | 7 |
| A' | 880.00 | 8 |
| - | silence | SPACE |

The first frequency is 440 Hz, called *A above middle C*. This is the international reference frequency for musical instruments using the equal-tempered scale (e.g., the piano). The frequency of all other notes is determined by multiplying this frequency by $2^{n/12}$, where $n$ is the number of steps, or semitones, to the note. The easiest example is A', one octave, or 12 steps above A, with a frequency of $440 \times 2^{12/12} = 880$ Hz. This is the last note in our musical scale. With reference to the bottom note in any major scale, called the root, the scale in steps is 2, 4, 5, 7, 9, 11, and 12. For example, the note E in Table 9-6 is 7 steps above A, so its frequency is $440 \times 2^{7/12} = 659.26$ Hz.

**Example 9-15.** Write a program called AMAJOR for the circuit of Figure 9-13 and Figure 9-15 to generate the frequencies of an "A major" musical scale using the console keyboard as shown in Table 9-6.

**Solution:** See below.

```
 1                    ************************************************************
 2                    * AMAJOR.SRC                                              *
 3                    *                                                         *
 4                    * This program allows a musical scale to be played by     *
 5                    * the console keyboard.   The mapping of keys is          *
 6                    *                                                         *
 7                    *         KEY       NOTE      FREQUENCY                   *
 8                    *         =====================================           *
 9                    *         SPACE     -         - (silence)                 *
10                    *         1         A         440.00 Hz                   *
11                    *         2         B         493.88 Hz                   *
12                    *         3         C#        554.37 Hz                   *
13                    *         4         D         587.33 Hz                   *
14                    *         5         E         659.26 Hz                   *
15                    *         6         F#        739.99 Hz                   *
16                    *         7         G#        930.61 Hz                   *
17                    *         8         A'        880.00 Hz                   *
18                    ************************************************************
19  0000C001          DUART   EQU     $00C001 ;68681 base address
20  00000008          ACR     EQU     4*2     ;auxiliary control register
21  0000000C          CTUR    EQU     6*2     ;counter/timer upper register
22  0000000E          CTLR    EQU     7*2     ;counter/timer lower register
23  0000000A          IMR     EQU     5*2     ;interrupt mask register
24  00000018          IVR     EQU     12*2    ;interrupt vector register
25  0000001E          STOP    EQU     15*2    ;timer stop command address
26  0000001A          I2VECTOR EQU    26      ;I2 autovector number
27  00010001          PIA     EQU     $10001  ;PIA base address
```

*Continued.*

```
28   00000002            CRA     EQU     1*2          ;Control Register A
29   0000000B            COUNT   EQU     11           ;timer interrupts @ 10472.7 Hz
30
31   00008000                    ORG     $8000
32   00008000 4EF90000   AMAJOR  JMP     >INIT
     00008004 800C
33   00008006 4EF90000           JMP     >L2ISR
     0000800A 805A
34   0000800C 207C0000   INIT    MOVEA.L #DUART,A0    ;A0 -> 68681 DUART
     00008010 C001
35   00008012 227C0000           MOVEA.L #TABLE,A1    ;A1 -> sine wave table
     00008016 808D
36   00008018 247C0001           MOVEA.L #PIA,A2      ;A2 -> DDRA
     0000801C 0001
37   0000801E 267C0000           MOVEA.L #SCALE,A3    ;A3 -> scale table
     00008022 8084
38   00008024 117C0008           MOVE.B  #$08,IMR(A0)
     00008028 000A
39   0000802A 117C001A           MOVE.B  #I2VECTOR,IVR(A0)
     0000802E 0018
40   00008030 303C000B           MOVE.W  #COUNT,D0
41   00008034 0188000C           MOVEP.W D0,CTUR(A0)
42   00008038 117C0070           MOVE.B  #$70,ACR(A0)
     0000803C 0008
43
44   0000803E 14BC00FF           MOVE.B  #$FF,(A2)    ;Port A = output
45   00008042 157C0004           MOVE.B  #$04,CRA(A2) ;A2 -> Port A
     00008046 0002
46   00008048 42790000           CLR.W   >STEP        ;begin with silence
     0000804C A000
47   0000804E 4241               CLR.W   D1           ;beginning of sine wave
48   00008050 007C0700           ORI.W   #$0700,SR    ;mask all interrupts
49   00008054 027CF9FF           ANDI.W  #$F9FF,SR    ;mask level 1 only
50   00008058 60FE               BRA     *            ;off we go!
51
52                       *********************************************************
53                       * LEVEL-2 INTERRUPT SERVICE ROUTINE                    *
54                       *                                                      *
55                       *      -issue STOP command to clear interrupt          *
56                       *      -send new DATA to MC1408L8 DAC using STEP        *
57                       *      -check if a key has been hit                     *
58                       *      -if a key has been hit, set new STEP value       *
59                       *********************************************************
60   0000805A 4A28001E   L2ISR   TST.B   STOP(A0)       ;stop cmd, clrs intrrpt
61   0000805E 10311000           MOVE.B  0(A1,D1.W),D0  ;get new data
62   00008062 1480               MOVE.B  D0,(A2)        ;sent to DAC
63   00008064 D2790000           ADD.W   >STEP,D1       ;increment index
     00008068 A000
64   0000806A 024103FF           ANDI.W  #$3FF,D1       ;reduce to 10 bits
65   0000806E 4E44       SKIP    TRAP    #4             ;has a key been hit?
66   00008070 64000010           BCC     DONE           ;no:  done
67   00008074 4E40               TRAP    #0             ;yes: get ASCII code
68   00008076 0240000F           ANDI.W  #$0F,D0        ;reduce to 4 bits
69   0000807A 13F30000           MOVE.B  0(A3,D0.W),>STEP+1 ;get new index
     0000807E 0000A001
70   00008082 4E73       DONE    RTE
71
72                       *********************************************************
73                       * The following scale table sets the increment         *
74                       * through the sine wave table for each note in an A     *
75                       * major scale.                                          *
```

*Continued.*

```
 76                          *                                                    *
 77                          * Each entry = fN x (1024 / fC), where fN is the note *
 78                          * frequency and fC is the conversion frequency.  For  *
 79                          * example the entry for A is 440 x (1024 / 10472.7) =  *
 80                          * 43.                                                  *
 81                          ********************************************************
 82   00008084 00     SCALE    DC.B     0               ;silence (SPACE)
 83   00008085 2B              DC.B     43              ;A
 84   00008086 30              DC.B     48              ;B
 85   00008087 36              DC.B     54              ;C#
 86   00008088 39              DC.B     57              ;D
 87   00008089 40              DC.B     64              ;E
 88   0000808A 48              DC.B     72              ;F#
 89   0000808B 51              DC.B     81              ;G#
 90   0000808C 56              DC.B     86              ;A'
 91
 92                          ********************************************************
 93                          * The following sine wave table contains 1024 entries *
 94                          * of integers between 0 and 255.                      *
 95                          ********************************************************
 96   0000808D 7F     TABLE    DC.B 127
 97   0000808E 80              DC.B 128
 98   0000808F 81              DC.B 129
 99   00008090 81              DC.B 129
100   00008091 82              DC.B 130
101                          * Turn listing off after first five entries
1118                         *─────────────────────────────────────────
1119                         * Turn listing on for last five entries
1120  00008488 7B              DC.B 123
1121  00008489 7C              DC.B 124
1122  0000848A 7D              DC.B 125
1123  0000848B 7D              DC.B 125
1124  0000848C 7E              DC.B 126
1125
1126  0000A000                 ORG      $A000
1127  0000A000 0001   STEP     DC.W     1
1128  0000A002                 END      AMAJOR
```

**Discussion:** Creating accurate musical frequencies is simplified through precisely timed interrupts. With a timer reload value of 11 (lines 29, 40–41), interrupts occur at a frequency of 10,472.7 Hz. The trick is calculating STEP—the index into the sine-wave table—to achieve the desired frequency. For example, the note A, with a frequency of 440 Hz, requires a STEP of $440 \times (1024/10472.7) = 43.02$, which we round to 43 (line 83).

The program uses two look-up tables: the sine-wave table presented earlier, and a SCALE look-up table containing the correct step for each note in our musical scale (lines 83–90). ASCII codes read from the console keyboard control the index into the SCALE table.

Interrupts occur every $1/10472.7 = 95.5$ μs. The level-2 ISR begins as follows: clear the interrupt source (line 60), fetch a new value from the sine-wave table using A1 as a pointer and D1 as an index (line 61), output the value to the DAC (line 62), increment D1 by STEP (line 63), reduce D1 to 10 bits just in case it overflowed (line 64), and check if a key was hit on the console keyboard (line 65). If no key was hit,

the ISR is finished (line 66). If a key was hit, the ASCII code is read into D0 (line 67), reduced to four bits (line 68), and used to fetch the new value of STEP from the SCALE table (line 69).

Note that checking the console to see if a key was hit (trap #4) is distinctly different from inputting a key from the console (trap #0). If no key was hit, the latter trap will sit in a loop waiting for one, and this would foul up the timing. Trap #4 is a simple status-check routine; it checks the serial port *receiver ready* status bit and returns with C = 1 if a key has been hit, or C = 0 otherwise. Once we know a key was hit, trap #0 is called with the assurance that it will return *immediately* with the ASCII code for the key. See IO.LST in Appendix E for more details.

Finally, note that we are living dangerously in this example. Since interrupts occur every 95.5 microseconds, the execution time of the level-2 ISR is critical. If the ISR is not finished when the next interrupt occurs, the new interrupt is made pending and is not serviced until the current ISR finishes. Meanwhile the 68681 timer continues to run, so the time available to the pending

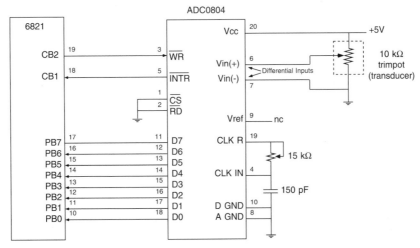

Figure 9-16.   Interface to ADC0804 analog-to-digital converter.

interrupt is reduced. This is not necessarily catastrophic because the ISR is not the same duration every time it executes. If no key was hit, the ISR is quite brief. If a key was hit, lines 67–69 execute, and this includes trap #0, so the duration of the ISR increases substantially. Of course, the safest approach is to ensure that the worst-case duration of the ISR is less than the interrupt period. See Question 17 at the end of this chapter.   ∎

## 9.16   ANALOG INPUT

Microcomputers are often called upon to sense analog conditions in the surrounding environment. An analog-to-digital converter (ADC) is a device that senses an analog condition, usually a voltage, and outputs a digital value proportional to the magnitude of the condition. In Figure 9-16, an ADC0804 8-bit ADC is interfaced to a 6821 PIA. As with the other components in our examples, the ADC0804 is inexpensive (less than $3) and readily available. Note that port B is used for the interface. After a brief introductory example, we'll combine the interface in Figure 9-16 with the DAC interface to port A of the 6821 described earlier.

The ADC0804 senses a differential input voltage on pins 6 and 7. In Figure 9-16, these inputs con-

nect to a trimpot presenting a DC signal between 0 volts and 5 volts. Any transducer, such as a thermistor, can be substituted for the trimpot. The analog input voltage is converted to a digital output through a series of comparisons against an internal reference voltage. The timing for the comparisons is controlled by an internal oscillator. The RC network at pins 4 and 19 sets the frequency of the oscillator. A conversion takes about 100 μs, for a conversion rate of 10 kHz.

The ADC0804 can directly interface to a microprocessor, through address decoding, and so on. Since we are using the 6821 PIA in this example, the chip select ($\overline{CS}$) and read ($\overline{RD}$) inputs are grounded. The timing for conversions is controlled by the ADC0804's $\overline{WR}$ input and $\overline{INTR}$ output. These connect to the 6821's CB2 and CB1 lines respectively. A start conversion command is issued to the ADC0804 by pulsing $\overline{WR}$ low for 0.1 μs minimum. When the conversion is complete, about 100 μs later, the ADC0804 asserts $\overline{INTR}$ (drives it low). The next pulse on $\overline{WR}$, to start the next conversion, de-asserts $\overline{INTR}$. The conversion timing is shown in Figure 9-17.

What remains is to satisfy the timing requirements of the ADC0804 with the interface to the PIA. As the next example illustrates, this is straightforward.

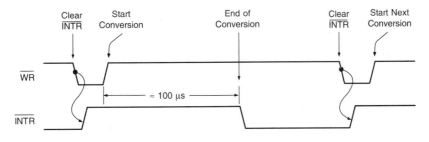

Figure 9-17.   Timing for ADC0804 conversions.

**Figure G.**

```
   1                              ************************************************
   2                              * ADCTEST.SRC                                 *
   3                              *                                             *
   4                              * This program reads the ADC0804 attached to Port B  *
   5                              * of the 6821 and reports the result on the console  *
   6                              * as a hexadecimal byte.                       *
   7                              ************************************************
   8   00010001     PIA     EQU      $10001         ;base address of 6821
   9   00000004     PORTB   EQU      2*2            ;6821 Port B
  10   00000006     CRB     EQU      3*2            ;Control Reg. B
  11   0000000D     CR      EQU      $0D            ;ASCII carriage ret.
  12   0000000A     LF      EQU      $0A            ;ASCII line feed
  13   00000B14     OUT2HX  EQU      $000B14        ;MON68K subroutine
  14
  15   00008000             ORG      $8000
  16   00008000 227C0000 ADCTEST MOVEA.L  #BANNER,A1     ;A1 -> message
       00008004 8038
  17   00008006 4E42              TRAP     #2             ;send it
  18   00008008 207C0001          MOVEA.L  #PIA,A0        ;A0 -> 6821 PIA
       0000800C 0001
  19   0000800E 117C003C          MOVE.B   #$3C,CRB(A0)   ;initialize CB2 = 1
       00008012 0006
  20   00008014 117C0034 REPEAT   MOVE.B   #$34,CRB(A0)   ;start conversion by
       00008018 0006
  21   0000801A 117C003C          MOVE.B   #$3C,CRB(A0)   ; toggling CB2 (-WR)
       0000801E 0006
  22   00008020 08280007 AGAIN    BTST.B   #7,CRB(A0)     ;IRQB flag set? (-INTR)
       00008024 0006
  23   00008026 67F8              BEQ      AGAIN          ;no:  check again
  24   00008028 10280004          MOVE.B   PORTB(A0),D0   ;yes: get ADC0804 data
  25   0000802C 4EB80B14          JSR      OUT2HX         ;send it to console
  26   00008030 103C000D          MOVE.B   #CR,D0         ;send CR too, to
  27   00008034 4E41              TRAP     #1             ; prepare for next
  28   00008036 60DC              BRA      REPEAT         ; conversion
  29
  30   00008038 0D0A     BANNER   DC.B     CR,LF
  31   0000803A 2A2A2A20          DC.B     '*** TEST ADC0804 ***',CR,LF,0
       0000803E 54455354
       00008042 20414443
       00008046 30383034
       0000804A 202A2A2A
       0000804E 0D0A00
  32   00008051             END      ADCTEST
```

**Example 9-16:** Write a program called ADCTEST to send a *start conversion* command to the ADC0804 in Figure 9-16 and report the result of the conversion on the console as a hexadecimal byte. Put the program in a loop such that the console is continually updated with the results of new conversions.

**Solution:** See Figure G.

**Discussion:** When this program executes, the following message is displayed on the console:

```
*** TEST ADC0804 ***
FF
```

The value FF is continually updated. As the trimpot is adjusted, the value changes in proportion to the voltage on pin 6 of the ADC0804. A smooth transition from 00 to FF is observed by adjusting the trimpot output from 0 volts to 5 volts.

Let's examine the program. The initialization for the PIA is slightly different from the previous examples. Since port B is an input port, it is not necessary to initialize DDRB. Recall that both ports default to input following a system reset. Control register B is initialized with $3C in line 19. The effect of each bit in this value is summarized in Figure 9-18. Details on other bit patterns for CRB are found in Appendix I.

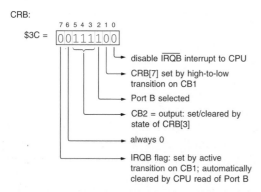

**Figure 9-18.** Initialization of control register B.

By writing $3C to CRB, the handshake signals, CB1 and CB2, are configured properly to achieve the timings in Figure 9-17. CB2 is configured as an output by writing $11_2$ to CRB[5:4]. The state of CB2 is then controlled by CRB[3]. Initially CB2 = 1, because CRB[3] = 1.

So, pulsing the ADC0804's $\overline{WR}$ is accomplished by writing $34 to control register B (line 20) following by writing $3C to control register B (line 21). This toggles CRB[3] which in turn toggles the output pin CB2 to initiate a conversion.

CB1 is always an input. It is used to set CRB[7], which is called the *IRQB flag*. Writing a 0 to CRB[1], sets the active transition on CB1 as *high-to-low*. That is, a high-to-low transition on CB1 sets bit 7 in control register B, the $\overline{IRQB}$ flag. CB1 is driven by the ADC0804's $\overline{INTR}$ output. A high-to-low transition on $\overline{INTR}$ signals *end of conversion* (see Figure 9-17), and this sets bit 7 in control register B. Note that the IRQB *flag* is not the same as the $\overline{IRQB}$ *signal* on the 6821 chip. The latter is disabled in our example by writing a 0 to CRB[0]. Interrupts are not used in this example.

The IRQB flag is interrogated in software to determine when a conversion is complete. This is done in lines 22–23 using a BTST (bit test) instruction followed by BEQ. These instructions

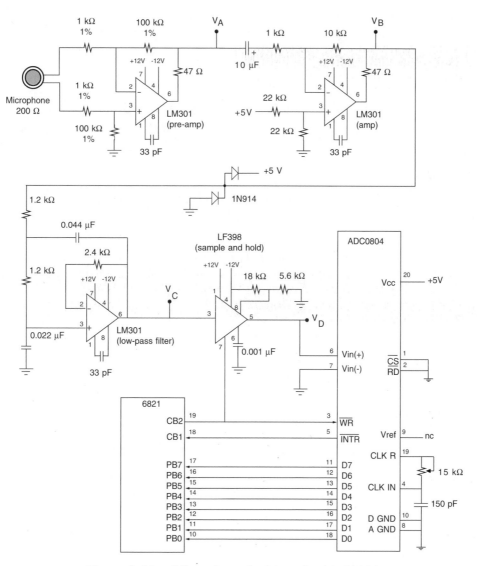

**Figure 9-19.** Microphone input to the ADC0804.

execute repeatedly while the ADC0804 converts the analog signal to a digital value. When the conversion is complete, the ADC0804 asserts $\overline{INTR}$, as shown in Figure 9-17. This sets CRB[7] inside the PIA. The test loop in lines 22–23 detects this and falls through to line 24 which reads the data at port B. The act of reading port B automatically resets the IRQB flag to prepare for the next conversion. The assertion on $\overline{INTR}$ follows the pulse on $\overline{WR}$ by about 100 μs, as stated in the ADC0804 data sheet. This is easily confirmed with an oscilloscope.

To facilitate observing and debugging the program, the converted data are sent to the console using MON68K's OUT2HX subroutine, as described earlier in Example 9-11. ■

## 9.17 DIGITIZED SPEECH INPUT AND PLAYBACK

As noted above, the conversion rate of the ADC0804 is about 10 kHz. This rate, sometimes called the **sampling rate,** is sufficient to capture and digitize AC input signals up to 5 kHz in frequency. Although insufficient for high-fidelity music, a 5 kHz bandwidth easily encompasses the frequency spectrum of speech. Speech signals digitized and transmitted in the telephone system, for example, are sampled at 8 kHz with 7-bit ADCs; so, similar (or better) quality can be expected using an ADC0804.

To expand the analog input of the previous example to capture speech input, we need a microphone and several stages of conditioning circuitry, including a preamplifier, amplifier, filter, and sample-and-hold. This is illustrated in Figure 9-19.

The following is a brief description of the operation of this circuit. A detailed analysis is beyond the scope of this text, however. (See the notes at the end of this chapter for design references.) Signals enter the circuit through a low-impedance microphone. The first LM301 op amp is a preamplifier stage with a gain of 40 dB and a common mode rejection ratio (CMRR) of 80 dB. The output can be observed on an oscilloscope at $V_A$. The second op-amp stage provides an additional 20 dB of gain and adds +2.5 volts of DC bias. Two 1N914 diodes are added at $V_B$ as a safety precaution to clamp the signal between −0.7 volts and 5.7 volts. The third op-amp stage is a second-order low-pass filter with a 4 kHz cutoff and a roll-off of 40 dB per decade. Finally, an LF398 samples the signal at $V_C$ and holds it at $V_D$ during the conversion period of the ADC0804.

The concept of **sample-and-hold** is critical for digitizing AC input signals, such as speech. Figure 9-20 illustrates the idea in more detail. The signal at the input to the LF398 is labeled $V_C$ in the figure. This is the electrical analog of the speech after amplification and filtering. During the 100 μs conversion period of the ADC, it is important that this signal is stable, or unchanging. At the beginning of each conversion period, the LF398 *samples* the signal at $V_C$ and stores the voltage level in a capacitor. Sampling is quick; it takes about 6 μs for the LF398 circuit in Figure 9-19. Then the LF398 isolates the capacitor from the input signal and switches it to the output, $V_D$. The capacitor maintains its charge (voltage) during the *hold* period. The signal presented to the ADC, therefore, is a sequence of "DC" voltages, each equal to the magnitude of the input signal at the beginning of the conversion period. A logic signal is required to switch the LF398 between its two states—sample and hold. In Figure 9-19, this signal is CB2 from the 6821 PIA, which is applied to pin 7 of the LF398.

From a software perspective, little is new in the circuit of Figure 9-19. Note that CB2 on the 6821 PIA connects to the $\overline{WR}$ input of the ADC0804 (as before) as well as to pin 7 of the LF398 sample-and-hold circuit. When CB2 = 0, the LF398 is in *sample* mode. This takes about 6 μs, so the instructions that toggle CB2 must include a few NOPs (no operation) to achieve the correct pulse duration on

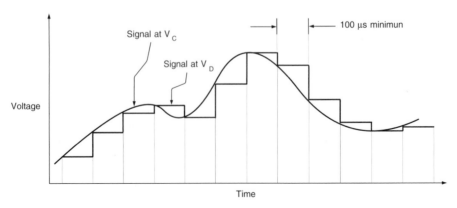

Figure 9-20.   Sample-and-hold waveforms.

$\overline{WR}$. When CB2 returns high the LF398 is in *hold* mode and the ADC0804 begins its conversion cycle.

If we combine the ADC0804 input circuit of Figure 9-19 with the MC1408L8 output circuits of Figure 9-13 and Figure 9-15, then some interesting applications are possible.

**Example 9-17:** Write a RECORD/PLAY program

for the combined circuits of Figures 9-13, 9-15, and 9-19. Name the program SPEECH. The program should include two routines with separate entry points. The RECORD routine digitizes speech from the microphone and stores the samples in a RAM buffer. The PLAY routine reads sample data from the RAM buffer and outputs the data to the loudspeaker driven by the MC1408L8.

**Solution:** See below.

```
 1                          * * * * * * * * * * * * * * * * * * * * * * * * * * * * * * * * * * * * * * * * *
 2                          * SPEECH.SRC                                                  *
 3                          *                                                             *
 4                          * This program has two entry points:                         *
 5                          *                                                             *
 6                          *      RECORD  - $8000                                        *
 7                          *      PLAY    - $800C                                        *
 8                          *                                                             *
 9                          * The RECORD routine digitizes speech from the               *
10                          * ADC0804 and stores the samples in a RAM buffer.            *
11                          *                                                             *
12                          * The PLAY routine outputs samples from the RAM              *
13                          * buffer to the MC1408L8.                                     *
14                          *                                                             *
15                          * The sample rate is 3686400 / 32 / COUNT = 7680 Hz.         *
16                          * The RAM buffer is 12K, starting at $8400.                   *
17                          * * * * * * * * * * * * * * * * * * * * * * * * * * * * * * * * * * * * * * * * *
18   0000C001              DUART    EQU     $00C001  ;68681 base address
19   00000008              ACR      EQU     4*2      ;auxiliary control register
20   0000000C              CTUR     EQU     6*2      ;counter/timer upper register
21   0000000E              CTLR     EQU     7*2      ;counter/timer lower register
22   0000000A              IMR      EQU     5*2      ;interrupt mask register
23   00000018              IVR      EQU     12*2     ;interrupt vector register
24   0000001E              STOP     EQU     15*2     ;timer stop command address
25   00010001              PIA      EQU     $010001  ;PIA base address
26   00000002              CRA      EQU     1*2      ;Control Register A
27   00000004              PORTB    EQU     2*2      ;Port B / DDRB
28   00000006              CRB      EQU     3*2      ;Control Register B
29   0000001A              I2VECTOR EQU     26       ;I2 autovector number
30   00008400              SAMPLES  EQU     $8400    ;sample buffer
31   00003000              SIZE     EQU     1024*12  ;12K sample buffer
32   0000000F              COUNT    EQU     15       ;interrupts @ 7680 Hz
33
34
35   00008000                       ORG     $8000
36   00008000 4EF90000    SPEECH   JMP     >RECORD
     00008004 8012
37   00008006 4EF90000             JMP     >L2ISR
     0000800A 8068
38   0000800C 1E3C0000    PLAY     MOVE.B  #0,D7       ;D7[0] = 0 = "play"
39   00008010 6004                 BRA.S   AHEAD
40   00008012 1E3C0001    RECORD   MOVE.B  #1,D7       ;D7[0] = 1 = "record"
41                        * init 68681 DUART
42   00008016 207C0000    AHEAD    MOVEA.L #DUART,A0   ;A0 -> 68681 DUART
     0000801A C001
43   0000801C 117C0008             MOVE.B  #$08,IMR(A0)
     00008020 000A
44   00008022 117C001A             MOVE.B  #I2VECTOR,IVR(A0)
     00008026 0018
45   00008028 303C000F             MOVE.W  #COUNT,D0
46   0000802C 0188000C             MOVEP.W D0,CTUR(A0)
```

*Continued.*

```
47   00008030 117C0070          MOVE.B    #$70,ACR(A0)
     00008034 0008
48                       * init 6821 PIA
49   00008036 247C0001          MOVEA.L   #PIA,A2        ;A2 -> 6821 PIA
     0000803A 0001
50   0000803C 14BC00FF          MOVE.B    #$FF,(A2)      ;Port A = output
51   00008040 157C0004          MOVE.B    #$04,CRA(A2)   ;enable Port A
     00008044 0002
52   00008046 157C003C          MOVE.B    #$3C,CRB(A2)   ;enable Port B
     0000804A 0006
53   0000804C 227C0000          MOVEA.L   #SAMPLES,A1    ;A1 -> sample buffer
     00008050 8400
54   00008052 007C0700          ORI.W     #$0700,SR      ;mask all interrupts
55   00008056 027CF9FF          ANDI.W    #$F9FF,SR      ;mask level 1 only
56                       * off we go!
57   0000805A B3FC0000  AGAIN   CMPA.L    #SAMPLES+SIZE,A1   ;end of buffer?
     0000805E B400
58   00008060 66F8              BNE       AGAIN          ;no:  check again
59   00008062 007C0700          ORI.W     #$0700,SR      ;yes: done
60   00008066 4E4E              TRAP      #14            ;return to MON68K
61
62                       ****************************************************
63                       * LEVEL-2 INTERRUPT SERVICE ROUTINE               *
64                       *                                                 *
65                       *       -issue STOP command to clear interrupt    *
66                       *       -check for PLAY vs. RECORD                 *
67                       *       -if PLAY: get a sample from RAM buffer and *
68                       *         send it to Port A (MC1408L8)             *
69                       *       -if RECORD: input a sample from ADC0804,   *
70                       *         store it in the RAM buffer, and pulse /WR *
71                       *         for 8 us to begin next conversion        *
72                       ****************************************************
73   00008068 4A28001E  L2ISR   TST.B     STOP(A0)       ;stop cmd, clrs intrrpt
74   0000806C 08070000          BTST      #0,D7          ;play or record?
75   00008070 66000008          BNE       R_ISR          ;1 = record
76   00008074 1019      P_ISR   MOVE.B    (A1)+,D0       ;0 = play (get sample)
77   00008076 1480              MOVE.B    D0,(A2)        ;send it
78   00008078 4E73              RTE
79
80   0000807A 102A0004  R_ISR   MOVE.B    PORTB(A2),D0   ;get sample
81   0000807E 12C0              MOVE.B    D0,(A1)+       ;put in buffer
82   00008080 157C0034          MOVE.B    #$34,CRB(A2)   ;start next conversion
     00008084 0006
83   00008086 4E71              NOP                      ;streeeeee
84   00008088 4E71              NOP                      ;   eeeeee
85   0000808A 4E71              NOP                      ;    eeeee
86   0000808C 4E71              NOP                      ;    eeeee
87   0000808E 4E71              NOP                      ;     eeeee
88   00008090 4E71              NOP                      ;      eeeee
89   00008092 4E71              NOP                      ;         eeeeeeeetch
90   00008094 157C003C          MOVE.B    #$3C,CRB(A2)   ;toggle CB2 for 8 us!
     00008098 0006
91   0000809A 4E73              RTE
92
93   00008400                   ORG       SAMPLES
94   00008400                   DS.B      SIZE           ;12 kbyte sample buffer
95   0000B400                   END       SPEECH
```

**Discussion:** The interface of Figure 9-19 combined with the program above captures and re-creates speech with surprising fidelity. When the RECORD routine at $8000 is started, the user has about 1.5 seconds to speak. Samples are taken, the RAM buffer fills, and the program returns to the monitor. Then, the PLAY routine is executed by restarting at $800C. The original speech is recreated through the DAC output channel. Although the available RAM on the 68KMB fills quickly, a 12K buffer is sufficient to demonstrate speech digitizing and playback.

Let's examine the program in detail. The first instruction of the record routine (line 36) jumps over the level-2 ISR entry point at $8006 to the label RECORD to begin the initialize sequence. The entry point for the PLAY routine is $800C (line 38). The distinction between record and play is implemented through bit 0 in data register D0, with bit 0 = 0 for play and bit 0 = 1 for record. This condition is tested in the level-2 ISR (lines 74–75) to determine which of two instruction sequences to execute.

After the setting or clearing D0[0], the 68681 and 6821 are initialized (lines 42–52). By initializing the timer registers with 15 (lines 45–46), interrupts occur at a rate of 3686400 / 32 / 15 = 7,680 Hz, for a period of 130 μs.

A1 is initialized as a pointer to the sample buffer (line 53) and level-2 interrupts are enabled (lines 54–55). The rest of the main loop (lines 57–58) simply checks the buffer pointer to determine if the buffer is full. This eventually occurs through the action of the level-2 ISR. When the buffer is full, the program terminates by setting the interrupt mask level to 7 (line 59) and returning to the monitor (line 60).

Level-2 interrupts occur every 130 μs through the continuous operation of the 68681 timer. The level-2 ISR is very simple. First, the 68681 timer interrupt signal is cleared (line 73), then D0[0] is tested for record vs. play (lines 74–75). The play instructions read a byte from the RAM buffer (line 76) and send it to the MC1408L8 (line 77). Note that the pointer register (A0) is incremented during the read operation in line 76.

The record instructions input a sample from the ADC0804 (line 80), put it in the RAM buffer (line 81), then toggle CB2 for about 8 μs to begin the next conversion (lines 82–90). Note that the end-of-conversion status flag in control register B (bit 7) is not tested. The interrupt period is sufficiently long (130 μs) to ensure an end-of-conversion condition each time an interrupt occurs. ■

## 9.18 CONCLUSIONS

This chapter has presented a variety of challenging interfaces between input/output devices and the 68000 microprocessor. Yet these examples represent only the beginning of a vast and exciting territory for students to explore. The value of hands-on experience cannot be overstressed. The excitement of putting together the examples for this chapter and developing interface software made this the most enjoyable chapter to develop for this text. The reader is encouraged to give the examples a try, and take them in new directions—just for the fun of it.

## 9.19 DESIGN AND IMPLEMENTATION NOTES

The following sources assisted in designing the interfaces for this chapter.

The low-pass filters in the DAC and ADC circuits of Examples 9-14, 9-15, and 9-17 were derived from Chapter 12 of

Coughlin, R. F., & Driscoll, F. F. (1977). *Operational amplifiers and linear integrated circuits.* Englewood Cliffs, NJ: Prentice Hall.

The preamplifier and amplifier circuits in the ADC circuit of Example 9-17 were based on designs in Chapter 6 of

Jung, W. G. (1976). *IC op amp cookbook.* New York: SAMS.

The LF398 sample-and-hold circuit of Example 9-17 was obtained from the following data book:

National Semiconductor Corp. (1982). *Linear databook.*

The MC14499 serial LED display driver in Examples 9-9 and 9-10 is described in the following data book:

Motorola Semiconductor Inc. (1984). *CMOS/NMOS special functions data.*

The DAC circuit of Example 9-13 was derived from application notes in the following databook:

Motorola Semiconductor, Inc. (1975). *Linear integrated circuits* (vol. 6).

Most of the hardware interfaces described in this chapter are available as six printed-circuit boards from URDA, Inc. (1-800-338-0517). These are illustrated in Figure 9-21. Figure 9-21a is I/O Board #1, which is the simple interface to switches and LEDs shown in Figure 9-3. Note that the 68681, which appears in the schematic in Figure 9-3, is implemented on the 68KMB and does not appear on I/O Board #1 in Figure 9-21a.

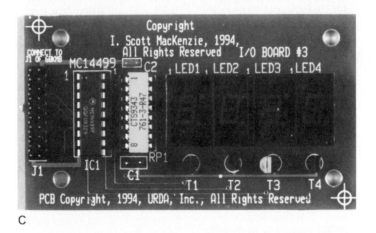

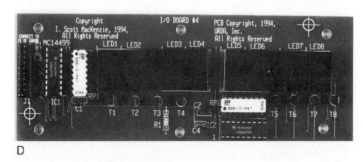

Figure 9-21. A–F. Printed-circuit board implementation of hardware interfaces. (See text for descriptions.)

E

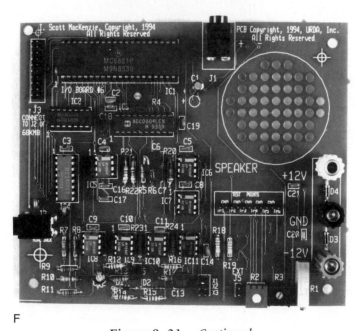

F

**Figure 9–21.** *Continued.*

Figure 9-21b is I/O Board #2, which implements the four switches and 7-segment LED display in Figure 9-4.

The 4-digit and 8-digit LED display interfaces in Figures 9-6 and 9-9 appear in Figures 9-21c (I/O Board #3) and 9-21d (I/O Board #4), respectively.

The hexadecimal keypad interface in Figure 9-12 is available as I/O Board #5 (see Figure 9-21e). This board also includes the signals and NAND gates shown in Figure 9-11 for interfacing to J2 on the 68KMB. Note as well, I/O Board #5 includes a wire wrap area with connections to Port B of the 6821.

The DAC and ADC interfaces are combined in I/O Board #6, as illustrated in Figure 9-21f. This board combines the circuitry shown in Figures 9-11, 9-13, 9-15, 9-16, and 9-19. There are a few additional features on the I/O boards that are not described in this chapter. These are described in the literature provided by URDA, Inc.

## 9.20   QUESTIONS

1. Write an instruction sequence to initialize channel B of the 68681 for operation at 9600 baud with 8 data bits, no parity, and 1.5 stop bits. Assume a 3.6864 MHz clock source is provided on the 68681's X1/CLK input. Put the solution in a file called INIT681A.SRC.

2. Write a program called MESSAGE3 that continually displays the alphabet on the console attached to channel A of the 68681. Each 26-character sequence should begin on a new line. While the alphabet is being displayed, monitor the keyboard for input and respond in the following manner:

    no key      continue
    U or u      uppercase alphabet is displayed
    L or l      lowercase alphabet is displayed
    Q or q      return to the monitor program

3. Write a program for the LED interface in Figure 9-3 that inputs a character from the console and displays the ASCII code for the character on the LEDs. Put the program in a loop and terminate to the monitor when 'q' is detected. Name the program KEYTEST.

4. Write program to test the switches in Figure 9-3. The program should read the switches and output their state to the console in binary. For example, if switch #1 is closed (0) and the others are open (1), then the program should display the following:

    1 1 1 1 0 1

    As switches change state, the console output should change accordingly. Name the program SWTEST.

5. Modify the program of Example 9-5 such that all eight LEDs attached to the output port flash, and the flash rate is 5 Hz. Name the program FIVEHZ.

6. Modify the program of Example 9-6 such that an asterisk is output to the console once every five seconds. Name the program STAR5.

7. In Example 9-6, the 68681 timer was configured to generate level-2 interrupts. The initialization sequence set the interrupt mask level to 1, thus enabling level-2 interrupts. This also enables level-3 through level-6 interrupts, although the possibility of spurious interrupts on these levels was not accommodated. Modify the program such that an appropriate error message is displayed on the console in the event a level-3 through level-6 interrupt occurs. Indicate the level of the spurious interrupt in the error message. Ignore the interrupt and continue on in the main program. Name the program STAR6.

8. Modify the program of Example 9-7 such that only BCD input codes are recognized. If the data read from the switches are in the range $A through $F, the display should remain blank. Name the program LED7A.

9. Write a *rotating segment* program for the 7-segment display in Figure 9-4. The program should light the segments in the following sequence: a, b, c, d, e, f, a, b, c, and on. Use the 68681 timer to establish a rotation rate of 5 Hz. Place the output instructions in an interrupt service routine. Name the program RSEGMENT.

10. Write a *countdown* program for 4-digit display in Figure 9-6. Design the program to be interrupt driven using the 68681 timer. Count down at a rate of 10 Hz. Name the program COUNT4D.

11. Modify the time-of-day clock program in Example 9-10 to include an alarm. Use memory locations to hold the time of the alarm, and allow the alarm to be set in a manner similar to setting the time (i.e., using the monitor's memory modify command). When the alarm time is reached, sound five beeps on the console at half-second intervals. The time should be continually displayed and updated during the alarm. Note: A beep is generated by sending the ASCII bell code ($07) to the console. Name the program ALARMCLK.

12. Consider the program for Example 9-11. If pin 13 of both 74LS165s in Figure 9-10 is grounded, what output value is displayed on the console?

13. Change the solution to Example 9-11 such that the output to the console is displayed in binary rather than in hexadecimal. Name the program LS165A.

14. Perform the following timing analyses on the subroutine RD165 in Example 9-11.

    (a) What is the formula for the execution time ($t$), given $t_{CPU}$ (the period of the CPU clock), and $n$ (the number of 74LS165s)?

    (b) How long does it take to read two 74LS165s connected to a 68000-based system operating at 3.6864 MHz?

(c) How long does it take to read ten 74LS165s connected to a 68000-based system operating at 12 MHz?

(d) Suppose RD165 must execute once every second on a very large data acquisition system with 500 sample points. If the host system is a 68000 operating at 16 MHz, what percentage of the CPU's execution time is consumed sampling the inputs?

15. For the sawtooth waveform in Example 9-13, construct a formula for the output frequency ($f$) given three variables: STEP, COUNT, and the CPU clock frequency ($f_C$).

16. Consider the sine-wave program in Example 9-14. What is the output frequency if the program is run on a 12-MHz system?

17. How long does the ISR in Example 9-15 take to execute? Give two estimates: one assuming a key has been hit, one assuming a key has not been hit.

18. What is the current sinking capability at the output port pins of the 68681 and the 6821?

19. The OUT2HX and HTOA subroutines from MON68K were used in the examples in this chapter. Suppose we also wished to use the subroutine ATOH (ASCII to hex) and IS-DIGIT (is a character an ASCII digit?). How would these subroutines be defined as equated symbols?

20. What exact size of buffer is required to store 10 seconds of speech using the program and interface in Example 9-17?

21. Modify the program in Example 9-17 as follows: Place the playback routine in a loop such that the content of the RAM buffer is continually sent to the DAC. During playback, monitor the console for keyboard input and respond in the following way when a key is pressed:

u        the frequency of playback increases (UP)

d        the frequency of playback decreases (DOWN)

SPACE    the frequency of playback is restored to normal

q        quit to MON68K

Ignore any other keystrokes. Name the program SPEECH2. (Hint: The frequency of playback can be controlled by altering the timer count.)

# 10. *Beyond the 68000*

## 10.1. INTRODUCTION

Underlying this text is the philosophy that in-depth study of one device is preferable to a family-level survey that fails to confront complex details of any one device. Our focus on one chip—the 68000—is deliberate. There is a tendency to overwhelm if too many advanced features are presented too soon. However, with the groundwork that the preceding chapters have established of the basic 68000 architecture, we are ready to conclude this text with a survey of 68000-family devices and a look beyond the 68000. Our aim is to make the text comprehensive, without claiming to study the complete 68000 family in depth.

The 68000-processor family is **upward compatible.** This means that every new member of the family is a superset of preceding members. For example, the 68010 will run 68000 programs, the 68020 will run 68010 or 68000 programs, and so on. Upward compatibility does not imply, for example, that 68020 programs will run on a 68000. In fact, this is generally not the case. New members of the family each include all the features of preceding members as well as new features or enhancements.

## 10.2. PROCESSORS

The primary processors in the 68000 family include the 68008, 68000, 68010, 68020, and 68030, and 68040. Table 10-1 highlights the major differences.

### 10.2.1. 68008

The 68008 is a scaled-down version of the 68000. The main difference is that the data bus is only 8 bits wide. With a simplified bus structure, the 68008 is an economical choice for many implementations since only byte-wide memories and peripherals are required. The non-multiplexed address and data buses eliminate the need for external demultiplexers to split accesses into upper and lower bytes (as with the 68000).

The instruction set of the 68008 is fully compatible with the 68000 at both the source- and object-code levels. The programmer's model is identical for both devices.

Savings also result from a smaller package. A 48-pin version includes a 20-bit address bus, and a 52-bit version includes a 22-bit address bus. This difference and the control bus differences are featured in Table 10-2.

Note in Table 10-2 that the 68008 includes address line A0 in lieu of $\overline{UDS}$ and $\overline{LDS}$. Since the data bus is 8 bits wide, every address is a byte-address; it is not necessary to distinguish between upper and lower bytes in the external memory interface. Further savings result from eliminating $\overline{VMA}$, a signal well known in the design community to be redundant.[1] $\overline{BGACK}$ is eliminated on the 48-pin 68008.

The function usually performed by $\overline{IPL2}$ and $\overline{IPL0}$ is combined in the 48-pin 68008. Internally the interrupt circuitry is the same except $\overline{IPL2}$ and $\overline{IPL0}$ are connected together. With only two interrupt inputs, the 48-pin version is limited to interrupt levels 0, 2, 5, and 7.

### 10.2.2 68010

The 68010 processor is fully object-code compatible with earlier members of the 68000 family (the 68000 and 68008). Additional features include virtual memory support and enhanced instruction execution timing. The 68010 is offered in a 68-pin package and is pin-for-pin compatible with the 68000. A 68010 device can replace a 68000 device in an existing 68000-based system.

There are a few changes for the 68000 programming model. A new register called the **vector base register** determines the location of the exception vector table in memory. By altering the vector base register, a 68010 can support multiple processes, each with independently managed exception tables.

---

[1]Rumors abound that VMA was added to the original 6800 8-bit microprocessor to correct a design bug.

Table 10-1.    68000-Family Features.

| | 48-pin 68008 | 52-pin 68008 | 68000 | 68010 | 68020 | 68030 | 68040 |
|---|---|---|---|---|---|---|---|
| Data Bus (bits) | 8 | 8 | 16 | 16 | 32 | 32 | 32 |
| Address Bus (bits) | 20 | 22 | 24 | 24 | 32 | 32 | 32 |
| Data Cache (bytes) | – | – | – | – | – | 256 | 4096 |
| Instruction Cache (bytes) | – | – | – | – | 256 | 256 | 4096 |
| On-Chip Memory Management | No | No | No | No | No | Yes | Yes |
| On-Chip Floating-Point Unit | No | No | No | No | No | No | Yes |

The two most significant changes are **virtual machine** support and **loop-mode** instruction execution. In a virtual memory system, a user program can be written as though it has more memory than the system contains. With a 24-bit address bus, the 68010 has a 16-megabyte address space. User programs can access this entire space even if only a fraction of that amount of memory is present. The mechanism to do this is exceptions. When a program accesses a memory location not physically present, a bus error or address error occurs. This may even occur in the middle of an instruction. The 68010's exception stack frame is quite substantial, capturing the complete internal state of the processor. The memory fault is corrected in the exception handler by reloading memory and reassigning addresses through external memory management hardware. When the exception handler has completed, the suspended instruction is continued. Complete details of the 68010's virtual machine implementation are found in Motorola's *M68000 8-/16-/32-Bit Microprocessor User's Manual* (M68000UM/AD).

Loop mode allows fast execution of tight loops by avoiding re-reading instruction words that are close to a DBcc instruction. Loop mode is invoked when the following three conditions occur: (1) a loopable instruction is executed, (2) the loopable instruction is followed immediately by DBcc, and (3) the branch destination is the loopable instruc-

tion. Thirty-seven instructions are identified as loopable.

The 68010 instruction set is summarized in Table 10-3. The maximum clock speed is 12.5 MHz.

## 10.2.3.   68020

The 68020 is the first full 32-bit implementation of a 68000-family microprocessor. All data paths are 32 bits wide, including the data bus and address bus. With a 32-bit address bus, the 68020 can directly access any location within a 4-gigabyte address space. With a 32-bit data bus, a longword operand can be transferred in a single bus cycle. Obviously, this greatly increases the overall bus bandwidth, and, therefore, overall processing power. As with the 68010, the 68020 is object-code compatible with preceding members of the 68000 family. Programs written for the 68000 microprocessor will execute unaltered on the 68020.

The 68020 includes far too many new features for a comprehensive treatment here. These include:

- new addressing-mode extensions
- a Bit Field data type to accelerate bit-oriented applications
- on-chip instruction cache to speed up instruction execution and increase bus bandwidth
- coprocessor interface to 68881 and 68882
- pipelined architecture supporting multiple concurrent instructions
- dynamic bus sizing to facilitate 8-/16-/32-bit data transfers
- full support of virtual-memory and virtual-machine architecture
- 4-gigabyte address space
- 33.33 MHz maximum clock speed

A 256-byte instruction cache allows a stream of instructions to be kept in the processor. This sub-

Table 10-2.    68008 vs. 68000 Signals.

| Signal | 68000 | 48-pin 68008 | 52-pin 68008 |
|---|---|---|---|
| $\overline{VMA}$ | • | | |
| $\overline{BGACK}$ | • | | |
| $\overline{IPL2}$ | • | $=\overline{IPL0}$ | • |
| $\overline{UDS}$ | • | | |
| $\overline{LDS}$ | • | | |
| A23, A22 | • | | |
| A21, A20 | • | | • |
| A0 | | • | • |

• = signal included

**Table 10-3.    68010 Instruction Set Summary.**

| Mnemonic | Description | Mnemonic | Description |
|---|---|---|---|
| ABCD[†] | Add decimal with extend | MOVE[†] | Move |
| ADD[†] | Add | MOVEC | Move control register |
| AND[†] | Logical AND | MOVES | Move address space |
| ASL[†] | Arithmetic shift left | MULS | Signed multiply |
| ASR[†] | Arithmetic shift right | MULU | Unsigned multiply |
| Bcc | Branch conditionally | NBCD[†] | Negate decimal with extend |
| BCHG | Bit test and change | NEG[†] | Negate |
| BCLR | Bit test and clear | NOP | No operation |
| BRA | Branch always | NOT[†] | Ones complement |
| BSET | Bit test and set | OR[†] | Logical OR |
| BSR | Branch to subroutine | PEA | Push effective address |
| BTST | Bit test | RESET | Reset external devices |
| CHK | Check register against bounds | ROL[†] | Rotate left |
| CLR[†] | Clear operand | ROR[†] | Rotate right |
| CMP | Compare | ROXL[†] | Rotate left with extend |
| DBcc | Test condition, decrement, branch | ROXR[†] | Rotate right with extend |
| DIVS | Signed divide | RTD | Return and deallocate |
| DIVU | Unsigned divide | RTE | Return from exception |
| EOR[†] | Exclusive OR | RTR | Return and restore CCR bits |
| EXG | Exchange registers | RTS | Return from subroutine |
| EXT | Sign extend | SBCD[†] | Subtract decimal with extend |
| ILLEGAL | Take illegal instruction trap | Scc | Set conditional |
| JMP | Jump | STOP | Stop |
| JSR | Jump to subroutine | SUB[†] | Subtract |
| LEA | Load effective address | SWAP | Swap data register halves |
| LINK | Link stack | TAS | Test and set operand |
| LSL[†] | Logical shift left | TRAP | Trap |
| LSR[†] | Logical shift right | TRAPV | Trap on overflow |
|  |  | TST[†] | Test |
|  |  | UNLK | Unlink |

▭ = new instructions from previous CPUs

[†] loopable instructions

stantially reduces the average instruction execution time and reduces the external bus activity. This means the system's buses are more accessible to other bus masters for DMA transfers.

Beginning with the 68020, conditional branch instructions support 32-bit signed offsets (as well as 8-bit and 16-bit signed offsets). Recall that a 16-bit signed offset is used if $00 appears as the 8-bit offset in the low-byte of the first instruction word. A 32-bit offset is now indicated if the 8-bit offset is $FF.

The 68020 architecture avoids the constraint that word and longword variables must reside at even addresses. **Dynamic bus sizing** allows word or longword operands to reside at odd addresses. If the operand is split over two consecutive 32-bit physical addresses, then two memory accesses are required. This is transparent to the programmer, however. The possibility of operand misalignment (among other things) complicates the calculation

of precise execution times for programs or instruction sequences. This is particularly troublesome for real-time applications that require careful timing analyses of interrupt service routines and other code sequences.

New operand sizes include bit fields, unpacked BCD digits, and quadword (64-bit) integers. A variety of new instructions are added to operate on strings of bits up to 32 bits long. These appear in the instruction set summary in Table 10-4 as bit-field instructions. A bit field may start in any bit position and may span any address boundary.

New binary-coded decimal operations include packing and unpacking digits. Packing reduces two bytes of data, with a BCD digit in the low-nibble of each, into a single byte with the digits in both nibbles. Unpacking reverses this process.

Beginning with the 68020, quadword operand sizes may be specified for multiply and divide operations. A longword multiply can now produce a

**Table 10-4.    68020 Instruction Set Summary.**

| Mnemonic | Description | Mnemonic | Description |
|---|---|---|---|
| ABCD | Add decimal with extend | MOVE | Move |
| ADD | Add | MOVEC | Move control register |
| AND | Logical AND | MOVES | Move address space |
| ASL | Arithmetic shift left | MULS | Signed multiply |
| ASR | Arithmetic shift right | MULU | Unsigned multiply |
| Bcc | Branch conditionally | NBCD | Negate decimal with extend |
| BCHG | Bit test and change | NEG | Negate |
| BCLR | Bit test and clear | NOP | No operation |
| BFCHG | Bit Field - test and change | NOT | Ones complement |
| BFCLR | Bit Field - test and clear | OR | Logical OR |
| BFEXTS | Bit Field - signed extract | PACK | Pack BCD |
| BFEXTU | Bit Field - unsigned extract | PEA | Push effective address |
| BFFFO | Bit Field - find first one | RESET | Reset external devices |
| BFINS | Bit Field - insert | ROL | Rotate left |
| BFSET | Bit Field - test and set | ROR | Rotate right |
| BFTST | Bit Field - test | ROXL | Rotate left with extend |
| BKPT | Breakpoint | ROXR | Rotate right with extend |
| BRA | Branch always | RTD | Return and deallocate |
| BSET | Bit test and set | RTM | Return from module |
| BSR | Branch to subroutine | RTE | Return from exception |
| BTST | Bit test | RTR | Return and restore CCR bits |
| CALLM | Call module | RTS | Return from subroutine |
| CAS | Compare and swap operands | SBCD | Subtract decimal with extend |
| CAS2 | Compare and swap dual operands | Scc | Set conditional |
| CHK | Check register against bounds | STOP | Stop |
| CHK2 | Check against upper & lower bounds | SUB | Subtract |
| CLR | Clear operand | SWAP | Swap data register halves |
| CMP | Compare | TAS | Test and set operand |
| CMP2 | Compare against upper/lower bounds | TRAP | Trap |
| DBcc | Test condition, decrement, branch | TRAPcc | Trap conditionally |
| DIVS | Signed divide | TRAPV | Trap on overflow |
| DIVU | Unsigned divide | TST | Test |
| EOR | Logical Exclusive OR | UNLK | Unlink |
| EXG | Exchange registers | UNPK | Unpack BCD |
| EXT | Sign extend | | |
| ILLEGAL | Take illegal instruction trap | Coprocessor | Instructions |
| JMP | Jump | cpBcc | Branch conditionally |
| JSR | Jump to subroutine | cpDBcc | Test condition, decrement and branch |
| LEA | Load effective address | cpGEN | General instruction |
| LINK | Link stack | cpRESTORE | Restore internal state |
| SL | Logical shift left | cpSAVE | Save internal state |
| LSR | Logical shift right | cpScc | Set conditionally |
| | | cpTRAPcc | Trap conditionally |

░░░░░ = new instructions from previous CPUs

quadword product. Division is now possible using a quadword dividend and a longword divisor; the result is a longword quotient and a longword remainder.

The 68020 introduces **scaled indices.** Consider the following 68000 instruction:

```
MOVE.W  TABLE(PC,D5),D6
```

To move item #5 in the table to D6, the index specified by D5 must be $5 \times 2 = 10$. Since the entries are words, each spans two byte-addresses, so indices must be adjusted accordingly to access the correct entry. With scaled indices, the adjustment occurs automatically by specifying a scaling factor following the index. For example

```
MOVE.W  TABLE(PC,D5*2),D6
```

or

```
MOVE.L  TABLE(PC,D5*4),D6
```

Table 10-5.   68030 Instruction Set Summary.

| Mnemonic | Description | Mnemonic | Description |
|---|---|---|---|
| ABCD | Add decimal with extend | NBCD | Negate decimal with extend |
| ADD | Add | NEG | Negate |
| AND | Logical AND | NOP | No operation |
| ASL | Arithmetic shift left | NOT | Ones complement |
| ASR | Arithmetic shift right | OR | Logical OR |
| Bcc | Branch conditionally | PACK | Pack BCD |
| BCHG | Bit test and change | PEA | Push effective address |
| BCLR | Bit test and clear | PFLUSH | Flush entries in ATC |
| BFCHG | Bit Field - test and change | PFLUSHA | Flush all entries in ATC |
| BFCLR | Bit Field - test and clear | PLOAD | Load entry into the ATC |
| BFEXTS | Bit Field - signed extract | PMOVE | Move to/from MMU registers |
| BFEXTU | Bit Field - unsigned extract | PMOVEFD | Move to/from MMU with flush disable |
| BFFFO | Bit Field - find first one | PTEST | Test a logical address |
| BFINS | Bit Field - insert | RESET | Reset external devices |
| BFSET | Bit Field - test and set | ROL | Rotate left |
| BFTST | Bit Field - test | ROR | Rotate right |
| BKPT | Breakpoint | ROXL | Rotate left with extend |
| BRA | Branch always | ROXR | Rotate right with extend |
| BSET | Bit test and set | RTD | Return and deallocate |
| BSR | Branch to subroutine | RTM | Return from module |
| BTST | Bit test | RTE | Return from exception |
| CALLM | Call module | RTR | Return and restore CCR bits |
| CAS | Compare and swap operands | RTS | Return from subroutine |
| CAS2 | Compare and swap dual operands | SBCD | Subtract decimal with extend |
| CHK | Check register against bounds | Scc | Set conditional |
| CHK2 | Check against upper & lower bounds | STOP | Stop |
| CLR | Clear operand | SUB | Subtract |
| CMP | Compare | SWAP | Swap data register halves |
| CMP2 | Compare against upper/lower bounds | TAS | Test and set operand |
| DBcc | Test condition, decrement, branch | TRAP | Trap |
| DIVS | Signed divide | TRAPcc | Trap conditionally |
| DIVU | Unsigned divide | TRAPV | Trap on overflow |
| EOR | Exclusive OR | TST | Test |
| EXG | Exchange registers | UNLK | Unlink |
| EXT | Sign extend | UNPK | Unpack BCD |
| ILLEGAL | Take illegal instruction trap | | |
| JMP | Jump | *Coprocessor Instructions* | |
| JSR | Jump to subroutine | cpBcc | Branch conditionally |
| LEA | Load effective address | cpDBcc | Test condition, decrement and branch |
| LINK | Link stack | cpGEN | General instruction |
| LSL | Logical shift left | cpRESTORE | Restore internal state |
| LSR | Logical shift right | cpSAVE | Save internal state |
| MOVE | Move | cpScc | Set conditionally |
| MOVEC | Move control register | cpTRAPcc | Trap conditionally |
| MOVES | Move address space | | |
| MULS | Signed multiply | | |
| MULU | Unsigned multiply | | |

▓▓▓▓ = new instructions from previous CPUs

The 68020 includes interface logic for a tightly coupled interface to the 68851 memory-management unit or the 68881 or 68882 coprocessors. A coprocessor is a peripheral IC that enables a CPU to perform complex mathematical operations without using (slow!) machine-language subroutines. From a programmer's perspective, the coprocessor is part of the CPU. Extra instructions be-come available that directly execute complex operations on floating-point numbers. With a coprocessor installed, the 68020 programming model includes an additional eight registers, FP0 through FP7. These registers are 80-bits each and conform to the IEEE[2] Standard for Binary Floating-Point

[2]Institute of Electrical and Electronics Engineers.

Table 10-6.    68040 Instruction Set Summary.

| Mnemonic | Description | Mnemonic | Description |
|----------|-------------|----------|-------------|
| ABCD | Add decimal with extend | FScc | Floating-point set by condition |
| ADD | Add | FSQRT | Floating-point square root |
| AND | Logical AND | FSUB | Floating-point subtract |
| ASL | Arithmetic shift left | FTRAPcc | Floating-point trap conditionally |
| ASR | Arithmetic shift right | FTST | Floating-point test |
| Bcc | Branch conditionally | ILLEGAL | Take illegal instruction trap |
| BCHG | Bit test and change | JMP | Jump |
| BCLR | Bit test and clear | JSR | Jump to subroutine |
| BFCHG | Bit Field - test and change | LEA | Load effective address |
| BFCLR | Bit Field - test and clear | LINK | Link stack |
| BFEXTS | Bit Field - signed extract | LSL | Logical shift left |
| BFEXTU | Bit Field - unsigned extract | LSR | Logical shift right |
| BFFFO | Bit Field - find first one | MOVE | Move |
| BFINS | Bit Field - insert | MOVE16 | Move 16-byte block |
| BFSET | Bit Field - test and set | MOVEC | Move control register |
| BFTST | Bit Field - test | MOVES | Move address space |
| BKPT | Breakpoint | MULS | Signed multiply |
| BRA | Branch always | MULU | Unsigned multiply |
| BSET | Bit test and set | NEG | Negate |
| BSR | Branch to subroutine | NOP | No operation |
| BTST | Bit test | NOT | Ones complement |
| CALLM | Call module | OR | Logical OR |
| CAS | Compare and swap operands | PACK | Pack BCD |
| CAS2 | Compare and swap dual operands | PEA | Push effective address |
| CHK | Check register against bounds | PFLUSH | Flush entries in ATC |
| CHK2 | Check against upper & lower bounds | PTEST | Test a logical address |
| CINV | Invalidate Cache Entries | RESET | Reset external devices |
| CLR | Clear operand | ROL | Rotate left |
| CMP | Compare | ROR | Rotate right |
| CMP2 | Compare against upper/lower bounds | ROXL | Rotate left with extend |
| CPUSH | Push then invalidate cache entries | ROXR | Rotate right with extend |
| DBcc | Test condition, decrement, branch | RTD | Return and deallocate |
| DIVS | Signed divide | RTM | Return from module |
| DIVU | Unsigned divide | RTE | Return from exception |
| EOR | Exclusive OR | RTR | Return and restore CCR bits |
| EXG | Exchange registers | RTS | Return from subroutine |
| EXT | Sign extend | SBCD | Subtract decimal with extend |
| FABS | Floating-point absolute value | Scc | Set conditional |
| FADD | Floating-point add | STOP | Stop |
| FBcc | Floating-point branch | SUB | Subtract |
| FCMP | Floating-point compare | SWAP | Swap data register halves |
| FDBcc | Floating-point decrement & branch | TAS | Test and set operand |
| FDIV | Floating-point divide | TRAP | Trap |
| FMOVE | Floating-point register move | TRAPcc | Trap conditionally |
| FMOVEM | Floating-point registers move | TRAPV | Trap on overflow |
| FMUL | Floating-point multiply | TST | Test |
| FNEG | Floating-point negate | UNLK | Unlink |
| FRESTORE | Restore floating-point internal state | UNPK | Unpack BCD |
| FSAVE | Save floating-point internal state | | |

▢ = new instructions from previous CPUs

Arithmetic (754). The additional instructions are implemented through 68000's F-line exception (as discussed in Chapter 6). A 68020 can execute a program using the extended floating-point instructions of the 68881 regardless of whether or not the coprocessor is present. If the coprocessor is not present, the instructions are directed to the appropriate machine language emulation routine through the F-line exception. The additional instructions implemented through the 68881 and 68882 coprocessors are presented later in this chapter.

## 10.2.4. 68030

Motorola refers to the 68030 as a *second-generation* 32-bit microprocessor. The architecture builds on the 68020—the first-generation—by adding an on-chip memory-management unit and an on-chip 256-byte data cache. There are some internal performance-boosting features, such as multiple data and address buses and a versatile bus controller. Bus accesses are now possible in two CPU cycles (rather than four). Burst cycles are possible in a single CPU cycle.

The added data cache means that both instruction and data accesses may be pipelined. This increases parallelism and boosts performance. For example, internal cache accesses may occur in parallel with external bus accesses.

The 68030 includes several new instructions in support of the page and pointer tables for the on-chip memory management unit (MMU). These are shown in Table 10-5. The new instructions are compatible with the instruction extensions added to the 68020 through the 68851 MMU. Since the memory management logic is on-chip with the 68030, an external 68851 is not needed. Complete details are found in Motorola's *MC68030 Enhanced 32-bit Microprocessor User's Manual* (MC68030UM/AD).

## 10.2.5. 68040

The most advanced processor in the 68000 family is the 68040—Motorola's third-generation 32-bit microprocessor. The 68040 is manufactured using a high-performance CMOS[3] technology that Motorola calls HCMOS. Although this is an implementation detail and has no bearing on the architecture per se, HCMOS devices combine high speed with low power and a small device size. There are performance benefits as well as cost benefits due to the simplified manufacturing process.

The most significant improvement with the 68040 is the on-chip floating-point unit (FPU). In addition, the instruction and data caches are now 4K bytes each. The performance of the 68040 is rated at 20 MIPS (million instructions per second) and 3.5 FLOPS (floating-point operations per second). The maximum clock frequency is 40 MHz.

Several new instructions are added to support cache memory and floating-point operations (see Table 10-6). Note that instructions missing from earlier processors are combined in the 68040's instruction set. Programs from any earlier member of the 68000 family will execute unaltered on the

68040. Complete details on the 68040 are found in Motorola's *M68040 Microprocessors User's Manual* (M68040UM/AD).

## 10.2.6. 68302, 68340, *and* 68306

A few members of the 68000 family form what Motorola calls the Integrated Group (IG). The 68302, 68340, and 68306 are examples of **embedded controllers**—computing devices intended for products other than general-purpose computers. Applications vary from washing machines to automobile ignition-control systems.

The 68340 is a highly specialized device, incorporating a 68000 core processor and myriad interface logic targeted at the communications industry. Applications include ISDN (integrated services digital network) channel control, terminal adapters, concurrent communications channel control, data concentrators, line cards, bridges, and gateways.

The 68302 is a general-purpose, highly integrated controller. As well as a 68000 core CPU, the 68302 includes a two-channel DMA controller, two serial I/O channels, two 16-bit timers, four programmable chip selects signals, and 16 programmable I/O pins.

The most recent IG device is the 68306, which includes a great deal of processing and interface circuitry in a single device. Complex systems can be designed around the 68306 with a minimum of additional components. A 68306 block diagram is shown in Figure 10-1.

On-chip features include the following:

- 68000 core processor
- two fully programmable serial ports
- 16-bit programmable timer
- dynamic RAM controller
- eight programmable chip select outputs
- programmable interrupt controller
- 8-bit I/O port
- watchdog timer
- 24 address lines
- 16 data lines

The maximum clock speed is 16.67 MHz, yielding a performance rating of 2.4 MIPS.

Much of the on-chip functionality incorporates the features of the 68681 DUART, presented in Chapter 9 and in Appendix H. A very significant additional on-chip feature is the dynamic RAM controller. Interfacing DRAMs to general-purpose CPUs (such as the 68000) has long been a thorn in the designer's side. The need to mesh refresh cycles with CPU cycles and maintain counters for re-

---

[3]CMOS stands for complementary metal-oxide semiconductor.

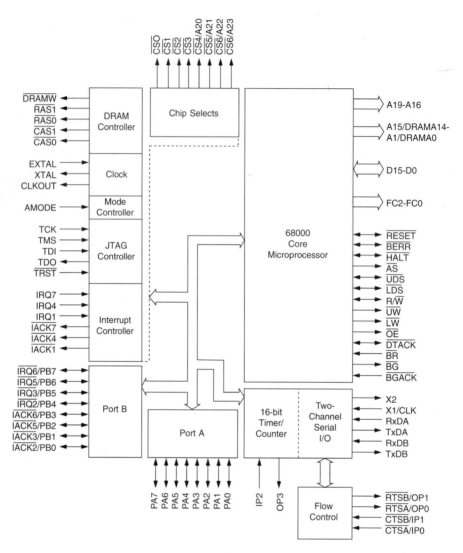

**Figure 10-1.   68306 block diagram.**

fresh addresses usually necessitates substantial external logic. The 68306's on-chip DRAM controller maintains its own refresh registers and provides the necessary $\overline{RAS}$ (row address strobe) and $\overline{CAS}$ (column address strobe) signals for two separate banks of DRAMs. Up to 64 megabytes of RAM can be interfaced to the 68306 *with no additional support circuitry.*

The eight programmable chip select outputs allow a variety of other peripheral interface ICs to connect to the 68306 without address decode logic. The lines are fully programmable, allowing the peripheral ICs to reside anywhere in the 68306's memory space.

## 10.3.   COPROCESSORS

The coprocessor bus interface supported by the 68020 and 68030 CPUs was designed with the 68881 and 68882 in mind. These devices can greatly increase the performance of 68020- or 68030-based systems, particularly if the application includes significant number crunching.

### 10.3.1.   68881

The first coprocessor introduced by Motorola was the 68881. This device implements the IEEE

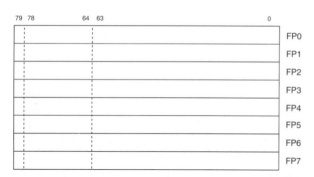

**Figure 10-2.   68881 floating-point data registers.**

### Table 10-7.  68881 Data Formats.

| Data Format | Exponent Size (bits) | Mantissa Size (bits) | Bias |
|---|---|---|---|
| Single | 8 | 23(+1) | 127 |
| Double | 11 | 52(+1) | 1023 |
| Extended | 15 | 64 | 16383 |

Standard for Binary Floating-Point Arithmetic (754). The 68881 provides a logical extension to the 68020 or 68030 CPUs through a high-performance floating-point unit and a set of floating-point data registers. Once a 68881 is interfaced to the system buses, the registers are accessed as though they were native to the CPU's programming model, with the 68881's instructions forming a natural extension to the CPU's in-

struction set. For example, all addressing modes are supported, as with the CPU's native instructions. From the programmer's perspective the 68881 and the 68020 (or 68030) are packaged on the same IC.

The programming model includes eight new floating-point data registers, designated FP0 through FP7. Each register is 80 bits wide, as shown in Figure 10-2.

Single-, double-, and extended-precision formats are supported. Each format uses a different size for the exponent and mantissa, and a different bias for the exponent (see Table 10.7). The instruction set of the 68881 is shown in Table 10-8. For a detailed description of the 68881, consult Motorola's *M68000 Family Reference Manual* (M68000FR/AD).

### Table 10-8.  68881 Instruction Set Summary.

| Mnemonic | Operation | Mnemonic | Operation |
|---|---|---|---|
| **Move Instructions** | | **Double-Operand Instructions** | |
| FMOVE | Move register | FADD | Add |
| FMOVEM | Move multiple registers | FCMP | Compare |
| | | FDIV | Divide |
| **Single-Operand Instructions** | | FMOD | Modulo remainder |
| FABS | Absolute value | FMUL | Multiply |
| FACOS | Arc cosine | FREM | IEEE remainder |
| FASIN | Arc sine | FSCALE | Scale exponent |
| FATAN | Arc tangent | FSGLDIV | Single-precision divide |
| FATANH | Hyperbolic arc tangent | FSGLMUL | Single-precision multiply |
| FCOS | Cosine | FSUB | Subtract |
| FCOSH | Hyperbolic Cosine | | |
| FETOX | e to the $x$ power | **Conditional Instructions** | |
| FETOXM1 | e to the $x$ power -1 | FBcc | Branch conditional |
| FGETEXP | Get exponent | FDBcc | Decrement and branch conditional |
| FGETMAN | Get mantissa | FScc | Set byte by condition |
| FINT | Integer part | FTRAPcc | Trap conditional |
| FINTRZ | Integer part (truncated) | | |
| FLOG10 | Log base 10 | **Miscellaneous Instructions** | |
| FLOG2 | Log base 2 | FMOVE FPcr | Move to/from control register |
| FLOGN | Log base e | FSAVE | Save virtual machine state |
| FLOGNP1 | Log base e of $(x + 1)$ | FRESTORE | Restore virtual machine state |
| FNEG | Negate | | |
| FSIN | Sine | | |
| FSINCOS | Simultaneous sine and cos. | | |
| FSINH | Hyperbolic Sine | | |
| FSQRT | Square root | | |
| FTAN | Tangent | | |
| FTANH | Hyperbolic tangent | | |
| FTENTOX | 10 to the power $x$ | | |
| FTST | Test | | |
| FTWOTX | 2 to the power $x$ | | |

Table 10-9.    68000 Peripheral/Memory Interface ICs.

| Device | Description |
|--------|-------------|
| 68851 | 32-bit paged memory management unit |
| 68440 | Dual-channel direct memory access controller |
| 68450 | Direct memory access controller |
| 68681 | Dual asynchronous receiver/transmitter |
| 68184 | Broadband interface controller |
| 68185 | Twisted-pair modem |
| 68194 | Carrierband modem |
| 68605 | X.25 protocol controller |
| 68606 | Multi-link LAPD protocol controller |
| 68824 | Token-passing bus controller |
| 68230 | Parallel interface/timer |
| 68901 | Multifunction peripheral |

## 10.3.2.    68882

The 68882 coprocessor is pin-for-pin and software compatible with the 68881. There is a variety of performance-boosting improvements, making the 68882 about 1.5 times faster than the 68881. This results from added hardware that speeds internal conversions of data formats, boosts throughput across the CPU interface, and executes multiple floating-point instructions concurrently.

## 10.4.    PERIPHERAL/MEMORY INTERFACE ICS

The 68000 family includes a variety of support ICs to facilitate interfaces to memory and peripheral devices. These are summarized in Table 10-9.

The last two devices—the 68230 and the 68901—are very popular devices and appear in a variety of general-purpose 68000-based systems.

The 68230—known as the PI/T—includes the following features:

- two bidirectional 8-bit I/O ports
- 24-bit programmable timer
- programmable handshaking options
- multiple interrupt sources
- five programmable interrupt vectors
- DMA compatibility

A block diagram is shown in Figure 10-3.

The 68901 multifunction peripheral provides yet another option to interface designers. Its features include:

- eight individually programmable I/O pins
- 16-source interrupt controller

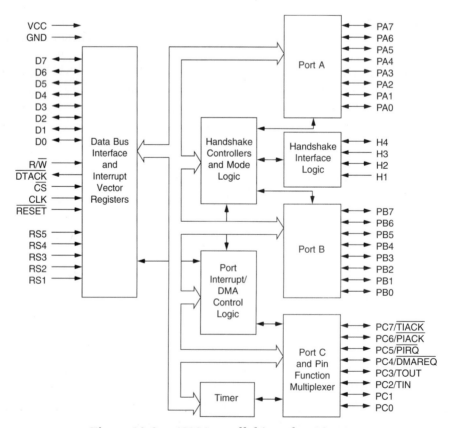

Figure 10-3.    68230 parallel interface/timer.

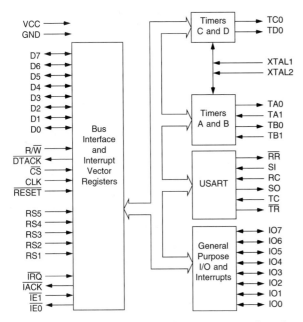

**Figure 10-4.   68901 multifunction peripheral.**

- four timers
- one serial I/O channel

A block diagram is shown in Figure 10-4.

---

## 10.5.   WHAT'S AHEAD?

We have now touched on most members of the 68000 family of high-performance CPUs and interface devices. Although the tour was quick, in the preceding chapters we have examined the functionality of the 68000 device in great detail. The reader is now well prepared for in-depth study of the advanced processors in the 68000 family or other processors conforming to a different architecture.

Keeping up-to-date with developments in microelectronics is a formidable task. As this text is written, there are many new processors appearing on the market featuring a staggering array of performance specifications, on-chip functionality, complexity, density, and so on.

A major architectural front has now emerged in the form of **RISC** technology. RISC, for **reduced instruction set computer,** is contrasted with **CISC** for **complex instruction set computer.** All the processors in the 68000 family are of the CISC variety. There are several very distinct architectural differences between RISC and CISC. CISC processors have variable-length instructions, a large number of addressing modes, and many instructions that combine memory accesses with arithmetic or logic operations. We have seen all this in the 68000 architecture. RISC processors, on the other hand, have fixed-length instructions, simple addressing modes, and instructions that segregate load/store memory accesses from register-to-register arithmetic or logic operations. RISC processors implement algorithms with many simple steps, whereas CISC processors implement algorithms with a few complex steps. Although many industry experts predict the demise of CISC over the next decade or so, the more pragmatic market-watchers see a healthy future for CISC-based systems. This is particularly true for portable computers and embedded controllers.

To place the current state of microprocessor technology in perspective, Table 10-10 compares

**Table 10-10.   Comparison of Five Recent Microprocessors[†].**

|  | 68040 | 80486 | PowerPC | Pentium | Alpha 21064 |
|---|---|---|---|---|---|
| Company | Motorola | Intel | IBM/Motorola | Intel | DEC |
| Introduced | 1989 | 6/91 | 4/93 | 3/93 | 2/92 |
| Architecture | CISC | CISC | RISC | CISC | RISC |
| Width (bits) | 32 | 32 | 32 | 32 | 64 |
| Registers (general/FP) | 16/8 | 8/8 | 32/32 | 8/8 | 32/32 |
| Multiprocessing Support? | No | No | Yes | Yes | Yes |
| Device Size (mm) | $10.8 \times 11.7$ | not available | $11 \times 11$ | $17.2 \times 17.2$ | $15.3 \times 12.7$ |
| Transistors (millions) | 1.2 | 1.2 | 2.8 | 3.1 | 1.68 |
| Clock (MHz) | 25 | 50 | 80 | 66 | 200 |
| SPECint 92[††] | 21 | 27.9 | 85 | 67.4 | 130 |
| SPECfp 92[††] | 15 | 13.1 | 105 | 63.6 | 184 |
| Peak Power (Watts) | 6 | 5 | 9.1 | 16 | 30 |
| Price ($US/1000 units) | $233 | $432 | $557 | $898 | $505 |

[†] Source: IEEE Spectrum, December 1993, p. 21
[††] Integer and floating-point performance benchmarks

five of today's leading devices—the 68040 from Motorola, the PowerPC from IBM and Motorola, the 80486 and Pentium from Intel, and the Alpha 21064 from Digital Equipment Corporation (DEC).

The Intel counterpart to the 68040 is the 80486. Although systems incorporating either of these devices are extremely powerful by the standards of, say, ten years ago, it is easy to see from the table that much more powerful systems are imminent. There are a number of interesting observations apparent from Table 10-10. The 68040 and 80486 processors perform about the same on the SPECint and SPECfp performance benchmarks, even though the 68040 device tested was operating at one-half the clock speed as the 80486 (25 MHz vs. 50 MHz). As well, there is a very significant leap forward in comparing the 68040 or 80486 to the PowerPC or Pentium, with the latter devices about three to four times more powerful than the older devices. The 64-bit DEC Alpha 21064 is easily the most powerful device; however, at 30 watts, peak power requirements are very demanding. The largest device in Table 10-10 is the Intel Pentium, sporting 3.1 million transistors on a 17.2 mm by 17.2 mm chip. This is contrasted with the Alpha 21064 which is considerably more powerful but uses about half as many transistors. This is primarily due to the Pentium's CISC design. The complexity in the instruction set, and architecture in general, brings with it a large device size. The Pentium is also the most expensive of the devices compared.

What's ahead for the next decade or two? We can speculate on this by calling upon Moore's Law, a well-known axiom to anticipate trends in the computer industry. Named after Gordon Moore, one of the founders of Intel Corp., Moore's Law states that every eighteen months computers get twice as powerful and half as expensive. This is a rough guideline based on simple market trends. More detailed predictions follow from several technology trend-lines, such as chip size, transistor size, number of pins per package, power dissipation, and so on. If these features continue current and previous patterns, we can expect that by the year 2000, microprocessors will contain 50–100 million transistors, chip size will be 25 mm by 25 mm, and the IC package will contain 800 pins. These are impressive figures, and they foretell the many exciting challenges that lie ahead.

# Appendix A

# Condition Codes Computation

This appendix provides a summary of the 68000 condition codes. The condition-code portion of the status register contains five bits:

X   Extend
N   Negative
Z   Zero
V   Overflow
C   Carry

The last four bits are true condition-code bits in that they reflect the condition of the results of a processor operation. The X bit is an operand for multi-precision computation. The carry bit (C) and the multi-precision operand extend bit (X) are separate in the 68000 to simplify the programming model.

The most common interpretation of the condition code bits follows:

X   Transparent to data movement. When affected, it is set the same as the C bit.
N   Set if the most-significant bit of the result is set. Cleared otherwise.
Z   Set if the result equals zero. Cleared otherwise.
V   Set if there was an arithmetic overflow. This implies that the result is not representable in the operand size. Cleared otherwise.
C   Set if a carry is generated out of the most-significant bit of the operands for an addition. Also set if a borrow is generated in a subtraction. Cleared otherwise.

Many instructions affect the condition-code bits in unique ways. The specific effect is given in Appendix B for each instruction.

Most operations take a source operand and a destination operand, compute an operation, and store the result in the destination location. Unary operations take a destination operand, compute an operation, and store the result in the destination location. Table A-1 details how each instruction affects the condition-code bits.

The 68000 includes the following conditional instructions:

Bcc    Branch if condition true
DBcc   Decrement and branch if condition true
Scc    Set destination to 1s if condition true otherwise set to 0s

For each of these, the mnemonic is completed by replacing "cc" with the mnemonic characters corresponding to the conditional tests supported by the 68000. These mnemonic characters are listed in Table A-2, along with condition names, encodings, and tests for the conditional branch and set instructions. The test associated with each condition is a logical formula based on the current state of the condition codes. If this formula evaluates to 1 (i.e., true), the condition is met. If the formula evaluates to 0 (i.e., false), the condition is not met. For example the T condition is always met, while the EQ condition is met only if the Z bit is currently set in the condition code register.

### Table A-1.   Condition-Code Computations.

| Operation | X | N | Z | V | C | Special Definitions |
|---|---|---|---|---|---|---|
| ABCD | * | U | ? | U | ? | $C$ = decimal carry, $Z = Z \cdot \overline{Rm} \cdot ... \cdot \overline{R0}$ |
| ADD, ADDI, ADDQ | * | * | * | ? | ? | $V = Sm \cdot Dm \cdot \overline{Rm} + \overline{Sm} \cdot \overline{Dm} \cdot Rm$ <br> $C = Sm \cdot Dm + \overline{Rm} \cdot Dm + Sm \cdot \overline{Rm}$ |
| ADDX | * | * | ? | ? | ? | $V = Sm \cdot Dm \cdot \overline{Rm} + \overline{Sm} \cdot \overline{Dm} \cdot Rm$ <br> $C = Sm \cdot Dm + \overline{Rm} \cdot Dm + Sm \cdot \overline{Rm}$ <br> $Z = Z \cdot \overline{Rm} \cdot ... \cdot \overline{R0}$ |
| AND, EOR, MOVE, OR, CLR, EXT, NOT, TAS, TST | - | * | * | 0 | 0 | |
| CHK | - | * | U | U | U | |
| SUB, SUBI, SUBQ | * | * | * | ? | ? | $V = \overline{Sm} \cdot Dm \cdot \overline{Rm} + Sm \cdot \overline{Dm} \cdot Rm$ <br> $C = Sm \cdot \overline{Dm} + Rm \cdot \overline{Dm} + Sm \cdot Rm$ |
| SUBX | * | * | ? | ? | ? | $V = \overline{Sm} \cdot Dm \cdot \overline{Rm} + Sm \cdot \overline{Dm} \cdot Rm$ <br> $C = Sm \cdot \overline{Dm} + Rm \cdot \overline{Dm} + Sm \cdot Rm$ <br> $Z = Z \cdot \overline{Rm} \cdot ... \cdot \overline{R0}$ |
| CMP, CMPI, CMPM | - | * | * | ? | ? | $V = \overline{Sm} \cdot Dm \cdot \overline{Rm} + Sm \cdot \overline{Dm} \cdot Rm$ <br> $C = Sm \cdot \overline{Dm} + Rm \cdot \overline{Dm} + Sm \cdot Rm$ |
| DIVS, DIVU | - | * | * | ? | 0 | $V$ = division overflow |
| MULS, MULU | - | * | * | 0 | 0 | |
| SBCD, NBCD | * | U | ? | U | ? | $C$ = decimal borrow, $Z = Z \cdot \overline{Rm} \cdot ... \cdot \overline{R0}$ |
| NEG | * | * | * | ? | ? | $V = Dm \cdot Rm$ <br> $C = Dm + Rm$ |
| NEGX | * | * | ? | ? | ? | $V = Dm \cdot Rm$ <br> $C = Dm + Rm$ <br> $Z = Z \cdot \overline{Rm} \cdot ... \cdot \overline{R0}$ |
| BTST, BCHG, BSET, BCLR | - | - | ? | - | - | $Z = \overline{Dm}$ |
| ASL | * | * | * | ? | ? | $V = Dm \cdot (\overline{D_{m-1}} + ... + \overline{D_{m-r}}) + \overline{Dm} \cdot (D_{m-1} + ... D_{m-r})$ <br> $C = D_{m-r+1}$ |
| ASL ($r = 0$) | - | * | * | 0 | 0 | |
| LSL, ROXL | * | * | * | 0 | ? | $C = D_{m-r+1}$ |
| LSR ($r = 0$) | - | * | * | 0 | 0 | |
| ROXL ($r = 0$) | - | * | * | 0 | ? | $C = X$ |
| ROL | - | * | * | 0 | ? | $C = D_{m-r+1}$ |
| ROL ($r = 0$) | - | * | * | 0 | 0 | |
| ASR, LSR, ROXR | * | * | * | 0 | ? | $C = D_{r-1}$ |
| ASR, LSR ($r = 0$) | - | * | * | 0 | 0 | |
| ROXR ($r = 0$) | - | * | * | 0 | ? | $C = X$ |
| ROR | - | * | * | 0 | ? | $C = D_{r-1}$ |
| ROR ($r = 0$) | - | * | * | 0 | 0 | |

| | | |
|---|---|---|
| - | Not affected | |
| U | Undefined | |
| ? | Other (see special definitions) | |
| * | General case: $\quad X = C, N = Rm, Z = \overline{Rn} \cdot ... \cdot \overline{R0}$ | |

| | |
|---|---|
| Sm | Source operand MSB |
| Dm | Destination operand MSB |
| Rm | Result operand MSB |
| n | bit number |
| r | shift count |

## Table A-2. Conditional Tests.

| Mnemonic | Condition | Encoding | Test |
|----------|-----------|----------|------|
| T[†] | true | 0000 | 1 |
| F[†] | false | 0001 | 0 |
| HI | high | 0010 | $\overline{C} \cdot \overline{Z}$ |
| LS | low or same | 0011 | $C + Z$ |
| CC(HS) | carry clear | 0100 | $\overline{C}$ |
| CS(LO) | carry set | 0101 | $C$ |
| NE | not equal | 0110 | $\overline{Z}$ |
| EQ | equal | 0111 | $Z$ |
| VC[††] | overflow clear | 1000 | $\overline{V}$ |
| VS[††] | overflow set | 1001 | $V$ |
| PL[††] | plus | 1010 | $\overline{N}$ |
| MI[††] | minus | 1011 | $N$ |
| GE[††] | greater or equal | 1100 | $N \cdot V + \overline{N} \cdot \overline{V}$ |
| LT[††] | less than | 1101 | $N \cdot \overline{V} + \overline{N} \cdot V$ |
| GT[††] | greater than | 1110 | $N \cdot V \cdot \overline{Z} + \overline{N} \cdot \overline{V} \cdot \overline{Z}$ |
| LE[††] | less or equal | 1111 | $Z + N \cdot \overline{V} + \overline{N} \cdot V$ |

[†] Not available for Bcc instruction

[††] Twos complement arithmetic, signed numbers

• = Boolean AND

+ = Boolean OR

# Appendix B

# Instruction Definitions

---

**ABCD**                      *Add Decimal with Extend*                      **ABCD**

*Operation:*    $source_{10}$ $destination_{10}$ + X $\rightarrow$ destination

*Assembler*    ABCD Dx,Dy
*Syntax:*      ABCD $-$ (Ax), $-$ (Ay)

*Attributes:*   Size=Byte

*Description:*   Adds the source operand to the destination operand along with the extend bit, and stores the result in the destination location. The addition is performed using binary coded decimal arithmetic. The operands, which are packed BCD numbers, are addressed in two ways:

1. Data register to data register: The operands are contained in the data registers specified in the instruction.
2. Memory to memory: The operands are addressed with the predecrement addressing mode using the address registers specified in the instruction.

This is a byte operation only.

*Condition Codes:*

| X | N | Z | V | C |
|---|---|---|---|---|
| * | U | * | U | * |

X   Set the same as the carry bit.
N   Undefined.
Z   Cleared if the result is non-zero. Unchanged otherwise.
V   Undefined.
C   Set if a decimal carry is generated.
    Cleared otherwise.

*Instruction Format:*

| 15 | 14 | 13 | 12 | 11  10  9 | 8 | 7 | 6 | 5 | 4 | 3 | 2  1  0 |
|----|----|----|----|-----------|---|---|---|---|---|-----|---------|
| 1 | 1 | 0 | 0 | Register Ry | 1 | 0 | 0 | 0 | 0 | R/M | Register Rx |

*Instruction Fields:*

Register Ry field—Specifies the destination register:
    if R/M = 0, specifies a data register
    if R/M = 1, specifies an address register for the predecrement addressing mode

R/M field—Specifies the operand addressing mode:

    0 = data register to data register

    1 = memory to memory

Register Rx field—Specifies the source register:

    if R/M = 0, specifies a data register

    if R/M = 1, specifies an address register for the predecrement addressing mode

*Note:*

1. Normally the Z condition code bit is set via programming before the start of an operation. This allows for successful tests for zero upon completion of a multi-precision operation.

**ADD**                    *Add*                    **ADD**

*Operation:*   source + destination → destination

*Assembler*   ADD <ea>,Dn
*Syntax:*   ADD Dn,<ea>

*Attributes:*   Size = Byte, Word, Long

*Description:*   Adds the source operand to the destination operand using binary addition, and stores the result in the destination location. The mode of the operation specifies which operand is the source and which is the destination as well as the operand size.

*Condition Codes:*

| X | N | Z | V | C |
|---|---|---|---|---|
| * | * | * | * | * |

X   Set the same as the carry bit.
N   Set if the result is negative (MSB = 1). Cleared otherwise.
Z   Set if the result is zero. Cleared otherwise.
V   Set if an overflow is generated. Cleared otherwise.
C   Set if a carry is generated. Cleared otherwise.

*Instruction Format:*

| 15 | 14 | 13 | 12 | 11 | 10 | 9 | 8 | 7 | 6 | 5 | 4 | 3 | 2 | 1 | 0 |
|----|----|----|----|----|----|---|---|---|---|---|---|---|---|---|---|
| 1 | 1 | 0 | 1 | Data Register | | | Op-mode | | | Effective Address | | | | | |
| | | | | | | | | | | Mode | | | Register | | |

*Instruction Fields:*

Data Register field—Specifies the data register for either the source or destination operand, depending of the Op-mode field.

Op-mode field—Specifies the operation mode, as follows:

| Byte | Word | Long | Operation |
|------|------|------|-----------|
| 000 | 001 | 010 | <Dn> + <ea> → <ea> |
| 100 | 101 | 110 | <ea> + <Dn> → <Dn> |

Effective Address field—Determines addressing mode. If the location specified is a source operand, all addressing modes are allowed, as shown:

| Addressing Mode | Mode | Register | Addressing Mode | Mode | Register |
|-----------------|------|----------|-----------------|------|----------|
| Dn | 000 | reg. number | xxx.W | 111 | 000 |
| An* | 001 | reg. number | xxx.L | 111 | 001 |
| (An) | 010 | reg. number | #data | 111 | 100 |
| (An)+ | 011 | reg. number | | | |
| −(An) | 100 | reg. number | | | |
| d16(An) | 101 | reg. number | d16(PC) | 111 | 010 |
| d8(An,Xn) | 110 | reg. number | d8(PC,Xn) | 111 | 011 |

*Word and Long only.

If the location specified is a destination operand, only memory alterable addressing modes are allowed, as shown:

| Addressing Mode | Mode | Register | Addressing Mode | Mode | Register |
|---|---|---|---|---|---|
| Dn | - | - | xxx.W | 111 | 000 |
| An | - | - | xxx.L | 111 | 001 |
| (An) | 010 | reg. number | #data | - | - |
| (An)+ | 011 | reg. number | | | |
| −(An) | 100 | reg. number | | | |
| d16(An) | 101 | reg. number | d16(PC) | - | - |
| d8(An,Xn) | 110 | reg. number | d8(PC,Xn) | - | - |

**Notes:**

1. The Dn mode is used when the destination is a data register. The destination <ea> is invalid for a data register.

2. ADDA is used when the destination is an address register. ADDI and ADDQ are used when the source is immediate data. Most assemblers automatically make this distinction.

# ADDA                          *Add Address*                          ADDA

*Operation:*    source + destination → destination

*Assembler*
*Syntax:*    ADDA <ea>,An

*Attributes:*    Size = Word, Long

*Description:*    Add the source operand to the destination address register, storing the result in an address register. For word data, the result is sign-extended to 32 bits.

*Condition Codes:*

   Not affected

*Instruction Format:*

| 15 | 14 | 13 | 12 | 11 | 10 | 9 | 8 | 7 | 6 | 5 | 4 | 3 | 2 | 1 | 0 |
|----|----|----|----|----|----|----|----|----|----|----|----|----|----|----|----|
| 1 | 1 | 0 | 1 | Address Register | | | Op-mode | | | Effective Address | | | | | |

| 15 | 14 | 13 | 12 | 11 | 10 | 9 | 8 | 7 | 6 | 5 | 4 | 3 | 2 | 1 | 0 |
|----|----|----|----|----|----|----|----|----|----|----|----|----|----|----|----|
| 1 | 1 | 0 | 1 | Address Register | | | Op-mode | | | Mode | | | Register | | |

*Instruction Fields:*

   Address Register field—Specifies the address register for either the destination operand

   Op-mode field—Specifies the operation mode, as follows:

| Word | Long | Operation |
|------|------|-----------|
| 011 | 111 | <ea> + <An> → <An> |

   Effective Address field—Specifies the source operand. All addressing modes are allowed, as shown:

| Addressing Mode | Mode | Register | Addressing Mode | Mode | Register |
|-----------------|------|----------|-----------------|------|----------|
| Dn | 000 | reg. number | xxx.W | 111 | 000 |
| An | 001 | reg. number | xxx.L | 111 | 001 |
| (An) | 010 | reg. number | #data | 111 | 100 |
| (An)+ | 011 | reg. number | | | |
| −(An) | 100 | reg. number | | | |
| d16(An) | 101 | reg. number | d16(PC) | 111 | 010 |
| d8(An,Xn) | 110 | reg. number | d8(PC,Xn) | 111 | 011 |

---

**ADDI**                            *Add Immediate*                            **ADDI**

***Operation:***      #data + destination → destination

***Assembler***
***Syntax:***        ADDI #data,<ea>

***Attributes:***    Size = Byte, Word, Long

***Description:***   Adds the immediate data to the destination operand, and stores the result in the destination location. The size of the immediate data matches the operand size.

***Condition Codes:***

| X | N | Z | V | C |
|---|---|---|---|---|
| * | * | * | * | * |

X   Set the same as the carry bit.
N   Set if the result is negative (MSB = 1). Cleared otherwise.
Z   Set if the result is zero. Cleared otherwise.
V   Set if an overflow is generated. Cleared otherwise.
C   Set if a carry is generated. Cleared otherwise.

***Instruction Format:***

| 15 | 14 | 13 | 12 | 11 | 10 | 9 | 8 | 7 | 6 | 5 | 4 | 3 | 2 | 1 | 0 |
|----|----|----|----|----|----|---|---|---|---|---|---|---|---|---|---|
| 0 | 0 | 0 | 0 | 0 | 1 | 1 | 0 | Size | | Effective Address | | | | | |
| | | | | | | | | | | Mode | | | Register | | |

***Instruction Fields:***

Size field—Specifies the size of data for the operation:

00 = byte

01 = word

10 = long

Effective Address field—Specifies the destination operand. Only data alterable addressing modes are allowed, as shown:

| Addressing Mode | Mode | Register | Addressing Mode | Mode | Register |
|-----------------|------|----------|-----------------|------|----------|
| Dn | 000 | reg. number | xxx.W | 111 | 000 |
| An | - | - | xxx.L | 111 | 001 |
| (An) | 010 | reg. number | #data | - | - |
| (An)+ | 011 | reg. number | | | |
| −(An) | 100 | reg. number | | | |
| d16(An) | 101 | reg. number | d16(PC) | - | - |
| d8(An,Xn) | 110 | reg. number | d8(PC,Xn) | - | - |

# ADDQ                          *Add Quick*                          ADDQ

**Operation:**   #data + destination → destination

**Assembler
Syntax:**   ADDQ #data,<ea>

**Attributes:**   Size = Byte, Word, Long

**Description:**   Adds an immediate value of one to eight to the operand at the destination location. When adding to address registers, the condition codes are not altered and the entire destination address register is used regardless of the operand size.

**Condition Codes:**

| X | N | Z | V | C |
|---|---|---|---|---|
| * | * | * | * | * |

X   Set the same as the carry bit.
N   Set if the result is negative (MSB = 1). Cleared otherwise.
Z   Set if the result is zero. Cleared otherwise.
V   Set if an overflow is generated. Cleared otherwise.
C   Set if a carry is generated. Cleared otherwise.

The condition codes are not affected when the destination is an address register.

**Instruction Format:**

| 15 | 14 | 13 | 12 | 11 | 10 | 9 | 8 | 7 | 6 | 5 | 4 | 3 | 2 | 1 | 0 |
|----|----|----|----|----|----|---|---|---|---|---|---|---|---|---|---|
| 0 | 1 | 0 | 1 | | Data | | 0 | | Size | | Effective Address | | | | |
| | | | | | | | | | | | Mode | | | Register | |

**Instruction Fields:**

Data field—Contains the immediate data with 0, 1–7, representing data values of 8, and 1 to 7 respectively

Size field—Specifies the size of the operation:

00 = byte
01 = word
10 = long

Effective Address field—Specifies the destination location. Only alterable addressing modes are allowed as shown:

| Addressing Mode | Mode | Register | Addressing Mode | Mode | Register |
|---|---|---|---|---|---|
| Dn | 000 | reg. number | xxx.W | 111 | 000 |
| An* | 001 | reg. number | xxx.L | 111 | 001 |
| (An) | 010 | reg. number | #data | - | - |
| (An)+ | 011 | reg. number | | | |
| −(An) | 100 | reg. number | | | |
| d16(An) | 101 | reg. number | d16(PC) | - | - |
| d8(An,Xn) | 110 | reg. number | d8(PC,Xn) | - | - |

*Word and Long only.

# **ADDX**                    *Add Extended*                    **ADDX**

*Operation:*    source + destination + X ➞ destination

*Assembler*    ADDX Dx,Dy
*Syntax:*       ADDX –(Ax),–(Ay)

*Attributes:*    Size = Byte, Word, Long

*Description:*    Adds the source operand to the destination operand along with the extend bit and stores the result in the destination location.  The operands are addressed in two ways:

1. Data register to data register: The operands are contained in the data registers specified in the instruction.
2. Memory to memory: The operands are addressed with the predecrement addressing mode using the address registers specified in the instruction.

*Condition Codes:*

| X | N | Z | V | C |
|---|---|---|---|---|
| * | * | * | * | * |

X   Set the same as the carry bit.
N   Set if the result is negative (MSB = 1). Cleared otherwise.
Z   Cleared if the result is non-zero. Unchanged otherwise.
V   Set if an overflow is generated. Cleared otherwise.
C   Set if a carry is generated. Cleared otherwise.

*Instruction Format:*

| 15 | 14 | 13 | 12 | 11 | 10 | 9 | 8 | 7 | 6 | 5 | 4 | 3 | 2 | 1 | 0 |
|----|----|----|----|----|----|----|----|----|----|----|----|----|----|----|----|
| 1 | 1 | 0 | 1 | Register Ry | | | 1 | Size | | 0 | 0 | R/M | Register Rx | | |

*Instruction Fields:*

Register Ry field—Specifies the destination register:
  if R/M = 0, specifies a data register
  if R/M = 1, specifies an address register for the predecrement addressing mode
Size field—Specifies the size of the operation:
  00—byte
  01—word
  10—long
R/M field—Specifies the operand addressing mode:
  0 = data register to data register
  1 = memory to memory
Register Rx field—Specifies the source register:
  if R/M = 0, specifies a data register
  if R/M = 1, specifies an address register for the predecrement addressing mode

*Note:*

1. Normally the Z condition code bit is set via programming before the start of an operation. This allows successful tests for zero upon completion of multiple-precision operations.

**AND**                               AND *Logical*                               **AND**

*Operation:*    source AND destination → destination

*Assembler*    AND <ea>,Dn
*Syntax:*       AND Dn,<ea>

*Attributes:*   Size = Byte, Word, Long

*Description:*  Performs a logical AND operation of the source operand with the destination operand and stores the result in the destination location. The contents of an address register may not be used as an operand.

*Condition Codes:*

| X | N | Z | V | C |
|---|---|---|---|---|
| - | * | * | 0 | 0 |

X   Not affected.
N   Set if the result is the most-significant bit of the result is set. Cleared otherwise.
Z   Set if the result is zero. Cleared otherwise.
V   Always cleared.
C   Always cleared.

*Instruction Format:*

| 15 | 14 | 13 | 12 | 11 | 10 | 9 | 8 | 7 | 6 | 5 | 4 | 3 | 2 | 1 | 0 |
|----|----|----|----|----|----|----|----|----|----|----|----|----|----|----|----|
| 1 | 1 | 0 | 0 | Data Register | | | Op-mode | | | Effective Address | | | | | |
| | | | | | | | | | | Mode | | | Register | | |

*Instruction Fields:*

Data Register field—Specifies the data register for either the source or destination operand, depending on the op-mode field.

Op-mode field—Specifies the operation mode, as follows:

| Byte | Word | Long | Operation |
|------|------|------|-----------|
| 000 | 001 | 010 | <Dn> AND <ea> → <ea> |
| 100 | 101 | 110 | <ea> AND <Dn> → <Dn> |

Effective Address field—Determines addressing mode. If the location specified is a source operand, only data addressing modes are allowed, as shown:

| Addressing Mode | Mode | Register | Addressing Mode | Mode | Register |
|-----------------|------|----------|-----------------|------|----------|
| Dn | 000 | reg. number | xxx.W | 111 | 000 |
| An | - | - | xxx.L | 111 | 001 |
| (An) | 010 | reg. number | #data | 111 | 100 |
| (An)+ | 011 | reg. number | | | |
| −(An) | 100 | reg. number | | | |
| d16(An) | 101 | reg. number | d16(PC) | 111 | 010 |
| d8(An,Xn) | 110 | reg. number | d8(PC,Xn) | 111 | 011 |

If the location specified is a destination operand, only memory alterable addressing modes are allowed, as shown:

| Addressing Mode | Mode | Register | Addressing Mode | Mode | Register |
|---|---|---|---|---|---|
| Dn | - | - | xxx.W | 111 | 000 |
| An | - | - | xxx.L | 111 | 001 |
| (An) | 010 | reg. number | #data | - | - |
| (An)+ | 011 | reg. number | | | |
| −(An) | 100 | reg. number | | | |
| d16(An) | 101 | reg. number | d16(PC) | - | - |
| d8(An,Xn) | 110 | reg. number | d8(PC,Xn) | - | - |

*Notes:*

1. The Dn mode is used when the destination is a data register. The destination <ea> is invalid for a data register.
2. Most assemblers use ANDI when the source is immediate data.

---

**ANDI**                        AND *Immediate*                        **ANDI**

---

*Operation:*     #data AND destination → destination

*Assembler*
*Syntax:*        ANDI #data,<ea>

*Attributes:*    Size = Byte, Word, Long

*Description:*   Performs a logical AND operation of the immediate data with the destination operand and stores the result in the destination location. The size of the immediate data matches the operand size.

*Condition Codes:*

| X | N | Z | V | C |
|---|---|---|---|---|
| - | * | * | 0 | 0 |

X   Not affected.
N   Set if the result is negative (MSB = 1). Cleared otherwise.
Z   Set if the result is zero. Cleared otherwise.
V   Always cleared.
C   Always cleared.

*Instruction Format:*

| 15 | 14 | 13 | 12 | 11 | 10 | 9 | 8 | 7 | 6 | 5 | 4 | 3 | 2 | 1 | 0 |
|----|----|----|----|----|----|---|---|---|---|---|---|---|---|---|---|
| 0 | 0 | 0 | 0 | 0 | 0 | 1 | 0 | Size | | Effective Address Mode | | | Register | | |

*Instruction Fields:*

Size field—Specifies the size of the immediate data for the operation:

   00 = byte (contained in low-byte of second instruction word, upper byte = 0)

   01 = word (contained in the entire second instruction word)

   10 = long (contained in the second and 3rd instruction words)

Effective Address field—Specifies the destination operand, Only data alterable addressing modes are allowed, as shown:

| Addressing Mode | Mode | Register | Addressing Mode | Mode | Register |
|---|---|---|---|---|---|
| Dn | 000 | reg. number | xxx.W | 111 | 000 |
| An | - | - | xxx.L | 111 | 001 |
| (An) | 010 | reg. number | #data | - | - |
| (An)+ | 011 | reg. number | | | |
| −(An) | 100 | reg. number | | | |
| d16(An) | 101 | reg. number | d16(PC) | - | - |
| d8(An,Xn) | 110 | reg. number | d8(PC,Xn) | - | - |

**ANDI**
**to CCR**

*AND Immediate to CCR*

**ANDI**
**to CCR**

*Operation:*    #data AND CCR → CCR

*Assembler*
*Syntax:*    ANDI #data,CCR

*Attributes:*    Size = Byte

*Description:*    Performs a logical AND operation of the immediate operand with the condition codes and stores the result in the low-byte of the status register.

*Condition Codes:*

| X | N | Z | V | C |
|---|---|---|---|---|
| * | * | * | * | * |

X    Cleared if bit 4 of immediate operand is zero. Unchanged otherwise.
N    Cleared if bit 3 of immediate operand is zero. Unchanged otherwise.
Z    Cleared if bit 2 of immediate operand is zero. Unchanged otherwise.
V    Cleared if bit 1 of immediate operand is zero. Unchanged otherwise.
C    Cleared if bit 0 of immediate operand is zero. Unchanged otherwise.

*Instruction Format:*

| 15 | 14 | 13 | 12 | 11 | 10 | 9 | 8 | 7 | 6 | 5 | 4 | 3 | 2 | 1 | 0 |
|----|----|----|----|----|----|---|---|---|---|---|---|---|---|---|---|
| 0  | 0  | 0  | 0  | 0  | 0  | 1 | 0 | 0 | 0 | 1 | 1 | 1 | 1 | 0 | 0 |

**ANDI
TO SR**

AND *Immediate to Status Register*

**ANDI
TO SR**

*Operation:*  if supervisor state
    #data AND SR → SR
  else
    TRAP

*Assembler
Syntax:*  ANDI #data,SR

*Attributes:*  Size = Word

*Description:*  Performs a logical AND operation of the immediate operand with the contents of the status register and stores the result in the status register. All implemented bits of the status register are affected.

*Condition Codes:*

| X | N | Z | V | C |
|---|---|---|---|---|
| * | * | * | * | * |

X  Cleared if bit 4 of immediate operand is zero. Unchanged otherwise.
N  Cleared if bit 3 of immediate operand is zero. Unchanged otherwise.
Z  Cleared if bit 2 of immediate operand is zero. Unchanged otherwise.
V  Cleared if bit 1 of immediate operand is zero. Unchanged otherwise.
C  Cleared if bit 0 of immediate operand is zero. Unchanged otherwise.

*Instruction Format:*

| 15 | 14 | 13 | 12 | 11 | 10 | 9 | 8 | 7 | 6 | 5 | 4 | 3 | 2 | 1 | 0 |
|----|----|----|----|----|----|---|---|---|---|---|---|---|---|---|---|
| 0 | 0 | 0 | 0 | 0 | 0 | 1 | 0 | 0 | 1 | 1 | 1 | 1 | 1 | 0 | 0 |

---

**ASL, ASR**                        *Arithmetic Shift*                        **ASL, ASR**

*Operation:*    destination shift left or right by count

*Assembler*     ASd Dx,Dy
*Syntax:*       ASd #data,Dy
                ASd <ea>
                where d is the shift direction, L (left) or R (right)

*Attributes:*   Size = Byte, Word, Long

*Description:*    Arithmetically shifts the bits of the operand in the direction specified. The carry bit receives the last bit shifted out of the operand. The shift count for the shifting of a register may be specified in two different ways:

1.  Immediate: The shift count is specified in the instruction (shift range, 1–8).
2.  Register: The shift count is contained in a data register specified in the instruction.

The size of the operand may be byte, word, or long. The content of memory may be shifted one bit only and the operand size is restricted to a word.

For ASL, the operand is shifted left; the number of positions shifted is the shift count. Bits shifted out of the high-order bit go to both the carry and the extend bits; zeros are shifted into the low-order bit. The overflow bit indicates if a sign change occurs during the shift.

For ASR, the operand is shifted right; the number of positions shifted is the shift count. Bits shifted out of the low-order bit go to both the carry and the extend bits; the sign-bit (MSB) is shifted into the high-order bit.

*Operation:*

ASL:

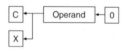

ASR:

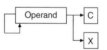

*Condition Codes:*

| X | N | Z | V | C |
|---|---|---|---|---|
| * | * | * | * | * |

X   Set according to the last bit shifted out of the operand. Unaffected for a shift count of zero.
N   Set if the result is negative (MSB = 1). Cleared otherwise.
Z   Set if the result is zero. Cleared otherwise.
V   Set if the most-significant bit is changed at any time during the shift operation. Cleared otherwise.
C   Set according to the last bit shifted out of the operand. Unaffected for a shift count of zero.

*Instruction Format (Register Shifts):*

| 15 | 14 | 13 | 12 | 11 | 10 | 9 | 8 | 7 | 6 | 5 | 4 | 3 | 2 | 1 | 0 |
|----|----|----|----|----|----|----|----|----|----|----|----|----|----|----|----|
| 1 | 1 | 1 | 0 | Count/<br>Register | | | dr | Size | | i/r | 0 | 0 | Data<br>Register | | |

## Instruction Fields (Register Shifts):

Count/Register field:

If i/r = 0, specifies shift count. (Note: Zero represents a shift count of 8.)

If i/r = 1, specifies a data register that contains the shift count.

dr field—Specifies the direction of the shift:

0 = right

1 = left

Size field—Specifies the size of the data to shift:

00 = byte

01 = word

10 = long

i/r field—Specifies the location of the shift count:

0 = immediate shift count

1 = register shift count

## Instruction Format (Memory Shifts):

| 15 | 14 | 13 | 12 | 11 | 10 | 9 | 8 | 7 | 6 | 5 | 4 | 3 | 2 | 1 | 0 |
|---|---|---|---|---|---|---|---|---|---|---|---|---|---|---|---|
| 1 | 1 | 1 | 0 | 0 | 0 | 0 | dr | 1 | 1 | Effective Address | | | | | |

Effective Address: Mode | Register

## Instruction Fields (Memory Shifts):

dr field—Specifies the direction of the shift:

0 = right

1 = left

Effective Address field—Specifies the operand to be shifted. Only memory alterable addressing modes are allowed, as shown:

| Addressing Mode | Mode | Register | Addressing Mode | Mode | Register |
|---|---|---|---|---|---|
| Dn | - | - | xxx.W | 111 | 000 |
| An | - | - | xxx.L | 111 | 001 |
| (An) | 010 | reg. number | #data | - | - |
| (An)+ | 011 | reg. number | | | |
| −(An) | 100 | reg. number | | | |
| d16(An) | 101 | reg. number | d16(PC) | - | - |
| d8(An,Xn) | 110 | reg. number | d8(PC,Xn) | - | - |

**BCC**                              *Branch Conditionally*                              **BCC**

*Operation:*    if condition true
                PC + offset → PC

*Assembler*
*Syntax:*       Bcc <label>

*Attributes:*   Size = Byte, Word

*Description:*   If the specified condition is met, program execution continues at location (PC) + offset.

The offset is a twos complement sign-extended integer which, when added to the PC, gives the destination address of the branch. Note: The PC contains the address *after the* Bcc instruction. The offset is either 8 or 16 bits, as necessary. 8-bit offsets are encoded in bits 0–7 of the opcode. 16-bit offsets are in the second instruction word (if bits 0–7 of the opcode = 0).

*Condition Codes:*

Not affected

*Instruction Format:*

| 15 | 14 | 13 | 12 | 11 | 10 | 9 | 8 | 7 | 6 | 5 | 4 | 3 | 2 | 1 | 0 |
|----|----|----|----|----|----|----|----|----|----|----|----|----|----|----|----|
| 0 | 1 | 1 | 0 | | Condition | | | | | 8-Bit Displacement | | | | | |

*Instruction Fields:*

Condition field—Specifies the branch test, as follows:

| Mnemonic | Condition | Encoding | Test |
|----------|-----------|----------|------|
| HI | high | 0010 | $\overline{C} \bullet \overline{Z}$ |
| LS | low or same | 0011 | $C + Z$ |
| CC(HS) | carry clear | 0100 | $\overline{C}$ |
| CS(LO) | carry set | 0101 | $C$ |
| NE | not equal | 0110 | $\overline{Z}$ |
| EQ | equal | 0111 | $Z$ |
| VC | overflow clear | 1000 | $\overline{V}$ |
| VS | overflow set | 1001 | $V$ |
| PL | plus | 1010 | $\overline{N}$ |
| MI | minus | 1011 | $N$ |
| GE | greater or equal | 1100 | $N \bullet V + \overline{N} \bullet \overline{V}$ |
| LT | less than | 1101 | $N \bullet \overline{V} + \overline{N} \bullet V$ |
| GT | greater than | 1110 | $N \bullet V \bullet \overline{Z} + \overline{N} \bullet \overline{V} \bullet \overline{Z}$ |
| LE | less or equal | 1111 | $Z + N \bullet \overline{V} + \overline{N} \bullet V$ |

• = Boolean AND
+ = Boolean OR

8-Bit Displacement field—Specifies the 8-bit signed offset for the branch, or, if 0, indicates that a 16-bit signed offset is contained in the second instruction word.

**BCHG**                     *Test a Bit and Change*                     **BCHG**

*Operation:*     test bit, then complement

*Assembler*      BCHG Dn,<ea>
*Syntax:*        BCHG #data,<ea>

*Attributes:*    Size = Byte, Long

*Description:*   A bit in the destination operand is tested to set or clear the Z bit in the CCR, then the bit is complemented. The source operand specifies the bit number. If the destination is a data register the bit number is modulo 32 (any bit can be tested). If the destination is a memory location, the bit number is modulo 8 (only bits 0—7 can be tested).

*Condition Codes:*

| X | N | Z | V | C |
|---|---|---|---|---|
| - | - | * | - | - |

X   Not affected.
N   Not affected.
Z   Set if the bit tested is zero. Cleared otherwise.
V   Not affected.
C   Not affected.

*Instruction Format (Bit Number Dynamic, specified in a register):*

| 15 | 14 | 13 | 12 | 11 | 10 | 9 | 8 | 7 | 6 | 5 | 4 | 3 | 2 | 1 | 0 |
|----|----|----|----|----|----|----|----|----|----|----|----|----|----|----|----|
| 0 | 0 | 0 | 0 | Data Register | | | 1 | 0 | 1 | Effective Address Mode | | | Register | | |

*Instruction Fields (Bit Number Dynamic):*

Data Register field—Specifies the data register that contains the bit number.

Effective Address field—Specifies the destination location. Only data alterable addressing modes are allowed, as shown:

| Addressing Mode | Mode | Register | Addressing Mode | Mode | Register |
|---|---|---|---|---|---|
| Dn* | 000 | reg. number | xxx.W | 111 | 000 |
| An | - | - | xxx.L | 111 | 001 |
| (An) | 010 | reg. number | #data | - | - |
| (An)+ | 011 | reg. number | | | |
| −(An) | 100 | reg. number | | | |
| d16(An) | 101 | reg. number | d16(PC) | - | - |
| d8(An,Xn) | 110 | reg. number | d8(PC,Xn) | - | - |

*Dn is long only, all others are byte only.

*Instruction Format (Bit Number Static, specified as immediate data):*

| 15 | 14 | 13 | 12 | 11 | 10 | 9 | 8 | 7 | 6 | 5 | 4 | 3 | 2 | 1 | 0 |
|----|----|----|----|----|----|----|----|----|----|----|----|----|----|----|----|
| 0 | 0 | 0 | 0 | 1 | 0 | 0 | 0 | 0 | 1 | Effective Address Mode | | | Register | | |

**Instruction Fields (Bit Number Static):**

Effective Address field—Specifies the destination location. Only data alterable addressing modes are allowed, as shown:

| Addressing Mode | Mode | Register | Addressing Mode | Mode | Register |
|---|---|---|---|---|---|
| Dn* | 000 | reg. number | xxx.W | 111 | 000 |
| An | - | - | xxx.L | 111 | 001 |
| (An) | 010 | reg. number | #data | - | - |
| (An)+ | 011 | reg. number | | | |
| −(An) | 100 | reg. number | | | |
| d16(An) | 101 | reg. number | d16(PC) | - | - |
| d8(An,Xn) | 110 | reg. number | d8(PC,Xn) | - | - |

*Dn is long only, all others are byte only.

**BCLR**                          *Test Bit and Clear*                          **BCLR**

*Operation:*     test bit, then clear

*Assembler*      BCLR Dn,<ea>
*Syntax:*        BCLR #data,<ea>

*Attributes:*    Size = Byte, Long

*Description:*   A bit in the destination operand is tested to set or clear the Z bit in the CCR, then the bit is cleared. The source operand specifies the bit number. If the destination is a data register the bit number is modulo 32 (any bit can be tested). If the destination is a memory location, the bit number is modulo 8 (only bits 0–7 can be tested).

*Condition Codes:*

| X | N | Z | V | C |
|---|---|---|---|---|
| - | - | * | - | - |

X  Not affected.
N  Not affected.
Z  Set if the bit tested is zero. Cleared otherwise.
V  Not affected.
C  Not affected.

### *Instruction Format (Bit Number Dynamic, specified in a register):*

| 15 | 14 | 13 | 12 | 11 | 10 | 9 | 8 | 7 | 6 | 5 | 4 | 3 | 2 | 1 | 0 |
|----|----|----|----|----|----|---|---|---|---|---|---|---|---|---|---|
| 0 | 0 | 0 | 0 | Data Register | | | 1 | 1 | 0 | Effective Address | | | | | |
| | | | | | | | | | | Mode | | | Register | | |

### *Instruction Fields (Bit Number Dynamic):*

Data Register Field—Specifies the data register that contains the bit number.

Effective Address field—Specifies the destination location. Only data alterable addressing modes are allowed, as shown:

| Addressing Mode | Mode | Register | Addressing Mode | Mode | Register |
|---|---|---|---|---|---|
| Dn* | 000 | reg. number | xxx.W | 111 | 000 |
| An | - | - | xxx.L | 111 | 001 |
| (An) | 010 | reg. number | #data | - | - |
| (An)+ | 011 | reg. number | | | |
| −(An) | 100 | reg. number | | | |
| d16(An) | 101 | reg. number | d16(PC) | - | - |
| d8(An,Xn) | 110 | reg. number | d8(PC,Xn) | - | - |

*Dn is long only, all others are byte only.

### *Instruction Format (Bit Number Static, specified as immediate data):*

| 15 | 14 | 13 | 12 | 11 | 10 | 9 | 8 | 7 | 6 | 5 | 4 | 3 | 2 | 1 | 0 |
|----|----|----|----|----|----|---|---|---|---|---|---|---|---|---|---|
| 0 | 0 | 0 | 0 | 1 | 0 | 0 | 0 | 1 | 0 | Effective Address | | | | | |
| | | | | | | | | | | Mode | | | Register | | |

### *Instruction Fields (Bit Number Static):*

Effective Address field—Specifies the destination location. Only data alterable addressing modes are allowed, as shown:

| Addressing Mode | Mode | Register | Addressing Mode | Mode | Register |
|---|---|---|---|---|---|
| Dn* | 000 | reg. number | xxx.W | 111 | 000 |
| An | - | - | xxx.L | 111 | 001 |
| (An) | 010 | reg. number | #data | - | - |
| (An)+ | 011 | reg. number | | | |
| −(An) | 100 | reg. number | | | |
| d16(An) | 101 | reg. number | d16(PC) | - | - |
| d8(An,Xn) | 110 | reg. number | d8(PC,Xn) | - | - |

*Dn is long only, all others are byte only.

**BRA**                        *Branch Always*                        **BRA**

*Operation:*     PC + offset → PC

*Assembler*
*Syntax:*        BRA <label>

*Attributes:*     Size = Byte, Word

*Description:*    Branch to the address identified by the label. Program execution continues at location (PC) + offset.

The offset is a twos complement sign-extended integer which when added to the PC gives the destination address of the branch. Note: The PC contains the address *after* the BRA instruction. The offset is either 8 or 16 bits, as necessary. 8-bit offsets are encoded in bits 0–7 of the opcode. 16-bit offsets are in the second instruction word (if bits 0–7 of the opcode = 0).

*Condition Codes:*

Not affected

*Instruction Format:*

| 15 | 14 | 13 | 12 | 11 | 10 | 9 | 8 | 7 | 6 | 5 | 4 | 3 | 2 | 1 | 0 |
|----|----|----|----|----|----|---|---|---|---|---|---|---|---|---|---|
| 0 | 1 | 1 | 0 | 0 | 0 | 0 | 0 | 8-Bit Displacement | | | | | | | |

*Instruction Fields:*

8-Bit Displacement field—Specifies the 8-bit signed offset for the branch, or, if 0, indicates that a 16-bit signed offset is contained in the second instruction word.

## BSET                           *Test a Bit and Set*                           BSET

**Operation:**    test bit, then set

**Assembler**    BSET Dn,<ea>
**Syntax:**       BSET #data,<ea>

**Attributes:**   Size = Byte, Long

**Description:**   Tests a bit in the destination operand and sets the Z condition code appropriately. Then the bit is set. The source operand specifies the bit number. If the destination is a data register the bit number is modulo 32 (any bit can be set). If the destination is a memory location, the bit number is modulo 8 (only bits 0–7 can be tested and set).

**Condition Codes:**

| X | N | Z | V | C |
|---|---|---|---|---|
| - | - | * | - | - |

X   Not affected.
N   Not affected.
Z   Set if the bit tested is zero. Cleared otherwise.
V   Not affected.
C   Not affected.

**Instruction Format (Bit Number Dynamic, specified in a register):**

| 15 | 14 | 13 | 12 | 11 | 10 | 9 | 8 | 7 | 6 | 5 | 4 | 3 | 2 | 1 | 0 |
|----|----|----|----|----|----|----|----|----|----|----|----|----|----|----|----|
| 0 | 0 | 0 | 0 | Data Register | | | 1 | 1 | 1 | Effective Address Mode | | | Register | | |

**Instruction Fields (Bit Number Dynamic):**

Data Register field—Specifies the data register that contains the bit number.

Effective Address field—Specifies the destination location. Only data alterable addressing modes are allowed, as shown:

| Addressing Mode | Mode | Register | Addressing Mode | Mode | Register |
|---|---|---|---|---|---|
| Dn* | 000 | reg. number | xxx.W | 111 | 000 |
| An | - | - | xxx.L | 111 | 001 |
| (An) | 010 | reg. number | #data | - | - |
| (An)+ | 011 | reg. number | | | |
| −(An) | 100 | reg. number | | | |
| d16(An) | 101 | reg. number | d16(PC) | - | - |
| d8(An,Xn) | 110 | reg. number | d8(PC,Xn) | - | - |

*Long only; all others are byte only.

**Instruction Format (Bit Number Static, specified as immediate data):**

| 15 | 14 | 13 | 12 | 11 | 10 | 9 | 8 | 7 | 6 | 5 | 4 | 3 | 2 | 1 | 0 |
|----|----|----|----|----|----|----|----|----|----|----|----|----|----|----|----|
| 0 | 0 | 0 | 0 | 1 | 0 | 0 | 0 | 1 | 1 | Effective Address Mode | | | Register | | |

### Instruction Fields (Bit Number Static):

Effective Address field—Specifies the destination location. Only data alterable addressing modes are allowed, as shown:

| Addressing Mode | Mode | Register | Addressing Mode | Mode | Register |
|---|---|---|---|---|---|
| Dn* | 000 | reg. number | xxx.W | 111 | 000 |
| An | - | - | xxx.L | 111 | 001 |
| (An) | 010 | reg. number | #data | - | - |
| (An)+ | 011 | reg. number | | | |
| −(An) | 100 | reg. number | | | |
| d16(An) | 101 | reg. number | d16(PC) | - | - |
| d8(An,Xn) | 110 | reg. number | d8(PC,Xn) | - | - |

*Long only; all others are byte only.

**BSR**                      *Branch to Subroutine*                      **BSR**

*Operation:*    PC → (SP)
                PC + offset → PC

*Assembler*
*Syntax:*    BSR <label>

*Attributes:*    Size = Byte, Word

*Description:*    The PC is pushed on the stack (low-word first), then the offset is added to the PC. The new PC is the first address of a subroutine.

The offset is a twos complement sign-extended integer which when added to the PC gives the destination address of the branch. Note: The PC contains the address after the BSR instruction. The offset is either 8 or 16 bits, as necessary. 8-bit offsets are encoded in bits 0–7 of the opcode. 16-bit offsets are in the second instruction word (if bits 0–7 of the opcode = 0).

*Condition Codes:*

Not affected

*Instruction Format:*

| 15 | 14 | 13 | 12 | 11 | 10 | 9 | 8 | 7 | 6 | 5 | 4 | 3 | 2 | 1 | 0 |
|----|----|----|----|----|----|---|---|---|---|---|---|---|---|---|---|
| 0 | 1 | 1 | 0 | 0 | 0 | 0 | 1 | 8-Bit Displacement | | | | | | | |

*Instruction Fields:*

8-Bit Displacement field—Specifies the 8-bit signed offset for the branch, or, if 0, indicates that a 16-bit signed offset is contained in the second instruction word.

**BTST**                              *Test a Bit*                              **BTST**

*Operation:*    test a bit

*Assembler*     BTST Dn,<ea>
*Syntax:*       BTST #data,<ea>

*Attributes:*   Size = Byte, Long

*Description:*   A bit in the destination operand is tested to set or clear the Z bit. The source operand specifies the bit number. If the destination is a data register the bit number is modulo 32 (any bit can be
tested). If the destination is a memory location, the bit number is modulo 8 (only bits 0–7 can be
tested).

*Condition Codes:*

| X | N | Z | V | C |
|---|---|---|---|---|
| - | - | * | - | - |

X   Not affected.
N   Not affected.
Z   Set if the bit tested is zero. Cleared otherwise.
V   Not affected.
C   Not affected.

*Instruction Format (Bit Number Dynamic, specified in a register):*

| 15 | 14 | 13 | 12 | 11 | 10 | 9 | 8 | 7 | 6 | 5 | 4 | 3 | 2 | 1 | 0 |
|----|----|----|----|----|----|---|---|---|---|---|---|---|---|---|---|
| 0 | 0 | 0 | 0 | Data Register | | | 1 | 0 | 0 | Effective Address Mode | | | Register | | |

*Instruction Fields (Bit Number Dynamic):*

Data Register field—Specifies the data register that contains the bit number.
Effective Address field—Specifies the destination location. Only data addressing modes are allowed,
as shown:

| Addressing Mode | Mode | Register | Addressing Mode | Mode | Register |
|-----------------|------|----------|-----------------|------|----------|
| Dn* | 000 | reg. number | xxx.W | 111 | 000 |
| An | - | - | xxx.L | 111 | 001 |
| (An) | 010 | reg. number | #data | 111 | 100 |
| (An)+ | 011 | reg. number | | | |
| −(An) | 100 | reg. number | | | |
| d16(An) | 101 | reg. number | d16(PC) | 111 | 010 |
| d8(An,Xn) | 110 | reg. number | d8(PC,Xn) | 111 | 011 |

*Long only; all others are byte only.

*Instruction Format (Bit Number Static, specified as immediate data):*

| 15 | 14 | 13 | 12 | 11 | 10 | 9 | 8 | 7 | 6 | 5 | 4 | 3 | 2 | 1 | 0 |
|----|----|----|----|----|----|---|---|---|---|---|---|---|---|---|---|
| 0 | 0 | 0 | 0 | 1 | 0 | 0 | 0 | 0 | 0 | Effective Address Mode | | | Register | | |

*Instruction Fields (Bit Number Static):*

Effective Address field—Specifies the destination location. Only data addressing modes are allowed, as shown:

| Addressing Mode | Mode | Register | Addressing Mode | Mode | Register |
|---|---|---|---|---|---|
| Dn | 000 | reg. number | xxx.W | 111 | 000 |
| An | - | - | xxx.L | 111 | 001 |
| (An) | 010 | reg. number | #data | - | - |
| (An)+ | 011 | reg. number | | | |
| −(An) | 100 | reg. number | | | |
| d16(An) | 101 | reg. number | d16(PC) | 111 | 010 |
| d8(An,Xn) | 110 | reg. number | d8(PC,Xn) | 111 | 011 |

# CHK                    *Check Register Against Bounds*                    CHK

**Operation:**     If Dn < 0 or Dn < (ea)
                   TRAP

**Assembler**
**Syntax:**        CHK <ea>,Dn

**Attributes:**    Size = Word

**Description:**   The content of the low word in the data register specified in the instruction is examined and compared to the upper bound. The upper bound is a twos complement integer. If the register value is < 0 or > the upper bound in the operand word, then the processor initiates exception processing.

**Condition Codes:**

| X | N | Z | V | C |
|---|---|---|---|---|
| - | * | U | U | U |

X   Not affected.
N   Set if Dn < 0; cleared if Dn > effective address operand.
Z   Undefined.
V   Undefined.
C   Undefined.

**Instruction Format:**

| 15 | 14 | 13 | 12 | 11 | 10 | 9 | 8 | 7 | 6 | 5 | 4 | 3 | 2 | 1 | 0 |
|----|----|----|----|----|----|----|----|----|----|----|----|----|----|----|----|
| 0 | 1 | 0 | 0 | | Data Register | | 1 | 1 | 0 | | | Effective Address Mode \| Register | | | |

**Instruction Fields:**

Data Register field—Specifies the data register that contains the value to check

Effective Address field—Specifies the upper bound operand. Only data addressing modes are allowed, as shown:

| Addressing Mode | Mode | Register | Addressing Mode | Mode | Register |
|---|---|---|---|---|---|
| Dn | 000 | reg. number | xxx.W | 111 | 000 |
| An | - | - | xxx.L | 111 | 001 |
| (An) | 010 | reg. number | #data | 111 | 100 |
| (An)+ | 011 | reg. number | | | |
| −(An) | 100 | reg. number | | | |
| d16(An) | 101 | reg. number | d16(PC) | 111 | 010 |
| d8(An,Xn) | 110 | reg. number | d8(PC,Xn) | 111 | 011 |

**CLR**                    *Clear an Operand*                    **CLR**

*Operation:*    0 → destination

*Assembler*
*Syntax:*    CLR <ea>

*Attributes:*    Size = Byte, Word, Long

*Description:*    The destination is cleared to all 0s.

*Condition Codes:*

| X | N | Z | V | C |
|---|---|---|---|---|
| - | 0 | 1 | 0 | 0 |

X    Not affected.
N    Always cleared.
Z    Always set.
V    Always cleared.
C    Always cleared.

*Instruction Format:*

| 15 | 14 | 13 | 12 | 11 | 10 | 9 | 8 | 7 | 6 | 5 | 4 | 3 | 2 | 1 | 0 |
|----|----|----|----|----|----|---|---|---|---|---|---|---|---|---|---|
| 0 | 1 | 0 | 0 | 0 | 0 | 1 | 0 | Size | | | Effective Address | | | | |
| | | | | | | | | | | | Mode | | Register | | |

*Instruction Fields:*

Size field—Specifies the size of the operand:

00 = byte

01 = word

10 = long

Effective Address field—Specifies the destination location. Only data alterable addressing modes are allowed, as shown:

| Addressing Mode | Mode | Register | Addressing Mode | Mode | Register |
|-----------------|------|----------|-----------------|------|----------|
| Dn | 000 | reg. number | xxx.W | 111 | 000 |
| An | - | - | xxx.L | 111 | 001 |
| (An) | 010 | reg. number | #data | - | - |
| (An)+ | 011 | reg. number | | | |
| −(An) | 100 | reg. number | | | |
| d16(An) | 101 | reg. number | d16(PC) | - | - |
| d8(An,Xn) | 110 | reg. number | d8(PC,Xn) | - | - |

**CMP**                         *Compare*                         **CMP**

*Operation:*    destination – source → CCR

*Assembler*
*Syntax:*    CMP <ea>,Dn

*Attributes:*    Size = Byte, Word, Long

*Description:*    Subtracts the source operand from the destination data register and sets the condition codes according to the result. The data register is not changed.

*Condition Codes:*

| X | N | Z | V | C |
|---|---|---|---|---|
| - | * | * | * | * |

X   Not affected.
N   Set if the result is negative (MSB = 1). Cleared otherwise.
Z   Set if the result is zero. Cleared otherwise.
V   Set if an overflow is generated. Cleared otherwise.
C   Set if a borrow occurs. Cleared otherwise.

*Instruction Format:*

| 15 | 14 | 13 | 12 | 11 | 10 | 9 | 8 | 7 | 6 | 5 | 4 | 3 | 2 | 1 | 0 |
|----|----|----|----|----|----|---|---|---|---|---|---|---|---|---|---|
| 1 | 0 | 1 | 1 | Data Register | | | Op-mode | | | Effective Address Mode | | | Register | | |

*Instruction Fields:*

Op-mode field—Specifies the operation mode, as follows:

| Byte | Word | Long | Operation |
|------|------|------|-----------|
| 000 | 001 | 010 | <Dn> – <ea> |

Effective Address field—Specifies the source operand. All addressing modes are allowed, as shown:

| Addressing Mode | Mode | Register | Addressing Mode | Mode | Register |
|-----------------|------|----------|-----------------|------|----------|
| Dn | 000 | reg. number | xxx.W | 111 | 000 |
| An* | 001 | reg. number | xxx.L | 111 | 001 |
| (An) | 010 | reg. number | #data | 111 | 100 |
| (An)+ | 011 | reg. number | | | |
| –(An) | 100 | reg. number | | | |
| d16(An) | 101 | reg. number | d16(PC) | 111 | 010 |
| d8(An,Xn) | 110 | reg. number | d8(PC,Xn) | 111 | 011 |

*Word and Long only.

*Note:*

1. CMPA is used when the destination is an address register. CMPI is used when the source is immediate data. CMPM is used for memory-to-memory compares. Most assemblers automatically make this distinction.

## CMPA                              *Compare Address*                              CMPA

*Operation:*    destination – source

*Assembler
Syntax:*    CMPA <ea>,An

*Attributes:*    Size = Word, Long

*Description:*    Subtracts the source operand from the destination address register and sets or clears CCR bits accordingly. Word-length source operands are sign-extended to 32 bits for the comparison.

*Condition Codes:*

| X | N | Z | V | C |
|---|---|---|---|---|
| – | * | * | * | * |

X    Not affected.
N    Set if the result is negative (MSB = 1). Cleared otherwise.
Z    Set if the result is zero. Cleared otherwise.
V    Set if an overflow is generated. Cleared otherwise.
C    Set if a borrow occurs. Cleared otherwise.

*Instruction Format:*

| 15 | 14 | 13 | 12 | 11 | 10 | 9 | 8 | 7 | 6 | 5 | 4 | 3 | 2 | 1 | 0 |
|----|----|----|----|----|----|---|---|---|---|---|---|---|---|---|---|
| 1 | 0 | 1 | 1 | Data Register | | | Op-mode | | | Effective Address Mode | | | Register | | |

*Instruction Fields:*

Op-mode field—Specifies the operation mode, as follows:

| Word | Long | Operation |
|------|------|-----------|
| 011 | 111 | <ea> – <An> |

Effective Address field—Specifies the source operand. All addressing modes are allowed, as shown:

| Addressing Mode | Mode | Register | Addressing Mode | Mode | Register |
|-----------------|------|----------|-----------------|------|----------|
| Dn | 000 | reg. number | xxx.W | 111 | 000 |
| A | 001 | reg. number | xxx.L | 111 | 001 |
| (An) | 010 | reg. number | #data | 111 | 100 |
| (An)+ | 011 | reg. number | | | |
| –(An) | 100 | reg. number | | | |
| d16(An) | 101 | reg. number | d16(PC) | 111 | 010 |
| d8(An,Xn) | 110 | reg. number | d8(PC,Xn) | 111 | 011 |

| **CMPI** | *Compare Immediate* | **CMPI** |
|---|---|---|

*Operation:*   destination – #data

*Assembler*
*Syntax:*   CMPI #data,<ea>

*Attributes:*   Size = Byte, Word, Long

*Description:*   Subtract the immediate data from the destination and set or clear CCR bits accordingly.

*Condition Codes:*

| X | N | Z | V | C |
|---|---|---|---|---|
| – | * | * | * | * |

X   Not affected.
N   Set if the result is negative (MSB = 1). Cleared otherwise.
Z   Set if the result is zero. Cleared otherwise.
V   Set if an overflow is generated. Cleared otherwise.
C   Set if a borrow occurs. Cleared otherwise.

*Instruction Format:*

| 15 | 14 | 13 | 12 | 11 | 10 | 9 | 8 | 7 | 6 | 5 | 4 | 3 | 2 | 1 | 0 |
|---|---|---|---|---|---|---|---|---|---|---|---|---|---|---|---|
| 0 | 0 | 0 | 0 | 1 | 1 | 0 | 0 | Size | | Effective Address Mode | | | Register | | |

*Instruction Fields:*

Size field—Specifies the size of the operand:

00 = byte
01 = word
10 = long

Effective Address field—Specifies the destination operand. Only data addressing modes are allowed, as shown:

| Addressing Mode | Mode | Register | Addressing Mode | Mode | Register |
|---|---|---|---|---|---|
| Dn | 000 | reg. number | xxx.W | 111 | 000 |
| An | - | - | xxx.L | 111 | 001 |
| (An) | 010 | reg. number | #data | - | - |
| (An)+ | 011 | reg. number | | | |
| –(An) | 100 | reg. number | | | |
| d16(An) | 101 | reg. number | d16(PC) | 111 | 010 |
| d8(An,Xn) | 110 | reg. number | d8(PC,Xn) | 111 | 011 |

---

**CMPM**                                   *Compare Memory*                                   **CMPM**

---

*Operation:*    destination – source → CCR

*Assembler*
*Syntax:*       CMPM (Ax)+,(Ay)+

*Attributes:*   Size = Byte, Word, Long

*Description:*  Subtracts the source from the destination and sets or clears CCR bits accordingly.

*Condition Codes:*

| X | N | Z | V | C |
|---|---|---|---|---|
| – | * | * | * | * |

X   Not affected.
N   Set if the result is negative (MSB = 1). Cleared otherwise.
Z   Set if the result is zero. Cleared otherwise.
V   Set if an overflow is generated. Cleared otherwise.
C   Set if a borrow occurs. Cleared otherwise.

*Instruction Format:*

| 15 | 14 | 13 | 12 | 11 | 10 | 9 | 8 | 7 | 6 | 5 | 4 | 3 | 2 | 1 | 0 |
|----|----|----|----|----|----|---|---|---|---|---|---|---|---|---|---|
| 1 | 0 | 1 | 1 | | Register Ry | | 1 | | Size | | 0 | 0 | 1 | | Register Rx | |

*Instruction Fields:*

Register Ry field—Specifies the destination address register used in the postincrement mode.
Size field—Specifies the size of the operand:
   00 = byte
   01 = word
   10 = long
Register Rx field—Specifies the source address register used in the postincrement mode.

---

**DBCC**                    *Test Condition, Decrement, and Branch*                    **DBCC**

**Operation:**    if condition false
                  Dn − 1 → Dn
                  if Dn != -1
                      PC + offset → PC

**Assembler
Syntax:**    DBcc Dn,<label>

**Attributes:**    Size = Word

**Description:**    This instruction is a looping primitive with 3 parameters: a condition, a data register, and an offset. The instruction first tests the condition to determine if the termination condition for the loop has been met, and if so, no operation is performed. If the termination condition is not true, the low-order 16 bits of the counter data register are decremented by one. If the result is −1, the count is exhausted and execution continues with the next instruction (PC + 2). If the result is not equal to −1, the branch occurs using the 16-bit sign-extended displacement in the second word of the instruction.

**Condition Codes:**

Not affected

**Instruction Format:**

| 15 | 14 | 13 | 12 | 11 | 10 | 9 | 8 | 7 | 6 | 5 | 4 | 3 | 2 | 1 | 0 |
|----|----|----|----|----|----|---|---|---|---|---|---|---|---|---|---|
| 0 | 1 | 0 | 1 | | Condition | | | 1 | 1 | 0 | 0 | 1 | | Data Register | |

**Instruction Fields:**

Condition field—Specifies the branch test, as follows:

| Mnemonic | Condition | Encoding | Test |
|----------|-----------|----------|------|
| T | true | 0000 | 1 |
| F | false | 0001 | 0 |
| HI | high | 0010 | $\overline{C}\bullet\overline{Z}$ |
| LS | low or same | 0011 | $C+Z$ |
| CC(HS) | carry clear | 0100 | $\overline{C}$ |
| CS(LO) | carry set | 0101 | $C$ |
| NE | not equal | 0110 | $\overline{Z}$ |
| EQ | equal | 0111 | $Z$ |
| VC | overflow clear | 1000 | $\overline{V}$ |
| VS | overflow set | 1001 | $V$ |
| PL | plus | 1010 | $\overline{N}$ |
| MI | minus | 1011 | $N$ |
| GE | greater or equal | 1100 | $N\bullet V+\overline{N}\bullet\overline{V}$ |
| LT | less than | 1101 | $N\bullet\overline{V}+\overline{N}\bullet V$ |
| GT | greater than | 1110 | $N\bullet V\bullet\overline{Z}+\overline{N}\bullet\overline{V}\bullet\overline{Z}$ |
| LE | less or equal | 1111 | $Z+N\bullet\overline{V}+\overline{N}\bullet V$ |

• = Boolean AND
+ = Boolean OR

Data Register field—Specifies the data register to decrement.

**Notes:**

1. The terminating condition is similar to the UNTIL loop clauses of high-level languages. For example, DBMI can be thought of as "decrement and branch until minus".

2. Most assemblers accept DBRA for DBF for use when only a count terminates the loop (no condition is tested). The count must be one less than the number of loop iterations.

3. A program can enter a loop at the beginning or by branching to the trailing DBcc instruction. Entering the loop at the beginning is useful for indexed addressing modes and dynamically specified bit operations. In this case, the control index count must be one less than the desired number of loop executions. However, when entering a loop by branching directly to the trailing DBcc instruction, the control count should equal the loop execution count. In this case, if a zero count occurs, the DBcc instruction does not branch, and the main loop is not executed.

**DIVS**                                   *Signed Divide*                                   **DIVS**

*Operation:*     destination / source → destination

*Assembler*
*Syntax:*     DIVS <ea>,Dn

*Attributes:*     Size = Word

*Description:*  Divides the destination operand by the source operand and stores the result in the destination. The destination is a long word and the source is a word. The operation is performed using signed arithmetic. The result is 32 bits, such that:

1. The quotient is in the lower word (least significant 16 bits).
2. The remainder is in the upper word.

The sign of the remainder is always the same as the dividend unless the remainder is 0. Two special conditions may arise:

1. Division by zero causes a trap.
2. Overflow may be detected and set before completion of the instruction. If overflow is detected, the condition is flagged but the operands are unaffected.

*Condition Codes:*

| X | N | Z | V | C |
|---|---|---|---|---|
| - | * | * | * | 0 |

X   Not affected.
N   Set if the quotient is negative (MSB = 1). Cleared otherwise. Undefined if overflow or divide-by-zero occurs.
Z   Set if the quotient is zero. Cleared otherwise. Undefined if overflow or divide-by-zero occurs.
V   Set if division overflow occurs; undefined if divide-by-zero occurs. Cleared otherwise.
C   Always cleared.

*Instruction Format:*

| 15 | 14 | 13 | 12 | 11 | 10 | 9 | 8 | 7 | 6 | 5 | 4 | 3 | 2 | 1 | 0 |
|----|----|----|----|----|----|---|---|---|---|---|---|---|---|---|---|
| 1 | 0 | 0 | 0 | Data Register | | | 1 | 1 | 1 | Effective Address Mode | | | Register | | |

*Instruction Fields:*

Data Register field—Specifies any of the eight data registers. This field always specifies the destination operand.

Effective Address field—Specifies the source operand, Only data addressing modes are allowed, as shown:

| Addressing Mode | Mode | Register | Addressing Mode | Mode | Register |
|---|---|---|---|---|---|
| Dn | 000 | reg. number | xxx.W | 111 | 000 |
| An | - | - | xxx.L | 111 | 001 |
| (An) | 010 | reg. number | #data | 111 | 100 |
| (An)+ | 011 | reg. number | | | |
| −(An) | 100 | reg. number | | | |
| d16(An) | 101 | reg. number | d16(PC) | 111 | 010 |
| d8(An,Xn) | 110 | reg. number | d8(PC,Xn) | 111 | 011 |

*Note:*

1. Overflow occurs if the quotient is larger than a 16-bit signed integer.

| **DIVU** | *Unsigned Divide* | **DIVU** |
|---|---|---|

**Operation:**    destination / source → destination

**Assembler
Syntax:**    DIVU <ea>,Dn

**Attributes:**    Size = Word

**Description:** Divides the destination operand by the source operand and stores the result in the destination. The destination is a long word and the source is a word. The operation is performed using unsigned arithmetic. The result is 32 bits, such that:

1. The quotient is in the lower word (least-significant 16 bits).
2. The remainder is in the upper word.

Two special conditions may arise:

1. Division by zero causes a trap.
2. Overflow may be detected and set before completion of the instruction. If overflow is detected, the condition is flagged but the operands are unaffected.

**Condition Codes:**

| X | N | Z | V | C |
|---|---|---|---|---|
| - | * | * | * | 0 |

X   Not affected.
N   Set if the quotient is negative (MSB = 1). Cleared otherwise. Undefined if overflow or divide by zero occurs.
Z   Set if the quotient is zero. Cleared otherwise. Undefined if overflow or divide-by-zero occurs.
V   Set if division overflow occurs; undefined if divide-by-zero occurs. Cleared otherwise.
C   Always cleared.

**Instruction Format:**

| 15 | 14 | 13 | 12 | 11 | 10 | 9 | 8 | 7 | 6 | 5 | 4 | 3 | 2 | 1 | 0 |
|---|---|---|---|---|---|---|---|---|---|---|---|---|---|---|---|
| 1 | 0 | 0 | 0 | Data Register | | | 0 | 1 | 1 | Effective Address Mode | | | Register | | |

**Instruction Fields:**

Data Register field—Specifies any of the eight data registers. This field always specifies the destination operand.

Effective Address field—Specifies the source operand. Only data addressing modes are allowed, as shown:

| Addressing Mode | Mode | Register | Addressing Mode | Mode | Register |
|---|---|---|---|---|---|
| Dn | 000 | reg. number | xxx.W | 111 | 000 |
| An | - | - | xxx.L | 111 | 001 |
| (An) | 010 | reg. number | #data | 111 | 100 |
| (An)+ | 011 | reg. number | | | |
| −(An) | 100 | reg. number | | | |
| d16(An) | 101 | reg. number | d16(PC) | 111 | 010 |
| d8(An,Xn) | 110 | reg. number | d8(PC,Xn) | 111 | 011 |

*Note:*

1. Overflow occurs if the quotient is larger than a 16-bit signed integer.

**EOR**                             *Exclusive* OR *Logical*                              **EOR**

*Operation:*      source $\oplus$ destination $\rightarrow$ destination

*Assembler*
*Syntax:*      EOR Dn,<ea>

*Attributes:*      Size = Byte, Word, Long

*Description:*   Performs an exclusive-OR operation of the source with the destination and stores the result in the destination.

*Condition Codes:*

| X | N | Z | V | C |
|---|---|---|---|---|
| - | * | * | 0 | 0 |

X   Not affected.
N   Set if the most-significant bit of the result is set. Cleared otherwise.
Z   Set if the result is zero. Cleared otherwise.
V   Always cleared.
C   Always cleared.

*Instruction Format:*

| 15 | 14 | 13 | 12 | 11 | 10 | 9 | 8 | 7 | 6 | 5 | 4 | 3 | 2 | 1 | 0 |
|----|----|----|----|----|----|---|---|---|---|---|---|---|---|---|---|
| 1 | 0 | 1 | 1 | Data Register | | | Op-mode | | | Effective Address Mode | | | Register | | |

*Instruction Fields:*

Data Register field—Specifies the source data register.

Op-mode field—Specifies the operation mode, as follows:

    100 = byte
    101 = word
    110 = long

Effective Address field—Specifies the destination operand. Only data alterable addressing modes are allowed, as shown:

| Addressing Mode | Mode | Register | Addressing Mode | Mode | Register |
|-----------------|------|----------|-----------------|------|----------|
| Dn | 000 | reg. number | xxx.W | 111 | 000 |
| An | - | - | xxx.L | 111 | 001 |
| (An) | 010 | reg. number | #data | - | - |
| (An)+ | 011 | reg. number | | | |
| -(An) | 100 | reg. number | | | |
| d16(An) | 101 | reg. number | d16(PC) | - | - |
| d8(An,Xn) | 110 | reg. number | d8(PC,Xn) | - | - |

*Note:*

1. Most assemblers use EORI when the source is immediate data.

**EORI**                     Exclusive OR Immediate                     **EORI**

*Operation:*     source ⊕ destination → destination

*Assembler*
*Syntax:*        EORI #data,<ea>

*Attributes:*    Size = Byte, Word, Long

*Description:*   Performs an exclusive-OR of the immediate source operand with the destination and stores the result in the destination.

*Condition Codes:*

| X | N | Z | V | C |
|---|---|---|---|---|
| - | * | * | 0 | 0 |

X   Not affected.
N   Set if the most-significant bit of the result is set. Cleared otherwise.
Z   Set if the result is zero. Cleared otherwise.
V   Always cleared.
C   Always cleared.

*Instruction Format:*

| 15 | 14 | 13 | 12 | 11 | 10 | 9 | 8 | 7 | 6 | 5 | 4 | 3 | 2 | 1 | 0 |
|----|----|----|----|----|----|---|---|---|---|---|---|---|---|---|---|
| 0 | 0 | 0 | 0 | 1 | 0 | 1 | 0 | Size | | Effective Address | | | | | |
| | | | | | | | | | | Mode | | | Register | | |

*Instruction Fields:*

Size field—Specifies the size of the operand:
   00 = byte
   01 = word
   10 = long

Effective Address field—Specifies the destination operand. Only data alterable addressing modes are allowed, as shown:

| Addressing Mode | Mode | Register | Addressing Mode | Mode | Register |
|---|---|---|---|---|---|
| Dn | 000 | reg. number | xxx.W | 111 | 000 |
| An | - | - | xxx.L | 111 | 001 |
| (An) | 010 | reg. number | #data | - | - |
| (An)+ | 011 | reg. number | | | |
| −(An) | 100 | reg. number | | | |
| d16(An) | 101 | reg. number | d16(PC) | - | - |
| d8(An,Xn) | 110 | reg. number | d8(PC,Xn) | - | - |

**EORI
TO CCR**                    *Exclusive OR Immediate to Condition Codes*                    **EORI
TO CCR**

*Operation:*    #data ⊕ CCR → CCR

*Assembler
Syntax:*        EORI #data,CCR

*Attributes:*   Size = Byte

*Description:*  Exclusive OR the source with the CCR and store the result in the CCR.

*Condition Codes:*

| X | N | Z | V | C |
|---|---|---|---|---|
| * | * | * | * | * |

X   Changed if bit 4 of the immediate operand is one. Unchanged otherwise.
N   Changed if bit 3 of the immediate operand is one. Unchanged otherwise.
Z   Changed if bit 2 of the immediate operand is one. Unchanged otherwise.
V   Changed if bit 1 of the immediate operand is one. Unchanged otherwise.
C   Changed if bit 0 of the immediate operand is one. Unchanged otherwise.

*Instruction Format:*

| 15 | 14 | 13 | 12 | 11 | 10 | 9 | 8 | 7 | 6 | 5 | 4 | 3 | 2 | 1 | 0 |
|----|----|----|----|----|----|---|---|---|---|---|---|---|---|---|---|
| 0 | 0 | 0 | 0 | 1 | 0 | 1 | 0 | 0 | 0 | 1 | 1 | 1 | 1 | 0 | 0 |

| **EORI**<br>**TO SR** | *Exclusive OR Immediate to Status Register* | **EORI**<br>**TO SR** |
|---|---|---|

**Operation:**   if supervisor state
                 #data ⊕ SR → SR
                 else TRAP

**Assembler**
**Syntax:**   EORI #data,SR

**Attributes:**   Size = Word

**Description:**   Exclusive OR the source with the status register and store the result in the status register.

**Condition Codes:**

| X | N | Z | V | C |
|---|---|---|---|---|
| * | * | * | * | * |

X   Changed if bit 4 of the immediate operand is one. Unchanged otherwise.
N   Changed if bit 3 of the immediate operand is one. Unchanged otherwise.
Z   Changed if bit 2 of the immediate operand is one. Unchanged otherwise.
V   Changed if bit 1 of the immediate operand is one. Unchanged otherwise.
C   Changed if bit 0 of the immediate operand is one. Unchanged otherwise.

**Instruction Format:**

| 15 | 14 | 13 | 12 | 11 | 10 | 9 | 8 | 7 | 6 | 5 | 4 | 3 | 2 | 1 | 0 |
|----|----|----|----|----|----|---|---|---|---|---|---|---|---|---|---|
| 0  | 0  | 0  | 0  | 1  | 0  | 1 | 0 | 0 | 1 | 1 | 1 | 1 | 1 | 0 | 0 |

**EXG**                 *Exchange Registers*                 **EXG**

*Operation:*    Rx $\longleftrightarrow$ Ry

*Assembler*
*Syntax:*      EXG Rx,Ry

*Attributes:*    Size = Long

*Description:*   Exchanges the contents of two 32-bit registers. Either operand may specify a data register or an address register.

*Condition Codes:*

  Not affected

*Instruction Format:*

| 15 | 14 | 13 | 12 | 11 | 10 | 9 | 8 | 7 | 6 | 5 | 4 | 3 | 2 | 1 | 0 |
|---|---|---|---|---|---|---|---|---|---|---|---|---|---|---|---|
| 1 | 1 | 0 | 0 | | Rx<br>Register | | 1 | | Op-mode | | | | | Ry<br>Register | |

*Instruction Fields:*

    Register Rx field—Specifies either a data register or an address register. If the exchange is between data and address registers, this field always specifies the data register.

    Op-mode field—Specifies the type of exchange:

       01000—data registers

       01001—address registers

       10001—data register and address register

    Register Ry field—Specifies either a data register of an address register. If the exchange is between data and address registers, this field always specifies the address register.

---

**EXT**            *Sign Extend*            **EXT**

*Operation:*  destination(sign-extended) → destination

*Assembler*  EXT.W Dn     extend byte to word
*Syntax:*  EXT.L Dn     extend word to long

*Attributes:*  Size = Word, Long

*Description:* Extend the sign bit of the data register from a byte to a word or from a word to a long word. If the operation is word, sign extend bit 7 into bits 8–15. If the operation is long, sign extend bit 15 into bits 16–31.

*Condition Codes:*

| X | N | Z | V | C |
|---|---|---|---|---|
| - | * | * | 0 | 0 |

X  Not affected.
N  Set if the result is negative (MSB = 1). Cleared otherwise.
Z  Set if the result is zero. Cleared otherwise.
V  Always cleared.
C  Always cleared.

*Instruction Format:*

| 15 | 14 | 13 | 12 | 11 | 10 | 9 | 8 7 6 | 5 | 4 | 3 | 2 1 0 |
|---|---|---|---|---|---|---|---|---|---|---|---|
| 0 | 1 | 0 | 0 | 1 | 0 | 0 | Op-mode | 0 | 0 | 0 | Data Register |

*Instruction Fields:*

Op-mode—Specifies the size of the sign-extension operation:
   010—sign-extend low-order byte of data register to word.
   011—sign-extend low-order word of data register to long.
Data Register field—Specifies the data register containing the operand.

## ILLEGAL        *Take Illegal Instruction Trap*        ILLEGAL

*Operation:*    PC → –(SSP)
                SR → –(SSP)
                Illegal Instruction Vector → PC

*Assembler*
*Syntax:*     ILLEGAL

*Attributes:*    Unsized

*Description:* This bit pattern causes an illegal instruction exception. All other illegal instruction bit patterns are reserved for future extensions of the instruction set.

*Condition Codes:*

   Not affected

*Instruction Format:*

| 15 | 14 | 13 | 12 | 11 | 10 | 9 | 8 | 7 | 6 | 5 | 4 | 3 | 2 | 1 | 0 |
|----|----|----|----|----|----|---|---|---|---|---|---|---|---|---|---|
| 0 | 1 | 0 | 0 | 1 | 0 | 1 | 0 | 1 | 1 | 1 | 1 | 1 | 1 | 0 | 0 |

**JMP**                                    *Jump*                                    **JMP**

*Operation:*    destination → PC

*Assembler*
*Syntax:*    JMP <ea>

*Attributes:*    Unsized

*Description:*    Program execution continues at the effective address specified by the instruction. The previous content of the PC is lost.

*Condition Codes:*

Not affected

*Instruction Format:*

| 15 | 14 | 13 | 12 | 11 | 10 | 9 | 8 | 7 | 6 | 5 | 4 | 3 | 2 | 1 | 0 |
|----|----|----|----|----|----|---|---|---|---|---|---|---|---|---|---|
| 0 | 1 | 0 | 0 | 1 | 1 | 1 | 0 | 1 | 1 | Effective Address | | | | | |

|  |  |  | Mode | | | Register | | |
|--|--|--|------|--|--|----------|--|--|

*Instruction Fields:*

Effective Address field—Specifies the address of the next instruction. Only control addressing modes are allowed, as shown:

| Addressing Mode | Mode | Register | Addressing Mode | Mode | Register |
|-----------------|------|----------|-----------------|------|----------|
| Dn | - | - | xxx.W | 111 | 000 |
| An | - | - | xxx.L | 111 | 001 |
| (An) | 010 | reg. number | #data | - | - |
| (An)+ | - | - | | | |
| −(An) | - | - | | | |
| d16(An) | 101 | reg. number | d16(PC) | 111 | 010 |
| d8(An,Xn) | 110 | reg. number | d8(PC,Xn) | 111 | 011 |

**JSR** **JSR**

*Jump to Subroutine*

*Operation:*    PC → -(SP)

*Assembler*
*Syntax:*    JSR <ea>

*Attributes:*    Unsized

*Description:*    The long word address of the instruction immediately following the PC is pushed onto the system stack. Program execution then continues at the address specified in the instruction.

*Condition Codes:*

Not affected.

*Instruction Format:*

| 15 | 14 | 13 | 12 | 11 | 10 | 9 | 8 | 7 | 6 | 5 | 4 | 3 | 2 | 1 | 0 |
|----|----|----|----|----|----|---|---|---|---|---|---|---|---|---|---|
| 0 | 1 | 0 | 0 | 1 | 1 | 1 | 0 | 1 | 0 | | Effective Address | | | | |
| | | | | | | | | | | | Mode | | | Register | |

*Instruction Fields:*

Effective Address field—Specifies the address of the next instruction. Only control addressing modes are allowed, as shown:

| Addressing Mode | Mode | Register | Addressing Mode | Mode | Register |
|-----------------|------|----------|-----------------|------|----------|
| Dn | - | - | xxx.W | 111 | 000 |
| An | - | - | xxx.L | 111 | 001 |
| (An) | 010 | reg. number | #data | - | - |
| (An)+ | - | - | | | |
| -(An) | - | - | | | |
| d16(An) | 101 | reg. number | d16(PC) | 111 | 010 |
| d8(An,Xn) | 110 | reg. number | d8(PC,Xn) | 111 | 011 |

---

# LEA                    *Load Effective Address*                    **LEA**

***Operation:***    destination address → An

***Assembler***
***Syntax:***    LEA <ea>,An

***Attributes:***    Size = Long

***Description:***    The effective address is loaded into the specified address register. All 32 bits of the address register are affected.

***Condition Codes:***

Not affected

***Instruction Format:***

| 15 | 14 | 13 | 12 | 11 | 10 | 9 | 8 | 7 | 6 | 5 | 4 | 3 | 2 | 1 | 0 |
|----|----|----|----|----|----|---|---|---|---|---|---|---|---|---|---|
| 0 | 1 | 0 | 0 | Address Register | | | 1 | 1 | 1 | Effective Address Mode | | | Register | | |

***Instruction Fields:***

Address Register field—Specifies the destination address register.

Effective Address field—Specifies the address of the next instruction. Only control addressing modes are allowed, as shown:

| Addressing Mode | Mode | Register | Addressing Mode | Mode | Register |
|---|---|---|---|---|---|
| Dn | - | - | xxx.W | 111 | 000 |
| An | - | - | xxx.L | 111 | 001 |
| (An) | 010 | reg. number | #data | - | - |
| (An)+ | - | - | | | |
| −(An) | - | - | | | |
| d16(An) | 101 | reg. number | d16(PC) | 111 | 010 |
| d8(An,Xn) | 110 | reg. number | d8(PC,Xn) | 111 | 011 |

**LINK**                  *Link and Allocate*                 **LINK**

*Operation:*     An → −(SP)
                  SP → An
                  SP + offset → SP

*Assembler*
*Syntax:*      LINK An,#offset

*Attributes:*    Size = Word

*Description:* The current content of the specified address register is pushed onto the stack. After the push, the address register is loaded with the updated stack pointer. Finally, the 16-bit sign-extended offset is added to the stack pointer. The content of the address register occupies two words on the stack (low word first). A negative displacement is specified to allocate stack area.

*Condition Codes:*

Not affected

*Instruction Format:*

| 15 | 14 | 13 | 12 | 11 | 10 | 9 | 8 | 7 | 6 | 5 | 4 | 3 | 2 | 1 | 0 |
|----|----|----|----|----|----|---|---|---|---|---|---|---|---|---|---|
| 0 | 1 | 0 | 0 | 1 | 1 | 1 | 0 | 0 | 1 | 0 | 1 | 0 | Address Register | | |

*Instruction Fields:*

Address Register field—Specifies the address register for the link operation.

*Notes:*

1. The 16-bit immediate operand following the instruction word contains the twos complement integer to be added to the stack pointer.
2. LINK and UNLK can be used to maintain a linked list of local data and parameter areas on the stack for nested subroutine calls.

## LSL, LSR                    *Logical Shift*                    LSL, LSR

**Operation:**    destination logical shifted left or right by count

**Assembler**    LSd Dx,Dy
**Syntax:**    LSd #data,Dy
  LSd <ea>,Dy
  where d is the shift direction, L (left) or R (right)

**Attributes:**    Size = Byte, Word, Long

**Description:**    Logically shifts the bits of the operand in the direction specified. The carry bit receives the last bit shifted out of the operand. The shift count for the shifting of a register may be specified in two different ways:

  1. Immediate: The shift count is specified in the instruction (shift range, 1–8).
  2. Register: The shift count is contained in a data register specified in the instruction.

The size of the operand may be byte, word, or long. The content of memory may be shifted one bit only and the operand size is restricted to a word.

The LSL instruction shifts the operand to the left the number of positions specified as the shift count. Bits shifted out of the high-order bit go to both the carry and the extend bits; zeros are shifted into the low-order bit.

The LSR instruction shifts the operand to the right the number of positions specified as the shift count. Bits shifted out of the low-order bit go to both the carry and the extend bits; zeros are shifted into the high-order bit.

Operation:

  LSL:

  LSR:

**Condition Codes:**

| X | N | Z | V | C |
|---|---|---|---|---|
| * | * | * | 0 | * |

  X   Set according to the last bit shifted out of the operand. Unaffected for a shift count of zero.
  N   Set if the result is negative (MSB = 1). Cleared otherwise.
  Z   Set if the result is zero. Cleared otherwise.
  V   Always cleared.
  C   Set according to the last bit shifted out of the operand. Unaffected for a shift count of zero.

***Instruction Format (Register Shifts):***

| 15 | 14 | 13 | 12 | 11 | 10 | 9 | 8 | 7 | 6 | 5 | 4 | 3 | 2 | 1 | 0 |
|----|----|----|----|----|----|---|---|---|---|---|---|---|---|---|---|
| 1 | 1 | 1 | 0 | Count/ Register | | | dr | Size | | i/r | 0 | 1 | Data Register | | |

***Instruction Fields (Register Shifts):***

Count/Register field:

If i/r = 0, specifies shift count. (Note: Zero represents a shift count of 8.)

If i/r = 1, specifies a data register that contains the shift count.

dr field—Specifies the direction to shift:

0 = right

1 = left

Size field—Specifies the size of the operand to shift:

00 = byte

01 = word

10 = long

i/r field—Specifies the location of the shift count:

0 = immediate shift count

1 = register shift count

Data Register field—Specifies the data register to be shifted.

***Instruction Format (Memory Shifts):***

| 15 | 14 | 13 | 12 | 11 | 10 | 9 | 8 | 7 | 6 | 5 | 4 | 3 | 2 | 1 | 0 |
|----|----|----|----|----|----|---|---|---|---|---|---|---|---|---|---|
| 1 | 1 | 1 | 0 | 0 | 0 | 1 | dr | 1 | 1 | Effective Address Mode | | | Register | | |

***Instruction Fields:***

dr field—Specifies the direction to shift:

0 = right

1 = left

Effective Address field—Specifies the operand to shift. Only memory alterable addressing modes are allowed, as shown:

| Addressing Mode | Mode | Register | Addressing Mode | Mode | Register |
|-----------------|------|----------|-----------------|------|----------|
| Dn | - | - | xxx.W | 111 | 000 |
| An | - | - | xxx.L | 111 | 001 |
| (An) | 010 | reg. number | #data | - | - |
| (An)+ | 011 | reg. number | | | |
| −(An) | 100 | reg. number | | | |
| d16(An) | 101 | reg. number | d16(PC) | - | - |
| d8(An,Xn) | 110 | reg. number | d8(PC,Xn) | - | - |

---

**MOVE**                    *Move Data from Source to Destination*                    **MOVE**

*Operation:*      source → destination

*Assembler*
*Syntax:*         MOVE <ea>,<ea>

*Attributes:*     Size = Byte, Word, Long

*Description:*    Move source to destination.

*Condition Codes:*

| X | N | Z | V | C |
|---|---|---|---|---|
| - | * | * | 0 | 0 |

X   Not affected.

N   Set if the result is negative (MSB = 1). Cleared otherwise.

Z   Set if the result is zero. Cleared otherwise.

V   Always cleared.

C   Always cleared.

*Instruction Format:*

| 15 | 14 | 13 | 12 | 11 | 10 | 9 | 8 | 7 | 6 | 5 | 4 | 3 | 2 | 1 | 0 |
|----|----|----|----|----|----|---|---|---|---|---|---|---|---|---|---|
| 0 | 0 | Size | | Destination EA | | | | | | Source EA | | | | | |
| | | | | Register | | | Mode | | | Mode | | | Register | | |

*Instruction Fields:*

Size field—Specifies the size of the operand to be moved:

  01—byte

  11—word

  10—long

Destination Effective Address field—Specifies the destination location. Only data alterable addressing modes are allowed, as shown:

| Addressing Mode | Mode | Register | Addressing Mode | Mode | Register |
|---|---|---|---|---|---|
| Dn | 000 | reg. number | xxx.W | 111 | 000 |
| An | - | - | xxx.L | 111 | 001 |
| (An) | 010 | reg. number | #data | - | - |
| (An)+ | 011 | reg. number | | | |
| −(An) | 100 | reg. number | | | |
| d16(An) | 101 | reg. number | d16(PC) | - | - |
| d8(An,Xn) | 110 | reg. number | d8(PC,Xn) | - | - |

Source Effective Address field—Specifies the source operand. All addressing modes are allowed, as shown:

| Addressing Mode | Mode | Register | Addressing Mode | Mode | Register |
|---|---|---|---|---|---|
| Dn | 000 | reg. number | xxx.W | 111 | 000 |
| An* | 001 | reg. number | xxx.L | 111 | 001 |
| (An) | 010 | reg. number | #data | 111 | 100 |
| (An)+ | 011 | reg. number | | | |
| −(An) | 100 | reg. number | | | |
| d16(An) | 101 | reg. number | d16(PC) | 111 | 010 |
| d8(An,Xn) | 110 | reg. number | d8(PC,Xn) | 111 | 011 |

*Word and Long only.

*Notes:*

1. Most assemblers use MOVEA when the destination is an address register.
2. MOVEQ can be used to move an immediate 8-bit value to a data register.

## MOVEA                    *Move to Address Register*                    **MOVEA**

*Operation:*    source → destination

*Assembler*
*Syntax:*    MOVEA <ea>,An

*Attributes:*    Size = Word, Long

*Description:* Moves source to destination address register. Word-size source operands are sign-extended to 32-bit quantities.

*Condition Codes:*

Not affected

*Instruction Format:*

| 15 | 14 | 13  12 | 11  10  9 | 8 | 7 | 6 | 5  4  3 | 2  1  0 |
|----|----|--------|-----------|---|---|---|---------|---------|
| 0 | 0 | Size | Destination Register | 0 | 0 | 1 | Source EA Mode | Register |

*Instruction Fields:*

Size field—Specifies the size of the operand to be moved:

11—word

10—long

Destination Register field—Specifies the destination address register.

Source Effective Address field—Specifies the location of the source operand. All addressing modes are allowed, as shown:

| Addressing Mode | Mode | Register | Addressing Mode | Mode | Register |
|-----------------|------|----------|-----------------|------|----------|
| Dn | 000 | reg. number | xxx.W | 111 | 000 |
| An | 001 | reg. number | xxx.L | 111 | 001 |
| (An) | 010 | reg. number | #data | 111 | 100 |
| (An)+ | 011 | reg. number | | | |
| −(An) | 100 | reg. number | | | |
| d16(An) | 101 | reg. number | d16(PC) | 111 | 010 |
| d8(An,Xn) | 110 | reg. number | d8(PC,Xn) | 111 | 011 |

| **MOVE TO CCR** | *Move to Condition Codes* | **MOVE TO CCR** |
|---|---|---|

*Operation:*     source → CCR

*Assembler*
*Syntax:*     MOVE <ea>,CCR

*Attributes:*     Size = Word

*Description:*  Move source to CCR. The upper byte of the source operand is discarded. The upper byte of the Status Register is not affected.

*Condition Codes:*

| X | N | Z | V | C |
|---|---|---|---|---|
| * | * | * | * | * |

X   Set to the value of bit 4 of the source operand.
N   Set to the value of bit 3 of the source operand.
Z   Set to the value of bit 2 of the source operand.
V   Set to the value of bit 1 of the source operand.
C   Set to the value of bit 0 of the source operand.

*Instruction Format:*

| 15 | 14 | 13 | 12 | 11 | 10 | 9 | 8 | 7 | 6 | 5 | 4 | 3 | 2 | 1 | 0 |
|----|----|----|----|----|----|---|---|---|---|---|---|---|---|---|---|
| 0 | 1 | 0 | 0 | 0 | 1 | 0 | 0 | 1 | 1 | Effective Address Mode | | | Register | | |

*Instruction Fields:*

Effective Address field—Specifies the location of the source operand. Only data addressing modes are allowed, as shown:

| Addressing Mode | Mode | Register | Addressing Mode | Mode | Register |
|---|---|---|---|---|---|
| Dn | 000 | reg. number | xxx.W | 111 | 000 |
| An | - | - | xxx.L | 111 | 001 |
| (An) | 010 | reg. number | #data | 111 | 100 |
| (An)+ | 011 | reg. number | | | |
| −(An) | 100 | reg. number | | | |
| d16(An) | 101 | reg. number | d16(PC) | 111 | 010 |
| d8(An,Xn) | 110 | reg. number | d8(PC,Xn) | 111 | 011 |

| MOVE FROM SR | *Move from the Status Register* | MOVE FROM SR |
|---|---|---|

**Operation:**    SR → destination

**Assembler
Syntax:**    MOVE SR,<ea>

**Attributes:**    Size = Word

**Description:**    Moves the data in the status register to the destination location. The destination is word length. Unimplemented bits are read as zero.

**Condition Codes:**

Not affected

**Instruction Format:**

| 15 | 14 | 13 | 12 | 11 | 10 | 9 | 8 | 7 | 6 | 5 | 4 | 3 | 2 | 1 | 0 |
|---|---|---|---|---|---|---|---|---|---|---|---|---|---|---|---|
| 0 | 1 | 0 | 0 | 0 | 0 | 0 | 0 | 1 | 1 | Effective Address | | | | | |
| | | | | | | | | | | Mode | | | Register | | |

**Instruction Fields:**

Effective Address field—Specifies the destination location. Only data alterable addressing modes are allowed, as shown:

| Addressing Mode | Mode | Register | Addressing Mode | Mode | Register |
|---|---|---|---|---|---|
| Dn | 000 | reg. number | xxx.W | 111 | 000 |
| An | - | - | xxx.L | 111 | 001 |
| (An) | 010 | reg. number | #data | - | - |
| (An)+ | 011 | reg. number | | | |
| −(An) | 100 | reg. number | | | |
| d16(An) | 101 | reg. number | d16(PC) | - | - |
| d8(An,Xn) | 110 | reg. number | d8(PC,Xn) | - | - |

**Notes:**

1. Use the MOVE from CCR instruction to access only the condition codes.
2. Memory destination is read before it is written to.
3. This is not a privileged instruction on the 68000 and 68008 microprocessors. It is a privileged instruction on the 68010, 68020, 68030, and 68040 microprocessors.

| **MOVE**<br>**TO SR** | MOVE *to the Status Register* | **MOVE**<br>**TO SR** |
|---|---|---|

*Operation:*   if supervisor state
                destination → SR
         else TRAP

*Assembler*
*Syntax:*     MOVE <ea>,SR

*Attributes:*   Size = Word

*Description:*  Moves the data in the source operand to the status register. The source operand is a word and all implemented bits of the status register are affected.

*Condition Codes:*

Set according to the source operand

*Instruction Format:*

| 15 | 14 | 13 | 12 | 11 | 10 | 9 | 8 | 7 | 6 | 5 | 4 | 3 | 2 | 1 | 0 |
|----|----|----|----|----|----|---|---|---|---|---|---|---|---|---|---|
| 0 | 1 | 0 | 0 | 0 | 1 | 1 | 0 | 1 | 1 | Effective Address | | | | | |

Effective Address: Mode / Register

*Instruction Fields:*

Effective Address field—Specifies the location of the source operand. Only data addressing modes are allowed, as shown:

| Addressing Mode | Mode | Register | Addressing Mode | Mode | Register |
|---|---|---|---|---|---|
| Dn | 000 | reg. number | xxx.W | 111 | 000 |
| An | - | - | xxx.L | 111 | 001 |
| (An) | 010 | reg. number | #data | 111 | 100 |
| (An)+ | 011 | reg. number | | | |
| −(An) | 100 | reg. number | | | |
| d16(An) | 101 | reg. number | d16(PC) | 111 | 010 |
| d8(An,Xn) | 110 | reg. number | d8(PC,Xn) | 111 | 011 |

## MOVE TO/FROM USP

*Move User Stack Pointer*

**Operation:**    if supervisor state
          USP → An or An → USP
        else TRAP

**Assembler**    MOVE USP,An
**Syntax:**    MOVE An,USP

**Attributes:**    Size = Long

**Description:**    Moves the contents of the user stack pointer to or from the specified address register.

**Condition Codes:**

  Not affected

**Instruction Format:**

| 15 | 14 | 13 | 12 | 11 | 10 | 9 | 8 | 7 | 6 | 5 | 4 | 3 | 2 | 1 | 0 |
|----|----|----|----|----|----|---|---|---|---|---|---|----|---|---|---|
| 0 | 1 | 0 | 0 | 1 | 1 | 1 | 0 | 0 | 1 | 1 | 0 | dr | Address Register | | |

**Instruction Fields:**

  dr field—Specifies the direction of transfer:
    0—transfer from the address register to the USP
    1—transfer from the USP to the address register
  Address Register Field—Specifies the address register for the transfer.

**MOVEM**             *Move Multiple Registers*             **MOVEM**

*Operation:*     registers → destination
                 source → registers

*Assembler*     MOVEM reg. list,\<ea\>
*Syntax:*        MOVEM \<ea\>, reg. list

*Attributes:*    Size = Word, Long

*Description:*    Selected registers are moved to or from consecutive memory locations starting at the address specified by the \<ea\>. A register list mask is provided in the second word of the instruction. The instruction size determines whether 16 or 32 bits are moved. In the case of word transfers to either address or data registers, each word is sign-extended to 32 bits, and the resulting long word is loaded into the associated register.

**Condition Codes:**

Not affected

**Instruction Format:**

| 15 | 14 | 13 | 12 | 11 | 10 | 9 | 8 | 7 | 6 | 5 | 4 | 3 | 2 | 1 | 0 |
|----|----|----|----|----|----|---|---|---|---|---|---|---|---|---|---|
| 0 | 1 | 0 | 0 | 1 | dr | 0 | 0 | 1 | Sz | | Effective Address | | | | |
| | | | | | | | | | | | Mode | | Register | | |

**Instruction Fields:**

dr field—Specifies the direction of the move:

0 = register to memory

1 = memory to register

Sz field—Specifies the size of the operands for the move:

0 = word transfer

1 = long transfer

Effective Address field—Specifies the memory address for the operation. For register-to-memory transfers, only control alterable addressing modes or the predecrement addressing mode are allowed, as shown:

| Addressing Mode | Mode | Register | Addressing Mode | Mode | Register |
|-----------------|------|----------|-----------------|------|----------|
| Dn | - | - | xxx.W | 111 | 000 |
| An | - | - | xxx.L | 111 | 001 |
| (An) | 010 | reg. number | #data | - | - |
| (An)+ | - | - | | | |
| −(An) | 100 | reg. number | | | |
| d16(An) | 101 | reg. number | d16(PC) | - | - |
| d8(An,Xn) | 110 | reg. number | d8(PC,Xn) | - | - |

For memory-to-register transfers, only control addressing modes or the postincrement addressing mode are allowed, as shown:

| Addressing Mode | Mode | Register | Addressing Mode | Mode | Register |
|:---:|:---:|:---:|:---:|:---:|:---:|
| Dn | - | - | xxx.W | 111 | 000 |
| An | - | - | xxx.L | 111 | 001 |
| (An) | 010 | reg. number | #data | - | - |
| (An)+ | 011 | reg. number | | | |
| −(An) | - | - | | | |
| d16(An) | 101 | reg. number | d16(PC) | 111 | 010 |
| d8(An,Xn) | 110 | reg. number | d8(PC,Xn) | 111 | 011 |

Register List Mask (second Instruction word)—Specifies the registers to be transferred. The low-order bit corresponds to the first register transferred; the high-order bit corresponds to the last register transferred. Thus, both for control modes and for the postincrement addressing mode, the mask correspondence is:

| 15 | 14 | 13 | 12 | 11 | 10 | 9 | 8 | 7 | 6 | 5 | 4 | 3 | 2 | 1 | 0 |
|:---:|:---:|:---:|:---:|:---:|:---:|:---:|:---:|:---:|:---:|:---:|:---:|:---:|:---:|:---:|:---:|
| A7 | A6 | A5 | A4 | A3 | A2 | A1 | A0 | D7 | D6 | D5 | D4 | D3 | D2 | D1 | D0 |

For the predecrement addressing mode, the mask correspondence is:

| 15 | 14 | 13 | 12 | 11 | 10 | 9 | 8 | 7 | 6 | 5 | 4 | 3 | 2 | 1 | 0 |
|:---:|:---:|:---:|:---:|:---:|:---:|:---:|:---:|:---:|:---:|:---:|:---:|:---:|:---:|:---:|:---:|
| D0 | D1 | D2 | D3 | D4 | D5 | D6 | D7 | A0 | A1 | A2 | A3 | A4 | A5 | A6 | A7 |

## MOVEP            *Move Peripheral Data*            MOVEP

**Operation:**     source → destination

**Assembler**     MOVEP Dx,d16(Ay)
**Syntax:**        MOVEP d16(Ay),Dx

**Attributes:**     Size = Word, Long

**Description:**     Data are transferred between a data register and alternate bytes of memory, starting at the location specified and incrementing by two. The high-order byte of the data register is transferred first and the low-order byte last. The memory address is specified using the address register indirect plus displacement addressing mode. If the address is even, all the transfers are made on the high-order half of the data bus; if the address is odd, all the transfers are made on the low-order half of the data bus.

Example: Long transfer to/from an even address:

### Byte Organization in Register

| 31 | 24 | 23 | 16 | 15 | 8 | 7 | 0 |
|---|---|---|---|---|---|---|---|
| HIGH BYTE | | MID UPPER BYTE | | MID LOWER BYTE | | LOW BYTE | |

### Byte Organization in 16-bit Memory

| Address | 15 | 8 | 7 | 0 |
|---|---|---|---|---|
| n+6 | LOW BYTE | | | |
| n+4 | MID LOWER BYTE | | | |
| n+2 | MID UPPER BYTE | | | |
| n | HIGH BYTE | | | |

**Condition Codes:**

Not affected

**Instruction Format:**

| 15 | 14 | 13 | 12 | 11 | 10 | 9 | 8 | 7 | 6 | 5 | 4 | 3 | 2 | 1 | 0 |
|---|---|---|---|---|---|---|---|---|---|---|---|---|---|---|---|
| 0 | 0 | 0 | 0 | Data Register | | | Op-mode | | | 0 | 0 | 1 | Address Register | | |

**Instruction Fields:**

Data Register field—Specifies the data register used for the source or destination of the move
Op-mode field—Specifies the operation mode, as follows:

    100 = transfer word from memory to register
    101 = transfer long from memory to register
    110 = transfer word from register to memory
    111 = transfer long from register to memory

Address Register field—Specifies the address register used in forming the source or destination effective address.

**MOVEQ**                               *Move Quick*                               **MOVEQ**

*Operation:*    #data → destination

*Assembler*
*Syntax:*    MOVEQ #data,Dn

*Attributes:*    Size = Long

*Description:*    Moves immediate data to a data register. The data are contained in an 8-bit field within the operation word. The data are sign-extended to a long operand. All 32 bits are transferred to the data register.

*Condition Codes:*

| X | N | Z | V | C |
|---|---|---|---|---|
| - | * | * | 0 | 0 |

X    Not affected.
N    Set if the result is negative (MSB=1). Cleared otherwise.
Z    Set if the result is zero. Cleared otherwise.
V    Always cleared.
C    Always cleared.

*Instruction Format:*

| 15 | 14 | 13 | 12 | 11 | 10 | 9 | 8 | 7 | 6 | 5 | 4 | 3 | 2 | 1 | 0 |
|----|----|----|----|----|----|----|----|----|----|----|----|----|----|----|----|
| 0 | 1 | 1 | 1 | Data Register | | | 0 | Data | | | | | | | |

*Instruction Fields:*

Data Register field—Specifies the destination data register.

Data field—Contains the immediate data. Data are sign-extended to a long operand and all 32 bits are transferred to the data register.

# MULS

**Signed Multiply**

**MULS**

**Operation:** source × destination → destination

**Assembler
Syntax:** MULS <ea>,Dn

**Attributes:** Size = Word

**Description:** Multiplies two signed 16-bit operands yielding a 32-bit signed result. A register operand is taken from the low-order word; the upper word is unused. All 32 bits of the product are saved in the destination register.

**Condition Codes:**

| X | N | Z | V | C |
|---|---|---|---|---|
| - | * | * | * | 0 |

X   Not affected.

N   Set if the result is negative (MSB = 1). Cleared otherwise.

Z   Set if the result is zero. Cleared otherwise.

V   Always cleared.

C   Always cleared.

**Instruction Format:**

| 15 | 14 | 13 | 12 | 11 | 10 | 9 | 8 | 7 | 6 | 5 | 4 | 3 | 2 | 1 | 0 |
|----|----|----|----|----|----|---|---|---|---|---|---|---|---|---|---|
| 1 | 1 | 0 | 0 | | Data Register | | 1 | 1 | 1 | | Effective Address Mode | | | Register | |

**Instruction Fields:**

Data Register field—Specifies the destination data register.

Effective Address field—Specifies the source operand. Only data addressing modes are allowed, as shown:

| Addressing Mode | Mode | Register | Addressing Mode | Mode | Register |
|-----------------|------|----------|-----------------|------|----------|
| Dn | 000 | reg. number | xxx.W | 111 | 000 |
| An | - | - | xxx.L | 111 | 001 |
| (An) | 010 | reg. number | #data | 111 | 100 |
| (An)+ | 011 | reg. number | | | |
| -(An) | 100 | reg. number | | | |
| d16(An) | 101 | reg. number | d16(PC) | 111 | 010 |
| d8(An,Xn) | 110 | reg. number | d8(PC,Xn) | 111 | 011 |

---

**MULU**                    *Unsigned Multiply*                    **MULU**

**Operation:**      source × destination → destination

**Assembler**
**Syntax:**      MULU <ea>,Dn

**Attributes:**      Size = Word

**Description:** Multiplies two unsigned 16-bit operands yielding a 32-bit unsigned result. A register operand is taken from the low-order word; the upper word is unused. All 32 bits of the product are saved in the destination data register.

**Condition Codes:**

| X | N | Z | V | C |
|---|---|---|---|---|
| - | * | * | * | 0 |

X   Not affected.
N   Set if the result is negative (MSB = 1). Cleared otherwise.
Z   Set if the result is zero. Cleared otherwise.
V   Always cleared.
C   Always cleared.

**Instruction Format:**

| 15 | 14 | 13 | 12 | 11 | 10 | 9 | 8 | 7 | 6 | 5 | 4 | 3 | 2 | 1 | 0 |
|----|----|----|----|----|----|---|---|---|---|---|---|---|---|---|---|
| 1 | 1 | 0 | 0 | | Data Register | | 0 | 1 | 1 | | | Effective Address Mode | | Register | |

**Instruction Fields:**

Data Register field—Specifies the destination data register.

Effective Address field—Specifies the source operand. Only data addressing modes are allowed, as shown:

| Addressing Mode | Mode | Register | Addressing Mode | Mode | Register |
|-----------------|------|----------|-----------------|------|----------|
| Dn | 000 | reg. number | xxx.W | 111 | 000 |
| An | - | - | xxx.L | 111 | 001 |
| (An) | 010 | reg. number | #data | 111 | 100 |
| (An)+ | 011 | reg. number | | | |
| −(An) | 100 | reg. number | | | |
| d16(An) | 101 | reg. number | d16(PC) | 111 | 010 |
| d8(An,Xn) | 110 | reg. number | d8(PC,Xn) | 111 | 011 |

## NBCD                     *Negate Decimal with Extend*                     NBCD

*Operation:*     $0 - \text{destination}_{10} - X \rightarrow \text{destination}$

*Assembler*
*Syntax:*        NBCD <ea>

*Attributes:*    Size = Byte

*Description:*   The operand addressed as the destination and the extend bit are subtracted from zero. The operation is performed using binary-coded-decimal arithmetic. The result is saved in the destination location. This instruction produces the tens complement of the destination if the extend bit is cleared, the nines complement if the extend bit is set.

*Condition Codes:*

| X | N | Z | V | C |
|---|---|---|---|---|
| * | U | * | U | * |

X   Set the same as the carry bit.
N   Undefined.
Z   Cleared if the result is non-zero. Unchanged otherwise.
V   Undefined.
C   Set if a decimal borrow occurs. Cleared otherwise.

*Instruction Format:*

| 15 | 14 | 13 | 12 | 11 | 10 | 9 | 8 | 7 | 6 | 5 | 4 | 3 | 2 | 1 | 0 |
|----|----|----|----|----|----|---|---|---|---|---|---|---|---|---|---|
| 0 | 1 | 0 | 0 | 1 | 0 | 0 | 0 | 0 | 0 | | Effective Address Mode | | | Register | |

*Instruction Fields:*

Effective Address field—Specifies the destination operand. Only data alterable addressing modes are allowed, as shown:

| Addressing Mode | Mode | Register | Addressing Mode | Mode | Register |
|---|---|---|---|---|---|
| Dn | 000 | reg. number | xxx.W | 111 | 000 |
| An | - | - | xxx.L | 111 | 001 |
| (An) | 010 | reg. number | #data | - | - |
| (An)+ | 011 | reg. number | | | |
| -(An) | 100 | reg. number | | | |
| d16(An) | 101 | reg. number | d16(PC) | - | - |
| d8(An,Xn) | 110 | reg. number | d8(PC,Xn) | - | - |

*Note:*

1. Normally the Z condition code bit is set via programming before the start of the operation. This allows for successful tests for zero results upon completion of a multi-precision operation.

---

**NEG**                                   *Negate*                                   **NEG**

**Operation:**    0 – destination → destination

**Assembler
Syntax:**    NEG <ea>

**Attributes:**    Size = Byte, Word, Long

**Description:**  The operand addressed as the destination is subtracted from zero. The result is stored in the destination location.

**Condition Codes:**

| X | N | Z | V | C |
|---|---|---|---|---|
| * | * | * | * | * |

X   Set the same as the carry bit.
N   Set if the result is negative (MSB = 1). Cleared otherwise.
Z   Set if the result is zero. Cleared otherwise.
V   Set if an overflow is generated. Cleared otherwise.
C   Cleared if the result is zero. Set otherwise.

**Instruction Format:**

| 15 | 14 | 13 | 12 | 11 | 10 | 9 | 8 | 7 | 6 | 5 | 4 | 3 | 2 | 1 | 0 |
|----|----|----|----|----|----|---|---|---|---|---|---|---|---|---|---|
| 0 | 1 | 0 | 0 | 0 | 1 | 0 | 0 | Size | | | Effective Address | | | | |
| | | | | | | | | | | | Mode | | | Register | |

**Instruction Fields:**

Size field—Specifies the size of the operand:

    00 = byte
    01 = word
    10 = long

Effective Address field—Specifies the destination operand. Only data alterable addressing modes are allowed, as shown:

| Addressing Mode | Mode | Register | Addressing Mode | Mode | Register |
|---|---|---|---|---|---|
| Dn | 000 | reg. number | xxx.W | 111 | 000 |
| An | - | - | xxx.L | 111 | 001 |
| (An) | 010 | reg. number | #data | - | - |
| (An)+ | 011 | reg. number | | | |
| –(An) | 100 | reg. number | | | |
| d16(An) | 101 | reg. number | d16(PC) | - | - |
| d8(An,Xn) | 110 | reg. number | d8(PC,Xn) | - | - |

# NEGX

**NEGX** *Negate with Extend* **NEGX**

**Operation:** 0 – destination – X → destination

**Assembler**
**Syntax:** NEGX <ea>

**Attributes:** Size = Byte, Word, Long

**Description:** The operand addressed as the destination and the extend bit are subtracted from zero. The result is stored in the destination location.

**Condition Codes:**

| X | N | Z | V | C |
|---|---|---|---|---|
| * | * | * | * | * |

X   Set the same as the carry bit.
N   Set if the result is negative (MSB = 1). Cleared otherwise.
Z   Cleared if the result is non-zero. Unchanged otherwise.
V   Set if an overflow is generated. Cleared otherwise.
C   Set if a borrow occurs. Cleared otherwise.

**Instruction Format:**

| 15 | 14 | 13 | 12 | 11 | 10 | 9 | 8 | 7 | 6 | 5 | 4 | 3 | 2 | 1 | 0 |
|----|----|----|----|----|----|---|---|---|---|---|---|---|---|---|---|
| 0 | 1 | 0 | 0 | 0 | 0 | 0 | 0 | Size | | | Effective Address Mode | | Register | | |

**Instruction Fields:**

Size field—Specifies the size of the operand:

00 = byte
01 = word
10 = long

Effective Address field—Specifies the destination operand. Only data alterable addressing modes are allowed, as shown:

| Addressing Mode | Mode | Register | Addressing Mode | Mode | Register |
|---|---|---|---|---|---|
| Dn | 000 | reg. number | xxx.W | 111 | 000 |
| An | - | - | xxx.L | 111 | 001 |
| (An) | 010 | reg. number | #data | - | - |
| (An)+ | 011 | reg. number | | | |
| −(An) | 100 | reg. number | | | |
| d16(An) | 101 | reg. number | d16(PC) | - | - |
| d8(An,Xn) | 110 | reg. number | d8(PC,Xn) | - | - |

**Note:**

1. Normally the Z condition code bit is set via programming before the start of the operation. This allows for successful tests for zero results upon completion of a multi-precision operation.

---

**NOP**                           *No Operation*                          **NOP**

*Operation:*    none

*Assembler*
*Syntax:*    NOP

*Attributes:*    Unsized

*Description:*    No operation occurs. The processor state, other than the program counter, is unaffected. Execution continues with the instruction following the NOP instruction.

*Condition Codes:*

  Not affected

*Instruction Format:*

| 15 | 14 | 13 | 12 | 11 | 10 | 9 | 8 | 7 | 6 | 5 | 4 | 3 | 2 | 1 | 0 |
|----|----|----|----|----|----|----|----|----|----|----|----|----|----|----|----|
| 0 | 1 | 0 | 0 | 1 | 1 | 1 | 0 | 0 | 1 | 1 | 1 | 0 | 0 | 0 | 1 |

**NOT**                         *Logical Complement*                         **NOT**

*Operation:*    complement-of-destination → destination

*Assembler*
*Syntax:*    NOT <ea>

*Attributes:*    Size = Byte, Word, Long

*Description:*    The ones complement of the destination operand is taken and the result is stored in the destination location.

*Condition Codes:*

| X | N | Z | V | C |
|---|---|---|---|---|
| - | * | * | 0 | 0 |

X    Not affected.
N    Set if the result is negative (MSB = 1). Cleared otherwise.
Z    Set if the result is zero. Cleared otherwise.
V    Always cleared.
C    Always cleared.

*Instruction Format:*

| 15 | 14 | 13 | 12 | 11 | 10 | 9 | 8 | 7 | 6 | 5 | 4 | 3 | 2 | 1 | 0 |
|----|----|----|----|----|----|---|---|---|---|---|---|---|---|---|---|
| 0 | 1 | 0 | 0 | 0 | 1 | 1 | 0 | Size | | Effective Address Mode | | | Register | | |

*Instruction Fields:*

Size field—Specifies the size of the operand:
    00 = byte
    01 = word
    10 = long

Effective Address field—Specifies the destination operand. Only data alterable addressing modes are allowed, as shown:

| Addressing Mode | Mode | Register | Addressing Mode | Mode | Register |
|-----------------|------|----------|-----------------|------|----------|
| Dn | 000 | reg. number | xxx.W | 111 | 000 |
| An | - | - | xxx.L | 111 | 001 |
| (An) | 010 | reg. number | #data | - | - |
| (An)+ | 011 | reg. number | | | |
| −(An) | 100 | reg. number | | | |
| d16(An) | 101 | reg. number | d16(PC) | - | - |
| d8(An,Xn) | 110 | reg. number | d8(PC,Xn) | - | - |

# OR

*Inclusive OR Logical*

# OR

**Operation:**    source OR destination → destination

**Assembler**    OR <ea>,Dn
**Syntax:**    OR Dn,<ea>

**Attributes:**    Size = Byte, Word, Long

**Description:**    The logical OR of the source and destination operands is computed and the result is stored in the destination.

**Condition Codes:**

| X | N | Z | V | C |
|---|---|---|---|---|
| - | * | * | 0 | 0 |

X    Not affected.
N    Set if the result is negative (MSB = 1). Cleared otherwise.
Z    Set if the result is zero. Cleared otherwise.
V    Always cleared.
C    Always cleared.

**Instruction Format:**

| 15 | 14 | 13 | 12 | 11 | 10 | 9 | 8 | 7 | 6 | 5 | 4 | 3 | 2 | 1 | 0 |
|----|----|----|----|----|----|---|---|---|---|---|---|---|---|---|---|
| 1 | 0 | 0 | 0 | Data Register | | | Op-mode | | | Effective Address Mode | | | Register | | |

**Instruction Fields:**

Data Register field—Specifies the source or destination data register, depending on the op-mode field.
Op-mode field—Specifies the operation mode, as follows:

| Byte | Word | Long | Operation |
|------|------|------|-----------|
| 000 | 001 | 010 | <ea> OR <Dn> → <Dn> |
| 100 | 101 | 110 | <Dn> OR <ea> → <ea> |

Effective Address field—If the location specified is a source operand, only data addressing modes are allowed, as shown:

| Addressing Mode | Mode | Register | Addressing Mode | Mode | Register |
|-----------------|------|----------|-----------------|------|----------|
| Dn | 000 | reg. number | xxx.W | 111 | 000 |
| An | - | - | xxx.L | 111 | 001 |
| (An) | 010 | reg. number | #data | 111 | 100 |
| (An)+ | 011 | reg. number | | | |
| −(An) | 100 | reg. number | | | |
| d16(An) | 101 | reg. number | d16(PC) | 111 | 010 |
| d8(An,Xn) | 110 | reg. number | d8(PC,Xn) | 111 | 011 |

If the location specified is a destination operand, only memory alterable addressing modes are allowed, as shown:

| Addressing Mode | Mode | Register | Addressing Mode | Mode | Register |
|---|---|---|---|---|---|
| Dn | - | - | xxx.W | 111 | 000 |
| An | - | - | xxx.L | 111 | 001 |
| (An) | 010 | reg. number | #data | - | - |
| (An)+ | 011 | reg. number | | | |
| −(An) | 100 | reg. number | | | |
| d16(An) | 101 | reg. number | d16(PC) | - | - |
| d8(An,Xn) | 110 | reg. number | d8(PC,Xn) | - | - |

*Notes:*

1. If the destination is a data register, it must be specified using the destination Dn mode, not the destination <ea> mode.
2. Most assemblers use ORI when the source is immediate data.

**ORI**                           *Inclusive OR Immediate*                          **ORI**

*Operation:*     #data OR destination → destination

*Assembler*
*Syntax:*        ORI #data,<ea>

*Attributes:*    Size = Byte, Word, Long

*Description:*   The logical OR of the source and destination operands is computed and the result is stored in the destination.

*Condition Codes:*

| X | N | Z | V | C |
|---|---|---|---|---|
| - | * | * | 0 | 0 |

X   Not affected.
N   Set if the most-significant bit of the result is set. Cleared otherwise.
Z   Set if the result is zero. Cleared otherwise.
V   Always cleared.
C   Always cleared.

*Instruction Format:*

| 15 | 14 | 13 | 12 | 11 | 10 | 9 | 8 | 7 | 6 | 5 | 4 | 3 | 2 | 1 | 0 |
|----|----|----|----|----|----|----|----|----|----|----|----|----|----|----|----|
| 0 | 0 | 0 | 0 | 0 | 0 | 0 | 0 | Size | | Effective Address | | | | | |
| | | | | | | | | | | Mode | | | Register | | |

*Instruction Fields:*

Size field—Specifies the size of the immediate data for the operation:

  00 = byte (contained in low-byte of second instruction word, upper byte = 0)

  01 = word (contained in the entire second instruction word)

  10 = long (contained in the second and 3rd instruction words)

Effective Address field—Specifies the destination operand. Only data alterable addressing modes are allowed, as shown:

| Addressing Mode | Mode | Register | Addressing Mode | Mode | Register |
|---|---|---|---|---|---|
| Dn | 000 | reg. number | xxx.W | 111 | 000 |
| An | - | - | xxx.L | 111 | 001 |
| (An) | 010 | reg. number | #data | - | - |
| (An)+ | 011 | reg. number | | | |
| −(An) | 100 | reg. number | | | |
| d16(An) | 101 | reg. number | d16(PC) | - | - |
| d8(An,Xn) | 110 | reg. number | d8(PC,Xn) | - | - |

**ORI**
**TO CCR**

*Inclusive OR Immediate to Condition Codes*

**ORI**
**TO CCR**

*Operation:*     #data OR CCR → CCR

*Assembler*
*Syntax:*     ORI #data,CCR

*Attributes:*     Size = Byte

*Description:* The logical OR of the immediate data and the CCR is computed and the result is stored in the CCR.

*Condition Codes:*

| X | N | Z | V | C |
|---|---|---|---|---|
| * | * | * | * | * |

X   Set if bit 4 of the immediate operand is one. Unchanged otherwise.
N   Set if bit 3 of the immediate operand is one. Unchanged otherwise.
Z   Set if bit 2 of the immediate operand is one. Unchanged otherwise.
V   Set if bit 1 of the immediate operand is one. Unchanged otherwise.
C   Set if bit 0 of the immediate operand is one. Unchanged otherwise.

*Instruction Format:*

| 15 | 14 | 13 | 12 | 11 | 10 | 9 | 8 | 7 | 6 | 5 | 4 | 3 | 2 | 1 | 0 |
|----|----|----|----|----|----|---|---|---|---|---|---|---|---|---|---|
| 0 | 0 | 0 | 0 | 0 | 0 | 0 | 0 | 0 | 0 | 1 | 1 | 1 | 1 | 0 | 0 |

## **ORI TO SR**                    *Inclusive OR Immediate to Status Register*                    **ORI TO SR**

*Operation:*    if supervisor state
             #data OR SR → SR
      else TRAP

*Assembler*
*Syntax:*       ORI #data,SR

*Attributes:*   Size = Word

*Description:*   The logical OR of the immediate data and the status register is computed and the result is stored in the status register. All implemented bits of the status register are affected.

*Condition Codes:*

| X | N | Z | V | C |
|---|---|---|---|---|
| * | * | * | * | * |

X    Set if bit 4 of the immediate operand is one. Unchanged otherwise.
N    Set if bit 3 of the immediate operand is one. Unchanged otherwise.
Z    Set if bit 2 of the immediate operand is one. Unchanged otherwise.
V    Set if bit 1 of the immediate operand is one. Unchanged otherwise.
C    Set if bit 0 of the immediate operand is one. Unchanged otherwise.

*Instruction Format:*

| 15 | 14 | 13 | 12 | 11 | 10 | 9 | 8 | 7 | 6 | 5 | 4 | 3 | 2 | 1 | 0 |
|----|----|----|----|----|----|---|---|---|---|---|---|---|---|---|---|
| 0  | 0  | 0  | 0  | 0  | 0  | 0 | 0 | 0 | 1 | 1 | 1 | 1 | 1 | 0 | 0 |

**PEA**                        *Push Effective Address*                        **PEA**

*Operation:*    destination → −(SP)

*Assembler*
*Syntax:*    PEA <ea>

*Attributes:*    Size = Long

*Description:*    The effective address is computed and pushed onto the stack.

*Condition Codes:*

Not affected

*Instruction Format:*

| 15 | 14 | 13 | 12 | 11 | 10 | 9 | 8 | 7 | 6 | 5 | 4 | 3 | 2 | 1 | 0 |
|----|----|----|----|----|----|---|---|---|---|---|---|---|---|---|---|
| 0 | 1 | 0 | 0 | 1 | 0 | 0 | 0 | 0 | 1 | | | | | | |

| Effective Address | |
|---|---|
| Mode | Register |

*Instruction Fields:*

Effective Address field—Specifies the address to be pushed onto the stack. Only control addressing modes are allowed, as shown:

| Addressing Mode | Mode | Register | Addressing Mode | Mode | Register |
|-----------------|------|----------|-----------------|------|----------|
| Dn | - | - | xxx.W | 111 | 000 |
| An | - | - | xxx.L | 111 | 001 |
| (An) | 010 | reg. number | #data | - | - |
| (An)+ | - | - | | | |
| −(An) | - | - | | | |
| d16(An) | 101 | reg. number | d16(PC) | 111 | 010 |
| d8(An,Xn) | 110 | reg. number | d8(PC,Xn) | 111 | 011 |

---

**RESET**                          *Reset External Devices*                          **RESET**

*Operation:*      if supervisor state
                      assert $\overline{\text{RESET}}$ line
                  else TRAP

*Assembler*
*Syntax:*      RESET

*Attributes:*   Unsized

*Description:*   The reset line is asserted for 124 clock cycles, resetting all external devices. The processor state, other than the program counter, is unaffected and execution continues with the next instruction.

*Condition Codes:*

   Not affected

*Instruction Format:*

| 15 | 14 | 13 | 12 | 11 | 10 | 9 | 8 | 7 | 6 | 5 | 4 | 3 | 2 | 1 | 0 |
|----|----|----|----|----|----|----|----|----|----|----|----|----|----|----|----|
| 0 | 1 | 0 | 0 | 1 | 1 | 1 | 0 | 0 | 1 | 1 | 1 | 0 | 0 | 0 | 0 |

**ROL, ROR**                  *Rotate (Without Extend)*                  **ROL, ROR**

***Operation:***    destination rotated left/right by count

***Assembler***    ROd Dx,Dy
***Syntax:***       ROd #data,Dy
             ROd <ea>
             where d is the rotate direction, L (left) or R (right)

***Attributes:***    Size = Byte, Word, Long

***Description:***    Rotates the bits of the operand in the direction specified. The extend bit is not included in the rotation. The rotate count for the rotating of a register may be specified in two different ways:

1. Immediate: The rotate count is specified in the instruction (shift range, 1–8).
2. Register: The rotate count is contained in a data register specified in the instruction.

The size of the operand may be byte, word, or long. The content of memory may be shifted one bit only and the operand size is restricted to a word.

The ROR instruction rotates the bits of the operand to the left; the rotate count determines the number of bit positions rotated. Bits rotated out of the high-order bit go to the carry bit and also back into the low-order bit.

The ROR instruction rotates the bits of the operand to the right; the rotate count determines the number of bit positions rotated. Bits rotated out of the low-order bit go to the carry bit and also back into the high-order bit.

Operation:

     ROL:

     ROR:

***Condition Codes:***

| X | N | Z | V | C |
|---|---|---|---|---|
| - | * | * | 0 | * |

X   Not affected.
N   Set if the most-significant bit of the result is set. Cleared otherwise.
Z   Set if the result is zero. Cleared otherwise.
V   Always cleared.
C   Set according to the last bit rotated out of the operand. Cleared when the rotate count is zero.

***Instruction Format (Register Rotates):***

| 15 | 14 | 13 | 12 | 11 | 10 | 9 | 8 | 7 | 6 | 5 | 4 | 3 | 2 | 1 | 0 |
|----|----|----|----|----|----|----|----|----|----|----|----|----|----|----|----|
| 1 | 1 | 1 | 0 | Count/ Register | | | dr | Size | | i/r | 1 | 1 | Data Register | | |

## Instruction Fields (Register Rotates):

Count/Register field:

If i/r = 0, specifies rotate count. (Note: Zero represents a rotate count of 8.)

If i/r = 1, specifies a data register that contains the rotate count.

dr field—Specifies the direction to rotate:

0 = right

1 = left

Size field—Specifies the size of the operand:

00 = byte

01 = word

10 = long

i/r field—Specifies the location of the rotate count:

0 = immediate rotate count

1 = register rotate count

## Instruction Format (Memory Rotates):

| 15 | 14 | 13 | 12 | 11 | 10 | 9 | 8 | 7 | 6 | 5 | 4 | 3 | 2 | 1 | 0 |
|----|----|----|----|----|----|----|----|----|----|----|----|----|----|----|----|
| 1 | 1 | 1 | 0 | 0 | 1 | 1 | dr | 1 | 1 | Effective Address | | | | | |
| | | | | | | | | | | Mode | | | Register | | |

## Instruction Fields (Memory Rotates):

dr field—Specifies the direction to rotate:

0 = right

1 = left

Effective Address field—Specifies the operand to be rotated. Only memory alterable addressing modes are allowed, as shown:

| Addressing Mode | Mode | Register | Addressing Mode | Mode | Register |
|-----------------|------|----------|-----------------|------|----------|
| Dn | - | - | xxx.W | 111 | 000 |
| An | - | - | xxx.L | 111 | 001 |
| (An) | 010 | reg. number | #data | - | - |
| (An)+ | 011 | reg. number | | | |
| −(An) | 100 | reg. number | | | |
| d16(An) | 101 | reg. number | d16(PC) | - | - |
| d8(An,Xn) | 110 | reg. number | d8(PC,Xn) | - | - |

# **ROXL**                    *Rotate with Extend*                    **ROXL**

**Operation:**    destination with X rotated by count

**Assembler**    ROXd Dx,Dy
**Syntax:**    ROXd #data,Dy
             ROXd <ea>
             where d is the direction to rotate, L (left) or R (right)

**Attributes:**    Size = Byte, Word, Long

**Description:**    Rotates the bits of the operand in the direction specified. The extend bit is included in the rotation. The rotate count for rotating a register may be specified in two different ways:

1. Immediate: The rotate count is specified in the instruction (range, 1–8).
2. Register: The rotate count is contained in a data register specified in the instruction.

The size of the operand may be byte, word, or long. The content of memory may be rotated one bit only and the operand size is restricted to a word.

The ROXL instruction rotates the bits of the operand to the left; the rotate count determines the number of bit positions rotated. Bits rotated out of the high-order bit go to the carry bit and the extend bit; the previous value of the extend bit rotates into the low-order bit.

The ROXR instruction rotates the bits of the operand to the right; the rotate count determines the number of bit positions rotated. Bits rotated out of the low-order bit go to the carry bit and the extend bit; the previous value of the extend bit rotates into the high-order bit.

Operation:

ROXL:

ROXR:

**Condition Codes:**

| X | N | Z | V | C |
|---|---|---|---|---|
| * | * | * | 0 | * |

X    Set to the last bit rotated out of the operand. Unaffected when the rotate count is zero.
N    Set if the most-significant bit of the result is set. Cleared otherwise.
Z    Set if the result is zero. Cleared otherwise.
V    Always cleared.
C    Set according to the last bit rotated out of the operand. When the rotate count is zero, set to the value of the extend bit.

**Instruction Format (Register Rotates):**

| 15 | 14 | 13 | 12 | 11 | 10 | 9 | 8 | 7 | 6 | 5 | 4 | 3 | 2 | 1 | 0 |
|----|----|----|----|----|----|---|---|---|---|---|---|---|---|---|---|
| 1 | 1 | 1 | 0 | Count/ Register | | | dr | Size | | i/r | 1 | 0 | Data Register | | |

### Instruction Fields (Register Rotates):

Count/Register field:

If i/r = 0, specifies rotate count. (Note: Zero represents a rotate count of 8.)

If i/r = 1, specifies a data register that contains the rotate count.

dr field—Specifies the direction to rotate:

0 = right

1 = left

Size field—Specifies the size of the operand:

00 = byte

01 = word

10 = long

i/r field—Specifies the location of the rotate count:

0 = immediate rotate count

1 = register rotate count

### Instruction Format (Memory Rotates):

| 15 | 14 | 13 | 12 | 11 | 10 | 9 | 8 | 7 | 6 | 5 | 4 | 3 | 2 | 1 | 0 |
|----|----|----|----|----|----|---|---|---|---|---|---|---|---|---|---|
| 1 | 1 | 1 | 0 | 0 | 1 | 0 | dr | 1 | 1 | Effective Address | | | | | |
| | | | | | | | | | | Mode | | | Register | | |

### Instruction Fields (Memory Rotates):

dr field—Specifies the direction of the rotate:

0 = right

1 = left

Effective Address field—Specifies the operand to be rotated. Only memory alterable addressing modes are allowed, as shown:

| Addressing Mode | Mode | Register | Addressing Mode | Mode | Register |
|-----------------|------|----------|-----------------|------|----------|
| Dn | - | - | xxx.W | 111 | 000 |
| An | - | - | xxx.L | 111 | 001 |
| (An) | 010 | reg. number | #data | - | - |
| (An)+ | 011 | reg. number | | | |
| −(An) | 100 | reg. number | | | |
| d16(An) | 101 | reg. number | d16(PC) | - | - |
| d8(An,Xn) | 110 | reg. number | d8(PC,Xn) | - | - |

**RTE**                    *Return from Exception*                    **RTE**

*Operation:*   if supervisor state
                   (SP)+ → SR
                   (SP)+ → PC
               else TRAP

*Assembler*
*Syntax:*      RTE

*Attributes:*  Unsized

*Description:*  The status register and program counter are pulled from the system stack. The previous status register and program counter are lost. All bits in the status register are affected.

*Condition Codes:*

  Not affected

*Instruction Format:*

| 15 | 14 | 13 | 12 | 11 | 10 | 9 | 8 | 7 | 6 | 5 | 4 | 3 | 2 | 1 | 0 |
|----|----|----|----|----|----|---|---|---|---|---|---|---|---|---|---|
| 0  | 1  | 0  | 0  | 1  | 1  | 1 | 0 | 0 | 1 | 1 | 1 | 0 | 0 | 1 | 1 |

**RTR**                    *Return and Restore Condition Codes*                    **RTR**

*Operation:*    (SP)+ → CCR
                (SP)+ → PC

*Assembler*
*Syntax:*       RTR

*Attributes:*   Unsized

*Description:*    The CCR and PC are pulled from the stack. The previous CCR and PC are lost. The supervisor portion of the status register is unaffected.

*Condition Codes:*

Set to the condition codes retrieved from the stack.

*Instruction Format:*

| 15 | 14 | 13 | 12 | 11 | 10 | 9 | 8 | 7 | 6 | 5 | 4 | 3 | 2 | 1 | 0 |
|----|----|----|----|----|----|---|---|---|---|---|---|---|---|---|---|
| 0  | 1  | 0  | 0  | 1  | 1  | 1 | 0 | 0 | 1 | 1 | 1 | 0 | 1 | 1 | 1 |

**RTS** *Return from Subroutine* **RTS**

*Operation:*    (SP)+ → PC

*Assembler*
*Syntax:*    RTS

*Attributes:*    Unsized

*Description:*    The PC is pulled from the stack. The previous value of the PC is lost.

*Condition Codes:*

  Not affected

*Instruction Format:*

| 15 | 14 | 13 | 12 | 11 | 10 | 9 | 8 | 7 | 6 | 5 | 4 | 3 | 2 | 1 | 0 |
|----|----|----|----|----|----|---|---|---|---|---|---|---|---|---|---|
| 0  | 1  | 0  | 0  | 1  | 1  | 1 | 0 | 0 | 1 | 1 | 1 | 0 | 1 | 0 | 1 |

---

**SBCD**                *Subtract Decimal with Extend*                **SBCD**

*Operation:*      $destination_{10} - source_{10} - X \rightarrow destination$

*Assembler*      SBCD Dx,Dy
*Syntax:*        SBCD -(Ax),-(Ay)

*Attributes:*    Size = Byte

*Description:*   The source is subtracted from the destination along with the X bit and the result is stored in the destination. The subtraction is performed using binary-coded-decimal arithmetic. The operands, which are packed BCD numbers, are addressed in two ways:

1. Data register to data register: The operands are contained in the data registers specified in the instruction.
2. Memory to memory: The operands are addressed with the predecrement addressing mode using the address registers specified in the instruction.

This is a byte operation only.

*Condition Codes:*

| X | N | Z | V | C |
|---|---|---|---|---|
| * | U | * | U | * |

X   Set the same as the carry bit.
N   Undefined
Z   Cleared if the result is non-zero. Unchanged otherwise.
V   Undefined
C   Set if a decimal borrow is generated. Cleared otherwise.

*Instruction Format:*

| 15 | 14 | 13 | 12 | 11 | 10 | 9 | 8 | 7 | 6 | 5 | 4 | 3 | 2 | 1 | 0 |
|----|----|----|----|----|----|----|----|----|----|----|----|-----|----|----|----|
| 1 | 0 | 0 | 0 | | Register Ry | | 1 | 0 | 0 | 0 | 0 | R/M | | Register Rx | |

*Instruction Fields:*

Register Ry field—Specifies the destination register:
   if R/M = 0, specifies a data register
   if R/M = 1, specifies an address register for the predecrement addressing mode
R/M field—Specifies the operand addressing mode:
   0 = data register to data register
   1 = memory to memory
Register Rx field—Specifies the source register:
   if R/M = 0, specifies a data register
   if R/M = 1, specifies an address register for the predecrement addressing mode

*Note:*

1. Normally the Z condition code bit is set via programming before the start of an operation. This allows for successful tests for zero results upon completion of a multi-precision operation.

**SCC**                     *Set According to Condition*                     **SCC**

*Operation:*    if condition true
        1s → destination
    else 0s → destination

*Assembler*
*Syntax:*    Scc <ea>

*Attributes:*    Size = Byte

*Description:*    The specified condition is tested and if it is true, the byte specified by the <ea> is set to all 1s, otherwise the byte is set to all 0s.

*Condition Codes:*

  Not affected

*Instruction Format:*

| 15 | 14 | 13 | 12 | 11 | 10 | 9 | 8 | 7 | 6 | 5 | 4 | 3 | 2 | 1 | 0 |
|----|----|----|----|----|----|----|----|----|----|----|----|----|----|----|----|
| 0 | 1 | 0 | 1 | | Condition | | | 1 | 1 | | Effective Address | | | | |
| | | | | | | | | | | | Mode | | | Register | |

*Instruction Fields:*

Condition field—Specifies the condition for setting, as follows:

| Mnemonic | Condition | Encoding | Test |
|----------|-----------|----------|------|
| T | true | 0000 | 1 |
| F | false | 0001 | 0 |
| HI | high | 0010 | $\overline{C} \cdot \overline{Z}$ |
| LS | low or same | 0011 | $C + Z$ |
| CC(HS) | carry clear | 0100 | $\overline{C}$ |
| CS(LO) | carry set | 0101 | $C$ |
| NE | not equal | 0110 | $\overline{Z}$ |
| EQ | equal | 0111 | $Z$ |
| VC | overflow clear | 1000 | $\overline{V}$ |
| VS | overflow set | 1001 | $V$ |
| PL | plus | 1010 | $\overline{N}$ |
| MI | minus | 1011 | $N$ |
| GE | greater or equal | 1100 | $N \cdot V + \overline{N} \cdot \overline{V}$ |
| LT | less than | 1101 | $N \cdot \overline{V} + \overline{N} \cdot V$ |
| GT | greater than | 1110 | $N \cdot V \cdot \overline{Z} + \overline{N} \cdot \overline{V} \cdot \overline{Z}$ |
| LE | less or equal | 1111 | $Z + N \cdot \overline{V} + \overline{N} \cdot V$ |

  • = Boolean AND
  + = Boolean OR

Effective Address field—Specifies the location into which the true/false byte is to be stored. Only data alterable addressing modes are allowed, as shown:

| Addressing Mode | Mode | Register | Addressing Mode | Mode | Register |
|---|---|---|---|---|---|
| Dn | 000 | reg. number | xxx.W | 111 | 000 |
| An | - | - | xxx.L | 111 | 001 |
| (An) | 010 | reg. number | #data | - | - |
| (An)+ | 011 | reg. number | | | |
| −(An) | 100 | reg. number | | | |
| d16(An) | 101 | reg. number | d16(PC) | - | - |
| d8(An,Xn) | 110 | reg. number | d8(PC,Xn) | - | - |

*Notes:*

1. A subsequent NEG.B instruction can be used with the same effective address to change the Scc result from TRUE or FALSE to the equivalent arithmetic value (TRUE = 1, FALSE = 0).

2. In the MC68000 and 68008, a memory address is read before it is written to.

**STOP**                    *Load Status Register and Stop*                    **STOP**

*Operation:*    if supervisor state
               #data → SR, STOP
        else TRAP

*Assembler*
*Syntax:*    STOP #data

*Attributes:*    Unsized

*Description:*    The immediate operand is moved into the entire SR; the PC is advanced to point to the next instruction and the processor stops fetching and executing instructions. Execution of instructions resumes when a trace, interrupt, or reset exception occurs. A trace exception will occur if the trace state is on when the STOP instruction is executed. If an interrupt arrives whose priority is higher than the current processor priority, an interrupt exception occurs; otherwise, the interrupt request has no effect. If the bit of the immediate data corresponding to the S-bit is off, execution of the instruction will cause a privilege violation. External reset will always initiate reset exception processing.

*Condition Codes:*

Set according to the immediate operand.

*Instruction Format:*

| 15 | 14 | 13 | 12 | 11 | 10 | 9 | 8 | 7 | 6 | 5 | 4 | 3 | 2 | 1 | 0 |
|----|----|----|----|----|----|---|---|---|---|---|---|---|---|---|---|
| 0  | 1  | 0  | 0  | 1  | 1  | 1 | 0 | 0 | 1 | 1 | 1 | 0 | 0 | 1 | 0 |

| **SUB** | *Subtract* | **SUB** |
|---|---|---|

**Operation:**    destination – source → destination

**Assembler**    SUB <ea>,Dn
**Syntax:**    SUB Dn,<ea>

**Attributes:**    Size = Byte, Word, Long

**Description:**    Subtract the source from the destination and stores the result in the destination.

**Condition Codes:**

| X | N | Z | V | C |
|---|---|---|---|---|
| * | * | * | * | * |

X    Set the same as the carry bit.
N    Set if the result is negative (MSB = 1). Cleared otherwise.
Z    Set if the result is zero. Cleared otherwise.
V    Set if an overflow is generated. Cleared otherwise.
C    Set if a borrow is generated. Cleared otherwise.

**Instruction Format:**

| 15 | 14 | 13 | 12 | 11 | 10 | 9 | 8 | 7 | 6 | 5 | 4 | 3 | 2 | 1 | 0 |
|---|---|---|---|---|---|---|---|---|---|---|---|---|---|---|---|
| 1 | 0 | 0 | 1 | Data Register | | | Op-mode | | | Effective Address | | | | | |
| | | | | | | | | | | Mode | | | Register | | |

**Instruction Fields:**

Data Register field—Specifies the source or destination data register, depending on the op-mode field.

Op-mode field—Specifies the operation mode, as follows:

| Byte | Word | Long | Operation |
|---|---|---|---|
| 000 | 001 | 010 | <Dn> – <ea> → <Dn> |
| 100 | 101 | 110 | <ea> – <Dn> → <ea> |

Effective Address field—Determines the addressing mode. If the location specified is a source operand, all addressing modes are allowed, as shown:

| Addressing Mode | Mode | Register | Addressing Mode | Mode | Register |
|---|---|---|---|---|---|
| Dn | 000 | reg. number | xxx.W | 111 | 000 |
| An | 001 | reg. number | xxx.L | 111 | 001 |
| (An) | 010 | reg. number | #data | 111 | 100 |
| (An)+ | 011 | reg. number | | | |
| –(An) | 100 | reg. number | | | |
| d16(An) | 101 | reg. number | d16(PC) | 111 | 010 |
| d8(An,Xn) | 110 | reg. number | d8(PC,Xn) | 111 | 011 |

*Word and Long only.

If the location specified is a destination operand, only memory alterable addressing modes are allowed, as shown:

| Addressing Mode | Mode | Register | Addressing Mode | Mode | Register |
|---|---|---|---|---|---|
| Dn | - | - | xxx.W | 111 | 000 |
| An | - | - | xxx.L | 111 | 001 |
| (An) | 010 | reg. number | #data | - | - |
| (An)+ | 011 | reg. number | | | |
| -(An) | 100 | reg. number | | | |
| d16(An) | 101 | reg. number | d16(PC) | - | - |
| d8(An,Xn) | 110 | reg. number | d8(PC,Xn) | - | - |

*Notes:*

1. If the destination is a data register, it must be specified as a destination Dn address, not as a destination <ea> address.
2. Most assemblers use SUBA when the destination is an address register, and SUBI or SUBQ when the source is immediate data.

---

**SUBA**                                    *Subtract Address*                                    **SUBA**

***Operation:***    destination – source → destination

***Assembler***
***Syntax:***    SUBA <ea>,An

***Attributes:***    Size = Word, Long

***Description:***    Subtracts the source from the destination address register and stores the result in the destination address register. Word-size operands are sign extended. All 32 bits of the address register are affected.

***Condition Codes:***

Not affected

***Instruction Format:***

| 15 | 14 | 13 | 12 | 11 | 10 | 9 | 8 | 7 | 6 | 5 | 4 | 3 | 2 | 1 | 0 |
|----|----|----|----|----|----|----|----|----|----|----|----|----|----|----|----|
| 1 | 0 | 0 | 1 | Data Register | | | Op-mode | | | Effective Address | | | | | |
| | | | | | | | | | | Mode | | | Register | | |

***Instruction Fields:***

Data Register field—Specifies the destination address register.

Op-mode field—Specifies the operation mode, as follows:

| Word | Long | Operation |
|------|------|-----------|
| 011  | 111  | <ea> – <An> → <An> |

Effective Address field—Specifies the source operand. All addressing modes are allowed, as shown:

| Addressing Mode | Mode | Register | Addressing Mode | Mode | Register |
|-----------------|------|----------|-----------------|------|----------|
| Dn | 000 | reg. number | xxx.W | 111 | 000 |
| An | 001 | reg. number | xxx.L | 111 | 001 |
| (An) | 010 | reg. number | #data | 111 | 100 |
| (An)+ | 011 | reg. number | | | |
| –(An) | 100 | reg. number | | | |
| d16(An) | 101 | reg. number | d16(PC) | 111 | 010 |
| d8(An,Xn) | 110 | reg. number | d8(PC,Xn) | 111 | 011 |

**SUBI**            *Subtract Immediate*            **SUBI**

**Operation:**     destination − #data → destination

**Assembler**
**Syntax:**     SUBI #data,<ea>

**Attributes:**     Size = Byte, Word, Long

**Description:**     Subtracts the immediate data from the destination and stores the result in the destination.

**Condition Codes:**

| X | N | Z | V | C |
|---|---|---|---|---|
| * | * | * | * | * |

X    Set the same as the carry bit.
N    Set if the result is negative (MSB = 1). Cleared otherwise.
Z    Set if the result is zero. Cleared otherwise.
V    Set if an overflow is generated. Cleared otherwise.
C    Set if a borrow is generated. Cleared otherwise.

**Instruction Format:**

| 15 | 14 | 13 | 12 | 11 | 10 | 9 | 8 | 7 | 6 | 5 | 4 | 3 | 2 | 1 | 0 |
|----|----|----|----|----|----|---|---|---|---|---|---|---|---|---|---|
| 0 | 0 | 0 | 0 | 0 | 1 | 0 | 0 | Size | | Effective Address | | | | | |
| | | | | | | | | | | Mode | | | Register | | |

**Instruction Fields:**

Size field—Specifies the size of the operand:

00 = byte (contained in low-byte of second instruction word, upper byte = 0)

01 = word (contained in the entire second instruction word)

10 = long (contained in the second and 3rd instruction words)

Effective Address field—Specifies the destination operand. Only data alterable addressing modes are allowed, as shown:

| Addressing Mode | Mode | Register | Addressing Mode | Mode | Register |
|-----------------|------|----------|-----------------|------|----------|
| Dn | 000 | reg. number | xxx.W | 111 | 000 |
| An | - | - | xxx.L | 111 | 001 |
| (An) | 010 | reg. number | #data | - | - |
| (An)+ | 011 | reg. number | | | |
| −(An) | 100 | reg. number | | | |
| d16(An) | 101 | reg. number | d16(PC) | - | - |
| d8(An,Xn) | 110 | reg. number | d8(PC,Xn) | - | - |

---

# SUBQ                      *Subtract Quick*                      SUBQ

**Operation:**      destination – #data → destination

**Assembler
Syntax:**      SUBQ #data,<ea>

**Attributes:**      Size = Byte, Word, Long

**Description:** Subtracts the immediate data from the destination and stores the result in the destination. The data range is from 1 to 8, as encoded in the first instruction word.

**Condition Codes:**

| X | N | Z | V | C |
|---|---|---|---|---|
| * | * | * | * | * |

X   Set the same as the carry bit.
N   Set if the result is negative (MSB = 1). Cleared otherwise.
Z   Set if the result is zero. Cleared otherwise.
V   Set if an overflow is generated. Cleared otherwise.
C   Set if a borrow is generated. Cleared otherwise.

**Instruction Format:**

| 15 | 14 | 13 | 12 | 11 | 10 | 9 | 8 | 7 | 6 | 5 | 4 | 3 | 2 | 1 | 0 |
|----|----|----|----|----|----|---|---|---|---|---|---|---|---|---|---|
| 0 | 1 | 0 | 1 | | Data | | 1 | | Size | | Mode | | | Register | |

(Effective Address: Mode | Register)

**Instruction Fields:**

Data field—Contains three bits of immediate data, 0, 1–7, representing a range of 8, 1 to 7 respectively.

Size field—Specifies the size of the operation:

00 = byte
01 = word
10 = long

Effective Address field—Specifies the destination location. Only alterable addressing modes are allowed, as shown:

| Addressing Mode | Mode | Register | Addressing Mode | Mode | Register |
|-----------------|------|----------|-----------------|------|----------|
| Dn | 000 | reg. number | xxx.W | 111 | 000 |
| An* | 001 | reg. number | xxx.L | 111 | 001 |
| (An) | 010 | reg. number | #data | – | – |
| (An)+ | 011 | reg. number | | | |
| –(An) | 100 | reg. number | | | |
| d16(An) | 101 | reg. number | d16(PC) | – | – |
| d8(An,Xn) | 110 | reg. number | d8(PC,Xn) | – | – |

*Word and Long only.

# SUBX

Subtract with Extend

**SUBX**

**Operation:** destination – source – X $\rightarrow$ destination

**Assembler**    SUBX Dy,Dx
**Syntax:**      SUBX -(Ay),-(Ax)

**Attributes:**   Size = Byte, Word, Long

**Description:** Subtracts the source from the destination along with the X bit and store the result in the destination. The operands are addressed in two ways:

1. Data register to data register: The operands are contained in the data registers specified in the instruction.
2. Memory to memory: The operands are addressed with the predecrement addressing mode using the address registers specified in the instruction.

**Condition Codes:**

| X | N | Z | V | C |
|---|---|---|---|---|
| * | * | * | * | * |

X   Set the same as the carry bit.
N   Set if the result is negative (MSB = 1). Cleared otherwise.
Z   Cleared if the result is non-zero. Unchanged otherwise.
V   Set if an overflow is generated. Cleared otherwise.
C   Set if a borrow is generated. Cleared otherwise.

**Instruction Format:**

| 15 | 14 | 13 | 12 | 11 | 10 | 9 | 8 | 7 | 6 | 5 | 4 | 3 | 2 | 1 | 0 |
|----|----|----|----|----|----|---|---|---|---|---|---|----|----|----|----|
| 1 | 0 | 0 | 1 | Register Ry | | | 1 | Size | | 0 | 0 | R/M | Register Rx | | |

**Instruction Fields:**

Register Ry field—Specifies the destination register:
   if R/M = 0, specifies a data register
   if R/M = 1, specifies an address register for the predecrement addressing mode
Size field—Specifies the size of the operation:
   00—byte
   01—word
   10—long
R/M field—Specifies the operand addressing mode:
   0 = data register to data register
   1 = memory to memory
Register Rx field—Specifies the source register:
   if R/M = 0, specifies a data register
   if R/M = 1, specifies an address register for the predecrement addressing mode

**Note:**

1. Normally the Z condition code bit is set via programming before the start of an operation. This allows for successful tests for zero results upon completion of a multi-precision operation.

**SWAP**                    *Swap Register Halves*                    **SWAP**

*Operation:*   $D_{31:16} \longleftrightarrow D_{15:0}$

*Assembler*
*Syntax:*   SWAP Dn

*Attributes:*   Size = Word

*Description:*   Exchange the 16-bit halves of a data register.

*Condition Codes:*

| X | N | Z | V | C |
|---|---|---|---|---|
| - | * | * | 0 | 0 |

X   Not affected.
N   Set if the result is negative (MSB = 1). Cleared otherwise.
Z   Set if the 32-bit result is zero. Cleared otherwise.
V   Always cleared.
C   Always cleared.

*Instruction Format:*

| 15 | 14 | 13 | 12 | 11 | 10 | 9 | 8 | 7 | 6 | 5 | 4 | 3 | 2 | 1 | 0 |
|----|----|----|----|----|----|---|---|---|---|---|---|---|---|---|---|
| 0 | 1 | 0 | 0 | 1 | 0 | 0 | 0 | 0 | 1 | 0 | 0 | 0 | Data Register | | |

*Instruction Fields:*

Register field—specifies the data register to swap

# TAS    *Test and Set and Operand*    TAS

**Operation:**    destination is tested → CCR
1 → bit 7 of destination

**Assembler
Syntax:**    TAS <ea>

**Attributes:**    Size = Byte

**Description:**    Test and set the byte operand addressed by the effective address field. The current value of the operand is tested and N and Z are set accordingly. The high order bit of the operand is set. The operation is indivisible (using a read-modify-write memory cycle) to allow synchronization of several processors.

**Condition Codes:**

| X | N | Z | V | C |
|---|---|---|---|---|
| - | * | * | 0 | 0 |

X    Not affected.
N    Set if the most-significant bit of the operand is currently set. Cleared otherwise.
Z    Set if the operand is zero. Cleared otherwise.
V    Always cleared.
C    Always cleared.

**Instruction Format:**

| 15 | 14 | 13 | 12 | 11 | 10 | 9 | 8 | 7 | 6 | 5 | 4 | 3 | 2 | 1 | 0 |
|----|----|----|----|----|----|---|---|---|---|---|---|---|---|---|---|
| 0 | 1 | 0 | 0 | 1 | 0 | 1 | 0 | 1 | 1 | Effective Address |||||

| | | | | | | | | | | Mode ||| Register |||

**Instruction Fields:**

Effective Address field—Specifies the location of the tested operand. Only data alterable addressing modes are allowed, as shown:

| Addressing Mode | Mode | Register | Addressing Mode | Mode | Register |
|---|---|---|---|---|---|
| Dn | 000 | reg. number | xxx.W | 111 | 000 |
| An | - | - | xxx.L | 111 | 001 |
| (An) | 010 | reg. number | #data | - | - |
| (An)+ | 011 | reg. number | | | |
| −(An) | 100 | reg. number | | | |
| d16(An) | 101 | reg. number | d16(PC) | - | - |
| d8(An,Xn) | 110 | reg. number | d8(PC,Xn) | - | - |

---

**TRAP**                                  *Trap*                                  **TRAP**

*Operation:*    PC → -(SSP)
                SR → -(SSP)
                (vector) → PC

*Assembler*
*Syntax:*       TRAP #vector

*Attributes:*   Unsized

*Description:*  The processor initiates exception processing. The vector number is generated to reference the TRAP instruction exception vector specified by the low-order four bits of the instruction. Sixteen TRAP instruction vectors are available.

*Condition Codes:*

   Not affected

*Instruction Format:*

| 15 | 14 | 13 | 12 | 11 | 10 | 9 | 8 | 7 | 6 | 5 | 4 | 3 | 2 | 1 | 0 |
|----|----|----|----|----|----|---|---|---|---|---|---|---|---|---|---|
| 0  | 1  | 0  | 0  | 1  | 1  | 1 | 0 | 0 | 1 | 0 | 0 | Vector |

*Instruction Fields:*

   Vector field—Specifies the trap vector to be taken.

**TRAPV**                    *Trap on Overflow*                    **TRAPV**

*Operation:*     If V then TRAP

*Assembler*
*Syntax:*       TRAPV

*Attributes:*    Unsized

*Description:*  The processor initiates exception processing if the V bit is set. If the V bit is not set, the processor performs no operation and execution continues with the next address.

*Condition Codes:*

   Not affected

*Instruction Format:*

| 15 | 14 | 13 | 12 | 11 | 10 | 9 | 8 | 7 | 6 | 5 | 4 | 3 | 2 | 1 | 0 |
|----|----|----|----|----|----|---|---|---|---|---|---|---|---|---|---|
| 0  | 1  | 0  | 0  | 1  | 1  | 1 | 0 | 0 | 1 | 1 | 1 | 0 | 1 | 1 | 0 |

---

**TST**                          *Test an Operand*                          **TST**

*Operation:*   destination tested → CCR

*Assembler*
*Syntax:*   TST <ea>

*Attributes:*   Size = Byte, Word, Long

*Description:*   Compares the operand with zero. No results are saved; however, the condition codes are set according to results of the test.

*Condition Codes:*

| X | N | Z | V | C |
|---|---|---|---|---|
| - | * | * | 0 | 0 |

X   Not affected.
N   Set if the operand is negative (MSB = 1). Cleared otherwise.
Z   Set if the operand is zero. Cleared otherwise.
V   Always cleared.
C   Always cleared.

*Instruction Format:*

| 15 | 14 | 13 | 12 | 11 | 10 | 9 | 8 | 7 | 6 | 5 | 4 | 3 | 2 | 1 | 0 |
|----|----|----|----|----|----|---|---|---|---|---|---|---|---|---|---|
| 0 | 1 | 0 | 0 | 1 | 0 | 1 | 0 | Size | | Effective Address | | | | | |
| | | | | | | | | | | Mode | | | Register | | |

*Instruction Fields:*

Size field—Specifies the size of the operation:

   00 = byte

   01 = word

   10 = long

Effective Address field—Specifies the addressing mode for the destination operand. Only data addressing modes are allowed, as shown:

| Addressing Mode | Mode | Register | Addressing Mode | Mode | Register |
|---|---|---|---|---|---|
| Dn | 000 | reg. number | xxx.W | 111 | 000 |
| An | - | - | xxx.L | 111 | 001 |
| (An) | 010 | reg. number | #data | - | - |
| (An)+ | 011 | reg. number | | | |
| −(An) | 100 | reg. number | | | |
| d16(An) | 101 | reg. number | d16(PC) | 111 | 010 |
| d8(An,Xn) | 110 | reg. number | d8(PC,Xn) | 111 | 011 |

# UNLK

Unlink

**UNLK**

*Operation:* An → SP

(SP)+ → An

*Assembler*
*Syntax:* UNLK An

*Attributes:* Unsized

*Description:* The stack pointer is loaded from the specified address register. The address register is then loaded with the long word pulled from the top of the stack.

*Condition Codes:*

Not affected

*Instruction Format:*

| 15 | 14 | 13 | 12 | 11 | 10 | 9 | 8 | 7 | 6 | 5 | 4 | 3 | 2 | 1 | 0 |
|----|----|----|----|----|----|----|----|----|----|----|----|----|----|----|----|
| 0 | 1 | 0 | 0 | 1 | 1 | 1 | 0 | 0 | 1 | 0 | 1 | 1 | Address Register | | |

*Instruction Fields:*

Address Register field—Specifies the address register for the unlink operation.

# Appendix C

# Machine-Language Summary

This appendix provides a summary of the binary encoding (machine language) of the 68000's instruction set. The binary encoding was also given in Appendix B; however, the presentation was alphabetical by instruction mnenomic. This appendix presents the machine language instructions sorted numerically by the binary representation, thus facilitating dissassembly of binary codes into instruction mnemonics.

Table C-1 is an opcode map which illustrates how bits 15 through 12 specify operations. Table C-2 provides the encoding of the 16-bit Effective Address field which appears in many of the instructions in this appendix. Table C-3 provides the encoding of the 16-bit extension word, required when the addressing mode is address-register-indirect-with-index or program-counter-with-displacement (see Table C-2).

### Table C-1.   Opcode Map.

| Bits 15 through 12 | Operation | See Page |
|---|---|---|
| 0000 | Bit Manipulation/MOVEP/Immediate | 366 |
| 0001 | Move Byte | 368 |
| 0010 | Move Long | 368 |
| 0011 | Move Word | 368 |
| 0100 | Miscellaneous | 369 |
| 0101 | ADDQ/SUBQ/Scc/DBcc | 372 |
| 0110 | Bcc/BSR | 373 |
| 0111 | MOVEQ | 373 |
| 1000 | OR/DIV/SBCD | 373 |
| 1001 | SUB/SUBX | 374 |
| 1010 | (Unassigned) | – |
| 1011 | CMP/EOR | 375 |
| 1100 | AND/MUL/ABCD/EXG | 375 |
| 1101 | ADD/ADDX | 376 |
| 1110 | Shift/Rotate | 377 |
| 1111 | (Unassigned) | – |

### Table C-2.   Effective Address Encoding Summary.

| Addressing Mode | Mode Bits | Register Bits |
|---|---|---|
| Data Register Direct | 000 | register number |
| Address Register Direct | 001 | register number |
| Address Register Indirect | 010 | register number |
| Address Register Indirect with Postincrement | 011 | register number |
| Address Register Indirect with Predecrement | 100 | register number |
| Address Register Indirect with Displacement† | 101 | register number |
| Address Register Indirect with Index* | 110 | register number |
| Absolute Short† | 111 | 000 |
| Absolute Long†† | 111 | 001 |
| Program Counter with Displacement† | 111 | 010 |
| Program Counter with Index* | 111 | 011 |
| Immediate or Status Register††† | 111 | 100 |

† One extension word required
†† Two extension words required
††† For Immediate addressing, one or two extension words required depending on the size of the operation
* One extension word required; see Table C-3 in Appendix C for the encoding

## Table C-3.   Extension Word to Specify Index Register and Displacement.

| 15 | 14 | 13 | 12 | 11 | 10 | 9 | 8 | 7 | 6 | 5 | 4 | 3 | 2 | 1 | 0 |
|---|---|---|---|---|---|---|---|---|---|---|---|---|---|---|---|
| D/A | Register | | | W/L | 0 | 0 | 0 | Displacement Integer | | | | | | | |

D/A field:
    0 = use a data register as the index
    1 = use an address register as the index
Register field:
    register number
W/L field:
    0 = sign-extended, low order word integer in index register
    1 = long value in index register
Displacement Integer Field:
    8-bit signed offset, sign-extended to 32 bits

## OR Immediate

| 15 | 14 | 13 | 12 | 11 | 10 | 9 | 8 | 7 | 6 | 5 | 4 | 3 | 2 | 1 | 0 |
|---|---|---|---|---|---|---|---|---|---|---|---|---|---|---|---|
| 0 | 0 | 0 | 0 | 0 | 0 | 0 | 0 | Size | | Effective Address | | | | | |
| | | | | | | | | | | Mode | | | Register | | |

Size field:
    00 = byte
    01 = word
    10 = longword

## OR Immediate to CCR

| 15 | 14 | 13 | 12 | 11 | 10 | 9 | 8 | 7 | 6 | 5 | 4 | 3 | 2 | 1 | 0 |
|---|---|---|---|---|---|---|---|---|---|---|---|---|---|---|---|
| 0 | 0 | 0 | 0 | 0 | 0 | 0 | 0 | 0 | 0 | 1 | 1 | 1 | 1 | 0 | 0 |

## OR Immediate to SR

| 15 | 14 | 13 | 12 | 11 | 10 | 9 | 8 | 7 | 6 | 5 | 4 | 3 | 2 | 1 | 0 |
|---|---|---|---|---|---|---|---|---|---|---|---|---|---|---|---|
| 0 | 0 | 0 | 0 | 0 | 0 | 0 | 0 | 0 | 1 | 1 | 1 | 1 | 1 | 0 | 0 |

## Dynamic Bit

| 15 | 14 | 13 | 12 | 11 | 10 | 9 | 8 | 7 | 6 | 5 | 4 | 3 | 2 | 1 | 0 |
|---|---|---|---|---|---|---|---|---|---|---|---|---|---|---|---|
| 0 | 0 | 0 | 0 | Data Register | | | 1 | Type | | Effective Address | | | | | |
| | | | | | | | | | | Mode | | | Register | | |

Type field:
    00 = TST
    01 = CHG
    10 = CLR
    11 = SET

## MOVEP

| 15 | 14 | 13 | 12 | 11 | 10 | 9 | 8 | 7 | 6 | 5 | 4 | 3 | 2 | 1 | 0 |
|---|---|---|---|---|---|---|---|---|---|---|---|---|---|---|---|
| 0 | 0 | 0 | 0 | Data Register | | | Op-mode | | | 0 | 0 | 1 | Address Register | | |

Op-mode field:
    100 = transfer word from memory to register
    101 = transfer longword from memory to register
    110 = transfer word from register to memory
    111 = transfer longword from register to memory

## AND Immediate

| 15 | 14 | 13 | 12 | 11 | 10 | 9 | 8 | 7 | 6 | 5 | 4 | 3 | 2 | 1 | 0 |
|----|----|----|----|----|----|---|---|---|---|---|---|---|---|---|---|
| 0 | 0 | 0 | 0 | 0 | 0 | 1 | 0 | Size | | Effective Address | | | | | |
| | | | | | | | | | | Mode | | | Register | | |

Size field:
  00 = byte
  01 = word
  10 = longword

## AND Immediate to CCR

| 15 | 14 | 13 | 12 | 11 | 10 | 9 | 8 | 7 | 6 | 5 | 4 | 3 | 2 | 1 | 0 |
|----|----|----|----|----|----|---|---|---|---|---|---|---|---|---|---|
| 0 | 0 | 0 | 0 | 0 | 0 | 1 | 0 | 0 | 0 | 1 | 1 | 1 | 1 | 0 | 0 |

## AND Immediate to SR

| 15 | 14 | 13 | 12 | 11 | 10 | 9 | 8 | 7 | 6 | 5 | 4 | 3 | 2 | 1 | 0 |
|----|----|----|----|----|----|---|---|---|---|---|---|---|---|---|---|
| 0 | 0 | 0 | 0 | 0 | 0 | 1 | 0 | 0 | 1 | 1 | 1 | 1 | 1 | 0 | 0 |

## SUB Immediate

| 15 | 14 | 13 | 12 | 11 | 10 | 9 | 8 | 7 | 6 | 5 | 4 | 3 | 2 | 1 | 0 |
|----|----|----|----|----|----|---|---|---|---|---|---|---|---|---|---|
| 0 | 0 | 0 | 0 | 0 | 1 | 0 | 0 | Size | | Effective Address | | | | | |
| | | | | | | | | | | Mode | | | Register | | |

Size field:
  00 = byte
  01 = word
  10 = longword

## ADD Immediate

| 15 | 14 | 13 | 12 | 11 | 10 | 9 | 8 | 7 | 6 | 5 | 4 | 3 | 2 | 1 | 0 |
|----|----|----|----|----|----|---|---|---|---|---|---|---|---|---|---|
| 0 | 0 | 0 | 0 | 0 | 1 | 1 | 0 | Size | | Effective Address | | | | | |
| | | | | | | | | | | Mode | | | Register | | |

Size field:
  00 = byte
  01 = word
  10 = longword

## Static Bit

| 15 | 14 | 13 | 12 | 11 | 10 | 9 | 8 | 7 | 6 | 5 | 4 | 3 | 2 | 1 | 0 |
|----|----|----|----|----|----|---|---|---|---|---|---|---|---|---|---|
| 0 | 0 | 0 | 0 | 1 | 0 | 0 | 0 | Type | | Effective Address | | | | | |
| | | | | | | | | | | Mode | | | Register | | |

Type field:
  00 = TST
  01 = CHG
  10 = CLR
  11 = SET

## EOR Immediate

| 15 | 14 | 13 | 12 | 11 | 10 | 9 | 8 | 7 | 6 | 5 | 4 | 3 | 2 | 1 | 0 |
|----|----|----|----|----|----|----|----|----|----|----|----|----|----|----|----|
| 0 | 0 | 0 | 0 | 1 | 0 | 1 | 0 | Size | | Effective Address | | | | | |
| | | | | | | | | | | Mode | | | Register | | |

Size field:
00 = byte
01 = word
10 = longword

## EOR Immediate to CCR

| 15 | 14 | 13 | 12 | 11 | 10 | 9 | 8 | 7 | 6 | 5 | 4 | 3 | 2 | 1 | 0 |
|----|----|----|----|----|----|----|----|----|----|----|----|----|----|----|----|
| 0 | 0 | 0 | 0 | 1 | 0 | 1 | 0 | 0 | 0 | 1 | 1 | 1 | 1 | 0 | 0 |

## EOR Immediate to SR

| 15 | 14 | 13 | 12 | 11 | 10 | 9 | 8 | 7 | 6 | 5 | 4 | 3 | 2 | 1 | 0 |
|----|----|----|----|----|----|----|----|----|----|----|----|----|----|----|----|
| 0 | 0 | 0 | 0 | 1 | 0 | 1 | 0 | 0 | 1 | 1 | 1 | 1 | 1 | 0 | 0 |

## CMP Immediate

| 15 | 14 | 13 | 12 | 11 | 10 | 9 | 8 | 7 | 6 | 5 | 4 | 3 | 2 | 1 | 0 |
|----|----|----|----|----|----|----|----|----|----|----|----|----|----|----|----|
| 0 | 0 | 0 | 0 | 1 | 1 | 0 | 0 | Size | | Effective Address | | | | | |
| | | | | | | | | | | Mode | | | Register | | |

Size field:
00 = byte
01 = word
10 = longword

## MOVE Byte

| 15 | 14 | 13 | 12 | 11 | 10 | 9 | 8 | 7 | 6 | 5 | 4 | 3 | 2 | 1 | 0 |
|----|----|----|----|----|----|----|----|----|----|----|----|----|----|----|----|
| 0 | 0 | 0 | 1 | Destination EA | | | | | | Source EA | | | | | |
| | | | | Register | | | | | | Mode | | | Mode | | |

Note register and mode locations.

## MOVEA Long

| 15 | 14 | 13 | 12 | 11 | 10 | 9 | 8 | 7 | 6 | 5 | 4 | 3 | 2 | 1 | 0 |
|----|----|----|----|----|----|----|----|----|----|----|----|----|----|----|----|
| 0 | 0 | 1 | 0 | Destination | | | 0 | 0 | 1 | Source EA | | | | | |
| | | | | Register | | | | | | Mode | | | Register | | |

## MOVE Long

| 15 | 14 | 13 | 12 | 11 | 10 | 9 | 8 | 7 | 6 | 5 | 4 | 3 | 2 | 1 | 0 |
|----|----|----|----|----|----|----|----|----|----|----|----|----|----|----|----|
| 0 | 0 | 1 | 0 | Destination EA | | | | | | Source EA | | | | | |
| | | | | Register | | | Mode | | | Mode | | | Register | | |

Note register and mode locations.

## MOVEA Word

| 15 | 14 | 13 | 12 | 11 | 10 | 9 | 8 | 7 | 6 | 5 | 4 | 3 | 2 | 1 | 0 |
|----|----|----|----|----|----|----|----|----|----|----|----|----|----|----|----|
| 0 | 0 | 1 | 1 | Destination | | | 0 | 0 | 1 | Source EA | | | | | |
| | | | | Register | | | | | | Mode | | | Register | | |

### MOVE Word

| 15 | 14 | 13 | 12 | 11 | 10 | 9 | 8 | 7 | 6 | 5 | 4 | 3 | 2 | 1 | 0 |
|---|---|---|---|---|---|---|---|---|---|---|---|---|---|---|---|
| 0 | 0 | 1 | 1 | Destination EA | | | | | | Source EA | | | | | |

Destination EA: Register | Mode.  Source EA: Mode | Register.

Note register and mode locations.

### NEGX

| 15 | 14 | 13 | 12 | 11 | 10 | 9 | 8 | 7 | 6 | 5 | 4 | 3 | 2 | 1 | 0 |
|---|---|---|---|---|---|---|---|---|---|---|---|---|---|---|---|
| 0 | 1 | 0 | 0 | 0 | 0 | 0 | 0 | Size | | Effective Address (Mode / Register) | | | | | |

Size field:
  00 = byte
  01 = word
  10 = longword

### MOVE from SR

| 15 | 14 | 13 | 12 | 11 | 10 | 9 | 8 | 7 | 6 | 5 | 4 | 3 | 2 | 1 | 0 |
|---|---|---|---|---|---|---|---|---|---|---|---|---|---|---|---|
| 0 | 1 | 0 | 0 | 0 | 0 | 0 | 0 | 1 | 1 | Effective Address (Mode / Register) | | | | | |

### CHK

| 15 | 14 | 13 | 12 | 11 | 10 | 9 | 8 | 7 | 6 | 5 | 4 | 3 | 2 | 1 | 0 |
|---|---|---|---|---|---|---|---|---|---|---|---|---|---|---|---|
| 0 | 1 | 0 | 0 | Data Register | | | 1 | 1 | 0 | Effective Address (Mode / Register) | | | | | |

### LEA

| 15 | 14 | 13 | 12 | 11 | 10 | 9 | 8 | 7 | 6 | 5 | 4 | 3 | 2 | 1 | 0 |
|---|---|---|---|---|---|---|---|---|---|---|---|---|---|---|---|
| 0 | 1 | 0 | 0 | Address Register | | | 1 | 1 | 1 | Effective Address (Mode / Register) | | | | | |

### CLR

| 15 | 14 | 13 | 12 | 11 | 10 | 9 | 8 | 7 | 6 | 5 | 4 | 3 | 2 | 1 | 0 |
|---|---|---|---|---|---|---|---|---|---|---|---|---|---|---|---|
| 0 | 1 | 0 | 0 | 0 | 0 | 1 | 0 | Size | | Effective Address (Mode / Register) | | | | | |

Size field:
  00 = byte
  01 = word
  10 = longword

### NEG

| 15 | 14 | 13 | 12 | 11 | 10 | 9 | 8 | 7 | 6 | 5 | 4 | 3 | 2 | 1 | 0 |
|---|---|---|---|---|---|---|---|---|---|---|---|---|---|---|---|
| 0 | 1 | 0 | 0 | 0 | 1 | 0 | 0 | Size | | Effective Address (Mode / Register) | | | | | |

Size field:
  00 = byte
  01 = word
  10 = longword

### MOVE to CCR

| 15 | 14 | 13 | 12 | 11 | 10 | 9 | 8 | 7 | 6 | 5 | 4 | 3 | 2 | 1 | 0 |
|---|---|---|---|---|---|---|---|---|---|---|---|---|---|---|---|
| 0 | 1 | 0 | 0 | 0 | 1 | 0 | 0 | 1 | 1 | Effective Address (Mode / Register) | | | | | |

## *NOT*

| 15 | 14 | 13 | 12 | 11 | 10 | 9 | 8 | 7 | 6 | 5 | 4 | 3 | 2 | 1 | 0 |
|----|----|----|----|----|----|---|---|---|---|---|---|---|---|---|---|
| 0 | 1 | 0 | 0 | 0 | 1 | 1 | 0 | Size | | Effective Address | | | | | |
| | | | | | | | | | | Mode | | | Register | | |

Size field:
  00 = byte
  01 = word
  10 = longword

## *MOVE to SR*

| 15 | 14 | 13 | 12 | 11 | 10 | 9 | 8 | 7 | 6 | 5 | 4 | 3 | 2 | 1 | 0 |
|----|----|----|----|----|----|---|---|---|---|---|---|---|---|---|---|
| 0 | 1 | 0 | 0 | 0 | 1 | 1 | 0 | 1 | 1 | Effective Address | | | | | |
| | | | | | | | | | | Mode | | | Register | | |

## *NBCD*

| 15 | 14 | 13 | 12 | 11 | 10 | 9 | 8 | 7 | 6 | 5 | 4 | 3 | 2 | 1 | 0 |
|----|----|----|----|----|----|---|---|---|---|---|---|---|---|---|---|
| 0 | 1 | 0 | 0 | 1 | 0 | 0 | 0 | 0 | 0 | Effective Address | | | | | |
| | | | | | | | | | | Mode | | | Register | | |

## *SWAP*

| 15 | 14 | 13 | 12 | 11 | 10 | 9 | 8 | 7 | 6 | 5 | 4 | 3 | 2 | 1 | 0 |
|----|----|----|----|----|----|---|---|---|---|---|---|---|---|---|---|
| 0 | 1 | 0 | 0 | 1 | 0 | 0 | 0 | 0 | 1 | 0 | 0 | 0 | Data | | |
| | | | | | | | | | | | | | Register | | |

## *PEA*

| 15 | 14 | 13 | 12 | 11 | 10 | 9 | 8 | 7 | 6 | 5 | 4 | 3 | 2 | 1 | 0 |
|----|----|----|----|----|----|---|---|---|---|---|---|---|---|---|---|
| 0 | 1 | 0 | 0 | 1 | 0 | 0 | 0 | 0 | 1 | Effective Address | | | | | |
| | | | | | | | | | | Mode | | | Register | | |

## *EXT Word*

| 15 | 14 | 13 | 12 | 11 | 10 | 9 | 8 | 7 | 6 | 5 | 4 | 3 | 2 | 1 | 0 |
|----|----|----|----|----|----|---|---|---|---|---|---|---|---|---|---|
| 0 | 1 | 0 | 0 | 1 | 0 | 0 | 0 | 1 | 0 | 0 | 0 | 0 | Data | | |
| | | | | | | | | | | | | | Register | | |

## *MOVEM*

| 15 | 14 | 13 | 12 | 11 | 10 | 9 | 8 | 7 | 6 | 5 | 4 | 3 | 2 | 1 | 0 |
|----|----|----|----|----|----|---|---|---|---|---|---|---|---|---|---|
| 0 | 1 | 0 | 0 | 1 | dr | 0 | 0 | 1 | Sz | Effective Address | | | | | |
| | | | | | | | | | | Mode | | | Register | | |

dr field:
  0 = register to memory
  1 = memory to register
Sz field:
  0 = word transfer
  1 = long transfer
Second instruction word contains Register List Mask, as follows:
  Register to memory: D0...D7 A0...A7
  Memory to register: A7...A0 D7...D0
  Register identified by LSB is transferred first

## *EXT Long*

| 15 | 14 | 13 | 12 | 11 | 10 | 9 | 8 | 7 | 6 | 5 | 4 | 3 | 2 | 1 | 0 |
|----|----|----|----|----|----|---|---|---|---|---|---|---|---|---|---|
| 0 | 1 | 0 | 0 | 1 | 0 | 0 | 0 | 1 | 1 | 0 | 0 | 0 | Data | | |
| | | | | | | | | | | | | | Register | | |

**TST**

| 15 | 14 | 13 | 12 | 11 | 10 | 9 | 8 | 7 | 6 | 5 | 4 | 3 | 2 | 1 | 0 |
|----|----|----|----|----|----|---|---|---|---|---|---|---|---|---|---|
| 0 | 1 | 0 | 0 | 1 | 0 | 1 | 0 | Size | | Effective Address | | | | | |
| | | | | | | | | | | Mode | | | Register | | |

Size field:
  00 = byte
  01 = word
  10 = longword

**TAS**

| 15 | 14 | 13 | 12 | 11 | 10 | 9 | 8 | 7 | 6 | 5 | 4 | 3 | 2 | 1 | 0 |
|----|----|----|----|----|----|---|---|---|---|---|---|---|---|---|---|
| 0 | 1 | 0 | 0 | 1 | 0 | 1 | 0 | 1 | 1 | Effective Address | | | | | |
| | | | | | | | | | | Mode | | | Register | | |

**ILLEGAL**

| 15 | 14 | 13 | 12 | 11 | 10 | 9 | 8 | 7 | 6 | 5 | 4 | 3 | 2 | 1 | 0 |
|----|----|----|----|----|----|---|---|---|---|---|---|---|---|---|---|
| 0 | 1 | 0 | 0 | 1 | 0 | 1 | 0 | 1 | 1 | 1 | 1 | 1 | 1 | 0 | 0 |

**TRAP**

| 15 | 14 | 13 | 12 | 11 | 10 | 9 | 8 | 7 | 6 | 5 | 4 | 3 | 2 | 1 | 0 |
|----|----|----|----|----|----|---|---|---|---|---|---|---|---|---|---|
| 0 | 1 | 0 | 0 | 1 | 1 | 1 | 0 | 0 | 1 | 0 | 0 | Vector | | | |

**LINK**

| 15 | 14 | 13 | 12 | 11 | 10 | 9 | 8 | 7 | 6 | 5 | 4 | 3 | 2 | 1 | 0 |
|----|----|----|----|----|----|---|---|---|---|---|---|---|---|---|---|
| 0 | 1 | 0 | 0 | 1 | 1 | 1 | 0 | 0 | 1 | 0 | 1 | 0 | Address Register | | |

**UNLK**

| 15 | 14 | 13 | 12 | 11 | 10 | 9 | 8 | 7 | 6 | 5 | 4 | 3 | 2 | 1 | 0 |
|----|----|----|----|----|----|---|---|---|---|---|---|---|---|---|---|
| 0 | 1 | 0 | 0 | 1 | 1 | 1 | 0 | 0 | 1 | 0 | 1 | 1 | Address Register | | |

**MOVE to USP**

| 15 | 14 | 13 | 12 | 11 | 10 | 9 | 8 | 7 | 6 | 5 | 4 | 3 | 2 | 1 | 0 |
|----|----|----|----|----|----|---|---|---|---|---|---|---|---|---|---|
| 0 | 1 | 0 | 0 | 1 | 1 | 1 | 0 | 0 | 1 | 1 | 0 | 0 | Address Register | | |

**MOVE from USP**

| 15 | 14 | 13 | 12 | 11 | 10 | 9 | 8 | 7 | 6 | 5 | 4 | 3 | 2 | 1 | 0 |
|----|----|----|----|----|----|---|---|---|---|---|---|---|---|---|---|
| 0 | 1 | 0 | 0 | 1 | 1 | 1 | 0 | 0 | 1 | 1 | 0 | 1 | Address Register | | |

**RESET**

| 15 | 14 | 13 | 12 | 11 | 10 | 9 | 8 | 7 | 6 | 5 | 4 | 3 | 2 | 1 | 0 |
|----|----|----|----|----|----|---|---|---|---|---|---|---|---|---|---|
| 0 | 1 | 0 | 0 | 1 | 1 | 1 | 0 | 0 | 1 | 1 | 1 | 0 | 0 | 0 | 0 |

**NOP**

| 15 | 14 | 13 | 12 | 11 | 10 | 9 | 8 | 7 | 6 | 5 | 4 | 3 | 2 | 1 | 0 |
|----|----|----|----|----|----|---|---|---|---|---|---|---|---|---|---|
| 0 | 1 | 0 | 0 | 1 | 1 | 1 | 0 | 0 | 1 | 1 | 1 | 0 | 0 | 0 | 1 |

### STOP

| 15 | 14 | 13 | 12 | 11 | 10 | 9 | 8 | 7 | 6 | 5 | 4 | 3 | 2 | 1 | 0 |
|---|---|---|---|---|---|---|---|---|---|---|---|---|---|---|---|
| 0 | 1 | 0 | 0 | 1 | 1 | 1 | 0 | 0 | 1 | 1 | 1 | 0 | 0 | 1 | 0 |

### RTE

| 15 | 14 | 13 | 12 | 11 | 10 | 9 | 8 | 7 | 6 | 5 | 4 | 3 | 2 | 1 | 0 |
|---|---|---|---|---|---|---|---|---|---|---|---|---|---|---|---|
| 0 | 1 | 0 | 0 | 1 | 1 | 1 | 0 | 0 | 1 | 1 | 1 | 0 | 0 | 1 | 1 |

### RTS

| 15 | 14 | 13 | 12 | 11 | 10 | 9 | 8 | 7 | 6 | 5 | 4 | 3 | 2 | 1 | 0 |
|---|---|---|---|---|---|---|---|---|---|---|---|---|---|---|---|
| 0 | 1 | 0 | 0 | 1 | 1 | 1 | 0 | 0 | 1 | 1 | 1 | 0 | 1 | 0 | 1 |

### TRAPV

| 15 | 14 | 13 | 12 | 11 | 10 | 9 | 8 | 7 | 6 | 5 | 4 | 3 | 2 | 1 | 0 |
|---|---|---|---|---|---|---|---|---|---|---|---|---|---|---|---|
| 0 | 1 | 0 | 0 | 1 | 1 | 1 | 0 | 0 | 1 | 1 | 1 | 0 | 1 | 1 | 0 |

### RTR

| 15 | 14 | 13 | 12 | 11 | 10 | 9 | 8 | 7 | 6 | 5 | 4 | 3 | 2 | 1 | 0 |
|---|---|---|---|---|---|---|---|---|---|---|---|---|---|---|---|
| 0 | 1 | 0 | 0 | 1 | 1 | 1 | 0 | 0 | 1 | 1 | 1 | 0 | 1 | 1 | 1 |

### JSR

| 15 | 14 | 13 | 12 | 11 | 10 | 9 | 8 | 7 | 6 | 5 | 4 | 3 | 2 | 1 | 0 |
|---|---|---|---|---|---|---|---|---|---|---|---|---|---|---|---|
| 0 | 1 | 0 | 0 | 1 | 1 | 1 | 0 | 1 | 0 | Effective Address Mode | | | Register | | |

### JMP

| 15 | 14 | 13 | 12 | 11 | 10 | 9 | 8 | 7 | 6 | 5 | 4 | 3 | 2 | 1 | 0 |
|---|---|---|---|---|---|---|---|---|---|---|---|---|---|---|---|
| 0 | 1 | 0 | 0 | 1 | 1 | 1 | 0 | 1 | 1 | Effective Address Mode | | | Register | | |

### ADDQ

| 15 | 14 | 13 | 12 | 11 | 10 | 9 | 8 | 7 | 6 | 5 | 4 | 3 | 2 | 1 | 0 |
|---|---|---|---|---|---|---|---|---|---|---|---|---|---|---|---|
| 0 | 1 | 0 | 1 | Data | | | 0 | Size | | Effective Address Mode | | | Register | | |

Data field:
    Three bits of immediate data, 0, 1–7, representing a range of 8, 1 to 7 respectively
Size field:
    00 = byte
    01 = word
    10 = longword

### Scc

| 15 | 14 | 13 | 12 | 11 | 10 | 9 | 8 | 7 | 6 | 5 | 4 | 3 | 2 | 1 | 0 |
|---|---|---|---|---|---|---|---|---|---|---|---|---|---|---|---|
| 0 | 1 | 0 | 1 | Condition† | | | | 1 | 1 | Effective Address Mode | | | Register | | |

† See Table A-2, page 263.

*DBcc*

| 15 | 14 | 13 | 12 | 11 | 10 | 9 | 8 | 7 | 6 | 5 | 4 | 3 | 2 | 1 | 0 |
|---|---|---|---|---|---|---|---|---|---|---|---|---|---|---|---|
| 0 | 1 | 0 | 1 | Condition† | | | | 1 | 1 | 0 | 0 | 1 | Data Register | | |

† See Table A-2, page 263.

*SUBQ*

| 15 | 14 | 13 | 12 | 11 | 10 | 9 | 8 | 7 | 6 | 5 | 4 | 3 | 2 | 1 | 0 |
|---|---|---|---|---|---|---|---|---|---|---|---|---|---|---|---|
| 0 | 1 | 0 | 1 | Data | | | 1 | Size | | Effective Address | | | | | |
| | | | | | | | | | | Mode | | | Register | | |

Data field:
  Three bits of immediate data, 0, 1–7, representing a range of 8, 1 to 7 respectively
Size field:
  00 = byte
  01 = word
  10 = longword

*Bcc*

| 15 | 14 | 13 | 12 | 11 | 10 | 9 | 8 | 7 | 6 | 5 | 4 | 3 | 2 | 1 | 0 |
|---|---|---|---|---|---|---|---|---|---|---|---|---|---|---|---|
| 0 | 1 | 1 | 0 | Condition† | | | | 8-Bit Displacement | | | | | | | |

† See Table A-2, page 263.

*BRA*

| 15 | 14 | 13 | 12 | 11 | 10 | 9 | 8 | 7 | 6 | 5 | 4 | 3 | 2 | 1 | 0 |
|---|---|---|---|---|---|---|---|---|---|---|---|---|---|---|---|
| 0 | 1 | 1 | 0 | 0 | 0 | 0 | 0 | 8-Bit Displacement | | | | | | | |

*BSR*

| 15 | 14 | 13 | 12 | 11 | 10 | 9 | 8 | 7 | 6 | 5 | 4 | 3 | 2 | 1 | 0 |
|---|---|---|---|---|---|---|---|---|---|---|---|---|---|---|---|
| 0 | 1 | 1 | 0 | 0 | 0 | 0 | 1 | 8-Bit Displacement | | | | | | | |

*MOVEQ*

| 15 | 14 | 13 | 12 | 11 | 10 | 9 | 8 | 7 | 6 | 5 | 4 | 3 | 2 | 1 | 0 |
|---|---|---|---|---|---|---|---|---|---|---|---|---|---|---|---|
| 0 | 1 | 1 | 1 | Data Register | | | 0 | Data | | | | | | | |

Data field:
  Data are sign-extended to a long operand and all 32 bits are transferred to the data register

*OR*

| 15 | 14 | 13 | 12 | 11 | 10 | 9 | 8 | 7 | 6 | 5 | 4 | 3 | 2 | 1 | 0 |
|---|---|---|---|---|---|---|---|---|---|---|---|---|---|---|---|
| 1 | 0 | 0 | 0 | Data Register | | | Op-mode | | | Effective Address | | | | | |
| | | | | | | | | | | Mode | | | Register | | |

Op-mode field:

| Byte | Word | Long | Operation |
|---|---|---|---|
| 000 | 001 | 010 | <ea> OR <Dn>→<Dn> |
| 100 | 101 | 110 | <Dn> OR <ea> →<ea> |

## *DIVU*

| 15 | 14 | 13 | 12 | 11 | 10 | 9 | 8 | 7 | 6 | 5 | 4 | 3 | 2 | 1 | 0 |
|---|---|---|---|---|---|---|---|---|---|---|---|---|---|---|---|
| 1 | 0 | 0 | 0 | Data Register | | | 0 | 1 | 1 | Effective Address | | | | | |
| | | | | | | | | | | Mode | | | Register | | |

## *SBCD*

| 15 | 14 | 13 | 12 | 11 | 10 | 9 | 8 | 7 | 6 | 5 | 4 | 3 | 2 | 1 | 0 |
|---|---|---|---|---|---|---|---|---|---|---|---|---|---|---|---|
| 1 | 0 | 0 | 0 | Destination Register* | | | 1 | 0 | 0 | 0 | 0 | R/M | Source Register* | | |

R/M field:

    0 = data register to data register

    1 = memory to memory

\* if R/M = 0, specifies a data register

    if R/M = 1, specifies an address register for the predecrement addressing mode.

## *DIVS*

| 15 | 14 | 13 | 12 | 11 | 10 | 9 | 8 | 7 | 6 | 5 | 4 | 3 | 2 | 1 | 0 |
|---|---|---|---|---|---|---|---|---|---|---|---|---|---|---|---|
| 1 | 0 | 0 | 0 | Data Register | | | 1 | 1 | 1 | Effective Address | | | | | |
| | | | | | | | | | | Mode | | | Register | | |

## *SUB*

| 15 | 14 | 13 | 12 | 11 | 10 | 9 | 8 | 7 | 6 | 5 | 4 | 3 | 2 | 1 | 0 |
|---|---|---|---|---|---|---|---|---|---|---|---|---|---|---|---|
| 1 | 0 | 0 | 1 | Data Register | | | Op-mode | | | Effective Address | | | | | |
| | | | | | | | | | | Mode | | | Register | | |

Op-mode field:

| Byte | Word | Long | Operation |
|---|---|---|---|
| 000 | 001 | 010 | <Dn>-<ea> → <Dn> |
| 100 | 101 | 110 | <ea>-<Dn> → <ea> |

## *SUBA*

| 15 | 14 | 13 | 12 | 11 | 10 | 9 | 8 | 7 | 6 | 5 | 4 | 3 | 2 | 1 | 0 |
|---|---|---|---|---|---|---|---|---|---|---|---|---|---|---|---|
| 1 | 0 | 0 | 1 | Address Register | | | Op-mode | | | Effective Address | | | | | |
| | | | | | | | | | | Mode | | | Register | | |

Op-mode field:

| Word | Long | Operation |
|---|---|---|
| 011 | 111 | (<ea>)-(<An>) → An |

## *SUBX*

| 15 | 14 | 13 | 12 | 11 | 10 | 9 | 8 | 7 | 6 | 5 | 4 | 3 | 2 | 1 | 0 |
|---|---|---|---|---|---|---|---|---|---|---|---|---|---|---|---|
| 1 | 0 | 0 | 1 | Destination Register* | | | 1 | Size | | 0 | 0 | R/M | Source Register* | | |

Size field:

    00 = byte

    01 = word

    10 = longword

R/M field:

    0 = data register to data register

    1 = memory to memory

\* if R/M = 0, specifies a data register

    if R/M = 1, specifies an address register for the predecrement addressing mode.

## CMP

| 15 | 14 | 13 | 12 | 11 | 10 | 9 | 8 | 7 | 6 | 5 | 4 | 3 | 2 | 1 | 0 |
|----|----|----|----|----|----|----|----|----|----|----|----|----|----|----|----|
| 1 | 0 | 1 | 1 | Data Register | | | Op-mode | | | Effective Address | | | | | |
| | | | | | | | | | | Mode | | | Register | | |

Op-mode field:

| Byte | Word | Long | Operation |
|------|------|------|-----------|
| 000 | 001 | 010 | \<Dn>→\<ea> |

## CMPA

| 15 | 14 | 13 | 12 | 11 | 10 | 9 | 8 | 7 | 6 | 5 | 4 | 3 | 2 | 1 | 0 |
|----|----|----|----|----|----|----|----|----|----|----|----|----|----|----|----|
| 1 | 0 | 1 | 1 | Address Register | | | Op-mode | | | Effective Address | | | | | |
| | | | | | | | | | | Mode | | | Register | | |

Op-mode field:

| Word | Long | Operation |
|------|------|-----------|
| 011 | 111 | \<ea>-\<An> |

## EOR

| 15 | 14 | 13 | 12 | 11 | 10 | 9 | 8 | 7 | 6 | 5 | 4 | 3 | 2 | 1 | 0 |
|----|----|----|----|----|----|----|----|----|----|----|----|----|----|----|----|
| 1 | 0 | 1 | 1 | Data Register | | | Op-mode | | | Effective Address | | | | | |
| | | | | | | | | | | Mode | | | Register | | |

Op-mode field:

| Byte | Word | Long | Operation |
|------|------|------|-----------|
| 100 | 101 | 110 | \<ea> EXOR \<Dn>→\<ea> |

## CMPM

| 15 | 14 | 13 | 12 | 11 | 10 | 9 | 8 | 7 | 6 | 5 | 4 | 3 | 2 | 1 | 0 |
|----|----|----|----|----|----|----|----|----|----|----|----|----|----|----|----|
| 1 | 0 | 1 | 1 | Destination Register | | | 1 | Size | | 0 | 0 | 1 | Source Register | | |

Size field:
- 00 = byte
- 01 = word
- 10 = longword

## AND

| 15 | 14 | 13 | 12 | 11 | 10 | 9 | 8 | 7 | 6 | 5 | 4 | 3 | 2 | 1 | 0 |
|----|----|----|----|----|----|----|----|----|----|----|----|----|----|----|----|
| 1 | 1 | 0 | 0 | Data Register | | | Op-mode | | | Effective Address | | | | | |
| | | | | | | | | | | Mode | | | Register | | |

Op-mode field:

| Byte | Word | Long | Operation |
|------|------|------|-----------|
| 000 | 001 | 010 | \<ea> AND \<Dn>→\<Dn> |
| 100 | 101 | 110 | \<Dn> AND \<ea>→\<ea> |

## MULU

| 15 | 14 | 13 | 12 | 11 | 10 | 9 | 8 | 7 | 6 | 5 | 4 | 3 | 2 | 1 | 0 |
|----|----|----|----|----|----|----|----|----|----|----|----|----|----|----|----|
| 1 | 1 | 0 | 0 | Data Register | | | 0 | 1 | 1 | Effective Address | | | | | |
| | | | | | | | | | | Mode | | | Register | | |

## ABCD

| 15 | 14 | 13 | 12 | 11 | 10 | 9 | 8 | 7 | 6 | 5 | 4 | 3 | 2 | 1 | 0 |
|----|----|----|----|----|----|----|----|----|----|----|----|----|----|----|----|
| 1 | 1 | 0 | 0 | Destination Register | | | 1 | 0 | 0 | 0 | 0 | R/M | Source Register* | | |

R/M field:

0 = data register to data register

1 = memory to memory

* if R/M = 0, specifies a data register

if R/M = 1, specifies an address register for the predecrement addressing mode.

## EXG Data Registers

| 15 | 14 | 13 | 12 | 11 10 9 | 8 | 7 | 6 | 5 | 4 | 3 | 2 1 0 |
|----|----|----|----|---------|---|---|---|---|---|---|-------|
| 1 | 1 | 0 | 0 | Data Register | 1 | 0 | 1 | 0 | 0 | 0 | Data Register |

## EXG Address Registers

| 15 | 14 | 13 | 12 | 11 10 9 | 8 | 7 | 6 | 5 | 4 | 3 | 2 1 0 |
|----|----|----|----|---------|---|---|---|---|---|---|-------|
| 1 | 1 | 0 | 0 | Address Register | 1 | 0 | 1 | 0 | 0 | 1 | Address Register |

## EXG Data Register and Address Register

| 15 | 14 | 13 | 12 | 11 10 9 | 8 | 7 | 6 | 5 | 4 | 3 | 2 1 0 |
|----|----|----|----|---------|---|---|---|---|---|---|-------|
| 1 | 1 | 0 | 0 | Data Register | 1 | 1 | 0 | 0 | 0 | 1 | Address Register |

## MULS

| 15 | 14 | 13 | 12 | 11 10 9 | 8 | 7 | 6 | 5 4 3 | 2 1 0 |
|----|----|----|----|---------|---|---|---|-------|-------|
| 1 | 1 | 0 | 0 | Data Register | 1 | 1 | 1 | Effective Address Mode | Register |

## ADD

| 15 | 14 | 13 | 12 | 11 10 9 | 8 7 6 | 5 4 3 | 2 1 0 |
|----|----|----|----|---------|-------|-------|-------|
| 1 | 1 | 0 | 1 | Data Register | Op-mode | Effective Address Mode | Register |

Op-mode field:

| Byte | Word | Long | Operation |
|------|------|------|-----------|
| 000 | 001 | 010 | <ea>+<Dn>→<Dn> |
| 100 | 101 | 110 | <Dn>+<ea>→<ea> |

## ADDA

| 15 | 14 | 13 | 12 | 11 10 9 | 8 7 6 | 5 4 3 | 2 1 0 |
|----|----|----|----|---------|-------|-------|-------|
| 1 | 1 | 0 | 1 | Address Register | Op-mode | Effective Address Mode | Register |

Op-mode field:

| Word | Long | Operation |
|------|------|-----------|
| 011 | 111 | (<ea>) + (<An>)→An |

## ADDX

| 15 | 14 | 13 | 12 | 11 10 9 | 8 | 7 6 | 5 | 4 | 3 | 2 1 0 |
|----|----|----|----|---------|---|-----|---|---|---|-------|
| 1 | 1 | 0 | 1 | Destination Register* | 1 | Size | 0 | 0 | R/M | Source Register* |

Size field:
  00 = byte
  01 = word
  10 = longword
R/M field:
  0 = data register to data register
  1 = memory to memory
* if R/M = 0, specifies a data register
  if R/M = 1, specifies an address register for the predecrement addressing mode.

## SHIFT/ROTATE - *Register*

| 15 | 14 | 13 | 12 | 11 | 10 | 9 | 8 | 7 | 6 | 5 | 4 | 3 | 2 | 1 | 0 |
|----|----|----|----|----|----|----|----|----|----|----|----|----|----|----|----|
| 1 | 1 | 1 | 0 | Count/ Register | | | dr | Size | | i/r | Type | | Data Register | | |

Count/register field:
   if i/r = 0, specifies shift count
   if i/r = 1, specifies a data register that contains the shift count
dr field:
   0 = right
   1 = left
i/r field:
   0 = immediate shift count
   1 = register shift count
Size field:
   00 = byte
   01 = word
   10 = longword
Type field:
   00 = arithmetic shift
   01 = logical shift
   10 = rotate with extend
   11 = rotate

## SHIFT/ROTATE - *Memory*

| 15 | 14 | 13 | 12 | 11 | 10 | 9 | 8 | 7 | 6 | 5 | 4 | 3 | 2 | 1 | 0 |
|----|----|----|----|----|----|----|----|----|----|----|----|----|----|----|----|
| 1 | 1 | 1 | 0 | 0 | Type | | dr | 1 | 1 | Effective Address Mode | | | Register | | |

Type field:
   00 = arithmetic shift
   01 = logical shift
   10 = rotate with extend
   11 = rotate
dr field:
   0 = right
   1 = left

# Appendix D

# Instruction Execution Times

This section contains a listing of the 68000 instruction execution times in terms of external clock (CLK) periods. It is assumed that both memory-read and memory-write cycles consist of four clock periods. A longer memory cycle causes the generation of wait states that must be added to the total instruction times.

The number of bus read and write cycles for each instruction is also included with the timing data. This is shown as

$$n(r/w)$$

where:

n  is the total number of clock periods
r  is the number of read cycles
w  is the number of write cycles

For example, a timing shown as 18(3/1) means the total number of clock periods is 18. Of these, 12 are for the three read cycles ($4 \times 3 = 12$). Four additional clock periods are for the single write cycle ($1 \times 4 = 4$), for a total of 16 clock periods. The bus is idle for two clock periods while the processor completes internal operations.

## Operand Effective Address Calculation Times

Table D-1 lists the number of clock periods required to compute the effective addresses for instructions. The total includes fetching any extension words, computing the address, and fetching the memory operand. The total number of clock periods, the number of read cycles, and the number of write cycles (zero for all effective address calculations) are shown in the format described above.

Table D-1.  Effective Address Calculation Times.

|  | Addressing Mode | Byte, Word | Long |
|---|---|---|---|
| Dn | Data Register Direct | 0(0/0) | 0(0/0) |
| An | Address Register Direct | 0(0/0) | 0(0/0) |
| (An) | Address Register Indirect | 4(1/0) | 8(2/0) |
| (An)+ | Address Register Indirect with Postincrement | 4(1/0) | 8(2/0) |
| -(An) | Address Register Indirect with Predecrement | 6(1/0) | 10(2/0) |
| d16(An) | Address Register Indirect with Displacement | 8(2/0) | 12(3/0) |
| d8(An,Xn)* | Address Register Indirect with Index | 10(2/0) | 14(3/0) |
| xxx.W | Absolute Short | 8(2/0) | 12(3/0) |
| xxx.L | Absolute Long | 12(3/0) | 16(4/0) |
| d16(PC) | Program Counter with Displacement | 8(2/0) | 12(3/0) |
| d8(PC,Xn)* | Program Counter with Index | 10(2/0) | 14(3/0) |
| #data | Immediate | 4(1/0) | 8(2/0) |

* The size of the index register (Xn) does not affect execution time.

**Table D-2.** Move Byte and Move Word Instruction Execution Times.

| Source | Destination | | | | | | | | |
|---|---|---|---|---|---|---|---|---|---|
| | Dn | An | (An) | (An)+ | -(An) | d16(An) | d8(An,Xn)* | xxx.W | xxx.L |
| Dn | 4(1/0) | 4(1/0) | 8(1/1) | 8(1/1) | 8(1/1) | 12(2/1) | 14(2/1) | 12(2/1) | 16(3/1) |
| An | 4(1/0) | 4(1/0) | 8(1/1) | 8(1/1) | 8(1/1) | 12(2/1) | 14(2/1) | 12(2/1) | 16(3/1) |
| (An) | 8(2/0) | 8(2/0) | 12(2/1) | 12(2/1) | 12(2/1) | 16(3/1) | 18(3/1) | 16(3/1) | 20(4/1) |
| (An)+ | 8(2/0) | 8(2/0) | 12(2/1) | 12(2/1) | 12(2/1) | 16(3/1) | 18(3/1) | 16(3/1) | 20(4/1) |
| -(An) | 10(2/0) | 10(2/0) | 14(2/1) | 14(2/1) | 14(2/1) | 18(3/1) | 20(3/1) | 18(3/1) | 22(4/1) |
| d16(An) | 12(3/0) | 12(3/0) | 16(3/1) | 16(3/1) | 16(3/1) | 20(4/1) | 22(4/1) | 20(4/1) | 24(5/1) |
| d8(An,Xn)* | 14(3/0) | 14(3/0) | 18(3/1) | 18(3/1) | 18(3/1) | 22(4/1) | 24(4/1) | 22(4/1) | 26(5/1) |
| xxx.W | 12(3/0) | 12(3/0) | 16(3/1) | 16(3/1) | 16(3/1) | 20(4/1) | 22(4/1) | 20(4/1) | 24(5/1) |
| xxx.L | 16(4/0) | 16(4/0) | 20(4/1) | 20(4/1) | 20(4/1) | 24(5/1) | 26(5/1) | 24(5/1) | 28(6/1) |
| d16(PC) | 12(3/0) | 12(3/0) | 16(3/1) | 16(3/1) | 16(3/1) | 20(4/1) | 22(4/1) | 20(4/1) | 24(5/1) |
| d8(PC,Xn)* | 14(3/0) | 14(3/0) | 18(3/1) | 18(3/1) | 18(3/1) | 22(4/1) | 24(4/1) | 22(4/1) | 26(5/1) |
| #data | 8(2/0) | 8(2/0) | 12(2/1) | 12(2/1) | 12(2/1) | 16(3/1) | 18(3/1) | 16(3/1) | 20(4/1) |

\* The size of the index register (Xn) does not affect execution time.

**Table D-3.** Move Long Instruction Execution Times.

| Source | Destination | | | | | | | | |
|---|---|---|---|---|---|---|---|---|---|
| | Dn | An | (An) | (An)+ | -(An) | d16(An) | d8(An,Xn)* | xxx.W | xxx.L |
| Dn | 4(1/0) | 4(1/0) | 12(1/2) | 12(1/2) | 12(1/2) | 16(2/2) | 18(2/2) | 16(2/2) | 20(3/2) |
| An | 4(1/0) | 4(1/0) | 12(1/2) | 12(1/2) | 12(1/2) | 16(2/2) | 18(2/2) | 16(2/2) | 20(3/2) |
| (An) | 12(3/0) | 12(3/0) | 20(3/2) | 20(3/2) | 20(3/2) | 24(4/2) | 26(4/2) | 24(4/2) | 28(5/2) |
| (An)+ | 12(3/0) | 12(3/0) | 20(3/2) | 20(3/2) | 20(3/2) | 24(4/2) | 26(4/2) | 24(4/2) | 28(5/2) |
| -(An) | 14(3/0) | 14(3/0) | 22(3/2) | 22(3/2) | 22(3/2) | 26(4/2) | 28(4/2) | 26(4/2) | 30(5/2) |
| d16(An) | 16(4/0) | 16(4/0) | 24(4/2) | 24(4/2) | 24(4/2) | 28(5/2) | 30(5/2) | 28(5/2) | 32(6/2) |
| d8(An,Xn)* | 18(4/0) | 18(4/0) | 26(4/2) | 26(4/2) | 26(4/2) | 30(5/2) | 32(5/2) | 30(5/2) | 34(6/2) |
| xxx.W | 16(4/0) | 16(4/0) | 24(4/2) | 24(4/2) | 24(4/2) | 28(5/2) | 30(5/2) | 28(5/2) | 32(6/2) |
| xxx.L | 20(5/0) | 20(5/0) | 28(5/2) | 28(5/2) | 28(5/2) | 32(6/2) | 34(6/2) | 32(6/2) | 36(7/2) |
| d16(PC) | 16(4/0) | 16(4/0) | 24(4/2) | 24(4/2) | 24(4/2) | 28(5/2) | 30(5/2) | 28(5/2) | 32(5/2) |
| d8(PC,Xn)* | 18(4/0) | 18(4/0) | 26(4/2) | 26(4/2) | 26(4/2) | 30(5/2) | 32(5/2) | 24(4/2) | 28(5/2) |
| #data | 12(3/0) | 12(3/0) | 20(3/2) | 20(3/2) | 20(3/2) | 24(4/2) | 26(4/2) | 30(5/2) | 34(6/2) |

\* The size of the index register (Xn) does not affect execution time.

## Table D-4. Standard Instruction Execution Times.

| Instruction | Size | <ea>,An[†] | <ea>,Dn | Dn,M[††] |
|---|---|---|---|---|
| ADD/ADDA | Byte, Word | 8(1/0)+ | 4(1/0)+ | 8(1/1)+ |
|  | Long | 6(1/0)+** | 6(1/0)+** | 12(1/2)+ |
| AND | Byte, Word | - | 4(1/0)+ | 8(1/1)+ |
|  | Long | - | 6(1/0)+** | 12(1/2)+ |
| CMP/CMPA | Byte, Word | 6(1/0)+ | 4(1/0)+ | - |
|  | Long | 6(1/0)+ | 6(1/0)+** | - |
| DIVS | - | - | 158(1/0)+* | - |
| DIVU | - | - | 140(1/0)+* | - |
| EOR | Byte, Word | - | 4(1/0)*** | 8(1/1)+ |
|  | Long | - | 8(1/0)*** | 12(1/2)+ |
| MULS | - | - | 70(1/0)+* | - |
| MULU | - | - | 70(1/0)+* | - |
| OR | Byte, Word | - | 4(1/0)+ | 8(1/1)+ |
|  | Long | - | 6(1/0)+** | 12(1/2)+ |
| SUB | Byte, Word | 8(1/0)+ | 4(1/0)+ | 8(1/1)+ |
|  | Long | 6(1/0)+** | 6(1/0)+** | 12(1/2)+ |

| | |
|---|---|
| + | Add effective address calculation time. |
| † | Word or long only. |
| †† | M is an effective address operand in memory. |
| * | Indicates maximum value. |
| ** | The base time of six clock periods is increased to eight if the effective address mode is register direct or immediate (effective address time should also be added). |
| *** | Only available effective address mode is data register direct. |
| DIVS,DIVU | The divide algorithm used by the MC68000 provides less than 10% difference between the best- and worst-case timings. |
| MULS,MULU | The multiply algorithm requires 38+2n clocks where n is defined as. |
| MULU: | n = the number of ones in the <ea>. |
| MULS: | n = concatenate the <ea> with a zero as the LSB; n is the resultant number of 10 or 01 patterns in the 17-bit source; i.e., worse case happens when the source is $5555. |

**Table D-5.    Immediate Instruction Execution Times.**

| Instruction | Size | #,Dn | #,An | #,M† |
|---|---|---|---|---|
| ADDI | Byte, Word | 8(2/0) | - | 12(2/1)+ |
|  | Long | 16(3/0) | - | 20(3/2)+ |
| ADDQ | Byte, Word | 4(1/0) | 4(1/0)* | 8(1/1)+ |
|  | Long | 8(1/0) | 8(1/0) | 12(1/2)+ |
| ANDI | Byte, Word | 8(2/0) | - | 12(2/1)+ |
|  | Long | 14(3/0) | - | 20(3/2)+ |
| CMPI | Byte, Word | 8(2/0) | - | 8(2/0)+ |
|  | Long | 14(3/0) | - | 12(3/0)+ |
| EORI | Byte, Word | 8(2/0) | - | 12(2/1)+ |
|  | Long | 16(3/0) | - | 20(3/2)+ |
| MOVEQ | Long | 4(1/0) | - | - |
| ORI | Byte, Word | 8(2/0) | - | 12(2/1)+ |
|  | Long | 16(3/0) | - | 20(3/2)+ |
| SUBI | Byte, Word | 8(2/0) | - | 12(2/1)+ |
|  | Long | 16(3/0) | - | 20(3/2)+ |
| SUBQ | Byte, Word | 4(1/0) | 8(1/0)* | 8(1/1)+ |
|  | Long | 8(1/0) | 8(1/0) | 12(1/2)+ |

+ Add effective address calculation time.
\* Word only.
† M is an effective address operand in memory.

**Table D-6.    Single Operand Instruction Execution Times.**

| Instruction | Size | Register | Memory |
|---|---|---|---|
| CLR | Byte, Word | 4(1/0) | 8(1/1)+ |
|  | Long | 6(1/0) | 12(1/2)+ |
| NBCD | Byte | 6(1/0) | 8(1/1)+ |
| NEG | Byte, Word | 4(1/0) | 8(1/1)+ |
|  | Long | 6(1/0) | 12(1/2)+ |
| NEGX | Byte, Word | 4(1/0) | 8(1/1)+ |
|  | Long | 6(1/0) | 12(1/2)+ |
| NOT | Byte, Word | 4(1/0) | 8(1/1)+ |
|  | Long | 6(1/0) | 12(1/2)+ |
| Scc | Byte, False | 4(1/0) | 8(1/1)+ |
|  | Byte, True | 6(1/0) | 8(1/1)+ |
| TAS | Byte | 4(1/0) | 14(2/1)+ |
| TST | Byte, Word | 4(1/0) | 4(1/0)+ |
|  | Long | 4(1/0) | 4(1/0)+ |

+ Add effective address calculation time.

Table D-7. Shift/Rotate Instruction Execution Times.

| Instruction | Size | Register | Memory |
|---|---|---|---|
| ASR, ASL | Byte, Word | 6+2n(1/0) | 8(1/1)+ |
|  | Long | 8+2n(1/0) | - |
| LSR, LSL | Byte, Word | 6+2n(1/0) | 8(1/1)+ |
|  | Long | 8+2n(1/0) | - |
| ROR, ROL | Byte, Word | 6+2n(1/0) | 8(1/1)+ |
|  | Long | 8+2n(1/0) | - |
| ROXR, ROXL | Byte, Word | 6+2n(1/0) | 8(1/1)+ |
|  | Long | 8+2n(1/0) | - |

+ Add effective address calculation time.
n is the shift count.

Table D-8. Bit Manipulation Instruction Execution Times.

| Instruction | Size | Dynamic | | Static | |
|---|---|---|---|---|---|
|  |  | Resister | Memory | Resister | Memory |
| BCHG | Byte | - | 8(1/1)+ | - | 12(2/1)+ |
|  | Long | 8(1/0)* | - | 12(2/0)* | - |
| BCLR | Byte | - | 8(1/1)+ | - | 12(2/1)+ |
|  | Long | 10(1/0)* | - | 14(2/0)* | - |
| BSET | Byte | - | 8(1/1)+ | - | 12(2/1)+ |
|  | Long | 8(1/0)* | - | 12(2/0)* | - |
| BTST | Byte | - | 4(1/0)+ | - | 8(2/0)+ |
|  | Long | 6(1/0) | - | 10(2/0) | - |

+ Add effective address calculation time.
* Indicates maximum value; data addressing mode only.

Table D-9. Conditional and Branch Instruction Execution Times.

| Instruction | Displacement | Branch Taken | Branch Not Taken |
|---|---|---|---|
| Bcc | Byte | 10(2/0) | 8(1/0) |
|  | Long | 10(2/0) | 12(2/0) |
| BRA | Byte | 10(2/0) | - |
|  | Long | 10(2/0) | - |
| BSR | Byte | 18(2/2) | - |
|  | Long | 18(2/2) | - |
| DBcc | cc True | - | 12(2/0) |
|  | cc false, Count Not Expired | 10(2/0) | - |
|  | cc false, Count Expired | - | 14(3/0) |

**Table D-10.    JMP, JSR, LEA, PEA, and MOVEM Instruction Execution Times.**

| Inst. | Size | (An) | (An)+ | -(An) | d16(An) | d8(An,Xn)* | xxx.W | xxx.L | d16(PC) | d8(PC,Xn)* |
|---|---|---|---|---|---|---|---|---|---|---|
| JMP | - | 8(2/0) | - | - | 10(2/0) | 14(3/0) | 10(2/0) | 12(3/0) | 10(2/0) | 14(3/0) |
| JSR | - | 16(2/2) | - | - | 18(2/2) | 22(2/2) | 18(2/2) | 20(3/2) | 18(2/2) | 22(2/2) |
| LEA | - | 4(1/0) | - | - | 8(2/0) | 12(2/0) | 8(2/0) | 12(3/0) | 8(2/0) | 12(2/0) |
| PEA | - | 12(1/2) | - | - | 16(2/2) | 20(2/2) | 16(2/2) | 20(3/2) | 16(2/2) | 20(2/2) |
| MOVEM M→R | Word | 12+4n (3+n/0) | 12+4n (3+n/0) | - | 16+4n (4+n/0) | 18+4n (4+n/0) | 16+4n (4+n/0) | 20+4n (5+n/0) | 16+4n (4n/0) | 18+4n (4+n/0) |
| | Long | 12+8n (3+2n/0) | 12+8n (3+2n/0) | - | 16+8n (4+2n/0) | 18+8n (4+2n/0) | 16+8n (4+2n/0) | 20+8n (5+2n/0) | 16+8n (4+2n/0) | 18+8n (4+2n/0) |
| MOVEM R→M | Word | 8+4n (2/n) | - | 8+4n (2/n) | 12+4n (3/n) | 14+4n (3/n) | 12+4n (3/n) | 16+4n (4/n) | - | - |
| | Long | 8+8n (2/2n) | - | 8+8n (2/2n) | 12+8n (3/2n) | (14+8n 3/2n) | 12+8n (3/2n) | 16+8n (4/2n) | - | - |

n is the number of registers to move.

\* The size of the index register (Xn) does not affect the instruction's execution time.

**Table D-11.    Multiprecision Instruction Execution Times.**

| Instruction | Size | Dn,Dn | M,M[†] |
|---|---|---|---|
| ADDX | Byte, Word | 4(1/0) | 18(3/1) |
| | Long | 8(1/0) | 30(5/2) |
| CMPM | Byte, Word | - | 12(3/0) |
| | Long | - | 20(5/0) |
| SUBX | Byte, Word | 4(1/0) | 18(3/1) |
| | Long | 8(1/0) | 30(5/2) |
| ABCD | Byte | 6(1/0) | 18(3/1) |
| SBCD | Byte | 6(1/0) | 18(3/1) |

[†] M is an effective address operand in memory.

Table D-12.    Miscellaneous Instruction
Execution Times.

| Instruction | Size | Register | Memory |
|---|---|---|---|
| ANDI to CCR | Byte | 20(3/0) | - |
| ANDI to SR | Word | 20(3/0) | - |
| CHK (No Trap) | - | 10(1/0)+ | - |
| EORI to CCR | Byte | 20(3/0) | - |
| EORI to SR | Word | 20(3/0) | - |
| ORI to CCR | Byte | 20(3/0) | - |
| ORI to SR | Word | 20(3/0) | - |
| MOVE from SR | - | 6(1/0) | 8(1/1)+ |
| MOVE to CCR | - | 12(1/0) | 12(1/0)+ |
| MOVE to SR | - | 12(2/0) | 12(2/0)+ |
| EXG | - | 6(1/0) | - |
| EXT | Word | 4(1/0) | - |
|  | Long | 4(1/0) | - |
| LINK | - | 16(2/2) | - |
| MOVE from USP | - | 4(1/0) | - |
| MOVE to USP | - | 4(1/0) | - |
| NOP | - | 4(1/0) | - |
| RESET | - | 132(1/0) | - |
| RTE | - | 20(5/0) | - |
| RTR | - | 20(2/0) | - |
| RTS | - | 16(4/0) | - |
| STOP | - | 4(0/0) | - |
| SWAP | - | 4(1/0) | - |
| TRAPV | - | 4(1/0) | - |
| UNLK | - | 12(3/0) | - |

+ add effective address calculation time.

Table D-13.    Move Peripheral Instruction Execution Times.

| Instruction | Size | Register →Memory | Memory→Register |
|---|---|---|---|
| MOVEP | Word | 16(2/2) | 16(4/0) |
|  | Long | 24(2/4) | 24(6/0) |

Table D-14.   Exception Processing
Execution Times.

| Exception | Periods |
|---|---|
| Address Error | 50(4/7) |
| Bus Error | 50(4/7) |
| CHK Instruction | 40(4/3)+ |
| Divide by Zero | 38(4/3)+ |
| Illegal Instruction | 34(4/3) |
| Interrupt | 44(5/3)* |
| Privilege Violation | 34(4/3) |
| RESET** | 40(6/0) |
| Trace | 34(4/3) |
| TRAP Instruction | 34(4/3) |
| TRAPV Instruction | 34(5/3) |

+   Add effective address  calculation time.
*   The interrupt acknowledge cycle is
    assumed to take four periods.
**  Indicates the time from when RESET
    and HALT are first sampled as negated
    to when instruction execution starts.

# Appendix E

# MON68K

This appendix contains the listing of a 68000 monitor program (MON68K) along with a general description of its design and operation. Many of the concepts in assembly-language programming developed earlier in short examples can be reinforced by reviewing this appendix.

MON68K is a monitor program written for the 68000 MiniBoard described in Chapter 8—the 68KMB. We begin with a description of the purpose of a monitor program, and then give a summary of MON68K commands.

The overall operation of MON68K and some design details are also described. The final pages of this appendix contain listings of MON68K files, including each assembled source file, the symbol table created by the linker/locator, and a dump of MON68K in hexadecimal S-records. These files are summarized in Table E-1.

A monitor program is not an operating system. It is a small program with commands that provide a primitive level of system control and user interaction. The major difference is that operating systems are found on large systems with disk drives, while monitor programs are found on small systems, such as the 68KMB, with a keyboard (or keypad) for input and a CRT (or LEDs) for output.

MON68K is a 68000 assembly-language program of approximately 10K bytes in length. It was written on an IBM PC-compatible system running MS-DOS version 5.0. Several development tools were used, including an editor, a cross assembler, a linker/locator, and a VT100 terminal emulation program. Both the cross assembler (A68K) and the linker/locator (XLINK) are products of Enertec Systems, Inc., Lansdale, PA. The VT100 terminal emulator (PC-VT) is a product of Athena Systems Development Group, San Diego, CA. Both Enertec and Athena allowed their programs to be distributed with this text and used in

Table E-1.   MON68K Files.

| File | Starting Page | Description |
|---|---|---|
| MON68K.LST | 415 | Main module for the monitor program |
| GETPAR.LST | 424 | Get parameters from the command line |
| CONVERT.LST | 426 | Subroutines to perform data conversions |
| IS.LST | 427 | Subroutines to check the type of data |
| IO.LST | 429 | Subroutines and traps for I/O operations |
| D_CMD.LST | 434 | D command code: disassemble instructions |
| G_CMD.LST | 436 | G command code: go to user program |
| L_CMD.LST | 438 | L command code: load S-records |
| M_CMD.LST | 441 | M command code: memory commands |
| R_CMD.LST | 446 | R command code: register display |
| T_CMD.LST | 449 | T command code: trace instructions |
| PERIOD.LST | 451 | .R command code: examine/alter user registers |
| DECODE68K.LST | 453 | Disassemble subroutine from TUTOR |
| MON68K.XLK | 454 | Command file for linker/locator |
| MON68K.MAP | 455 | Absolute symbol table for MON68K |
| MON68K.HEX | 461 | Hexadecimal S-records for MON68K |

educational settings free of charge. These programs are found on the disk accompanying this text. MON68K is also available free of charge for non-profit educational use. The file MON68K.HEX is also included on the companion disk.

Testing and debugging of MON68K were performed using the 68KMB single-board computer connected to the host system's serial communications, or "COM," port. The terminal emulation program includes a file transmit command to transfer S-records through the COM port to a target system. This permitted incremental development of MON68K, whereby new commands were tested and debugged in RAM before being incorporated into MON68K and burned into EPROM.

MON68K was developed using modular programming techniques. Thirteen source files were used. To keep the listing files relatively short for this appendix, the symbol tables have been deleted at the end of each listing. These tables are of limited use in any case, since all files are relocatable. The symbol table created by the linker/locator is much more useful and is included near the end of this appendix. This file is called MON68K.MAP. The linker/locator creates two output files: the symbol table, or link map, and an absolute version of the program in hexadecimal S-records. The latter file, called MON68K.HEX can be burned into an EPROM or executed with an in-circuit emulator. Some EPROM programmers may require an extra stage of translation through a conversion utility supplied with the programmer.

**Table E-2.   MON68K Command Summary.**

| Command | PAR1 | PAR2 | PAR3 | Name | Description |
|---|---|---|---|---|---|
| DI | address | count | | Disassemble | Disassemble *count* instructions starting at *address*. |
| GO | address | | | Go | Go to user program starting at *address*. If address not specified, user PC is used. |
| GT | address | | | Go To | Go to temporary breakpoint at *address*. Execution begins at address in user PC. |
| HE | | | | Help | Display help screen. |
| LG | | | | Load and Go | Load S-records and begin execution at address specified in S8 or S9 record. |
| LO | | | | Load | Load S-records and return to monitor. |
| MC | start | end | destination | Memory Copy | Copy memory from *start* address up to *end* address. Copy to *destination* address. |
| MD | start | count | | Memory Display | Display *count* bytes of memory beginning at *start* address. |
| MF | start | end | byte | Memory Fill | Fill memory with *byte*, beginning at start address and proceeding to *end* address. |
| MM | address | | | Memory Modify | Memory display/modify at *address*. |
| MT | start | end | | Memory Test | Test RAM from *start* address to *end* address. |
| RD | | | | Register Display | Dump user register set to console. |
| SZ | size | | | Size | Set *size* of data for MD command (1=byte, 2=word, 4=longword; default=word). |
| TD | delay | | | Trace Delay | Set delay for TR command. |
| TR | count | | | Trace | Trace *count* instructions.  Display user registers after each instruction. |
| R | X | | | Register | Change user register R.  Hexadecimal value X is written to register R. |
| ? | | | | Help | Display help screen. |

## Commands and Specifications

MON68K was written for the 68KMB single-board computer described in Chapter 8. System requirements are as follows:

- 68000 CPU (any frequency)
- MON68K installed in EPROM starting at address 0
- 16K bytes of RAM from address $008000 to $00BFFF
- 68681 DUART clocked a 3.6864 MHz and selected at odd addresses from $00C001 to $00C01F
- Host computer/terminal operating at 9600 baud, 7 data bits, odd parity

MON68K supports 17 commands. These are summarized in Table E-2.
Before describing each command in detail, the following points should be considered:

- When the system is powered-up or reset, the following prompt appears:

```
MON68K
V4.4>
```

The version number (4.4) may change as MON68K is updated.

- Commands are entered on the keyboard and terminated by pressing the ENTER key.
- Uppercase and lowercase characters are treated the same.
- During command entry, mistakes may be corrected by using the BACKSPACE or DELETE key.
- Maximum line length is 39 characters, including the ENTER key.
- Each command uses from 0 to 3 parameters entered in hexadecimal ("$" is not needed).
- Parameters are separated by commas or spaces.
- If a command requires parameters and none are entered, a brief syntax message is displayed.
- If the MONITOR switch is depressed during a user program, the program is terminated and the user register set is saved and displayed on the console. (The MONITOR switch generates a level-7 interrupt.)
- The 68KMB does not include a watchdog timer. If a memory access is made to a vacant memory location, the system hangs.

## Command Descriptions

This section describes each MON68K command in detail and provides examples of typical invocations of each command.

In the following paragraphs, the term *console* refers to the device attached to the serial port of the 68KMB. This device is most likely a PC-compatible host computer running a terminal emulation program, such as PC-VT. Any RS232C dumb terminal may be used as well.

The examples provided for each command show real instances of using MON68K. A screen capture program assisted in creating the output. For convenience, user input is underlined.

**DI**                          *Disassemble Instructions*                          **DI**

*Syntax:*      `DI address count`

*Description*:   The DI command disassembles binary words in memory and displays the disassembled instructions on the console. The first parameter is the memory location to begin disassembling. The second parameter is the number of instructions to disassemble.

If a word is read that corresponds to an undefined 68000 instruction, it is assembled as a DC.W directive.

*Example:*

```
V4.4>     DI 400 11
-----     000400    027CF8FF              AND.W    #-1793,SR
-----     000404    007C0700              OR.W     #1792,SR
-----     000408    4EB80A5E              JSR.S    $00000A5E
-----     00040C    23FC000000020000B8FA  MOVE.L   #2,$0000B8FA
-----     000416    23FC000000010000B918  MOVE.L   #1,$0000B918
-----     000420    207C0000B800          MOVE.L   #47104,A0
-----     000426    4E60                  MOVE.L   A0,USP
-----     000428    33FC27000000B8B8      MOVE.W   #9984,$0000B8B8
-----     000430    23FC000080000000B8B4  MOVE.L   #32768,$0000B8B4
-----     00043A    303C000E              MOVE.W   #14,D0
-----     00043E    207C0000B8BA          MOVE.L   #47290,A0
-----     000444    4298                  CLR.L    (A0)+
-----     000446    51C8FFFC              DBF.L    D0,$000444
-----     00044A    43FA04C2              LEA.L    $0000090E(PC),A1
-----     00044E    4E42                  TRAP     #2
-----     000450    2E7C0000C000          MOVE.L   #49152,A7
-----     000456    43FA04BF              LEA.L    $00000917(PC),A1
V4.4>
```

The example above disassembles the first 17 instructions in MON68K. These begin at address $400, just above the 68000's reset and exception vector space.

**GO**                          *Go to User Program*                          **GO**

*Syntax:*        `GO address`

*Description:*    The GO command begins execution of a user program. The user register set is loaded into the 68000's internal registers before execution begins. If an address is entered as a command-line parameter, that address is loaded into the user PC before the user register set is loaded. If no address is entered on the command line, the current value of the user PC is the address where execution begins.

*Example:*

```
V4.4>LO
Load S-records...   Module: EXAMPLE    Entry: 00008000
V4.4>DI 8000 3
----- 008000    227C0000800A           MOVE.L   #32778,A1
----- 008006    4E42                   TRAP     #2
----- 008008    4E4E                   TRAP     #14
V4.4>MD 8000 22
00008000   227C 0000 800A 4E42 4E4E 0D0A 2A2A 2A20   "|....NBNN..***
00008010   4449 5350 4C41 5920 5448 4953 204D 4553   DISPLAY THIS MES
00008020   5341 4745 202A 2A2A 00F0 F0F0 F0F0 F0F0   SAGE ***.ppppppp
V4.4>GO 8000
*** DISPLAY THIS MESSAGE ***
V4.4>
```

The example shows a sequence of four MON68K commands. First, the LO command is used to load a program from the host system into RAM. (See the LO command for more details.) The program has only three instructions and begins at address $8000. The second command disassembles the three instructions. (MON68K's TRAP instructions are discussed later in this appendix.) The third command displays the RAM locations containing the program. The fourth command is GO 8000 which executes the user program.

---

**GT**                          *Go to Temporary Breakpoint*                          **GT**

*Syntax:*        GT address

*Description:*   The GT command begins execution of a user program and sets a temporary breakpoint at
                 the address specified in the first command-line parameter. The user register set is loaded
                 into the 68000's internal registers before execution begins. Execution begins at the address
                 contained in the user PC.

*Example:*

```
V4.4>LO
Load S-records...   Module: EXAMPLE    Entry: 00008000
V4.4>DI 8000 5
----- 008000     103C0005              MOVE.B   #5,D0
----- 008004     D03C0019              ADD.B    #25,D0
----- 008008     1200                  MOVE.B   D0,D1
----- 00800A     E309                  LSL.B    #1,D1
----- 00800C     4E4E                  TRAP     #14
V4.4>.PC 8000

V4.4>GT 800C
 PC=0000800C SR=2700=.S7..... US=0000B800 SS=0000BFD2
 D0=0000001E D1=0000003C D2=00000000 D3=00000000
 D4=00000000 D5=00000000 D6=00000000 D7=00000000
 A0=00000000 A1=00000000 A2=00000000 A3=00000000
 A4=00000000 A5=00000000 A6=00000000 A7=0000BFD2
----- 00800C     4E4E                  TRAP     #14
V4.4>
```

The example above uses four MON68K commands. First, the LO command is used to load a program into
RAM. (See the LO command for more details.) The program is five instructions long beginning at address
$8000. Next, the DI command is used to disassemble the program. The user PC is set to $8000 in the third
command. Then, GT is used to begin execution of the program (at $8000) until the temporary breakpoint
is reached at address $800C. When the temporary breakpoint is reached, execution terminates and the
user register set is displayed on the console. Note that the effect of the program is easily verified by examining registers D0 and D1. The address, opcode, and mnemonic for the next instruction to execute are also
displayed, just after the user register set.

**HE**                                    *Help*                                    **HE**

*Syntax:*        HE

*Description:*   The HE command displays a summary of all MON68K commands on the console.

*Example:*

```
V4.4>HE
***** MON68K COMMAND SUMMARY *****
==================================
DI     disassemble instructions
GO     go to user program
GT     go to temporary breakpoint
HE     help (display this message)
LG     load S-records and go
LO     load S-records
MC     memory copy
MD     memory dump
MF     memory fill
MM     memory modify
MT     memory test
RD     register dump
SZ     size of data for MD command
TD     trace delay
TR     trace instructions
.R X   set register R to value X
?      display this message
==================================
V4.4>
```

---

**LG**                         *Load and Go*                         **LG**

*Syntax:*      LG

*Description*:   The LG command loads S-records from the 68KMB serial port, then begins execution of the
              user program at the address specified in the S8 or S9 record that terminates the hexadecimal
              transmission. If no entry point is found in the S8 or S9 record, control returns to MON68K.

*Example:*

```
V4.4>LG
Load S-records...   Module: EXAMPLE    Entry: 00008000
*** DISPLAY THIS MESSAGE ***
V4.4>
```

In the example above, the program loaded is called EXAMPLE and the entry point for execution is address
$8000. The example program is very simple; it displays a one-line message and returns to MON68K.

Most 68000 assemblers allow a program entry point to be specified by following the END directive with a
label corresponding to the instruction where execution should begin. This address is automatically inserted into the S8 or S9 record when the program is converted to S-records.

The format for Motorola S-records is described in detail in Chapter 1 of this text.

## LO                                    *Load*                                    **LO**

*Syntax:*        LO

*Description*:    The LO command loads S-records from the 68KMB serial port and then returns control to the monitor program.

*Example:*

```
V4.4>LO
Load S-records...    Module: EXAMPLE    Entry: 00008000
V4.4>
```

When the LO command is entered, MON68K displays the message "Load S-records. . . ." and then enters a loop waiting for S-records to arrive from the console. Assuming the console is a host computer running a terminal-emulation program, the user should issue the appropriate command to transmit a file. (With PC-VT, CONTROL+4 is the file transmit command.) As the file is received by MON68K, the name of the module appearing in the S0 record is displayed. As S1 or S2 records are received, the data are extracted and placed into memory. The data records will be followed with an S8 or S9 end-of-data record. If a module entry point is specified in the S8 or S9 record, it too is displayed. After all S-records have been received, MON68K waits for a CONTROL+Z character as an end-of-transmission indicator. This usually occurs as part of the file transmit protocol; otherwise, CONTROL+Z may be entered on the keyboard to terminate the LO command and return to MON68K.

If at any time the LO command computes a checksum different from that in an S-record, an error message is displayed and the load is terminated.

The format for Motorola S-records is described in detail in Chapter 1 of this text.

---

**MC** *Memory Copy* **MC**

*Syntax:*        MC start end destination

*Description:*  The MC command copies a block of memory from a source location to a destination. The first command-line parameter identifies the starting address of the source block. The second command-line parameter identifies the ending address of the source block. The third command-line parameter identifies the starting address of the destination block.

*Example:*

```
V4.4>MD 5A0 22
000005A0   4E42 6000 FEAC 0D0A 2A2A 2A2A 2A20 4D4F   NB`.~,..***** MO
000005B0   4E36 384B 2043 4F4D 4D41 4E44 2053 554D   N68K COMMAND SUM
000005C0   4D41 5259 202A 2A2A 2A2A 0D0A 3D3D 3D3D   MARY *****..====
V4.4>MC 5A0 5CF 8000
V4.4>MD 8000 33
00008000   4E42 6000 FEAC 0D0A 2A2A 2A2A 2A20 4D4F   NB`.~,..***** MO
00008010   4E36 384B 2043 4F4D 4D41 4E44 2053 554D   N68K COMMAND SUM
00008020   4D41 5259 202A 2A2A 2A2A 0D0A 3D3D 3D3D   MARY *****..====
00008030   B6B6 B6B6 B6B6 B6B6 B6B6 B6B6 B6B6 B6B6   6666666666666666
V4.4>
```

The example above consists of three MON68K commands. First, the MD command is used to display 48 bytes of the MON68K EPROM. (The data displayed contain a portion of MON68K containing the HE command string.) The second command copies these 48 bytes to RAM beginning at address $8000. Finally, the MD command is used again to verify the copy.

**MD**                           *Memory Display*                           **MD**

*Syntax:*        MD start count

*Description:*   The MD command dumps (displays) a block of memory to the console. The first command-line parameter identifies the starting address of the block. The second command-line parameter is a count of the number of bytes to dump.

The MD command always outputs a multiple of sixteen bytes. The count, which is specified in hexadecimal, is rounded up to the next multiple-of-sixteen. For example, a count of 11 will cause 32 bytes to be displayed to the console.

The output data are grouped by bytes, words, or longwords, depending on the setting of the parameter SIZE. SIZE defaults to word, but may be altered to byte or longword using the SZ command.

An ASCII interpretation of the displayed data appears on the right of the display. Data bytes in the range $20_{16}$ to $7E_{16}$ correspond to displayable ASCII characters and are displayed as such. All other data bytes are displayed as a period.

If a console key is pressed during the dump, the command is terminated.

*Example:*

```
V4.4>MD 880 1111
00000880   3131 2045 6D75 6C61 7465 2054 7261 7000   11 Emulate Trap.
00000890   0D0A 0746 6F72 6D61 7420 4572 726F 7200   ...Format Error.
000008A0   0D0A 0755 6E69 6E69 7469 616C 697A 6564   ...Uninitialized
000008B0   2049 6E74 6572 7275 7074 2056 6563 746F    Interrupt Vecto
000008C0   720D 0A07 5370 7572 696F 7573 2049 6E74   r...Spurious Int
000008D0   6572 7275 7074 000D 0A07 556E 696D 706C   errupt....Unimpl
000008E0   656D 656E 7465 6420 4578 6365 7074 696F   emented Exceptio
000008F0   6E00 0D0A 5043 203D 2000 0D0A 4163 6365   n...PC = ...Acce
00000900   7373 2061 6464 7265 7373 203D 2000 0D0A   ss address = ...
00000910   4D4F 4E36 384B 000D 0A56 342E 343E 000D   MON68K...V4.4>..
00000920   0A3F 0000 227C 0000 B800 247C 0000 B828   .?.."|..8.$|..8(
00000930   4239 0000 B831 1019 B03C 0020 67F8 6002   B9..81..0<. gx`.
00000940   1019 6100 007A 14C0 0C00 000D 6604 4222   ..a..z.@....f.B"
00000950   605A 0C00 0020 6702 60E6 4222 247C 0000   `Z... g.`fB"$|..
00000960   B832 1E3C 0004 0883 0000 4281 1019 0C00   82.<......B.....
00000970   000D 6606 1E3C 0001 6024 0C00 0020 6714   ..f..<...`$... g.
00000980   0C00 002C 670E 08C3 0000 6100 0022 8280   ...,g..C..a..".
00000990   E9
V4.4>
```

The MD command above displays a region of the MON68K EPROM containing various messages, including the prompt string. Although the count was specified as "1111", the output was halted prematurely at address $00990 by pressing a key.

---

**MF**                                    *Memory Fill*                                    **MF**

*Syntax:*        `MF start end byte`

*Description:*   The MF command fills a block of memory with a specified byte. The first command-line parameter is the starting address of the block of memory to fill. The second command-line parameter is the ending address of the block of memory to fill. The third command-line parameter is the byte of data to write to the specified block.

The data written are not checked. No message is displayed if, for example, the specified block is a region of EPROM.

The address specified may be odd or even.

*Example:*

```
V4.4>MD 8100 22
00008100   0F0F 0F0F 0F0F 0F0F 0F0F 0F0F 0F0F 0F0F   ................
00008110   4949 4949 4949 4949 4949 4949 4949 4949   IIIIIIIIIIIIIIII
00008120   F0F0 F0F0 F0F0 F0F0 F0F0 F0F0 F0F0 F0F0   pppppppppppppppp
V4.4>MF 8100 810F 39
V4.4>MD 8100 22
00008100   3939 3939 3939 3939 3939 3939 3939 3939   9999999999999999
00008110   4949 4949 4949 4949 4949 4949 4949 4949   IIIIIIIIIIIIIIII
00008120   F0F0 F0F0 F0F0 F0F0 F0F0 F0F0 F0F0 F0F0   pppppppppppppppp
V4.4>
```

The example above uses three MON68K commands. First, a 48-byte region of RAM is displayed using the MD command. Then, the MF command is used to write the hexadecimal byte $39 to RAM addresses $008100 through to $00810F. Finally, the MD command is issued to verify the memory-fill operation.

**MM**                          *Memory Modify*                          **MM**

*Syntax:*      MM address

*Description:*  The MM command is used to examine and/or modify memory locations. The command-line parameter is the address of the first memory location to examine. The MM command always operates on byte-size data.

After the content of the first memory location is displayed, several responses are possible:

| | |
|---|---|
| ENTER | Examine next location |
| data ENTER | Write data to location, then examine next location |
| ↑ | Examine previous location |
| ↓ | Examine next location |
| . | Exit to monitor program |

*Example:*

```
V4.4>MM 9000
00009000 0F 55 ENTER
00009001 0F ↑
00009000 55 ENTER
00009001 0F ENTER
00009002 0F ENTER
00009003 0F ENTER
00009004 0F .
V4.4>
```

In the example above, the MM command is used to examine and change memory location $009000. After issuing the MM command, the address specified is read and its content is displayed on the following line. Initially, the value in location $009000 is $0F. The user responds with "55" followed by the ENTER key. The hexadecimal value 55 is written to address $009000 and then the content of the following address is displayed. To verify the change, the up-arrow key is pressed on the console keyboard. This decrements the memory pointer, causing location $009000 to be redisplayed. The new content, $55, appears. Then the ENTER key is pressed four more times to examine the following four memory locations. Finally, a period is entered to terminate the MM command.

The up-arrow function is implemented using the ANSI escape sequence for "cursor up." The byte sequence is $1B, $5B, $41 (ESC [ A). The down-arrow sequence is $1B, $5B, $42 (ESC [ B). Most PC-compatible systems and terminal-emulation programs implement these and other ANSI escape sequences for cursor control.

| MT | Memory Test | MT |
|---|---|---|

*Syntax:*    `MT start end`

*Description:*    The MT command tests a block of RAM. The first command-line parameter specifies the starting address of the block. The second command-line parameter specifies the ending address of the block.

If the block of RAM is OK, an appropriate message is displayed on the console. If a read/write error occurs, the address of the error is displayed on the console along with an appropriate message.

The data in the region of RAM tested are left intact at the end of the test.

*Example:*

```
V4.4>MT 8000 BFFF
Memory OK
V4.4>MT 8000 C000
Memory error at address 0000C000
V4.4>
```

Since the 68KMB has RAM from $008000 to $00BFFF, the first test above passed. The second test attempted to test an area beyond the top of RAM; this caused a read/write error at address $00C000.

**RD**                     *Register Dump*                     **RD**

*Syntax*:       RD

*Description*:   The RD command is used to dump the user register set on the console. The user register set is maintained by MON68K. Whenever a user program is started, this register set is loaded into the 68000 CPU's internal registers before execution begins.

User registers may be changed using the PERIOD (.) command.

*Example*:

```
V4.4>RD
 PC=00009000 SR=2700=.S7..... US=0000B800 SS=0000BFD8
 D0=00000000 D1=00000000 D2=00000000 D3=00000000
 D4=00000000 D5=00000000 D6=00000000 D7=00000000
 A0=00000000 A1=00000000 A2=00000000 A3=00000000
 A4=00000000 A5=00000000 A6=00000000 A7=0000BFD8
 -----  009000     207C0000C000          MOVE.L #49152,A0
V4.4>
```

In addition to displaying the user register set, the RD command displays the disassembled instruction pointed at by the user PC.

**SZ**                              *Size of Data*                              **SZ**

*Syntax:*        `SZ size`

*Description:*   The SZ command sets the size of data for the MD command. The default size is word. The first command-line parameter changes the size as follows:

1 = byte

2 = word

4 = longword

*Example:*

```
V4.4>SZ 1
V4.4>MD 0 11
00000000  00 00 C0 00 00 00 04 00 00 00 05 06 00 00 05 0C   ..@.............
00000010  00 00 05 18 00 00 05 22 00 00 05 2C 00 00 05 36   .......".....,...6
V4.4>SZ 2
V4.4>MD 0 11
00000000  0000 C000 0000 0400 0000 0506 0000 050C   ..@.............
00000010  0000 0518 0000 0522 0000 052C 0000 0536   .......".....,...6
V4.4>SZ 4
V4.4>MD 0 11
00000000  0000C000 00000400 00000506 0000050C   ..@.............
00000010  00000518 00000522 0000052C 00000536   .......".....,...6
V4.4>
```

All three MD commands above display the first 32 bytes in the 68000's memory space. These locations hold the first eight longwords in the 68000's reset and exception vector space. The last MD command is preceded with SZ = 4. This allows the eight longwords to be displayed in the most appropriate format.

**TD**                            *Trace Delay*                            **TD**

*Syntax:*        `TD delay`

*Description:*   The TD command sets the delay between each instruction for the TR command. The command-line parameter sets the delay as follows:

$$1 = 1 \text{ second}$$
$$2 = 2 \text{ seconds}$$
$$3 = 4 \text{ seconds}$$
$$4 = 8 \text{ seconds}$$
$$5 = 16 \text{ seconds}$$
$$6 = 32 \text{ seconds}$$
$$7 = 64 \text{ seconds}$$

*Example:*

```
V4.4>TD
SYNTAX: TD delay
V4.4>TD 3
V4.4>
```

The first TD command above is issued without a parameter; so, an appropriate reminder message is displayed. The second TD command specifies a delay of 3. Subsequent instruction tracing with the TR command inserts a 4-second delay between each instruction executed.

**TR**                              *Trace Instructions*                              **TR**

*Syntax:*        TR count

*Description:*    The TR command traces instructions in the user program. The first command-line parameter specifies the number of instructions to trace. Execution begins at the address in the user
PC. After the trace count is exhausted, a colon (:) prompt is displayed. The following responses are supported:

> ENTER    trace next instruction
>
> .        exit to monitor

*Example:*

```
V4.4>LO
Load S-records...   Module: EXAMPLE
V4.4>DI 8000 5
----- 008000     103C0005            MOVE.B   #5,D0
----- 008004     123C00FF            MOVE.B   #255,D1
----- 008008     D200                ADD.B    D0,D1
----- 00800A     C3FC0006            MULS.W   #6,D1
----- 00800E     4E4E                TRAP     #14
V4.4>.PC 8000

V4.4>TR 2
 PC=00008004 SR=A710=TS7X.... US=0000B800 SS=0000BFD2
 D0=00000005 D1=00000018 D2=00000000 D3=00000000
 D4=00000000 D5=00000000 D6=00000000 D7=00000000
 A0=00000000 A1=00000000 A2=00000000 A3=00000000
 A4=00000000 A5=00000000 A6=00000000 A7=0000BFD2
----- 008004     123C00FF               MOVE.B   #255,D1
:
 PC=00008008 SR=A718=TS7XN... US=0000B800 SS=0000BFD2
 D0=00000005 D1=000000FF D2=00000000 D3=00000000
 D4=00000000 D5=00000000 D6=00000000 D7=00000000
 A0=00000000 A1=00000000 A2=00000000 A3=00000000
 A4=00000000 A5=00000000 A6=00000000 A7=0000BFD2
----- 008008     D200                   ADD.B    D0,D1
: ENTER
 PC=0000800A SR=A711=TS7X...C US=0000B800 SS=0000BFD2
 D0=00000005 D1=00000004 D2=00000000 D3=00000000
 D4=00000000 D5=00000000 D6=00000000 D7=00000000
 A0=00000000 A1=00000000 A2=00000000 A3=00000000
 A4=00000000 A5=00000000 A6=00000000 A7=0000BFD2
----- 00800A     C3FC0006               MULS.W   #6,D1
: ENTER
 PC=0000800E SR=A710=TS7X.... US=0000B800 SS=0000BFD2
 D0=00000005 D1=00000018 D2=00000000 D3=00000000
 D4=00000000 D5=00000000 D6=00000000 D7=00000000
 A0=00000000 A1=00000000 A2=00000000 A3=00000000
 A4=00000000 A5=00000000 A6=00000000 A7=0000BFD2
----- 00800E     4E4E                   TRAP     #14
:.
V4.4>
```

This example begins by loading a program that performs a few simple arithmetic operations. The program
is disassembled using the DI command, and then the user PC is initialized to $008000—the start of the
program. The TR command is issued with a count of 2. Two instructions are traced and output halts at PC-

address $008008 with the colon (:) prompt displayed. The ENTER key is pressed two times to single-step through subsequent instructions. Finally, a period is pressed to return to MON68K.

After each instruction is traced, the user-register set is displayed on the console along with a disassembled listing of the next instruction to execute. Note that the effect of each instruction is easily seen in the display of the user registers.

---

*User Register Modify*

*Syntax:*       .R X

*Description:*   The PERIOD command is used to modify user registers. The following entries are supported
              for R:

>       Dn   data register in range D0–D7
>       An   address register in range A0–A6
>       PC   program counter
>       SR   status register
>       US   user stack pointer

              The hexadecimal entry provided as X is written to the specified user register.

*Example:*

```
V4.4>.PC 8000

V4.4>.D0 55555555

V4.4>RD
 PC=00008000  SR=2700=.S7..... US=0000B800  SS=0000BFD8
 D0=55555555 D1=00000000 D2=00000000 D3=00000000
 D4=00000000 D5=00000000 D6=00000000 D7=00000000
 A0=00000000 A1=00000000 A2=00000000 A3=00000000
 A4=00000000 A5=00000000 A6=00000000 A7=0000BFD8
 ----- 008000    0F0F0F0F             MOVEP.W $0F0F(A7),D7
V4.4>
```

First, the user program counter is initialized with $00008000, then the user register D0 is initialized with
$55555555. The results are verified by issuing the RD command.

**?**                                   *Help*                                        **?**

*Syntax:*        ?

*Description:*    The ? command is the same as the HE command.

*Example:*

See HE command.

## MON68K Resources

MON68K includes numerous traps and subroutines that can be incorporated into user programs. All exception conditions are accommodated to facilitate debugging or implementing user-defined traps or interrupts.

## Traps

Of the 68000's sixteen trap instructions, six are implemented, one is reserved, and nine are unimplemented. The traps are summarized in Table E-3.

Note that the unimplemented traps are available for user applications. The entry point for each is a location within the 68KMB's RAM space. The entry points are spaced six bytes apart to provide just enough room for a JMP instruction to the user-implemented code. Consult the MON68K.LST and IO.LST listings later in this appendix for specific details on each trap.

## Subroutines

A variety of subroutines defined in MON68K can be incorporated into user programs. These are identified in Table E-4.

These subroutines are easily included in user programs by equating the name of the subroutine to the appropriate address and then calling the subroutine in the usual way.

Figure A (p. 409) illustrates how user programs can benefit by using MON68K's subroutines and traps. The program UECHO in Figure A uses one MON68K subroutine (TOUPPER) and four traps (0, 1, 2, and 14). First, a banner message is output to the console using TRAP #2 (lines 6–7). Then the program enters a loop. A character is input to D0 using TRAP #0 (line 8), then it is converted to uppercase using MON68K's TOUPPER subroutine (line 9). The symbol TOUPPER is equated to the correct address, $000992, in line 3. Note that TOUPPER does not affect D0 if the code is not a lowercase character. The character is echoed to the

Table E-3.    MON68K Traps.

| Trap | Name | Parameters | | Description |
|------|------|-------|------|-------------|
| | | Enter | Exit | |
| 0 | INCHR | – | D0=ASCII char. | Input character from console keyboard; return with ASCII code in D0 |
| 1 | OUTCHR | D0 = ASCII char. | – | Output ASCII code in D0 to console |
| 2 | OUTSTR | A1 points to string | – | Output null-terminated ASCII string pointed at by A1 to console |
| 3 | INLINE | A1 points to buffer | – | Input line of characters from keyboard. Store line in RAM buffer pointed at by A1. Terminate with a null character |
| 4 | KEYHIT | – | C=1 (key hit) C=0 (no key hit) | Check keyboard status; return with C=1 if a key is hit or with C=0 otherwise |
| 5 | – | – | – | User: begin at $008024 |
| 6 | – | – | – | User: begin at $00802A |
| 7 | – | – | – | User: begin at $008030 |
| 8 | – | – | – | User: begin at $008036 |
| 9 | – | – | – | User: begin at $00803C |
| 10 | – | – | – | User: begin at $008042 |
| 11 | – | – | – | User: begin at $008048 |
| 12 | – | – | – | User: begin at $00804E |
| 13 | – | – | – | User: begin at $008054 |
| 14 | MON68K | – | – | Return to MON68K |
| 15 | reserved | – | – | Used for temporary breakpoints by MON68K (do not use) |

Table E-4.    MON68K Subroutines.

| Name | Address[†] | Parameters Enter | Parameters Exit | Listing | Description |
|---|---|---|---|---|---|
| ATOH | $000982 | D0=ASCII char. | D0=hex nibble | CONVERT.LST | Convert ASCII character (0–9 or A–F) to hex nibble |
| TOUPPER | $000992 | D0=ASCII char. | D0=ASCII char. (uppercase) | CONVERT.LST | Convert lowercase ASCII char. to uppercase |
| HTOA | $00099E | D0=hex nibble | D0=ASCII char. | CONVERT.LST | Convert hex nibble to ASCII char. |
| ISHEX | $0009BE | D0=ASCII char. | C=0 (not hex) C=1 (is hex) | IS.LST | Test if ASCII character is in range 0–9, a–f, or A–F |
| ISDIGIT | $0009D2 | D0=ASCII char. | C=0 (not digit) C=1 (is digit) | IS.LST | Test if ASCII char. is in range 0–9 |
| ISALPH | $0009EA | D0=ASCII char. | C=0 (not alpha) C=1 (is alpha) | IS.LST | Test if ASCII char. is in range a–z or A–Z |
| ISGRAPH | $000A0E | D0=ASCII char. | C=0 (not graphic) C=1 (is graphic) | IS.LST | Test if ASCII char. is in range $20–$7E |
| OUT2HX | $000B14 | D0=byte | – | IO.LST | Output byte to console as two hex characters |
| OUTHEX | $000B20 | D0=nibble | – | IO.LST | Output nibble to console as hex character |
| OUTADD | $000B2C | A0=address | – | IO.LST | Output address to console as 8 hex character |
| SPACE | $000B44 | – | – | IO.LST | Output $20 to console |
| NEWLINE | $000B52 | – | – | IO.LST | Output CR/LF to console |
| GETHEX | $000B62 | – | D0=hex byte | IO.LST | Read two char. from console; return as hex byte |

[†] MON68K, version 4.4

```
Figure A.   1   0000000D              CR        EQU       $0D            ;ASCII carriage return
            2   0000000A              LF        EQU       $0A            ;ASCII line feed
            3   00000992              TOUPPER   EQU       $0992          ;MON68K V4.4 subroutine
            4
            5   00008000                        ORG       $8000
            6   00008000 227C0000     UECHO     MOVEA.L   #BANNER,A1     ;send banner message
                00008004 801A
            7   00008006 4E42                   TRAP      #2
            8   00008008 4E40         LOOP      TRAP      #0             ;get at character
            9   0000800A 4EB80992               JSR       TOUPPER        ;convert to uppercase
           10   0000800E 4E41                   TRAP      #1             ;echo character
           11   00008010 B03C0051               CMP.B     #'Q',D0        ;is it 'Q' or 'q'?
           12   00008014 6702                   BEQ.S     EXIT           ;yes: exit to MON68K
           13   00008016 60F0                   BRA       LOOP           ;no:  repeat
           14   00008018 4E4E         EXIT      TRAP      #14
           15   0000801A 0D0A2A2A     BANNER    DC.B      CR,LF,'*** UPPERCASE ECHO ***'
                0000801E 2A205550
                00008022 50455243
                00008026 41534520
                0000802A 4543484F
                0000802E 202A2A2A
           16   00008032 0D0A00                 DC.B      CR,LF,0
           17   00008035                        END       UECHO
```

console using TRAP #1 in line 10. Before looping back, the character in D0 is checked in lines 11–12. If the character is 'Q' or 'q,' the program terminates to MON68K using TRAP #14 in line 14. Otherwise, the program branches back to repeat the loop (line 13).

This program is a good example of the effective use of MON68K resources to simplify programming tasks.

**Interrupts**

The 68000 architecture supports seven interrupt levels. Four of these have designated purposes with MON68K, and three are uncommitted. Table E-5 illustrates MON68K's implementation of interrupts.

The physical connections for interrupt levels 1, 2, 3, and 7 are shown in Chapter 8. A jumper called X16 is used to force MON68K to begin execution at address $004000 immediately after a system reset. Address $004000 is the first address of the user EPROMs. This is a useful feature that allows user programs in EPROM to coexist with MON68K. The main benefit is that the user program in EPROM can execute immediately after reset, thus avoiding the need to connect a terminal or host computer simply to issue "GO 4000" to MON68K.

The 68681 DUART is hard-wired to generate a level-2 interrupt on the 68KMB. Since the 68681 is designed to generate a user vector during IACK cycles (as opposed to an autovector), the interrupt vector register inside the 68681 should be initialized with $26_{10}$ to benefit from MON68K's defined entry points. This done, the first instruction will execute from address $008006 when a 68681 interrupt is responded to. See Chapter 9 for programming examples.

The I/O expansion connector on the 68KMB includes the level-3 interrupt signal, $\overline{INT3}$, and the autovector handshake signal, $\overline{VPA}$. As configured through MON68K, the first instruction to execute in response to a level-3 interrupt is at address $00800C. See Chapter 9 for programming examples.

Interrupt levels 4, 5, and 6 are not used by the 68KMB. Interrupt sources may be added to generate these signals, and the interrupt handlers may be written to begin at the entry points in Table E-5.

The MONITOR switch on the 68KMB generates a non-maskable level-7 interrupt. The main purpose of this switch is to terminate a user program. The user register set is saved and displayed on the console prior to returning to MON68K.

**Exceptions**

All 68000 exceptions are accommodated in one form or another by MON68K. Most of the 255 exceptions are designated *errors* and output an appropriate message on the console in the event the exception occurs. Obviously, this is not the case for traps and interrupts, as discussed above. Consult the MON68K.LST listing later in this appendix for complete details.

Table E-5.    MON68K Implementation of Interrupts.

| Interrupt | Use | Entry Point | Description |
|---|---|---|---|
| 1 | RESET jumper | $004000 | If the jumper X16 is installed in the 68KMB, begin execution at address $4000 immediately after system reset |
| 2 | 68681 DUART | $008006 | The 68681 DUART is wired to interrupt on level-2 with the 68KMB |
| 3 | I/O expansion board | $00800C | The expansion connector J2 includes the level-3 interrupt signal |
| 4 | – | $008012 | Available to the user |
| 5 | – | $008018 | Available to the user |
| 6 | – | $00801E | Available to the user |
| 7 | MONITOR switch | – | Terminate user program; save user register set; display user register set on console; return to MON68K |

## User-Program Organization

User programs may reside anywhere in the bottom 14K bytes of system RAM—from address $008000 to $00B7FF. The most logical starting address of user programs is the beginning of RAM, at address $008000. If interrupts or user-defined traps are not used, then programs may start at $8000 and proceed upward through the RAM space to address $00B7FF. This will be the case for most introductory student programs.

If user-defined traps and/or interrupts are used, then the user program must be organized to accommodate the entry points defined by MON68K and listed in Table E-3 and Table E-5. As an example, let's assume a user program implements all available traps and interrupts. This is unlikely; however, the following organization would be used if this were the case:

```
  1   00008000                         ORG      $8000
  2   00008000 4EF90000   EXAMPLE JMP   >BEGIN           ;jump to user program
      00008004 805A
  3                         *
  4                         * Entry points for interrupt service routines
  5                         *
  6   00008006 4EF90000             JMP   >DUART_ISR    ;68681 DUART
      0000800A 805C
  7   0000800C 4EF90000             JMP   >IOEB_ISR     ;I/O exp. board
      00008010 805E
  8   00008012 4EF90000             JMP   >L4_ISR       ;level-4 interrupt
      00008016 8060
  9   00008018 4EF90000             JMP   >L5_ISR       ;level-5 interrupt
      0000801C 8062
 10   0000801E 4EF90000             JMP   >L6_ISR       ;level-6 interrupt
      00008022 8064
 11                         *
 12                         * Entry points for user-defined traps
 13                         *
 14   00008024 4EF90000             JMP   >TRAP5
      00008028 8066
 15   0000802A 4EF90000             JMP   >TRAP6
      0000802E 8068
 16   00008030 4EF90000             JMP   >TRAP7
      00008034 806A
 17   00008036 4EF90000             JMP   >TRAP8
      0000803A 806C
 18   0000803C 4EF90000             JMP   >TRAP9
      00008040 806E
 19   00008042 4EF90000             JMP   >TRAP10
      00008046 8070
 20   00008048 4EF90000             JMP   >TRAP11
      0000804C 8072
 21   0000804E 4EF90000             JMP   >TRAP12
      00008052 8074
 22   00008054 4EF90000             JMP   >TRAP13
      00008058 8076
 23                         *
 24                         * Code for user program begins above jump table
 25                         *
 26   0000805A 4E71       BEGIN    NOP    ;expand as necessary
 27                         *             ;end with TRAP #14
 28                         *
 29                         * Code for interrupts and user-defined traps
 30                         *
 31   0000805C 4E71       DUART_ISR NOP   ;expand as necessary (end with RTE)
 32   0000805E 4E71       IOEB_ISR NOP
 33   00008060 4E71       L4_ISR   NOP
 34   00008062 4E71       L5_ISR   NOP
```

**Continued.**
```
35   00008064  4E71     L6_ISR    NOP
36   00008066  4E71     TRAP5     NOP
37   00008068  4E71     TRAP6     NOP
38   0000806A  4E71     TRAP7     NOP
39   0000806C  4E71     TRAP8     NOP
40   0000806E  4E71     TRAP9     NOP
41   00008070  4E71     TRAP10    NOP
42   00008072  4E71     TRAP11    NOP
43   00008074  4E71     TRAP12    NOP
44   00008076  4E71     TRAP13    NOP
45   00008078                     END       EXAMPLE
```

The program begins at $008000 with a jump instruction to skip over the entry points for interrupts and user-defined traps. The following 14 instructions are also jump instructions. Each leads to the appropriate place later on where the code for the interrupt or user-defined trap appears. Note that in all cases the jump instructions use absolute long addressing. This ensures the instructions are precisely three words (six bytes). The effect is to position each jump instruction in the correct address for each entry point. This is verified by examining the address column beside the line number. For example, the interrupt service routine for a level-5 interrupt is set up through MON68K to begin at address $008018 (see Table E-5). In line 9 of the program above, the jump instruction leading to the level-5 ISR is correctly positioned at address $008018. Note that the entry points are defined in MON68K.LST. For the level-5 interrupt, the vector number is 29 and the vector address is $000074 (see Table 6-2 in Chapter 6). In line 60 of MON68K.LST, a DC.L directive appears that puts the entry point address ($00008018) in address $000074 (see page 416).

The user program, the ISRs, and the traps are all shown with a single NOP instruction. Of course, these would expand as per the user application. Remember that ISRs and traps must terminate with return-from-exception (RTE) instructions. The best way to terminate a user program is with TRAP #14, which returns control to MON68K.

### Customizing MON68K

There are a variety of ways users may customize MON68K for their own purpose. The primary mechanism is a **patch.** Usually a patch is defined as a change made to the binary image of a program to correct a bug. For our purpose, a patch is a change introduced to the binary image of MON68K to alter its operation to suit a user's need.

The simplest example, perhaps, is a patch to alter the baud rate of the serial interface to the 68681 DUART. By default, MON68K operates at 9600 baud. This rate is set in the routine that initializes the 68681. Specifically, the following instruction is found in the INIT_DUART subroutine:

```
MOVE.B   #B9600,CSRA(A0)
```

See line 42 in IO.LST. The symbol B9600 is equated to the constant $BB near the top of IO.LST, in line 22 (see page 429). This instruction sets the baud rate for the 68681's serial port. With a bit of investigation (see IO.LST and MON68K.MAP later in this appendix), it is easy to determine that the immediate data reside at byte-address $000A47 in MON68K. Alternate baud rates are set through other patterns, as listed in the 68681 data sheet in Appendix H. The most common baud rates are summarized in Table E-6.

Table E-6.   Customizing MON68K's
Baud Rate.

| MON68K Address | Byte | Baud Rate |
|---|---|---|
| $000A47 | $44 | 300 |
| $000A47 | $66 | 1200 |
| $000A47 | $88 | 2400 |
| $000A47 | $99 | 4800 |
| $000A47 | $BB | 9600 |

Note that the 68KMB is capable of accepting continuous input at 9600 baud. This occurs, for example, while loading S-records. However, it is possible that the host computer/terminal cannot receive continuous characters at 9600 baud. This might occur, for example, during a memory display (MD) command. Some systems may experience buffer overflow problems. If this is the case, reduce the baud rate of MON68K (or get a faster host!).

A patch may be introduced easily during EPROM programming. After MON68K is loaded into the EPROM programmer's RAM buffer, use the software's memory display/edit commands to display address $000A47 and then introduce the appropriate patch. The file called MON68K.HEX, on the accompanying disk, contains MON68K as a series of S-records.

The data format for the 68681 DUART is set through the byte at address $000A3B, which is written to Mode Register 1A (MR1A) during the initialization sequence. The current format is 7 data bits with odd parity. Different formats are possible by altering this byte in conformance with the bit patterns given in Appendix H for register MR1A.

One change that is particularly powerful is to expand MON68K's command set. Currently, MON68K commands are implemented through a look-up table (see MON68K.LST lines 167–192). Each entry corresponds to a letter of the alphabet. Of the 26 possible command types, most are unimplemented. The user could, for example, add a command that begins with the letter P by changing the word in address $0004D2 (see MON68K.LST, line 182). The new word should be the 16-bit address of the new command. The code must be added to the end of MON68K. The last address of MON68K is read from the link map in the listing MON68K.MAP. For version 4.4, the first empty address is $001490 + $000CBC = $00214C.

Before adding a command in EPROM, it may be tested in RAM using MON68K's Y-command. Any command beginning with the letter Y automatically begins execution at address $8000. This is preferable to testing through the command "GO 8000," since the Y-command also inputs command-line parameters for use in the command. Once the command is debugged in RAM, it may be added to MON68K and assigned the desired letter. Make sure the code is position-independent, otherwise the object image will not execute properly when repositioned in MON68K.

MON68K's command-line parameters are longword RAM locations defined in the GETPAR module (see GETPAR.LST, lines 65–69). The absolute address of each parameter is given in the MON68K's link map (see MON68K.MAP). For example, PAR1 is at longword address $00B832 in MON68K version 4.4.

The more ambitious reader may even wish to redesign some of MON68K's exception routines. For example, routines to implement complex arithmetic operations could be added to MON68K and accessed through the F-line emulation exception. The patch—the address of the start of the exception routine— must be placed at the longword address $002C in MON68K (see MON68K.LST, line 48).

### Listings

The following pages contains the listing files for MON68K. The overall shape of the program is determined in the first module—MON68K. This module contains the following parts in order:

- Comment header (lines 1–15)
- Symbol definitions (lines 16–26)
- Declaration of external symbols (lines 28–33)
- Declaration of public symbols (line 34)
- RSEG directive to begin relocatable code segment named EPROM (line 36)
- Reset SP and PC values (lines 37–38)
- Exception vectors (lines 39–81)
- Initialization instructions (lines 110–129)
- Command processing code (lines 122–165)
- Command look-up table (lines 167–192)
- Exception code (lines 194–255)
- Code for HE command (lines 259–261)

- Message strings (lines 262–301)
- RSEG directive to begin relocatable data segment named RAM (line 303)
- DS directive to create command-line buffer

The rest of the modules contain code supporting MON68K's commands.

A particularly important listing is the link map—MON68K.MAP. This listing is the primary reference to determine *what is where* in MON68K. It contains the absolute address of all MON68K symbols.

Note that the listing for the subroutine to disassemble a 68000 instruction—DCODE68K.LST—has been deleted. This subroutine was extracted from an electronic bulletin board maintained by Motorola. The DCODE68K subroutine originally appeared in a 68000 monitor program from Motorola. Motorola's permission to use the code in MON68K is greatly appreciated.

# MON68K.LST

```
1     ***********************************************************
2        * MON68K.SRC                                           *
3        *                  68000 Monitor Program               *
4        *                  =====================               *
5        *                                                      *
6        * System Configuration:                                *
7        *                                                      *
8        *    CPU            68000, 3.6864 MHz                  *
9        *    Monitor EPROM  $000000-$003FFF (16K)             *
10       *    User EPROM     $004000-$007FFF (16K)             *
11       *    RAM            $008000-$00BFFF (16K)             *
12       *    I/O            $00C001-$00C01F (68681 DUART)     *
13       *                                                      *
14       *                        (c) I. Scott MacKenzie, 1993, 1994 *
15       ***********************************************************
16   0000C000       SP_INIT    EQU     $C000          ;top-of-stack (+1)
17   00000400       PC_INIT    EQU     $400           ;above exception vectors
18   00002700       SR_INIT    EQU     $2700          ;default user SR
19   0000B800       USTACK     EQU     $B800          ;default value of user SP
20   00008000       URAM       EQU     $8000          ;default value of user PC
21   00004000       UEPROM     EQU     $4000          ;user EPROM entry point
22   00000028       BUFFSIZ    EQU     40             ;command line buffer size
23   0000001A       EOF        EQU     $1A            ;control-Z
24   0000000D       CR         EQU     $0D            ;carriage return
25   0000000A       LF         EQU     $0A            ;line feed
26   00000007       BEL        EQU     $07            ;bell code
27
28   00000000       EXTERN   OUTCHR,INCHR,OUTSTR,INLINE
29   00000000       EXTERN   INIT_DUART,ISALPH,GETPAR,UA7
30   00000000       EXTERN   PAR1,SIZE,PERIOD,KEYHIT
31   00000000       EXTERN   UPC,USR,UD0,TRE,COMMAND,TBP,RDS
32   00000000       EXTERN   OUTADD,BREAK,T_DELAY
33   00000000       EXTERN   D_CMD,G_CMD,L_CMD,M_CMD,R_CMD,S_CMD,T_CMD
34   00000000       PUBLIC   MON68K,MON68K2,BUFFER
35
36   00000000                RSEG     EPROM          ;begin at $000000
37   00000000 0000C000       DC.L     SP_INIT        ;supervisor SP
38   00000004 00000400       DC.L     PC_INIT        ;reset PC value
39   00000008 00000506       DC.L     BUS_ERROR
40   0000000C 0000050C       DC.L     ADDRESS_ERROR
41   00000010 00000518       DC.L     ILLEGAL_INSTRUCTION
42   00000014 0000051E       DC.L     ZERO_DIVIDE
43   00000018 00000524       DC.L     CHK_INSTRUCTION
44   0000001C 0000052A       DC.L     TRAPV_INSTRUCTION
45   00000020 00000530       DC.L     PRIVILEGE_VIOLATION
46   00000024 00000000       DC.L     TRE            ;TRace Exeception code
47   00000028 00000536       DC.L     LINE_0101_EMULATOR
48   0000002C 0000053C       DC.L     LINE_1111_EMULATOR
49   00000030 00000566       DC.L     ERROR
50   00000034 00000566       DC.L     ERROR
51   00000038 00000542       DC.L     FORMAT_ERROR
52   0000003C 00000548       DC.L     UNINITIALIZED_INTERRUPT_VECTOR
53   00000040 00000566       DC.L     ERROR,ERROR,ERROR,ERROR
     00000044 00000566
     00000048 00000566
     0000004C 00000566
54   00000050 00000566       DC.L     ERROR,ERROR,ERROR,ERROR
     00000054 00000566
     00000058 00000566
     0000005C 00000566
```

```
55   00000060 0000054E              DC.L    SPURIOUS_INTERRUPT
56   00000064 00004000              DC.L    UEPROM          ;Interrupt 1: reset jumper
57   00000068 00008006              DC.L    URAM+6          ;Interrupt 2: 68681
58   0000006C 0000800C              DC.L    URAM+12         ;Interrupt 3: I/O exp. board
59   00000070 00008012              DC.L    URAM+18         ;Interrupt 4: user
60   00000074 00008018              DC.L    URAM+24         ;Interrupt 5: user
61   00000078 0000801E              DC.L    URAM+30         ;Interrupt 6: user
62   0000007C 000004E8              DC.L    NMI             ;Interrupt 7: Monitor Switch
63   00000080 00000000              DC.L    INCHR           ;Trap 0: INput CHaRacter
64   00000084 00000000              DC.L    OUTCHR          ;Trap 1: OUTput CHaRacter
65   00000088 00000000              DC.L    OUTSTR          ;Trap 2: OUTput STRing
66   0000008C 00000000              DC.L    INLINE          ;Trap 3: INput LINE
67   00000090 00000000              DC.L    KEYHIT          ;Trap 4: is a KEY HIT?
68   00000094 00008024              DC.L    URAM+36         ;Trap 5
69   00000098 0000802A              DC.L    URAM+42         ;Trap 6
70   0000009C 00008030              DC.L    URAM+48         ;Trap 7
71   000000A0 00008036              DC.L    URAM+54         ;Trap 8
72   000000A4 0000803C              DC.L    URAM+60         ;Trap 9
73   000000A8 00008042              DC.L    URAM+66         ;Trap 10
74   000000AC 00008048              DC.L    URAM+72         ;Trap 11
75   000000B0 0000804E              DC.L    URAM+78         ;Trap 12
76   000000B4 00008054              DC.L    URAM+84         ;Trap 13
77   000000B8 00000000              DC.L    BREAK           ;Trap 14: end user program
78   000000BC 00000000              DC.L    TBP             ;Trap 15: Temporary BrkPoint
79                           *
80                           * Listing turned off on following line (all vectors = "ERROR")
81                           *
110  00000400 027CF8FF              ANDI.W  #$F8FF,SR       ;enable all interrupts
111                           *                             ;if reset jumper in, INT1
112  00000404 007C0700              ORI.W   #$0700,SR       ;mask all interrupts
113  00000408 4EB80000              JSR     INIT_DUART      ;init 68681
114  0000040C 23FC0000              MOVE.L  #2,>SIZE        ;init SIZE to 2 (word)
     00000410 00020000
     00000414 0000
115  00000416 23FC0000              MOVE.L  #1,>T_DELAY     ;init trace delay to 0 sec.
     0000041A 00010000
     0000041E 0000
116  00000420 207C0000              MOVEA.L #USTACK,A0
     00000424 B800
117  00000426 4E60                  MOVE.L  A0,USP          ;default user SP value
118  00000428 33FC2700              MOVE.W  #SR_INIT,>USR   ;default user SR value
     0000042C 00000000
119  00000430 23FC0000              MOVE.L  #URAM,>UPC      ;default user PC value
     00000434 80000000
     00000438 0000
120  0000043A 303C000E              MOVE.W  #14,D0          ;initialize user reg. to 0
121  0000043E 207C0000              MOVEA.L #UD0,A0         ;NOTE: UA7 left as is
     00000442 0000
122  00000444 4298         LOOP     CLR.L   (A0)+
123  00000446 51C8FFFC              DBRA    D0,LOOP         ;dec. D0[0:15] until -1
124
125  0000044A 43FA0496              LEA     PROMPT1(PC),A1  ;MON68K
126  0000044E 4E42                  TRAP    #2
127                           *
128                           * Soft re-entry (INT7, ABORT, some exceptions, etc.)
129                           *
130  00000450 2E7C0000     MON68K   MOVEA.L #SP_INIT,A7
     00000454 C000
131  00000456 43FA0493              LEA     PROMPT2(PC),A1  ;Vn>
132  0000045A 4E42                  TRAP    #2
```

```
133  0000045C 227C0000         MOVEA.L  #BUFFER,A1       ;A1 = command address
     00000460 0000
134  00000462 7228             MOVEQ.L  #BUFFSIZ,D1      ;D1 = buffer size
135  00000464 4E43             TRAP     #3               ;get a command
136                    *
137            * Enter here to re-interpret current command (SP re-initialized)
138                    *
139  00000466 2E7C0000 MON68K2 MOVEA.L  #SP_INIT,A7
     0000046A C000
140  0000046C 4EB80000         JSR      GETPAR
141  00000470 227C0000         MOVEA.L  #COMMAND,A1      ;A1 points to command
     00000474 0000
142  00000476 1011             MOVE.B   (A1),D0          ;D0 contains 1st character
143  00000478 0C00002E         CMPI.B   #'.',D0          ;1st character = '.'?
144  0000047C 6606             BNE.S    SKIP             ;no:  leave as is
145  0000047E 103C005A         MOVE.B   #'Z',D0          ;yes: change to Z
146  00000482 600A             BRA.S    SKIP1
147  00000484 0C00003F SKIP    CMPI.B   #'?',D0          ;1st char. = '?'
148  00000488 6604             BNE.S    SKIP1            ;no:  leave as is
149  0000048A 103C0048         MOVE.B   #'H',D0          ;yes: change to H (Help)
150  0000048E 4A00     SKIP1   TST.B    D0               ;if no command ...
151  00000490 67BE             BEQ      MON68K           ;   get another
152  00000492 61000000 SKIP2   BSR      ISALPH           ;1st char. must be alpha
153  00000496 64B8             BCC      MON68K           ;if not, get a new command
154  00000498 5300             SUBQ.B   #1,D0            ;adjust: $41 - 1 = $40 ("A")
155  0000049A 0200001F         ANDI.B   #$1F,D0          ;reduce to 5 bits
156  0000049E E318             ROL.B    #1,D0            ;word align
157  000004A0 43FA0012         LEA      TABLE(PC),A1     ;A1 points to table
158  000004A4 30310000         MOVE     0(A1,D0),D0      ;build command address
159  000004A8 2240             MOVEA.L  D0,A1            ;point to command address
160                    *                                 ;Note: A1[16:31] = 0
161  000004AA 4ED1             JMP      (A1)             ;execute command
162
163  000004AC 43FA0445 NOCMD   LEA      PROMPT3(PC),A1   ;no command
164  000004B0 4E42             TRAP     #2               ;send '?' and
165  000004B2 609C             BRA      MON68K           ;return to monitor
166
167  000004B4 04AC     TABLE   DC.W     NOCMD            ;A
168  000004B6 04AC             DC.W     NOCMD            ;B
169  000004B8 04AC             DC.W     NOCMD            ;C
170  000004BA 0000             DC.W     D_CMD            ;D: disassemble instructions
171  000004BC 04AC             DC.W     NOCMD            ;E
172  000004BE 04AC             DC.W     NOCMD            ;F
173  000004C0 0000             DC.W     G_CMD            ;G: go to user program
174  000004C2 0570             DC.W     HELP             ;H: help (display commands)
175  000004C4 04AC             DC.W     NOCMD            ;I
176  000004C6 04AC             DC.W     NOCMD            ;J
177  000004C8 04AC             DC.W     NOCMD            ;K
178  000004CA 0000             DC.W     L_CMD            ;L: load S-records
179  000004CC 0000             DC.W     M_CMD            ;M: memory commands
180  000004CE 04AC             DC.W     NOCMD            ;N
181  000004D0 04AC             DC.W     NOCMD            ;O
182  000004D2 04AC             DC.W     NOCMD            ;P
183  000004D4 04AC             DC.W     NOCMD            ;Q
184  000004D6 0000             DC.W     R_CMD            ;R: register dump
185  000004D8 0000             DC.W     S_CMD            ;S: size of data
186  000004DA 0000             DC.W     T_CMD            ;T: trace instructions
187  000004DC 04AC             DC.W     NOCMD            ;U
188  000004DE 04AC             DC.W     NOCMD            ;V
189  000004E0 04AC             DC.W     NOCMD            ;W
190  000004E2 04AC             DC.W     NOCMD            ;X
191  000004E4 8000             DC.W     URAM             ;Y: (use for testing)
```

```
192    000004E6 0000                      DC.W     PERIOD           ;Z: . command
193
194    000004E8 48F97FFF   NMI            MOVEM.L  D0-D7/A0-A6,>UD0
       000004EC 00000000
195    000004F0 23EF0002                  MOVE.L   2(A7),>UPC
       000004F4 00000000
196    000004F8 33D70000                  MOVE.W   (A7),>USR
       000004FC 0000
197    000004FE 4EB80000                  JSR      RDS
198    00000502 6000FF4C                  BRA      MON68K
199                        *
200                        * Bus Error or Address Error: Send a message to the console,
201                        * dump the access address, beep, then return to MON68K.
202                        *
203    00000506 43FA02A5   BUS_ERROR      LEA      MESSAGE1(PC),A1
204    0000050A 6004                      BRA.S    SEND2              ;dump access address
205    0000050C            ADDRESS_ERROR
206    0000050C 43FA02AC                  LEA MESSAGE2(PC),A1
207    00000510 4E42       SEND2          TRAP     #2
208    00000512 43FA03BA                  LEA      MESSAGE13(PC),A1
209    00000516 6040                      BRA.S    AHEAD
210                        *
211                        * The following exceptions send a message to the console,
212                        * dump the PC, beep, then return to MON68K.
213                        *
214    00000518            ILLEGAL_INSTRUCTION
215    00000518 43FA02B1                  LEA MESSAGE3(PC),A1
216    0000051C 6034                      BRA.S    SEND
217    0000051E            ZERO_DIVIDE
218    0000051E 43FA02C2                  LEA MESSAGE4(PC),A1
219    00000522 602E                      BRA.S    SEND
220    00000524            CHK_INSTRUCTION
221    00000524 43FA02CB                  LEA MESSAGE5(PC),A1
222    00000528 6028                      BRA.S    SEND
223    0000052A            TRAPV_INSTRUCTION
224    0000052A 43FA02D8                  LEA MESSAGE6(PC),A1
225    0000052E 6022                      BRA.S    SEND
226    00000530            PRIVILEGE_VIOLATION
227    00000530 43FA02E7                  LEA MESSAGE7(PC),A1
228    00000534 601C                      BRA.S    SEND
229    00000536            LINE_0101_EMULATOR
230    00000536 43FA02F8                  LEA MESSAGE7A(PC),A1
231    0000053A 6016                      BRA.S    SEND
232    0000053C            LINE_1111_EMULATOR
233    0000053C 43FA030C                  LEA MESSAGE7B(PC),A1
234    00000540 6010                      BRA.S    SEND
235    00000542            FORMAT_ERROR
236    00000542 43FA0320                  LEA   MESSAGE9(PC),A1
237    00000546 600A                      BRA.S    SEND
238    00000548            UNINITIALIZED_INTERRUPT_VECTOR
239    00000548 43FA032A                  LEA MESSAGE10(PC),A1
240    0000054C 6004                      BRA.S    SEND
241    0000054E            SPURIOUS_INTERRUPT
242    0000054E 43FA0345                  LEA MESSAGE10A(PC),A1
243    00000552 4E42       SEND           TRAP     #2               ;send exception message
244    00000554 43FA0370                  LEA      MESSAGE12(PC),A1
245    00000558 4E42       AHEAD          TRAP     #2               ;send contents of PC
246    0000055A 206F0002                  MOVEA.L  2(A7),A0  ;stacked PC value
247    0000055E 61000000                  BSR      OUTADD
248    00000562 6000FEEC                  BRA      MON68K
249                        *
```

```
250                             * All other exceptions, are unimplemented. Send a message
251                             * to the console, beep, then return to MON68K.
252                             *
253   00000566 43FA0343  ERROR      LEA       MESSAGE11(PC),A1
254   0000056A 4E42                 TRAP      #2
255   0000056C 6000FEE2             BRA       MON68K
256                             *
257                             * Help: Send command summary to console
258                             *
259   00000570 43FA0008  HELP       LEA       HELP_STR(PC),A1
260   00000574 4E42                 TRAP      #2
261   00000576 6000FED8             BRA       MON68K
262   0000057A 0D0A      HELP_STR   DC.B      CR,LF
263   0000057C 2A2A2A2A             DC.B      '***** MON68K COMMAND SUMMARY *****',CR,LF
      00000580 2A204D4F
      00000584 4E36384B
      00000588 20434F4D
      0000058C 4D414E44
      00000590 2053554D
      00000594 4D415259
      00000598 202A2A2A
      0000059C 2A2A0D0A
264   000005A0 3D3D3D3D             DC.B      '====================================',CR,LF
      000005A4 3D3D3D3D
      000005A8 3D3D3D3D
      000005AC 3D3D3D3D
      000005B0 3D3D3D3D
      000005B4 3D3D3D3D
      000005B8 3D3D3D3D
      000005BC 3D3D3D3D
      000005C0 3D3D0D0A
265   000005C4 44492020             DC.B      'DI      disassemble instructions',CR,LF
      000005C8 20202064
      000005CC 69736173
      000005D0 73656D62
      000005D4 6C652069
      000005D8 6E737472
      000005DC 75637469
      000005E0 6F6E730D
      000005E4 0A
266   000005E5 474F2020             DC.B      'GO      go to user program',CR,LF
      000005E9 20202067
      000005ED 6F20746F
      000005F1 20757365
      000005F5 72207072
      000005F9 6F677261
      000005FD 6D0D0A
267   00000600 47542020             DC.B      'GT      go to temporary breakpoint',CR,LF
      00000604 20202067
      00000608 6F20746F
      0000060C 2074656D
      00000610 706F7261
      00000614 72792062
      00000618 7265616B
      0000061C 706F696E
      00000620 740D0A
268   00000623 48452020             DC.B      'HE      help (display this message)',CR,LF
      00000627 20202068
      0000062B 656C7020
      0000062F 28646973
      00000633 706C6179
```

```
        00000637 20746869
        0000063B 73206D65
        0000063F 73736167
        00000643 65290D0A
269     00000647 4C472020          DC.B    'LG      load S-records and go',CR,LF
        0000064B 2020206C
        0000064F 6F616420
        00000653 532D7265
        00000657 636F7264
        0000065B 7320616E
        0000065F 6420676F
        00000663 0D0A
270     00000665 4C4F2020          DC.B    'LO      load S-records',CR,LF
        00000669 2020206C
        0000066D 6F616420
        00000671 532D7265
        00000675 636F7264
        00000679 730D0A
271     0000067C 4D432020          DC.B    'MC      memory copy',CR,LF
        00000680 2020206D
        00000684 656D6F72
        00000688 7920636F
        0000068C 70790D0A
272     00000690 4D442020          DC.B    'MD      memory dump',CR,LF
        00000694 2020206D
        00000698 656D6F72
        0000069C 79206475
        000006A0 6D700D0A
273     000006A4 4D462020          DC.B    'MF      memory fill',CR,LF
        000006A8 2020206D
        000006AC 656D6F72
        000006B0 79206669
        000006B4 6C6C0D0A
274     000006B8 4D4D2020          DC.B    'MM      memory modify',CR,LF
        000006BC 2020206D
        000006C0 656D6F72
        000006C4 79206D6F
        000006C8 64696679
        000006CC 0D0A
275     000006CE 4D542020          DC.B    'MT      memory test',CR,LF
        000006D2 2020206D
        000006D6 656D6F72
        000006DA 79207465
        000006DE 73740D0A
276     000006E2 52442020          DC.B    'RD      register dump',CR,LF
        000006E6 20202072
        000006EA 65676973
        000006EE 74657220
        000006F2 64756D70
        000006F6 0D0A
277     000006F8 535A2020          DC.B    'SZ      size of data for MD command',CR,LF
        000006FC 20202073
        00000700 697A6520
        00000704 6F662064
        00000708 61746120
        0000070C 666F7220
        00000710 4D442063
        00000714 6F6D6D61
        00000718 6E640D0A
278     0000071C 54442020          DC.B    'TD      trace delay',CR,LF
        00000720 20202074
```

```
          00000724 72616365
          00000728 2064656C
          0000072C 61790D0A
279       00000730 54522020            DC.B      'TR      trace instructions',CR,LF
          00000734 20202074
          00000738 72616365
          0000073C 20696E73
          00000740 74727563
          00000744 74696F6E
          00000748 730D0A
280       0000074B 2E522058            DC.B      '.R X    set register R to value X',CR,LF
          0000074F 20202073
          00000753 65742072
          00000757 65676973
          0000075B 74657220
          0000075F 5220746F
          00000763 2076616C
          00000767 75652058
          0000076B 0D0A
281       0000076D 3F202020            DC.B      '?       display this message',CR,LF
          00000771 20202064
          00000775 6973706C
          00000779 61792074
          0000077D 68697320
          00000781 6D657373
          00000785 6167650D
          00000789 0A
282       0000078A 3D3D3D3D3D          DC.B      '===================================',0
          0000078E 3D3D3D3D
          00000792 3D3D3D3D
          00000796 3D3D3D3D
          0000079A 3D3D3D3D
          0000079E 3D3D3D3D
          000007A2 3D3D3D3D
          000007A6 3D3D3D3D
          000007AA 3D3D00
283
284       000007AD 0D0A0742   MESSAGE1 DC.B      CR,LF,BEL,'Bus Error',0
          000007B1 75732045
          000007B5 72726F72
          000007B9 00
285       000007BA 0D0A0741   MESSAGE2 DC.B      CR,LF,BEL,'Address Error',0
          000007BE 64647265
          000007C2 73732045
          000007C6 72726F72
          000007CA 00
286       000007CB 0D0A0749   MESSAGE3 DC.B      CR,LF,BEL,'Illegal Instruction',0
          000007CF 6C6C6567
          000007D3 616C2049
          000007D7 6E737472
          000007DB 75637469
          000007DF 6F6E00
287       000007E2 0D0A075A   MESSAGE4 DC.B      CR,LF,BEL,'Zero Divide',0
          000007E6 65726F20
          000007EA 44697669
          000007EE 646500
288       000007F1 0D0A0743   MESSAGE5 DC.B      CR,LF,BEL,'CHK Instruction',0
          000007F5 484B2049
          000007F9 6E737472
          000007FD 75637469
          00000801 6F6E00
```

```
289   00000804  0D0A0754   MESSAGE6    DC.B      CR,LF,BEL,'TRAPV Instruction',0
      00000808  52415056
      0000080C  20496E73
      00000810  74727563
      00000814  74696F6E
      00000818  00
290   00000819  0D0A0750   MESSAGE7    DC.B      CR,LF,BEL,'Privilege Violation',0
      0000081D  72697669
      00000821  6C656765
      00000825  2056696F
      00000829  6C617469
      0000082D  6F6E00
291   00000830  0D0A074C   MESSAGE7A   DC.B      CR,LF,BEL,'Line 0101 Emulate Trap',0
      00000834  696E6520
      00000838  30313031
      0000083C  20456D75
      00000840  6C617465
      00000844  20547261
      00000848  7000
292   0000084A  0D0A074C   MESSAGE7B   DC.B      CR,LF,BEL,'Line 1111 Emulate Trap',0
      0000084E  696E6520
      00000852  31313131
      00000856  20456D75
      0000085A  6C617465
      0000085E  20547261
      00000862  7000
293   00000864  0D0A0746   MESSAGE9    DC.B      CR,LF,BEL,'Format Error',0
      00000868  6F726D61
      0000086C  74204572
      00000870  726F7200
294   00000874  0D0A0755   MESSAGE10   DC.B      CR,LF,BEL,'Uninitialized Interrupt Vector'
      00000878  6E696E69
      0000087C  7469616C
      00000880  697A6564
      00000884  20496E74
      00000888  65727275
      0000088C  70742056
      00000890  6563746F
      00000894  72
295   00000895  0D0A0753   MESSAGE10A  DC.B      CR,LF,BEL,'Spurious Interrupt',0
      00000899  70757269
      0000089D  6F757320
      000008A1  496E7465
      000008A5  72727570
      000008A9  7400
296   000008AB  0D0A0755   MESSAGE11   DC.B      CR,LF,BEL,'Unimplemented Exception',0
      000008AF  6E696D70
      000008B3  6C656D65
      000008B7  6E746564
      000008BB  20457863
      000008BF  65707469
      000008C3  6F6E00
297   000008C6  0D0A5043   MESSAGE12   DC.B      CR,LF,'PC = ',0
      000008CA  203D2000
298   000008CE  0D0A4163   MESSAGE13   DC.B      CR,LF,'Access address = ',0
      000008D2  63657373
      000008D6  20616464
      000008DA  72657373
      000008DE  203D2000
299   000008E2  0D0A4D4F   PROMPT1     DC.B      CR,LF,'MON68K',0
      000008E6  4E36384B
      000008EA  00
```

```
300   000008EB 0D0A5634   PROMPT2   DC.B   CR,LF,'V4.4>',0
      000008EF 2E343E00
301   000008F3 0D0A3F00   PROMPT3   DC.B   CR,LF,'?',0
302
303   00000000            RSEG   RAM
304   00000000   BUFFER   DS.B   BUFFSIZ   ;command line buffer
305   00000028            END
```

# GETPAR.LST

```
 1                          *****************************************************************
 2                          * GETPAR    GET PARameters from input line                    *
 3                          *****************************************************************
 4  0000000D               CR        EQU       $0D
 5  00000020               SPACE     EQU       $20
 6
 7  00000000                         EXTERN    BUFFER,ATOH,ISHEX,TOUPPER
 8  00000000                         PUBLIC    GETPAR,COMMAND,PAR1,PAR2,PAR3,PAR4,NPAR
 9
10   00000000                        RSEG      EPROM
11  00000000 227C0000      GETPAR    MOVEA.L   #BUFFER,A1      ;A1 points to input buffer
    00000004 0000
12  00000006 247C0000                MOVEA.L   #COMMAND,A2     ;A2 points to commmand buff.
    0000000A 0000
13  0000000C 42390000                CLR.B     >NPAR           ;init. # of parameters to 0
    00000010 0009
14                         *
15                         * Get command
16                         *
17  00000012 1019          AGAIN22   MOVE.B    (A1)+,D0        ;first, get command char.
18  00000014 B03C0020                CMP.B     #SPACE,D0       ;ignore leading spaces
19  00000018 67F8                    BEQ.S     AGAIN22
20  0000001A 6002                    BRA.S     SKIP99
21  0000001C 1019          AGAIN     MOVE.B    (A1)+,D0
22  0000001E 61000000      SKIP99    BSR       TOUPPER         ;convert to upperca se
23  00000022 14C0                    MOVE.B    D0,(A2)+        ;put in command buffer
24  00000024 0C00000D                CMPI.B    #CR,D0
25  00000028 6604                    BNE.S     SKIP3           ;carriage return?
26  0000002A 4222                    CLR.B     -(A2)           ;yes: put 0 at end of commnd
27  0000002C 605A                    BRA.S     EXIT            ;          and exit
28  0000002E 0C000020      SKIP3     CMPI.B    #SPACE,D0       ;no:  space?
29  00000032 6702                    BEQ.S     SKIP2           ;yes: get parameters
30  00000034 60E6                    BRA       AGAIN           ;no:  get next command char.
31                         *
32                         * Get parameters (arrive here when a space is found)
33                         *
34  00000036 4222          SKIP2     CLR.B     -(A2)           ;put 0 at end of command
35  00000038 247C0000                MOVEA.L   #PAR1,A2        ;A2 = pointer to parameters
    0000003C 000A
36  0000003E 1E3C0004                MOVE.B    #COUNT,D7       ;D7 = max. # of parameters
37  00000042 08830000                BCLR.B    #0,D3           ;D3[0] = "in parameter" flag
38  00000046 4281          AGAIN2    CLR.L     D1              ;D1 = parameter (binary)
39  00000048 1019          AGAIN3    MOVE.B    (A1)+,D0
40  0000004A 0C00000D                CMPI.B    #CR,D0
41  0000004E 6606                    BNE.S     SKIP8
42  00000050 1E3C0001                MOVE.B    #1,D7
43  00000054 6024                    BRA.S     STORE
44  00000056 0C000020      SKIP8     CMPI.B    #SPACE,D0
45  0000005A 6714                    BEQ.S     SKIP9
46  0000005C 0C00002C                CMPI.B    #',',D0
47  00000060 670E                    BEQ.S     SKIP9
48  00000062 08C30000                BSET.B    #0,D3
49  00000066 61000000                BSR       ATOH
50  0000006A 8280                    OR.L      D0,D1
51  0000006C E999                    ROL.L     #4,D1
52  0000006E 60D8                    BRA       AGAIN3
53  00000070 08030000      SKIP9     BTST      #0,D3
54  00000074 67D2                    BEQ       AGAIN3
55  00000076 08830000                BCLR.B    #0,D3
```

```
56   0000007A 52390000   STORE      ADDQ.B    #1,>NPAR
     0000007E 0009
57   00000080 E899                  ROR.L     #4,D1          ;undo last rotate
58   00000082 24C1                  MOVE.L    D1,(A2)+
59   00000084 5307                  SUBQ.B    #1,D7
60   00000086 66BE                  BNE       AGAIN2
61   00000088 4E75       EXIT       RTS
62
63   00000000                       RSEG      RAM
64   00000000            COMMAND    DS.B      9              ;command characters copied here
65   00000009            NPAR       DS.B      1              ;number of parameters entered
66   0000000A            PAR1       DS.L      1              ;binary parameters stored here
67   0000000E            PAR2       DS.L      1
68   00000012            PAR3       DS.L      1
69   00000016            PAR4       DS.L      1
70   00000004            COUNT      EQU       (*-PAR1)/4
71   0000001A                       END
```

# CONVERT.LST

```
 1                       ***********************************************************
 2                       * CONVERT.SRC                                            *
 3                       ***********************************************************
 4  00000000                        EXTERN   ISALPH
 5  00000000                        PUBLIC   ATOH,TOUPPER,HTOA
 6  00000000                        RSEG     EPROM
 7                       ***********************************************************
 8                       * ATOH      ASCII-to-hex: convert a single hex-ASCII      *
 9                       *           character to a hex nibble                     *
10                       *                                                         *
11                       *           ENTER:   D0[0:7] contains hex-ASCII character in  *
12                       *                      range '0'-'9' or 'A' to 'F'        *
13                       *           EXIT:    D0[0:3] contains hex nibble          *
14                       *                    D0[4:7] clear                        *
15                       *                    D0[8:31] unchanged                   *
16                       *           USES:    no subroutines                       *
17                       ***********************************************************
18  00000000 0C00003A    ATOH      CMPI.B   #'9'+1,D0
19  00000004 6504                   BCS.S    ATOH2
20  00000006 D03C0009               ADD.B    #9,D0         ;'A': $41 & $0F + 9 = $0A
21  0000000A 0200000F    ATOH2     ANDI.B   #$0F,D0
22  0000000E 4E75                   RTS
23
24                       ***********************************************************
25                       * TOUPPER   convert character TO UPPER case               *
26                       *                                                         *
27                       *           ENTER:   ASCII code in D0[0:7]                *
28                       *           EXIT:    converted to uppercase if alphabetic *
29                       *                      (left as is otherwise)             *
30                       *           USES:    ISALPH                               *
31                       ***********************************************************
32  00000010 61000000    TOUPPER   BSR      ISALPH        ;is character alphabetic?
33  00000014 6404                   BCC.S    EXIT          ;no:   leave as is
34  00000016 020000DF               ANDI.B   #$DF,D0       ;yes: clear bit 5 for uppercase
35  0000001A 4E75        EXIT      RTS
36
37                       ***********************************************************
38                       * HTOA      Hex-TO-Ascii conversion                       *
39                       *                                                         *
40                       *           ENTER:   D0[0:3] contains hex nibble          *
41                       *           EXIT:    D0[0:7] contains ASCII for hex nibble *
42                       *                    D0[8:31] unchanged                   *
43                       *           USES:    no subroutines                       *
44                       ***********************************************************
45  0000001C 0200000F    HTOA      ANDI.B   #$0F,D0       ;ensure bits 4-7 are clear
46  00000020 0C00000A               CMPI.B   #$0A,D0
47  00000024 6504                   BCS.S    HTOA2
48  00000026 06000007               ADDI.B   #7,D0
49  0000002A 06000030    HTOA2     ADDI.B   #'0',D0
50  0000002E 4E75                   RTS
51  00000030                        END
```

# IS.LST

```
 1                        ************************************************************
 2                        * IS        "Is" subroutines (check type of data)        *
 3                        ************************************************************
 4   00000000                     PUBLIC   ISHEX,ISDIGIT,ISALPH,ISGRAPH
 5   00000000                     RSEG     EPROM
 6                        ************************************************************
 7                        * ISHEX     IS character HEX-ascii?                       *
 8                        *                                                         *
 9                        *           ENTER:  ASCII code in D0[0:7]                 *
10                        *           EXIT:   C = 1 if yes (code in range '0'-'9',  *
11                        *                        'A'-'F', or 'a'-'f')             *
12                        *                   C = 0 if no                           *
13                        *                   D0[8:31] cleared                      *
14                        *           USES:   ISDIGIT                               *
15                        ************************************************************
16   00000000 02800000    ISHEX     ANDI.L   #$7F,D0       ;clear bits 8-31
     00000004 007F
17   00000006 6118                  BSR.S    ISDIGIT
18   00000008 6514                  BCS.S    SKIP
19   0000000A 00000020              ORI.B    #$20,D0       ;convert to lowercase
20   0000000E 0C000061              CMPI.B   #'a',D0
21   00000012 6506                  BCS.S    SKIP2
22   00000014 0C000067              CMPI.B   #'f'+1,D0
23   00000018 6504                  BCS.S    SKIP
24   0000001A 023C00FE  SKIP2       ANDI.B   #$FE,CCR      ;not hex
25   0000001E 4E75      SKIP        RTS
26
27                        ************************************************************
28                        * ISDIGIT   IS character an ascii DIGIT?                  *
29                        *                                                         *
30                        *           ENTER:  ASCII code in D0[0:7]                 *
31                        *           EXIT:   C = 1 if yes (code in range '0' to '9') *
32                        *                   C = 0 if no                           *
33                        *                   D0[8:31] cleared                      *
34                        *           USES:   no subroutines                        *
35                        ************************************************************
36   00000020 02800000    ISDIGIT   ANDI.L   #$7F,D0       ;clears bits 8-31
     00000024 007F
37   00000026 0C000030              CMPI.B   #'0',D0
38   0000002A 6506                  BCS.S    SKIP3
39   0000002C 0C00003A              CMPI.B   #'9'+1,D0
40   00000030 6504                  BCS.S    SKIP4         ;carry set if digit
41   00000032 023C00FE  SKIP3       ANDI.B   #$FE,CCR
42   00000036 4E75      SKIP4       RTS
43
44                        ************************************************************
45                        * ISALPH     IS character an ALPHabetic ascii code?       *
46                        *                                                         *
47                        *           ENTER:  ASCII code in D0[0:7]                 *
48                        *           EXIT:   C = 1 if yes (code in range 'a'-'z' or *
49                        *                        'A'-'Z'                          *
50                        *                   C = 0 if no                           *
51                        *                   D0[8:31] cleared                      *
52                        *           USES:   no subroutines                        *
53                        ************************************************************
54   00000038 02800000    ISALPH    ANDI.L   #$7F,D0       ;clear bits 8-31
     0000003C 007F
55   0000003E 0C000061              CMPI.B   #'a',D0
56   00000042 6506                  BCS.S    SKIP5
```

```
57  00000044 0C00007B           CMPI.B   #'z'+1,D0
58  00000048 650A               BCS.S    YES
59  0000004A 0C000041  SKIP5    CMPI.B   #'A',D0
60  0000004E 6506               BCS.S    NO
61  00000050 0C00005B           CMPI.B   #'Z'+1,D0
62  00000054 4E75      YES      RTS
63  00000056 023C00FE  NO       ANDI.B   #$FE,CCR
64  0000005A 4E75               RTS
65
66                    *****************************************************************
67                    * ISGRAPH    IS character an ascii GRAPHic code?                *
68                    *                                                               *
69                    *            ENTER:   ASCII code in D0[0:7]                     *
70                    *            EXIT:    C = 1 if yes (code in range $20 to $7E)   *
71                    *                     C = 0 if no                               *
72                    *                     D0[8:31] cleared                          *
73                    *            USES:    no subroutines                            *
74                    *****************************************************************
75  0000005C 40E7      ISGRAPH  MOVE.W   SR,-(A7)
76  0000005E 3F00               MOVE.W   D0,-(A7)
77  00000060 0240007F           ANDI.W   #$7F,D0        ;clear bits 8-31
78  00000064 0C000020           CMPI.B   #$20,D0
79  00000068 650A               BCS.S    NO2
80  0000006A 0C00007F           CMPI.B   #$7E+1,D0
81  0000006E 40EF0002           MOVE.W   SR,2(A7)       ;update carry bit
82  00000072 6006               BRA.S    ISGRAPH2
83  00000074 026FFFFE  NO2      ANDI.W   #$FFFE,2(A7)   ;clear carry bit
    00000078 0002
84  0000007A 301F      ISGRAPH2 MOVE.W   (A7)+,D0
85  0000007C 46DF               MOVE.W   (A7)+,SR
86  0000007E 4E75               RTS
87  00000080                    END
```

# IO.LST

```
 1            ***************************************************************
 2            * IO.SRC                                                      *
 3            ***************************************************************
 4            * 68681 address and register offsets (even-byte aligned)
 5   0000C001    DUART    EQU    $C001
 6   00000000    MR1A     EQU    0*2              ;mode reg. 1A
 7   00000000    MR2A     EQU    0*2              ;mode reg. 2A
 8   00000002    CSRA     EQU    1*2              ;clock select reg. A
 9   00000002    SRA      EQU    1*2              ;status reg. A
10   00000004    CRA      EQU    2*2              ;command reg. A
11   00000006    TBA      EQU    3*2              ;tx buffer A
12   00000006    RBA      EQU    3*2              ;rx buffer A
13   00000008    ACR      EQU    4*2              ;auxillary control reg.
14
15   0000001A    EOF      EQU    $1A              ;control-Z
16   0000000D    CR       EQU    $0D              ;carriage return
17   0000000A    LF       EQU    $0A              ;line feed
18   0000001B    ESC      EQU    $1B              ;escape
19   00000004    BS       EQU    $4               ;back space (VT100)
20   0000007F    DEL      EQU    $7F              ;delete
21   00000099    B4800    EQU    $99              ;4800 baud init value
22   000000BB    B9600    EQU    $BB              ;9600 baud init value
23
24   00000000             EXTERN  HTOA,ATOH
25   00000000             PUBLIC  OUTCHR,INCHR,OUTSTR,INLINE,INIT_DUART
26   00000000             PUBLIC  OUT2HX,OUTHEX,KEYHIT,NEWLINE,SPACE
27   00000000             PUBLIC  OUTADD,GETHEX
28
29   00000000             RSEG    EPROM
30
31            ***************************************************************
32            * INIT_DUART   INITialize 68681 DUART channel A               *
33            *                                                             *
34            *             ENTER:  no conditions                           *
35            *             EXIT:   68681 initialized                       *
36            *                     A0 contains address of 68681            *
37            *             USES:   no subroutines                          *
38            ***************************************************************
39   00000000 207C0000  INIT_DUART  MOVEA.L  #DUART,A0       ;A0 points to DUART
     00000004 C001
40   00000006 117C0006              MOVE.B   #$06,MR1A(A0)   ;7 data bits, odd parity
     0000000A 0000
41   0000000C 117C000F              MOVE.B   #$0F,MR2A(A0)   ;2 stop bits (Tx only)
     00000010 0000
42   00000012 117C00BB              MOVE.B   #B9600,CSRA(A0) ;set baud rate
     00000016 0002
43   00000018 117C0005              MOVE.B   #$05,CRA(A0)    ;Tx/Rx enabled
     0000001C 0004
44   0000001E 4E75                  RTS
45
46            ***************************************************************
47            * TRAP 0:                                                     *
48            * INCHR     INput CHaRacter from serial port into D0          *
49            *                                                             *
50            *           ENTER:  no conditions                            *
51            *           EXIT:   D0[0:7] contains ASCII character          *
52            *                   D0[8:31] unchanged                        *
53            *           USES:   no subroutines                            *
54            ***************************************************************
```

```
 55   00000020 2F08      INCHR     MOVE.L   A0,-(A7)        ;save A0
 56   00000022 3F07                MOVE.W   D7,-(A7)        ;save D7
 57   00000024 207C0000            MOVEA.L  #DUART,A0       ;A0 points to 68681
      00000028 C001
 58   0000002A 1E280002  INCHR2    MOVE.B   SRA(A0),D7
 59   0000002E 02070001            ANDI.B   #1,D7
 60   00000032 67F6                BEQ.S    INCHR2
 61   00000034 10280006            MOVE.B   RBA(A0),D0
 62   00000038 0200007F            ANDI.B   #$7F,D0         ;ensure bit 7 = 0
 63   0000003C 3E1F                MOVE.W   (A7)+,D7        ;restore D7
 64   0000003E 205F                MOVEA.L  (A7)+,A0        ;restore A7
 65   00000040 4E73                RTE
 66
 67                      **********************************************************
 68                      * TRAP 1:                                                *
 69                      * OUTCHR    OUTput CHaRacter in D0 to serial port         *
 70                      *                                                        *
 71                      *           ENTER:   D0[0:8] contains ASCII character    *
 72                      *           EXIT:    D0[0:8] unchanged                    *
 73                      *                    D0[8:31] cleared                    *
 74                      *           USES:    no subroutines                      *
 75                      **********************************************************
 76   00000042 2F08      OUTCHR    MOVE.L   A0,-(A7)        ;save A0
 77   00000044 3F07                MOVE.W   D7,-(A7)        ;save D7
 78   00000046 207C0000            MOVEA.L  #DUART,A0       ;A0 points to 68681
      0000004A C001
 79   0000004C 1E280002  OUTCHR2   MOVE.B   SRA(A0),D7
 80   00000050 02070004            ANDI.B   #4,D7
 81   00000054 67F6                BEQ.S    OUTCHR2
 82   00000056 11400006            MOVE.B   D0,TBA(A0)
 83   0000005A 3E1F                MOVE.W   (A7)+,D7        ;restore D7
 84   0000005C 205F                MOVE.L   (A7)+,A0        ;restore A0
 85   0000005E 4E73                RTE
 86
 87                      **********************************************************
 88                      * TRAP 2:                                                *
 89                      * OUTSTR    OUTput null-terminated STRing to serial port  *
 90                      *                                                        *
 91                      *           ENTER:   A1 points to string                 *
 92                      *           EXIT:    A1 points to null-terminator        *
 93                      *           USES:    OUTCHR                               *
 94                      **********************************************************
 95   00000060 2F00      OUTSTR    MOVE.L   D0,-(A7)        ;save D0 on stack
 96   00000062 1019      OUTSTR2   MOVE.B   (A1)+,D0
 97   00000064 6704                BEQ.S    EXIT
 98   00000066 4E41                TRAP     #1              ;outchr
 99   00000068 60F8                BRA.S    OUTSTR2
100   0000006A 201F      EXIT      MOVE.L   (A7)+,D0        ;restore D0
101   0000006C 4E73                RTE
102
103                      **********************************************************
104                      * TRAP 3:                                                *
105                      * INLINE    INput LINE from keyboard and save in input buffer *
106                      *                                                        *
107                      *           ENTER:   A1 = address of input buffer        *
108                      *                    D1 = buffer size (including CR & null) *
109                      *           EXIT:    all registers intact                *
110                      *           USES:    TOUPPR, TRAP 0, TRAP 1, TRAP 2      *
111                      **********************************************************
112   0000006E 48E7E040  INLINE    MOVEM.L  D0-D2/A1,-(SP)  ;save registers
113   00000072 4242                CLR.W    D2              ;D1 counts characters
114   00000074 5541                SUBQ.W   #2,D1           ;leave room for CR & null
```

```
115   00000076 4E40      INLINE5   TRAP     #0                ;get a char. from keyboard
116   00000078 0C000004            CMPI.B   #BS,D0            ;check for backspace
117   0000007C 6706                BEQ.S    INLINE3
118   0000007E 0C00007F            CMPI.B   #DEL,D0           ;check for delete
119   00000082 6618                BNE.S    INLINE4
120   00000084 4A42      INLINE3   TST.W    D2                ;if count = 0,
121   00000086 67EE                BEQ.S    INLINE5           ;ignore, otherwise,
122   00000088 43E9FFFF            LEA      -1(A1),A1         ;decrement pointer
123   0000008C 2F09                MOVE.L   A1,-(A7)          ;save on stack
124   0000008E 227C0000            MOVEA.L  #BACKUP,A1        ;backup cursor
      00000092 00BE
125   00000094 4E42                TRAP     #2                ;outstr
126   00000096 225F                MOVEA.L  (A7)+,A1          ;restore from stack
127   00000098 5342                SUBQ.W   #1,D2             ;decrement count
128   0000009A 60DA                BRA      INLINE5           ;get another
129   0000009C 4E41      INLINE4   TRAP     #1                ;echo character
130   0000009E 5242                ADDQ.W   #1,D2             ;increment count
131   000000A0 12C0                MOVE.B   D0,(A1)+          ;put in line buffer
132   000000A2 B242                CMP.W    D2,D1             ;buffer full?
133   000000A4 660A                BNE.S    INLINE6           ;no:  continue
134   000000A6 103C000D            MOVE.B   #CR,D0            ;yes: put CR at end
135   000000AA 4E41                TRAP     #1
136   000000AC 12C0                MOVE.B   D0,(A1)+
137   000000AE 6006                BRA.S    INLINE7           ;and exit
138   000000B0 0C00000D  INLINE6   CMPI.B   #CR,D0
139   000000B4 66C0                BNE      INLINE5
140   000000B6 4211      INLINE7   CLR.B    (A1)
141   000000B8 4CDF0207  EXIT2     MOVEM.L  (SP)+,D0-D2/A1    ;restore registers
142   000000BC 4E73                RTE
143   000000BE 1B5B44    BACKUP    DC.B     ESC,'[D'          ;ANSI: backup cursor
144   000000C1 1B5B4B00            DC.B     ESC,'[K',0        ;ANSI: erase to end of line
145
146                               ****************************************************************
147                               * TRAP 4:                                                      *
148                               * KEYHIT    has a KEY been HIT on the terminal?                 *
149                               *                                                              *
150                               *           ENTER:   no conditions                             *
151                               *           EXIT:    C = 1 if a key has been hit               *
152                               *                    C = 0 if no key has been hit              *
153                               *                    all registers intact                     *
154                               *           USES:    no subroutines                            *
155                               ****************************************************************
156   000000C6 2F08      KEYHIT    MOVE.L   A0,-(A7)          ;save A0
157   000000C8 3F00                MOVE.W   D0,-(A7)          ;save D0
158   000000CA 207C0000            MOVEA.L  #DUART,A0         ;A0 points to 68681
      000000CE C001
159   000000D0 10280002            MOVE.B   SRA(A0),D0        ;copy SRA bits to D0
160   000000D4 02000001            ANDI.B   #1,D0             ;bit 0 = key hit status
161   000000D8 1F400007            MOVE.B   D0,7(A7)          ;copy to CCR on stack
162   000000DC 301F                MOVE.W   (A7)+,D0          ;restore D0
163   000000DE 205F                MOVEA.L  (A7)+,A0          ;restore A0
164   000000E0 4E73                RTE
165
166                               ****************************************************************
167                               * OUT2HX    OUTput 2 HeX characters to terminal                *
168                               *                                                              *
169                               *           ENTER:   D0[0:7] contains byte of data             *
170                               *           EXIT:    D0 intact                                 *
171                               *           USES:    HTOA, OUTCHR                              *
172                               ****************************************************************
173   000000E2 2F00      OUT2HX    MOVE.L   D0,-(A7)          ;save data on stack
174   000000E4 E818                ROR.B    #4,D0             ;send high nibble first
```

```
175  000000E6 61000000              BSR     HTOA        ;convert to ASCII first
176  000000EA 4E41                  TRAP    #1          ;send it
177  000000EC 201F                  MOVE.L  (A7)+,D0    ;retrieve data from stack
178  000000EE 2F00     OUTHEX        MOVE.L  D0,-(A7)
179  000000F0 61000000              BSR     HTOA        ;convert lower nibble
180  000000F4 4E41                  TRAP    #1          ;send it
181  000000F6 201F                  MOVE.L  (A7)+,D0    ;restore D0
182  000000F8 4E75                  RTS
183
184                    ******************************************************************
185                    * OUTADD    OUTput ADDress to terminal                          *
186                    *                                                                *
187                    *           ENTER:   A0 contains address                        *
188                    *           EXIT:    all registers intact                       *
189                    *           USES:    OUT2HX                                     *
190                    ******************************************************************
191  000000FA 2F00     OUTADD        MOVE.L  D0,-(A7)    ;save D0 on stack
192  000000FC 3F01                  MOVE.W  D1,-(A7)    ;save D1 on stack
193  000000FE 2008                  MOVE.L  A0,D0
194  00000100 323C0004              MOVE.W  #4,D1       ;D1 = byte counter
195  00000104 E198     OUTADD2       ROL.L   #8,D0
196  00000106 61DA                  BSR     OUT2HX
197  00000108 5341                  SUBQ    #1,D1       ;last nibble?
198  0000010A 66F8                  BNE     OUTADD2     ;no:  do again
199  0000010C 321F                  MOVE.W  (A7)+,D1    ;yes: restore data registers
200  0000010E 201F                  MOVE.L  (A7)+,D0
201  00000110 4E75                  RTS
202
203                    ******************************************************************
204                    * SPACE     send SPACE code to terminal (all registers intact) *
205                    ******************************************************************
206  00000112 2F09     SPACE         MOVE.L  A1,-(A7)
207  00000114 43FA0008              LEA     SPACE1(PC),A1
208  00000118 4E42                  TRAP    #2              ;outstr
209  0000011A 225F                  MOVEA.L (A7)+,A1
210  0000011C 4E75                  RTS
211  0000011E 2000     SPACE1        DC.B    ' ',0
212
213                    ******************************************************************
214                    * NEWLINE   send NEW LINE chars to terminal (all reg. intact)  *
215                    ******************************************************************
216  00000120 2F09     NEWLINE       MOVE.L  A1,-(A7)
217  00000122 43FA0008              LEA     NEWLINE1(PC),A1
218  00000126 4E42                  TRAP    #2              ;outstr
219  00000128 225F                  MOVEA.L (A7)+,A1
220  0000012A 4E75                  RTS
221  0000012C 0D0A00   NEWLINE1      DC.B    CR,LF,0
222
223                    ******************************************************************
224                    * GETHEX -  read two hex-ASCII characters from the serial       *
225                    *           input port and convert to a single                  *
226                    *           hexadecimal byte                                     *
227                    *                                                                *
228                    *           ENTER:   no conditions                              *
229                    *           EXIT:    D0[0:7] contains hex byte                   *
230                    *                    D0[8:31] cleared                           *
231                    *           USES:    ATOH                                       *
232                    ******************************************************************
233  00000130 4E40     GETHEX        TRAP    #0          ;get char. into D0
234  00000132 61000000              BSR     ATOH        ;convert to hex
235  00000136 E918                  ROL.B   #4,D0       ;put in upper nibble
236  00000138 3F00                  MOVE.W  D0,-(A7)    ;save it
```

```
237  0000013A 4E40              TRAP     #0
238  0000013C 61000000          BSR      ATOH
239  00000140 805F              OR.W     (A7)+,D0
240  00000142 02800000          ANDI.L   #$FF,D0      ;ensure bits 8-31 clear
     00000146 00FF
241  00000148 4E75              RTS
242  0000014A                   END
```

# D_CMD.LST

```
1             ***********************************************************
2             * D_CMD.SRC   DIsassemble 68000 instructions            *
3             ***********************************************************
4    0000000D     CR      EQU     $0D
5    0000000A     LF      EQU     $0A
6    00000050     BUFSIZE EQU     80              ;(TUTOR)
7    00000004     EOT     EQU     4               ;(TUTOR)
8    0000000A     FDATA   EQU     10              ;(TUTOR)
9    0000001F     FOC     EQU     31              ;(TUTOR)
10   00000027     FOP     EQU     39              ;(TUTOR)
11   00000010     LOCVARSZ EQU    16              ;(TUTOR)
12
13   00000000     EXTERN  PAR1,PAR2,NPAR,DCODE68K,MON68K
14   00000000     PUBLIC  D_CMD,DI_N,DIBUFFER,BUFSIZE,OFFSET
15
16   00000000     RSEG    EPROM
17            ***********************************************************
18            * DI       DIassemble command                           *
19            *                                                        *
20            * Syntax:  DI PAR1,PAR2                                  *
21            *                                                        *
22            *          PAR1 = address of instruction to disassemble  *
23            *          PAR2 = number of instructions to disassemble   *
24            ***********************************************************
25   00000000 28790000  D_CMD  MOVEA.L  >PAR1,A4   ;put address in A4
     00000004 0000
26   00000006 2E390000         MOVE.L   >PAR2,D7   ;use D7 as counter
     0000000A 0000
27   0000000C 4A390000         TST.B    >NPAR      ;zero parameters entered?
     00000010 0000
28   00000012 6704            BEQ.S    DI_SYNTAX  ;yes: send syntax message
29   00000014 6128            BSR.S    DI_N        ;no:  do it!
30   00000016 6006            BRA.S    DI_EXIT     ;return to MON68K
31   00000018 43FA0008 DI_SYNTAX LEA    DI_MESS(PC),A1
32   0000001C 4E42            TRAP     #2
33   0000001E 60000000 DI_EXIT  BRA     MON68K
34   00000022 0D0A5359 DI_MESS  DC.B    CR,LF,'SYNTAX: DI address count',0
     00000026 4E544158
     0000002A 3A204449
     0000002E 20616464
     00000032 72657373
     00000036 20636F75
     0000003A 6E7400
35
36            ***********************************************************
37            * DI_N   DIsassemble N 68000 instructions               *
38            *                                                        *
39            *          ENTER:   A4 = address of instruction          *
40            *                   D7 = number of instructions          *
41            *          EXIT:    A4 = address of next instruction      *
42            *                   all other registers intact           *
43            *          USES:    TUTOR's DCODE68K subroutine (modified)*
44            ***********************************************************
45   0000003E 48E7FFF6 DI_N    MOVEM.L  D0-D7/A0-A3/A5-A6,-(SP)
46   00000042 207C0000        MOVEA.L  #OFFSET,A0         ;clear offset registers
     00000046 0000
47   00000048 303C0007        MOVE.W   #7,D0             ;(TUTOR artifact:
48   0000004C 4298     LOOP   CLR.L    (A0)+             ; Sorry, but it's
49   0000004E 51C8FFFC        DBRA     D0,LOOP           ; necessary)
```

```
50   00000052 201C      LOOP2      MOVE.L     (A4)+,D0                  ;D0 = words 1 & 2
51   00000054 221C                 MOVE.L     (A4)+,D1                  ;D1 = words 3 & 4
52   00000056 241C                 MOVE.L     (A4)+,D2                  ;D2 = words 5 & 6
53   00000058 49ECFFF4             LEA        -12(A4),A4                ;align pointer
54   0000005C 2A7C0000             MOVEA.L    #DIBUFFER,A5              ;buffer for output
     00000060 0020
55   00000062 61000000             BSR        DCODE68K                 ;thank you TUTOR!
56   00000066 42390000             CLR.B      >DIBUFFER+BUFSIZE-2 ;put null byte at end
     0000006A 006E
57   0000006C 227C0000             MOVEA.L    #NEWLINE,A1              ;OK, let's have a look
     00000070 0086
58   00000072 4E42                 TRAP       #2                       ;pretty it up a bit
59   00000074 224D                 MOVEA.L    A5,A1                    ;A1 points to output
60   00000076 4E42                 TRAP       #2                       ;send it!
61   00000078 4E44                 TRAP       #4                       ;console key hit?
62   0000007A 6504                 BCS.S      SKIP2                    ;yes: done
63   0000007C 5347                 SUBQ       #1,D7                    ;no:  last instruction?
64   0000007E 66D2                 BNE        LOOP2                    ;no:  repeat
65   00000080 4CDF6FFF  SKIP2      MOVEM.L    (SP)+,D0-D7/A0-A3/A5-A6 ;yes: clean up
66   00000084 4E75                 RTS
67   00000086 0D0A2D2D  NEWLINE    DC.B       CR,LF,'--- ',0
     0000008A 2D2D2D20
     0000008E 00
68
69   00000000            RSEG      RAM
70   00000000            OFFSET    DS.L       8                  ;(TUTOR)
71   00000020            DIBUFFER  DS.B       BUFSIZE            ;disassembled line goes here
72   00000070            END
```

# G_CMD.LST

```
 1                        ***********************************************************
 2                        * G_CMD.SRC     GO to user program                       *
 3                        *                                                         *
 4                        * The following code begins execution of a user program.  The  *
 5                        * operations are:                                         *
 6                        *                                                         *
 7                        * 1. Load all data and address registers with the user values *
 8                        * 2. Push the SR and PC onto the stack                     *
 9                        * 3. Execute RETURN AND RESTORE (RTR) to pop the CCR and   *
10                        *    PC from the user stack                               *
11                        *                                                         *
12                        * NOTES:                                                  *
13                        * 1. If the user stack pointer (A7) has not been set to any *
14                        *    value, it will contain B800 (as initialized upon SYSTEM *
15                        *    RESET).                                               *
16                        * 2. By default, user programs execute in supervisor mode. *
17                        ***********************************************************
18  0000001A    EOF       EQU      $1A              ;control-Z
19  0000000D    CR        EQU      $0D              ;carriage return
20  0000000A    LF        EQU      $0A              ;line feed
21  00004E4F    TRAP15    EQU      $4E4F
22
23  00000000              EXTERN   NPAR,PAR1,BUFFER,RDS,COMMAND,MON68K
24  00000000              PUBLIC   UD0,UD1,UD2,UD3,UD4,UD5,UD6,UD7
25  00000000              PUBLIC   UA0,UA1,UA2,UA3,UA4,UA5,UA6,UA7
26  00000000              PUBLIC   G_CMD,UPC,USR,TBP,BREAK
27
28  00000000              RSEG     EPROM
29  00000000 207C0000 G_CMD  MOVEA.L  #COMMAND,A0      ;find out which G command
    00000004 0000
30  00000006 10280001      MOVE.B   1(A0),D0         ;get 2nd character
31  0000000A 0C000054      CMPI.B   #'T',D0          ;GT command?
32  0000000E 6728          BEQ.S    GT               ;yes:  Go To breakpoint
33                        *                          ;no:   default to GO
34                        ***********************************************************
35                        * GO        GO to user program                           *
36                        ***********************************************************
37  00000010 4A390000 GO     TST.B    >NPAR           ;GO entered without address?
    00000014 0000
38  00000016 670A          BEQ.S    GO2              ;yes: use existing UPC
39  00000018 23F90000      MOVE.L   >PAR1,>UPC       ;no:  load UPC with address
    0000001C 00000000
    00000020 0002
40  00000022 4CF97FFF GO2    MOVEM.L  >UD0,D0-D7/A0-A6     ;load register set
    00000026 00000008
41                        *                          ;NOTE: SSP left as is
42  0000002A 2F390000      MOVE.L   >UPC,-(A7)       ;push user PC on stack
    0000002E 0002
43  00000030 3F390000      MOVE.W   >USR,-(A7)       ;push user SR on stack
    00000034 0006
44  00000036 4E73          RTE                       ;pop into SR & PC
45
46                        ***********************************************************
47                        * GT        Go To temporary breakpoint                   *
48                        ***********************************************************
49  00000038 4A390000 GT     TST.B    >NPAR           ;address entered?
    0000003C 0000
50  0000003E 6712          BEQ.S    GT_SYNTAX        ;no:  send syntax message
51  00000040 20790000      MOVEA.L  >PAR1,A0         ;yes: put it in A0
    00000044 0000
52  00000046 33D00000      MOVE.W   (A0),>SAVE       ;save instruction
    0000004A 0000
```

```
53  0000004C 30BC4E4F                  MOVE.W    #TRAP15,(A0)   ;replace with Trap #15
54  00000050 60D0                      BRA       GO2
55  00000052 43FA0008  GT_SYNTAX  LEA  GT_MESS(PC),A1 ;send syntax message
56  00000056 4E42                      TRAP      #2             ;OUTSTR trap
57  00000058 60000000                  BRA       MON68K         ;return to monitor
58  0000005C 0D0A5359  GT_MESS    DC.B CR,LF,'SYNTAX: GT address',0
    00000060 4E544158
    00000064 3A204754
    00000068 20616464
    0000006C 72657373
    00000070 00
59
60                     ****************************************************************
61                     * TRAP 14:                                                     *
62                     * BREAK     BREAK from user program (save register set)         *
63                     ****************************************************************
64  00000072 48F97FFF  BREAK      MOVEM.L  D0-D7/A0-A6,>UD0  ;save register set
    00000076 00000008
65  0000007A 207C0000             MOVEA.L  #UPC,A0
    0000007E 0002
66  00000080 20AF0002             MOVE.L   2(A7),(A0)     ;save UPC, then...
67  00000084 5590                 SUBQ.L   #2,(A0)        ;re-align
68  00000086 31570004             MOVE.W   (A7),4(A0)     ;save USR
69  0000008A 60000000             BRA      MON68K         ;return to monitor
70
71                     ****************************************************************
72                     * TRAP 15:                                                     *
73                     * TBP       Temporary BreakPoint                                *
74                     ****************************************************************
75  0000008E 48F97FFF  TBP        MOVEM.L  D0-D7/A0-A6,>UD0  ;save register set
    00000092 00000008
76  00000096 207C0000             MOVEA.L  #UPC,A0
    0000009A 0002
77  0000009C 20AF0002             MOVE.L   2(A7),(A0)     ;save UPC, then...
78  000000A0 5590                 SUBQ.L   #2,(A0)        ;re-align
79  000000A2 31570004             MOVE.W   (A7),4(A0)     ;save USR
80  000000A6 20790000             MOVEA.L  >PAR1,A0
    000000AA 0000
81  000000AC 30B90000             MOVE.W   >SAVE,(A0)     ;restore instruction
    000000B0 0000
82  000000B2 61000000             BSR      RDS            ;dump registers
83  000000B6 60000000             BRA      MON68K         ;return to monitor
84
85  00000000             RSEG   RAM
86  00000000  SAVE       DS.W   1         ;save opcode (temp. brkpnt)
87  00000002  UPC        DS.L   1         ;user program counter
88  00000006  USR        DS.W   1         ;user status register
89  00000008  UD0        DS.L   1         ;user data registers
90  0000000C  UD1        DS.L   1
91  00000010  UD2        DS.L   1
92  00000014  UD3        DS.L   1
93  00000018  UD4        DS.L   1
94  0000001C  UD5        DS.L   1
95  00000020  UD6        DS.L   1
96  00000024  UD7        DS.L   1
97  00000028  UA0        DS.L   1         ;user address registers
98  0000002C  UA1        DS.L   1
99  00000030  UA2        DS.L   1
100 00000034  UA3        DS.L   1
101 00000038  UA4        DS.L   1
102 0000003C  UA5        DS.L   1
103 00000040  UA6        DS.L   1
104 00000044  UA7        DS.L   1
105 00000048             END
```

# L_CMD.LST

```
 1                        ******************************************************************
 2                        * L_CMD.SRC                                                     *
 3                        *                                                               *
 4                        *          Load S-records from serial port and place binary     *
 5                        *          bytes in memory.  Data records are preceded with     *
 6                        *          S1 (16-bit address) or S2 (24-bit address).          *
 7                        *          Load terminates when an S8 or S9 record is           *
 8                        *          received.                                            *
 9                        *                                                               *
10                        * SYNTAX:  LO       load (and return to monitor)                *
11                        *          LG       load and go (execute program)               *
12                        ******************************************************************
13  0000000D      CR       EQU      $0D              ;carriage return
14  0000000A      LF       EQU      $0A              ;line feed
15  00000013      CTRL_S   EQU      $13              ;XOFF
16  00000011      CTRL_Q   EQU      $11              ;XON
17  0000001A      EOF      EQU      $1A              ;end-of-file
18  00000007      BEL      EQU      $07              ;ASCII bell code
19
20  00000000               EXTERN   GETHEX,MON68K,TOUPPER,OUTADD,COMMAND
21  00000000               PUBLIC   L_CMD
22
23  00000000               RSEG     EPROM
24  00000000 43FA00F8  L_CMD LEA    MESS1(PC),A1     ;A1 points to message
25  00000004 4E42             TRAP   #2               ;outstr
26  00000006 4E40      LOAD1  TRAP   #0               ;inchr
27  00000008 0C000053         CMPI.B #'S',D0          ;found 'S'?
28  0000000C 66F8             BNE.S  LOAD1            ;no:  check again
29  0000000E 4E40             TRAP   #0               ;yes: get next character
30  00000010 0C000030         CMPI.B #'0',D0          ;header record?
31  00000014 676C             BEQ.S  S0               ;yes: get module name
32  00000016 0C000031         CMPI.B #'1',D0          ;S1 data record?
33  0000001A 6716             BEQ.S  S1S2             ;yes: get data (a16)
34  0000001C 0C000032         CMPI.B #'2',D0          ;S2 data record?
35  00000020 6710             BEQ.S  S1S2             ;yes: get data (a24)
36  00000022 0C000038         CMPI.B #'8',D0          ;S8 record?
37  00000026 67000086         BEQ    S8S9             ;yup: we're out of here
38  0000002A 0C000039         CMPI.B #'9',D0          ;S9 record?
39  0000002E 677E             BEQ.S  S8S9             ;yea: toot-a-loo!
40  00000030 60D4             BRA    LOAD1            ;nope: start again
41                    *
42                    * S1 or S2 record
43                    *
44  00000032 1800      S1S2   MOVE.B D0,D4            ;save record type
45  00000034 61000000         BSR    GETHEX           ;get count
46  00000038 1600             MOVE.B D0,D3            ;D3 = checksum
47  0000003A 1400             MOVE.B D0,D2            ;D2 = count
48  0000003C 61000000         BSR    GETHEX           ;get 1st address byte
49  00000040 5502             SUBQ.B #2,D2            ;dec. count (twice)
50  00000042 D600             ADD.B  D0,D3            ;update checksum
51  00000044 E198             ROL.L  #8,D0            ;put in bits 8-15
52  00000046 2440             MOVEA.L D0,A2           ;A2 = load address
53  00000048 61000000         BSR    GETHEX           ;get 2nd address byte
54  0000004C 5302             SUBQ.B #1,D2            ;dec. count
55  0000004E D600             ADD.B  D0,D3            ;update checksum
56  00000050 D08A             ADD.L  A2,D0            ;A2 = load address
57  00000052 B83C0032         CMP.B  #'2',D4          ;S2 record?
58  00000056 660E             BNE.S  SKIP3            ;no:  16-bit address
59  00000058 E198             ROL.L  #8,D0            ;put in bits 8-23
```

```
60   0000005A 2040                  MOVEA.L    D0,A0              ;A2 = load address
61   0000005C 61000000             BSR        GETHEX             ;get 3rd address byte
62   00000060 5302                 SUBQ.B     #1,D2              ;update count
63   00000062 D600                 ADD.B      D0,D3              ;update checksum
64   00000064 D08A                 ADD.L      A2,D0              ;A2 = load address
65   00000066 2440     SKIP3       MOVEA.L    D0,A2              ;(done!)
66   00000068 61000000 LOAD3       BSR        GETHEX             ;get data byte
67   0000006C D600                 ADD.B      D0,D3              ;update checksum
68   0000006E 14C0                 MOVE.B     D0,(A2)+           ;put in RAM
69   00000070 5302                 SUBQ.B     #1,D2              ;dec. count
70   00000072 66F4                 BNE        LOAD3              ;if !0, do get next byte
71   00000074 61000000             BSR        GETHEX             ;get checksum
72   00000078 B103                 EOR.B      D0,D3              ;XOR with sum
73   0000007A 0C0300FF             CMPI.B     #$FF,D3            ;error?
74   0000007E 6670                 BNE.S      CHKERR             ;yes: send message
75   00000080 6084                 BRA        LOAD1              ;no:  get next record
76                        *
77                        * S0 record
78                        *
79   00000082 43FA009C S0          LEA        MESS3(PC),A1       ;send "Module" message
80   00000086 4E42                 TRAP       #2
81   00000088 61000000             BSR        GETHEX             ;get count
82   0000008C 1600                 MOVE.B     D0,D3
83   0000008E 4883                 EXT.W      D3
84   00000090 5743                 SUBQ.W     #3,D3              ;adjust count
85   00000092 61000000             BSR        GETHEX             ;get add-H (discard)
86   00000096 61000000             BSR        GETHEX             ;get add-L (discard)
87   0000009A 600A                 BRA.S      SKIP01
88   0000009C 61000000 LOAD4       BSR        GETHEX             ;get module name char.
89   000000A0 61000000             BSR        TOUPPER            ;uppercase looks good
90   000000A4 4E41                 TRAP       #1                 ;send module name char.
91   000000A6 51CBFFF4 SKIP01      DBRA       D3,LOAD4
92   000000AA 6000FF5A             BRA        LOAD1
93                        *
94                        * S8 or S9 record
95                        *
96   000000AE 61000000 S8S9        BSR        GETHEX             ;get count
97   000000B2 1600                 MOVE.B     D0,D3
98   000000B4 4883                 EXT.W      D3
99   000000B6 5543                 SUBQ.W     #2,D3              ;adjust count
100  000000B8 4282                 CLR.L      D2                 ;build address in D2
101  000000BA 61000000 DONE1       BSR        GETHEX             ;get address byte
102  000000BE E18A                 LSL.L      #8,D2              ;adjust build address
103  000000C0 1400                 MOVE.B     D0,D2              ;insert new add. byte
104  000000C2 51CBFFF6             DBRA       D3,DONE1           ;repeat, until done
105  000000C6 4A82                 TST.L      D2                 ;address = 0?
106  000000C8 670C                 BEQ.S      DONE2              ;yes: don't send message
107  000000CA 43FA0061             LEA        MESS4(PC),A1       ;no:  send "Entry" message
108  000000CE 4E42                 TRAP       #2
109  000000D0 2042                 MOVEA.L    D2,A0
110  000000D2 61000000             BSR        OUTADD
111  000000D6 4E40     DONE2       TRAP       #0                 ;if done, look for EOF
112  000000D8 0C00001A             CMPI.B     #EOF,D0            ;end of file?
113  000000DC 66F8                 BNE        DONE2              ;no:  check again
114  000000DE 0C390047             CMPI.B     #'G',>COMMAND+1    ;load and GO command?
     000000E2 00000001
115  000000E6 660E                 BNE.S      LD_EXIT            ;no:  exit
116  000000E8 4A82                 TST.L      D2                 ;yes: address = 0?
117  000000EA 670A                 BEQ.S      LD_EXIT            ;yes: exit
118  000000EC 2F08                 MOVE.L     A0,-(SP)           ;OK loaded, push address
119  000000EE 4E75                 RTS                           ;pop into PC
120
121  000000F0 43FA001C CHKERR      LEA        MESS2(PC),A1       ;send error message
```

```
122    000000F4 4E42                       TRAP      #2                    ;outstr
123    000000F6 4EF80000    LD_EXIT         JMP       MON68K                ;return to MON68K
124
125    000000FA 0D0A4C6F    MESS1           DC.B      CR,LF,'Load S-records...',0
       000000FE 61642053
       00000102 2D726563
       00000106 6F726473
       0000010A 2E2E2E00
126    0000010E 0D0A0743    MESS2           DC.B      CR,LF,BEL,'Checksum Error',0
       00000112 6865636B
       00000116 73756D20
       0000011A 4572726F
       0000011E 7200
127    00000120 1320204D    MESS3           DC.B      CTRL_S,'  Module: ',CTRL_Q,0
       00000124 6F64756C
       00000128 653A2011
       0000012C 00
128    0000012D 2020456E    MESS4           DC.B      '  Entry: ',0
       00000131 7472793A
       00000135 2000
129    00000137                             END
```

# M_CMD.LST

```
1                          *************************************************************
2                          * M_CMD.SRC Memory CoMmanDs (MM, MD, MT, MC, MF, & SZ)      *
3                          *************************************************************
4    0000000D       CR        EQU      $0D              ;ASCII carriage return
5    0000000A       LF        EQU      $0A              ;ASCII line feed
6    00000007       BEL       EQU      $07              ;ASCII bell
7    0000001B       ESC       EQU      $1B              ;ASCII escape charcter
8
9    00000000                 EXTERN   NEWLINE,OUTADD,SPACE,MON68K,OUT2HX,ATOH
10   00000000                 EXTERN   COMMAND,TOUPPER,PAR1,PAR2,PAR3
11   00000000                 EXTERN   ISGRAPH,NPAR
12   00000000                 PUBLIC   SIZE,S_CMD,M_CMD
13
14   00000000                 RSEG     EPROM
15   00000000 20790000  M_CMD  MOVEA.L  >PAR1,A0     ;A0 = parameter #1
     00000004 0000
16   00000006 22790000         MOVEA.L  >PAR2,A1     ;A1 = parameter #2
     0000000A 0000
17   0000000C 24790000         MOVEA.L  >PAR3,A2     ;A2 = parameter #3
     00000010 0000
18   00000012 1E390000         MOVE.B   >NPAR,D7     ;D7 = # of parameters entered
     00000016 0000
19   00000018 10390000         MOVE.B   >COMMAND+1,D0 ;get 2nd char. in command
     0000001C 0001
20   0000001E 0C000043         CMPI.B   #'C',D0      ;MC command?
21   00000022 6722            BEQ.S    MC           ;yes: memory copy
22   00000024 0C000044         CMPI.B   #'D',D0      ;MD command?
23   00000028 6700019A         BEQ      MD           ;yes: memory dump
24   0000002C 0C000046         CMPI.B   #'F',D0      ;MF command?
25   00000030 670000D2         BEQ      MF           ;yes: memory fill
26   00000034 0C00004D         CMPI.B   #'M',D0      ;MM command?
27   00000038 67000102         BEQ      MM           ;yes: memory modifiy
28   0000003C 0C000054         CMPI.B   #'T',D0      ;no:  MT command?
29   00000040 6742            BEQ.S    MT           ;yes: memory test
30   00000042 60000000         BRA      MON68K       ;unknown command
31
32                          *************************************************************
33                          * MC        Memory Copy command                            *
34                          *************************************************************
35   00000046 4A07      MC     TST.B    D7           ;zero parameters entered?
36   00000048 670C            BEQ.S    MC_SYNTAX    ;yes: send syntax message
37   0000004A 43E90001         LEA      1(A1),A1     ;adjust end pointer
38   0000004E 14D8      MC3    MOVE.B   (A0)+,(A2)+  ;move byte
39   00000050 B3C8            CMPA.L   A0,A1        ;reached last address?
40   00000052 66FA            BNE.S    MC3          ;no:  move another byte
41   00000054 6006            BRA.S    MC_EXIT      ;yes: return to monitor
42   00000056 43FA0008  MC_SYNTAX LEA   MC_MESS(PC),A1 ;send syntax message
43   0000005A 4E42            TRAP     #2           ;OUTSTR trap
44   0000005C 60000000  MC_EXIT  BRA    MON68K       ;return to monitor
45   00000060 0D0A      MC_MESS  DC.B   CR,LF
46   00000062 53594E54         DC.B     'SYNTAX: MC start end destination',0
     00000066 41583A20
     0000006A 4D432073
     0000006E 74617274
     00000072 20656E64
     00000076 20646573
     0000007A 74696E61
     0000007E 74696F6E
     00000082 00
```

```
47
48                        ************************************************************
49              * MT          Memory Test command                              *
50                        ************************************************************
51   00000084 4A07   MT        TST.B   D7            ;zero parameters entered?
52   00000086 6726            BEQ.S   MT_SYNTAX     ;yes: send syntax message
53   00000088 43E90001        LEA     1(A1),A1      ;adjust address pointer
54   0000008C 1C10   MT2       MOVE.B  (A0),D6       ;read byte from RAM
55   0000008E 4606            NOT.B   D6            ;complement it and
56   00000090 1086            MOVE.B  D6,(A0)       ;write it back to RAM
57   00000092 BC10            CMP.B   (A0),D6       ;now check it
58   00000094 6620            BNE.S   MT_ERROR      ;if different, error
59   00000096 4606            NOT.B   D6            ;if OK, complement it again and
60   00000098 1086            MOVE.B  D6,(A0)       ;write original value to RAM
61   0000009A BC10            CMP.B   (A0),D6       ;check it again
62   0000009C 6618            BNE.S   MT_ERROR      ;if different, error
63   0000009E 41E80001        LEA     1(A0),A0      ;increment address pointer
64   000000A2 B3C8            CMPA.L  A0,A1         ;last address?
65   000000A4 66E6            BNE     MT2                ;no:  repeat
66   000000A6 43FA0033        LEA     MT_MESS2(PC),A1 ;yes: send OK message
67   000000AA 4E42            TRAP    #2
68   000000AC 6012            BRA.S   MT_EXIT            ;return to monitor
69   000000AE 43FA0014 MT_SYNTAX LEA   MT_MESS(PC),A1  ;send sytax message
70   000000B2 4E42            TRAP    #2
71   000000B4 600A            BRA.S   MT_EXIT
72   000000B6 43FA002F MT_ERROR  LEA   MT_MESS3(PC),A1 ;send error message
73   000000BA 4E42            TRAP    #2
74   000000BC 61000000        BSR     OUTADD
75   000000C0 60000000 MT_EXIT   BRA   MON68K
76   000000C4 0D0A5359 MT_MESS   DC.B  CR,LF,'SYNTAX: MT start end',0
     000000C8 4E544158
     000000CC 3A204D54
     000000D0 20737461
     000000D4 72742065
     000000D8 6E6400
77   000000DB 0D0A4D65 MT_MESS2  DC.B  CR,LF,'Memory OK',0
     000000DF 6D6F7279
     000000E3 204F4B00
78   000000E7 0D0A074D MT_MESS3  DC.B  CR,LF,BEL,'Memory error at address ',0
     000000EB 656D6F72
     000000EF 79206572
     000000F3 726F7220
     000000F7 61742061
     000000FB 64647265
     000000FF 73732000
79
80                        ************************************************************
81              * MF          Memory Fill command                              *
82                        ************************************************************
83   00000104 4A07   MF        TST.B   D7            ;zero parameters entered?
84   00000106 670E            BEQ.S   MF_SYNTAX     ;yes: send syntax message
85   00000108 43E90001        LEA     1(A1),A1      ;adjust address pointer
86   0000010C 3C0A            MOVE.W  A2,D6
87   0000010E 10C6   MF_LOOP   MOVE.B  D6,(A0)+
88   00000110 B3C8            CMPA.L  A0,A1
89   00000112 66FA            BNE     MF_LOOP
90   00000114 6006            BRA.S   MF_EXIT
91   00000116 43FA0008 MF_SYNTAX LEA   MF_MESS(PC),A1
92   0000011A 4E42            TRAP    #2
93   0000011C 60000000 MF_EXIT   BRA   MON68K
94   00000120 0D0A5359 MF_MESS   DC.B  CR,LF,'SYNTAX: MF start end byte',0
     00000124 4E544158
```

```
          00000128 3A204D46
          0000012C 20737461
          00000130 72742065
          00000134 6E642062
          00000138 79746500
 95
 96                      ************************************************************
 97                      * MM         Memory Modify command                        *
 98                      ************************************************************
 99  0000013C 4A07       MM          TST.B       D7              ;zero parameters entered?
100  0000013E 6764                   BEQ.S       MM_SYNTAX       ;yes: send syntax message
101  00000140 61000000   BACK        BSR         NEWLINE
102  00000144 61000000               BSR         OUTADD          ;send the address
103  00000148 61000000               BSR         SPACE
104  0000014C 1018                   MOVE.B      (A0)+,D0        ;get byte of data
105  0000014E 1200                   MOVE.B      D0,D1           ;build code in D1
106  00000150 61000000               BSR         OUT2HX          ;send as two hex characters
107  00000154 61000000               BSR         SPACE
108  00000158 4E40       BACK2       TRAP        #0              ;get a response
109  0000015A 0C00002E               CMPI.B      #'.',D0         ;PERIOD?
110  0000015E 6740                   BEQ.S       DONE            ;yes: return to monitor
111  00000160 0C000020               CMPI.B      #' ',D0         ;SPACE?
112  00000164 673A                   BEQ.S       DONE            ;yes: return to monitor
113  00000166 0C00000D               CMPI.B      #CR,D0          ;no:  if RETURN,
114  0000016A 671C                   BEQ.S       ENTER           ;       examine next
115  0000016C 0C00001B               CMPI.B      #ESC,D0         ;check for arrow key
116  00000170 6622                   BNE.S       AHEAD
117  00000172 4E40                   TRAP        #0              ;inchr
118  00000174 0C00005B               CMPI.B      #'[',D0
119  00000178 6626                   BNE.S       DONE            ;if not 'ESC [', abort
120  0000017A 4E40                   TRAP        #0
121  0000017C 0C000041               CMPI.B      #'A',D0         ;cursor up? (ESC [ A)
122  00000180 660C                   BNE.S       AHEAD1          ;no:  check for down arrow
123  00000182 41E8FFFE               LEA         -2(A0),A0       ;yes: back up memory pointer
124  00000186 60B8                   BRA         BACK
125  00000188 1141FFFF   ENTER       MOVE.B      D1,-1(A0)       ;write data to memory
126  0000018C 60B2                   BRA         BACK
127  0000018E 0C000042   AHEAD1      CMPI.B      #'B',D0         ;cursor down? (ESC [ B)
128  00000192 67AC                   BEQ         BACK            ;yes: display next data
129                      *                                       ;no:  must be data
130  00000194 4E41       AHEAD       TRAP        #1              ;echo ASCII code
131  00000196 61000000               BSR         ATOH            ;convert to hex nibble
132  0000019A E909                   LSL.B       #4,D1
133  0000019C 8200                   OR.B        D0,D1
134  0000019E 60B8                   BRA         BACK2
135  000001A0 4E41       DONE        TRAP        #1              ;echo last entry
136  000001A2 6006                   BRA.S       MM_EXIT         ;return to monitor
137  000001A4 43FA0008   MM_SYNTAX   LEA         MM_MESS(PC),A1
138  000001A8 4E42                   TRAP        #2
139  000001AA 6000FF70   MM_EXIT     BRA         MF_EXIT
140  000001AE 0D0A5359   MM_MESS     DC.B        CR,LF,'SYNTAX: MM address',0
     000001B2 4E544158
     000001B6 3A204D4D
     000001BA 20616464
     000001BE 72657373
     000001C2 00
141
142                      ************************************************************
143                      * MD         Memory Dump command                          *
144                      ************************************************************
145  000001C4 4A07       MD          TST.B       D7              ;zero parameters entered?
146  000001C6 67000086               BEQ         MD_SYNTAX       ;yes: send syntax message
147  000001CA 2008                   MOVE.L      A0,D0           ;D0 contains address of data
```

```
148  000001CC 020000F0                 ANDI.B   #$F0,D0           ;align to 16-byte boundary
149  000001D0 2640                     MOVEA.L  D0,A3             ;put copy in A3
150  000001D2 2209                     MOVE.L   A1,D1             ;use D1 to count bytes
151  000001D4 D27C0010                 ADD.W    #16,D1            ;round to next highest
152  000001D8 0241FFF0                 ANDI.W   #$FFF0,D1         ;16-byte count
153  000001DC E859                     ROR.W    #4,D1             ;D1 = row counter
154  000001DE 61000000     LOOP2       BSR      NEWLINE
155  000001E2 2040                     MOVEA.L  D0,A0
156  000001E4 61000000                 BSR      OUTADD            ;send address
157  000001E8 287C0000                 MOVEA.L  #ASCII_BUF,A4
     000001EC 0004
158  000001EE 343C0010                 MOVE.W   #16,D2            ;use D2 as byte counter
159  000001F2 2A7C0000                 MOVEA.L  #SIZE,A5          ;A5 points to space param.
     000001F6 0000
160  000001F8 2615                     MOVE.L   (A5),D3           ;use D3 as space counter
161  000001FA 61000000                 BSR      SPACE
162  000001FE 61000000                 BSR      SPACE
163  00000202 101B         LOOP        MOVE.B   (A3)+,D0          ;load data in address
164  00000204 61000000                 BSR      OUT2HX
165  00000208 5303                     SUBQ.B   #1,D3             ;decrement space counter
166  0000020A 6606                     BNE.S    SKIP6
167  0000020C 61000000                 BSR      SPACE
168  00000210 2615                     MOVE.L   (A5),D3
169  00000212 61000000     SKIP6       BSR      ISGRAPH           ;is code displayable ASCII?
170  00000216 6508                     BCS.S    SKIP3             ;yes: leave as is
171  00000218 19BC002E                 MOVE.B   #'.',-1(A4,D2)    ;no:  replace with '.'
     0000021C 20FF
172  0000021E 6004                     BRA.S    SKIP5
173  00000220 198020FF     SKIP3       MOVE.B   D0,-1(A4,D2)      ;put in ASCII buffer
174  00000224 4E44         SKIP5       TRAP     #4                ;key hit?
175  00000226 6404                     BCC.S    SKIP2             ;no:  continue
176  00000228 4E40                     TRAP     #0                ;yes: flush input buffer &
177  0000022A 6028                     BRA.S    MD_EXIT           ;       return to MON68K
178  0000022C 200B         SKIP2       MOVE.L   A3,D0             ;retrieve address
179  0000022E 5302                     SUBQ.B   #1,D2             ;last byte in row?
180  00000230 66D0                     BNE      LOOP              ;no:  repeat
181  00000232 143C0010                 MOVE.B   #16,D2            ;yes: flush ASCII buffer
182  00000236 61000000                 BSR      SPACE
183  0000023A 103420FF     SKIP4       MOVE.B   -1(A4,D2),D0
184  0000023E 4E41                     TRAP     #1
185  00000240 5302                     SUBQ.B   #1,D2
186  00000242 66F6                     BNE      SKIP4
187  00000244 5341                     SUBQ.W   #1,D1             ;last row of data?
188  00000246 670C                     BEQ.S    MD_EXIT
189  00000248 200B                     MOVE.L   A3,D0             ;copy address into D0
190  0000024A 6092                     BRA      LOOP2             ;no:  repeat
191  0000024C 6006                     BRA.S    MD_EXIT           ;yes: return to monitor
192  0000024E 43FA0008     MD_SYNTAX   LEA      MD_MESS(PC),A1
193  00000252 4E42                     TRAP     #2
194  00000254 60000000     MD_EXIT     BRA      MON68K
195  00000258 0D0A5359     MD_MESS     DC.B     CR,LF,'SYNTAX: MD start count',0
     0000025C 4E544158
     00000260 3A204D44
     00000264 20737461
     00000268 72742063
     0000026C 6F756E74
     00000270 00
196
197                                    ***********************************************************
198                                    * S_CMD      select Size of data for MD command          *
199                                    ***********************************************************
200  00000272 4A390000     S_CMD       TST.B    >NPAR             ;zero parameters entered?
     00000276 0000
```

```
201  00000278 672E                        BEQ.S     SZ_SYNTAX        ;yes: send syntax message
202  0000027A 207C0000                     MOVEA.L   #PAR1,A0         ;A0 points to cmd parameters
     0000027E 0000
203  00000280 227C0000                     MOVEA.L   #SIZE,A1         ;A1 points to SIZE param.
     00000284 0000
204  00000286 2010                         MOVE.L    (A0),D0
205  00000288 02800000                     ANDI.L    #7,D0            ;reduce to 3 bits
     0000028C 0007
206  0000028E 0C000001                     CMPI.B    #1,D0            ;only allow 1, 2, or 4
207  00000292 6710                         BEQ.S     SKIP7
208  00000294 0C000002                     CMPI.B    #2,D0
209  00000298 670A                         BEQ.S     SKIP7
210  0000029A 0C000004                     CMPI.B    #4,D0
211  0000029E 6704                         BEQ.S     SKIP7
212  000002A0 103C0002                     MOVE.B    #2,D0            ;use "2" as a default
213  000002A4 2280          SKIP7          MOVE.L    D0,(A1)          ;store SIZE parameter
214  000002A6 6006                         BRA.S     SZ_EXIT          ;return to monitor
215  000002A8 43FA0008      SZ_SYNTAX      LEA       SZ_MESS(PC),A1
216  000002AC 4E42                         TRAP      #2
217  000002AE 60000000      SZ_EXIT        BRA       MON68K
218  000002B2 0D0A5359      SZ_MESS        DC.B      CR,LF,'SYNTAX: SZ n (1 = byte, 2 = word, '
     000002B6 4E544158
     000002BA 3A20535A
     000002BE 206E2028
     000002C2 31203D20
     000002C6 62797465
     000002CA 2C203220
     000002CE 3D20776F
     000002D2 72642C20
219  000002D6 34203D20                     DC.B      '4 = longword)',0
     000002DA 6C6F6E67
     000002DE 776F7264
     000002E2 2900
220
221  00000000                              RSEG      RAM
222  00000000      SIZE                    DS.L      1                ;size of data for MD command
223                *                                                    1 = byte
224                *                                                    2 = word
225                *                                                    4 = long word
226  00000004      ASCII_BUF               DS.B      16
227  00000014                              END
```

# R_CMD.LST

```
 1                        *******************************************************************
 2                        * R_CMD.SRC Register Dump command                                 *
 3                        *******************************************************************
 4  00000000                        EXTERN   UPC,NEWLINE,OUTADD,MON68K,OUT2HX,UA7,DI_N
 5  00000000                        PUBLIC   R_CMD,RDS,MESSAGE
 6
 7  00000000                        RSEG     EPROM
 8
 9  00000000 6104       R_CMD       BSR.S    RDS                   ;register dump subroutine
10  00000002 4EF80000               JMP      MON68K
11
12                        *******************************************************************
13                        * RDS        Register Dump Subroutine                              *
14                        *                                                                  *
15                        *     ENTER:   no conditions                                      *
16                        *     EXIT:    all registers intact                               *
17                        *     USES:    OUTADD,NEWLINE,SPACE,OUT2HX                         *
18                        *******************************************************************
19  00000006 48E7F0F8    RDS         MOVEM.L  D0-D3/A0-A4,-(A7)  ;save registers on stack
20  0000000A 61000000                BSR      NEWLINE
21  0000000E 267C0000                MOVEA.L  #UPC,A3               ;A3 = address of data
    00000012 0000
22  00000014 247C0000                MOVEA.L  #MESSAGE,A2           ;A2 = address of strings
    00000018 0128
23  0000001A 143C0010                MOVE.B   #16,D2               ;D2 = register counter
24  0000001E 224A                    MOVEA.L  A2,A1                ;send "PC=" string
25  00000020 4E42                    TRAP     #2
26  00000022 45EA0005                LEA      5(A2),A2
27  00000026 205B                    MOVE.L   (A3)+,A0             ;use OUTADD subroutine to
28  00000028 61000000                BSR      OUTADD               ; dump user register values
29  0000002C 224A                    MOVEA.L  A2,A1                ;send "SR=" string
30  0000002E 4E42                    TRAP     #2
31  00000030 45EA0005                LEA      5(A2),A2
32  00000034 101B                    MOVE.B   (A3)+,D0
33  00000036 61000000                BSR      OUT2HX
34  0000003A 101B                    MOVE.B   (A3)+,D0
35  0000003C 61000000                BSR      OUT2HX
36  00000040 103C003D                MOVE.B   #'=',D0
37  00000044 4E41                    TRAP     #1
38                        *
39                        * Build ASCII string for status register bits
40                        *
41  00000046 227C0000                MOVEA.L  #STATUS_BUF,A1
    0000004A 0000
42  0000004C 103C0008                MOVE.B   #8,D0
43  00000050 12FC002E    LOOP1       MOVE.B   #'.',(A1)+
44  00000054 5300                    SUBQ.B   #1,D0
45  00000056 66F8                    BNE      LOOP1
46  00000058 4211                    CLR.B    (A1)
47  0000005A 227C0000                MOVEA.L  #STATUS_BUF,A1
    0000005E 0000
48  00000060 102BFFFE                MOVE.B   -2(A3),D0            ;get SR high byte
49  00000064 E318                    ROL.B    #1,D0                ;check 'T' bit
50  00000066 6404                    BCC.S    SKIP0
51  00000068 12BC0054                MOVE.B   #'T',(A1)
52  0000006C 43E90001    SKIP0       LEA      1(A1),A1
53  00000070 E518                    ROL.B    #2,D0                ;check 'S' bit
54  00000072 6404                    BCC.S    SKIP2
55  00000074 12BC0053                MOVE.B   #'S',(A1)
```

```
56   00000078 43E90001   SKIP2   LEA      1(A1),A1
57   0000007C E618               ROR.B    #3,D0        ;check 'I' bits (& encode)
58   0000007E 02000007           ANDI.B   #$07,D0
59   00000082 00000030           ORI.B    #$30,D0      ;convert to ASCII digit
60   00000086 12C0               MOVE.B   D0,(A1)+
61   00000088 102BFFFF           MOVE.B   -1(A3),D0    ;get SR low byte
62   0000008C E918               ROL.B    #4,D0        ;check 'X' bit
63   0000008E 6404               BCC.S    SKIP3
64   00000090 12BC0058           MOVE.B   #'X',(A1)
65   00000094 43E90001   SKIP3   LEA      1(A1),A1
66   00000098 E318               ROL.B    #1,D0        ;check 'N' bit
67   0000009A 6404               BCC.S    SKIP4
68   0000009C 12BC004E           MOVE.B   #'N',(A1)
69   000000A0 43E90001   SKIP4   LEA      1(A1),A1
70   000000A4 E318               ROL.B    #1,D0        ;check 'Z' bit
71   000000A6 6404               BCC.S    SKIP5
72   000000A8 12BC005A           MOVE.B   #'Z',(A1)
73   000000AC 43E90001   SKIP5   LEA      1(A1),A1
74   000000B0 E318               ROL.B    #1,D0        ;check 'V' bit
75   000000B2 6404               BCC.S    SKIP6
76   000000B4 12BC0056           MOVE.B   #'V',(A1)
77   000000B8 43E90001   SKIP6   LEA      1(A1),A1
78   000000BC E318               ROL.B    #1,D0        ;check 'C' bit
79   000000BE 6404               BCC.S    SKIP7
80   000000C0 12BC0043           MOVE.B   #'C',(A1)
81   000000C4 227C0000   SKIP7   MOVEA.L  #STATUS_BUF,A1
     000000C8 0000
82   000000CA 4E42               TRAP     #2
83   000000CC 224A               MOVEA.L  A2,A1        ;send 'US=' string
84   000000CE 4E42               TRAP     #2
85   000000D0 45EA0005           LEA      5(A2),A2
86   000000D4 4E68               MOVE.L   USP,A0
87   000000D6 61000000           BSR      OUTADD       ;send user SP contents
88   000000DA 23CF0000           MOVE.L   A7,>UA7      ;set user A7 = system A7
     000000DE 0000
89   000000E0 224A               MOVEA.L  A2,A1        ;send 'SS=' string
90   000000E2 4E42               TRAP     #2
91   000000E4 45EA0005           LEA      5(A2),A2
92   000000E8 20790000           MOVE.L   >UA7,A0
     000000EC 0000
93   000000EE 61000000           BSR      OUTADD       ;send system SP contents
94   000000F2 61000000           BSR      NEWLINE
95   000000F6 224A       LOOP    MOVEA.L  A2,A1
96   000000F8 4E42               TRAP     #2           ;outstr
97   000000FA 45EA0005           LEA      5(A2),A2
98
99   000000FE 205B               MOVE.L   (A3)+,A0     ;use OUTADD subroutine to
100  00000100 61000000           BSR      OUTADD       ; dump 32-bit reg. values
101
102  00000104 5302               SUBQ.B   #1,D2
103  00000106 670E               BEQ.S    DONE
104  00000108 3202               MOVE     D2,D1
105  0000010A C23C0003           AND.B    #$03,D1
106  0000010E 6604               BNE.S    SKIP
107  00000110 61000000           BSR      NEWLINE
108  00000114 60E0       SKIP    BRA      LOOP
109  00000116 28790000   DONE    MOVEA.L  >UPC,A4      ;address of next instruction
     0000011A 0000
110  0000011C 7E01               MOVE.L   #1,D7        ;count = 1
111  0000011E 61000000           BSR      DI_N         ;disassemble instruction
112  00000122 4CDF1F0F           MOVEM.L  (A7)+,D0-D3/A0-A4 ;restore registers
113  00000126 4E75               RTS
```

```
114
115   00000128 2050433D   MESSAGE    DC.B     ' PC=',0
      0000012C 00
116   0000012D 2053523D              DC.B     ' SR=',0
      00000131 00
117   00000132 2055533D              DC.B     ' US=',0
      00000136 00
118   00000137 2053533D              DC.B     ' SS=',0
      0000013B 00
119   0000013C 2044303D              DC.B     ' D0=',0
      00000140 00
120   00000141 2044313D              DC.B     ' D1=',0
      00000145 00
121   00000146 2044323D              DC.B     ' D2=',0
      0000014A 00
122   0000014B 2044333D              DC.B     ' D3=',0
      0000014F 00
123   00000150 2044343D              DC.B     ' D4=',0
      00000154 00
124   00000155 2044353D              DC.B     ' D5=',0
      00000159 00
125   0000015A 2044363D              DC.B     ' D6=',0
      0000015E 00
126   0000015F 2044373D              DC.B     ' D7=',0
      00000163 00
127   00000164 2041303D              DC.B     ' A0=',0
      00000168 00
128   00000169 2041313D              DC.B     ' A1=',0
      0000016D 00
129   0000016E 2041323D              DC.B     ' A2=',0
      00000172 00
130   00000173 2041333D              DC.B     ' A3=',0
      00000177 00
131   00000178 2041343D              DC.B     ' A4=',0
      0000017C 00
132   0000017D 2041353D              DC.B     ' A5=',0
      00000181 00
133   00000182 2041363D              DC.B     ' A6=',0
      00000186 00
134   00000187 2041373D              DC.B     ' A7=',0
      0000018B 00
135
136   00000000              RSEG     RAM
137   00000000   STATUS_BUF DS.B     9
138   00000009              END
```

# T_CMD.LST

```
 1                        ***********************************************************
 2                        * T_CMD.SRC    Trace commands                            *
 3                        ***********************************************************
 4   00000000                      EXTERN    BUFFER,ATOH,ISHEX,NPAR,PAR1,MON68K2
 5   00000000                      EXTERN    UPC,USR,UD0,RDS,MON68K,COMMAND
 6   00000000                      PUBLIC    T_CMD,TRE,T_DELAY
 7
 8   0000000D         CR           EQU       $0D
 9   0000000A         LF           EQU       $0A
10
11   00000000                      RSEG      EPROM
12   00000000 10390000 T_CMD       MOVE.B    >COMMAND+1,D0
     00000004 0001
13   00000006 B03C0052             CMP.B     #'R',D0
14   0000000A 676A                 BEQ.S     TR
15   0000000C B03C0044             CMP.B     #'D',D0
16   00000010 6704                 BEQ.S     TD
17   00000012 4EF80000             JMP       MON68K
18                        *
19                        * Trace Delay command
20                        *
21   00000016 4A390000 TD          TST.B     >NPAR                 ;zero parameters entered?
     0000001A 0000
22   0000001C 671A                 BEQ.S     TD_SYNTX              ;yes: send syntax message
23   0000001E 20390000             MOVE.L    >PAR1,D0              ;no:  get trace delay
     00000022 0000
24   00000024 C07C0007             AND.W     #7,D0                 ;reduce to 3 bits
25   00000028 E508                 LSL.B     #2,D0                 ;longword align
26   0000002A 203B002A             MOVE.L    TD_ZERO(PC,D0),D0     ;get delay count
27   0000002E 23C00000             MOVE.L    D0,>T_DELAY           ;store it
     00000032 0000
28   00000034 4EF80000             JMP       MON68K               ;return to monitor
29
30   00000038 43FA0008 TD_SYNTX LEA         TD_MESS(PC),A1        ;send syntax message
31   0000003C 4E42                 TRAP      #2                    ;OUTSTR trap
32   0000003E 4EF80000             JMP       MON68K
33
34   00000042 0D0A5359 TD_MESS     DC.B      CR,LF,'SYNTAX: TD delay',0
     00000046 4E544158
     0000004A 3A205444
     0000004E 2064656C
     00000052 617900
35   00000056 00000001 TD_ZERO     DC.L      1                     ;0 = zero delay
36   00025800         ONE_SEC      EQU       153600                ;count for 1 s delay
37   0000005A 00025800 TD_ONE      DC.L      ONE_SEC               ;1 = 1 s delay
38   0000005E 0004B000             DC.L      ONE_SEC*2             ;2 = 2 s delay
39   00000062 00096000             DC.L      ONE_SEC*4             ;3 = 4 s delay
40   00000066 0012C000             DC.L      ONE_SEC*8             ;4 = 8 s delay
41   0000006A 00258000             DC.L      ONE_SEC*16            ;5 = 16 s delay
42   0000006E 004B0000             DC.L      ONE_SEC*32            ;6 = 32 s delay
43   00000072 00960000             DC.L      ONE_SEC*64            ;7 = 64 s delay
44   00000000                      RSEG      RAM
45   00000000         T_DELAY      DS.L      1
46                        *
47                        * TRace command
48                        *
49   00000076                      RSEG      EPROM
50   00000076 4A390000 TR          TST.B     >NPAR                 ;zero parameters entered?
     0000007A 0000
```

```
51  0000007C 671E                    BEQ.S     TR_SYNTX           ;yes: send syntax message
52  0000007E 00798000                ORI.W     #$8000,>USR        ;set TRACE bit in user SR
    00000082 00000000
53  00000086 4CF97FFF                MOVEM.L   >UD0,D0-D7/A0-A6   ;load register set (not A7)
    0000008A 00000000
54  0000008E 2F390000                MOVE.L    >UPC,-(A7)         ;push user PC on stack
    00000092 0000
55  00000094 3F390000                MOVE.W    >USR,-(A7)         ;push user SR on stack
    00000098 0000
56  0000009A 4E73                    RTE
57  0000009C 43FA0008      TR_SYNTX  LEA       TR_MESS(PC),A1     ;send syntax message
58  000000A0 4E42                    TRAP      #2                 ;OUTSTR trap
59  000000A2 4EF80000                JMP       MON68K
60  000000A6 0D0A5359      TR_MESS   DC.B      CR,LF,'SYNTAX: TR count',0
    000000AA 4E544158
    000000AE 3A205452
    000000B2 20636F75
    000000B6 6E7400
61                         *
62                         * Trace Exception code follows
63                         *
64  000000BA 48F97FFF      TRE       MOVEM.L   D0-D7/A0-A6,>UD0   ;save user register set
    000000BE 00000000
65  000000C2 23EF0002                MOVE.L    2(A7),>UPC         ;NOTE: UA7 not updated
    000000C6 00000000
66  000000CA 33D70000                MOVE.W    (A7),>USR
    000000CE 0000
67  000000D0 61000000                BSR       RDS                ;Register Dump Subroutine
68  000000D4 43FA0046                LEA       TRPROMPT(PC),A1
69  000000D8 4E42                    TRAP      #2                 ;outstr
70  000000DA 4A390000                TST.B     >NPAR              ;trace count specified?
    000000DE 0000
71  000000E0 6712                    BEQ.S     SKIP               ;no: onward (trace 1 inst.)
72  000000E2 2E390000                MOVE.L    >T_DELAY,D7        ;yes: trace another, but...
    000000E6 0000
73  000000E8 5387          TRE2      SUBQ.L    #1,D7              ;    first, delay a bit
74  000000EA 66FC                    BNE       TRE2
75  000000EC 53B90000                SUBQ.L    #1,>PAR1           ;decrement trace count
    000000F0 0000
76  000000F2 6E12                    BGT.S     AGAIN2             ;trace until count <= 0
77  000000F4 227C0000      SKIP      MOVEA.L   #BUFFER,A1
    000000F8 0000
78  000000FA 4E43                    TRAP      #3                 ;get keyboard response
79  000000FC 0C39000D                CMPI.B    #CR,>BUFFER        ;CR?
    00000100 00000000
80  00000104 660A                    BNE.S     EXIT               ;no: leave trace mode
81  00000106 4CF97FFF      AGAIN2    MOVEM.L   >UD0,D0-D7/A0-A6   ;yes: restore user register
    0000010A 00000000
82  0000010E 4E73                    RTE                          ;    set and do again
83  00000110 02797FFF      EXIT      ANDI.W    #$7FFF,>USR        ;clear trace bit in USR
    00000114 00000000
84  00000118 60000000                BRA       MON68K2            ;and return to monitor
85  0000011C 0D0A3A00      TRPROMPT  DC.B      CR,LF,':',0
86  00000120                         END
```

# PERIOD.LST

```
 1                        ************************************************************
 2                        * PERIOD command for register examine/change              *
 3                        ************************************************************
 4  0000000D      CR       EQU      $0D
 5  00000020      SPACE    EQU      $20
 6
 7  00000000               EXTERN   MON68K,MESSAGE,UPC,OUTADD,COMMAND
 8  00000000               EXTERN   NEWLINE,PAR1,OUT2HX
 9  00000000               PUBLIC   PERIOD
10
11  00000000               RSEG     EPROM
12  00000000 61000000 PERIOD BSR     NEWLINE
13  00000004 24390000      MOVE.L   >PAR1,D2        ;D2     modify value (if needed)
    00000008 0000
14  0000000A 08810000      BCLR.B   #0,D1           ;D1[0] examine/!modify flag
15  0000000E 227C0000      MOVEA.L  #COMMAND,A1     ;A1     pointer to command
    00000012 0000
16  00000014 267C0000      MOVEA.L  #UPC,A3         ;A3     pointer to register set
    00000018 0000
17  0000001A 287C0000      MOVEA.L  #MESSAGE,A4     ;A4     pointer to message set
    0000001E 0000
18  00000020 10290003      MOVE.B   3(A1),D0        ;check 3rd char. of cmd line
19  00000024 0C00000D      CMPI.B   #CR,D0          ;3rd char. = CR?
20  00000028 6604          BNE.S    SKIP            ;yes: examine (leave flag = 0)
21  0000002A 08C10000      BSET.B   #0,D1           ;no:  modify (set flag)
22  0000002E 10290002 SKIP  MOVE.B  2(A1),D0        ;now check 2nd command char.
23  00000032 0C000053      CMPI.B   #'S',D0         ;SS or US command?
24  00000036 6638          BNE.S    SKIP2           ;no:  check for others
25  00000038 10290001      MOVE.B   1(A1),D0        ;yes: check 1st command char.
26  0000003C 0C000053      CMPI.B   #'S',D0         ;SS command?
27  00000040 6616          BNE.S    SKIP3           ;no:  must be US
28  00000042 08010000      BTST.B   #0,D1           ;yes: check for examine/!modify
29  00000046 670A          BEQ.S    SKIP4
30  00000048 43EC000F      LEA      15(A4),A1       ;examine SSP
31  0000004C 204F          MOVEA.L  A7,A0
32  0000004E 600000A8      BRA      EXAMINE
33  00000052 2E42     SKIP4 MOVEA.L D2,A7           ;modify SSP
34  00000054 600000A8      BRA      EXIT
35  00000058 08010000 SKIP3 BTST    #0,D1           ;US command
36  0000005C 670A          BEQ.S    SKIP5
37  0000005E 43EC000A      LEA      10(A4),A1       ;examine USP
38  00000062 4E68          MOVE.L   USP,A0
39  00000064 60000092      BRA      EXAMINE
40  00000068 2842     SKIP5 MOVEA.L D2,A4
41  0000006A 4E64          MOVE.L   A4,USP          ;modify USP
42  0000006C 60000090      BRA      EXIT
43  00000070 0C000043 SKIP2 CMPI.B  #'C',D0         ;PC command?
44  00000074 6616          BNE.S    SKIP6
45  00000076 08010000      BTST     #0,D1           ;examine/!modify?
46  0000007A 670A          BEQ.S    SKIP7
47  0000007C 43EC0000      LEA      0(A4),A1        ;examine PC
48  00000080 206B0000      MOVEA.L  0(A3),A0
49  00000084 6072          BRA.S    EXAMINE
50  00000086 27420000 SKIP7 MOVE.L  D2,0(A3)        ;modify PC
51  0000008A 6072          BRA.S    EXIT
52  0000008C 0C000052 SKIP6 CMPI.B  #'R',D0         ;SR command?
53  00000090 6624          BNE.S    SKIP9
54  00000092 08010000      BTST     #0,D1           ;examine/!modify?
55  00000096 6718          BEQ.S    SKIP8
56  00000098 43EC0005      LEA      5(A4),A1        ;examine SR
```

```
57  0000009C 4E42              TRAP    #2
58  0000009E 302B0004          MOVE.W  4(A3),D0
59  000000A2 E158              ROL.W   #8,D0
60  000000A4 61000000          BSR     OUT2HX
61  000000A8 E158              ROL.W   #8,D0
62  000000AA 61000000          BSR     OUT2HX
63  000000AE 604E              BRA.S   EXIT
64  000000B0 37420004  SKIP8   MOVE.W  D2,4(A3)        ;modify SR
65  000000B4 6048              BRA.S   EXIT
66                    *
67                    *Must be .Dn or .An
68                    *
69  000000B6 4284      SKIP9   CLR.L   D4              ;D4 = register set index
70  000000B8 4285              CLR.L   D5              ;D5 = message set index
71  000000BA 16290001          MOVE.B  1(A1),D3        ;check 1st command char.
72  000000BE 18290002          MOVE.B  2(A1),D4        ;2nd char. = register number
73  000000C2 02840000          ANDI.L  #$07,D4         ;reduce ASCII to binary
    000000C6 0007
74  000000C8 1A04              MOVE.B  D4,D5           ;put copy in D5
75  000000CA E59C              ROL.L   #2,D4           ;long-word align
76  000000CC CAFC0005          MULU    #5,D5           ;build index
77  000000D0 0C030041          CMPI.B  #'A',D3
78  000000D4 660C              BNE.S   SKIP10
79  000000D6 D8BC0000          ADD.L   #32,D4          ;D1 = reg. set index (complete)
    000000DA 0020
80  000000DC DABC0000          ADD.L   #40,D5          ;D5 = message set index (done!)
    000000E0 0028
81  000000E2 08010000  SKIP10  BTST    #0,D1           ;examine/!modify?
82  000000E6 670A              BEQ.S   SKIP11
83  000000E8 43F45014          LEA     20(A4,D5),A1    ;examine Dn or An
84  000000EC 20734006          MOVEA.L 6(A3,D4),A0
85  000000F0 6006              BRA.S   EXAMINE
86  000000F2 27824006  SKIP11  MOVE.L  D2,6(A3,D4)     ;modify Dn or An
87  000000F6 6006              BRA.S   EXIT
88  000000F8 4E42      EXAMINE TRAP    #2              ;A1 points to string
89  000000FA 61000000          BSR     OUTADD          ;A0 contains data to display
90  000000FE 60000000  EXIT    BRA     MON68K
91  00000102                   END
```

# DCODE68K.LST

The listing for the DCODE68K subroutine is about 40 pages. It has been removed to keep this appendix "small". The DCODE68K subroutine is copyright Motorola, Inc. It is available on bulletin boards at 1-416-497-3733 or 1-512-891-3733.

# MON68K.XLK

```
DEF-CPU        68K
LOAD           MON68K.OBJ
LOAD           GETPAR.OBJ
LOAD           CONVERT.OBJ
LOAD           IS.OBJ
LOAD           IO.OBJ
LOAD           D_CMD.OBJ
LOAD           G_CMD.OBJ
LOAD           L_CMD.OBJ
LOAD           M_CMD.OBJ
LOAD           R_CMD.OBJ
LOAD           T_CMD.OBJ
LOAD           PERIOD.OBJ
LOAD           DCODE68K.OBJ
DEF-SEG        (EPROM,TUTOR)=0
DEF-SEG        (RAM)=B800
MAP            MON68K.MAP
DUMP           MON68K.HEX
EXIT
```

# MON68K.MAP

| Segments | Loc | Siz | Typ | Org | P/N | Al |
|----------|-----|-----|-----|-----|-----|-----|
| ======== | === | === | === | === | === | == |
| EPROM | 00000000 | 00001490 | Rel | Stc | Pos | 01 |
| TUTOR | 00001490 | 00000CBC | Rel | Flt | Pos | 02 |
| RAM | 0000B800 | 0000011C | Rel | Stc | Pos | 01 |

| Modules/Entries | | Values |
|-----------------|---|--------|
| =============== | | ====== |

mon68k

| | | |
|---|---|---|
| MON68K | E | 00000450 |
| MON68K2 | E | 00000466 |
| BUFFER | E | 0000B800 |
| SP_INIT | L | 0000C000 |
| PC_INIT | L | 00000400 |
| SR_INIT | L | 00002700 |
| USTACK | L | 0000B800 |
| URAM | L | 00008000 |
| UEPROM | L | 00004000 |
| BUFFSIZ | L | 00000028 |
| EOF | L | 0000001A |
| CR | L | 0000000D |
| LF | L | 0000000A |
| BEL | L | 00000007 |
| LOOP | L | 00000444 |
| SKIP | L | 00000484 |
| SKIP1 | L | 0000048E |
| SKIP2 | L | 00000492 |
| NOCMD | L | 000004AC |
| TABLE | L | 000004B4 |
| NMI | L | 000004E8 |
| BUS_ERROR | L | 00000506 |
| ADDRESS_ERROR | L | 0000050C |
| SEND2 | L | 00000510 |
| ILLEGAL_INSTRUCTION | | |
| | L | 00000518 |
| ZERO_DIVIDE | L | 0000051E |
| CHK_INSTRUCTION | L | 00000524 |
| TRAPV_INSTRUCTION | | |
| | L | 0000052A |
| PRIVILEGE_VIOLATION | | |
| | L | 00000530 |
| LINE_0101_EMULATOR | | |
| | L | 00000536 |
| LINE_1111_EMULATOR | | |
| | L | 0000053C |
| FORMAT_ERROR | L | 00000542 |
| UNINITIALIZED_INTERRUPT_VECTOR | | |
| | L | 00000548 |
| SPURIOUS_INTERRUPT | | |
| | L | 0000054E |
| SEND | L | 00000552 |
| AHEAD | L | 00000558 |
| ERROR | L | 00000566 |
| HELP | L | 00000570 |
| HELP_STR | L | 0000057A |
| MESSAGE1 | L | 000007AD |

```
          MESSAGE2          L   000007BA
          MESSAGE3          L   000007CB
          MESSAGE4          L   000007E2
          MESSAGE5          L   000007F1
          MESSAGE6          L   00000804
          MESSAGE7          L   00000819
          MESSAGE7A         L   00000830
          MESSAGE7B         L   0000084A
          MESSAGE9          L   00000864
          MESSAGE10         L   00000874
          MESSAGE10A        L   00000895
          MESSAGE11         L   000008AB
          MESSAGE12         L   000008C6
          MESSAGE13         L   000008CE
          PROMPT1           L   000008E2
          PROMPT2           L   000008EB
          PROMPT3           L   000008F3
getpar
          GETPAR            E   000008F8
          COMMAND           E   0000B828
          PAR1              E   0000B832
          PAR2              E   0000B836
          PAR3              E   0000B83A
          PAR4              E   0000B83E
          NPAR              E   0000B831
          CR                L   0000000D
          SPACE             L   00000020
          AGAIN22           L   0000090A
          AGAIN             L   00000914
          SKIP99            L   00000916
          SKIP3             L   00000926
          SKIP2             L   0000092E
          AGAIN2            L   0000093E
          AGAIN3            L   00000940
          SKIP8             L   0000094E
          SKIP9             L   00000968
          STORE             L   00000972
          EXIT              L   00000980
          COUNT             L   00000004
convert
          ATOH              E   00000982
          TOUPPER           E   00000992
          HTOA              E   0000099E
          ATOH2             L   0000098C
          EXIT              L   0000099C
          HTOA2             L   000009AC
is
          ISHEX             E   000009B2
          ISDIGIT           E   000009D2
          ISALPH            E   000009EA
          ISGRAPH           E   00000A0E
          SKIP2             L   000009CC
          SKIP              L   000009D0
          SKIP3             L   000009E4
          SKIP4             L   000009E8
          SKIP5             L   000009FC
          YES               L   00000A06
          NO                L   00000A08
          NO2               L   00000A26
          ISGRAPH2          L   00000A2C
io
          OUTCHR            E   00000A74
```

```
    INCHR           E    00000A52
    OUTSTR          E    00000A92
    INLINE          E    00000AA0
    INIT_DUART      E    00000A32
    OUT2HX          E    00000B14
    OUTHEX          E    00000B20
    KEYHIT          E    00000AF8
    NEWLINE         E    00000B52
    SPACE           E    00000B44
    OUTADD          E    00000B2C
    GETHEX          E    00000B62
    DUART           L    0000C001
    MR1A            L    00000000
    MR2A            L    00000000
    CSRA            L    00000002
    SRA             L    00000002
    CRA             L    00000004
    TBA             L    00000006
    RBA             L    00000006
    ACR             L    00000008
    EOF             L    0000001A
    CR              L    0000000D
    LF              L    0000000A
    ESC             L    0000001B
    BS              L    00000004
    DEL             L    0000007F
    B4800           L    00000099
    B9600           L    000000BB
    INCHR2          L    00000A5C
    OUTCHR2         L    00000A7E
    OUTSTR2         L    00000A94
    EXIT            L    00000A9C
    INLINE5         L    00000AA8
    INLINE3         L    00000AB6
    INLINE4         L    00000ACE
    INLINE6         L    00000AE2
    INLINE7         L    00000AE8
    EXIT2           L    00000AEA
    BACKUP          L    00000AF0
    OUTADD2         L    00000B36
    SPACE1          L    00000B50
    NEWLINE1        L    00000B5E
d_cmd
    D_CMD           E    00000B7C
    DI_N            E    00000BBA
    DIBUFFER        E    0000B862
    BUFSIZE         E    00000050
    OFFSET          E    0000B842
    CR              L    0000000D
    LF              L    0000000A
    EOT             L    00000004
    FDATA           L    0000000A
    FOC             L    0000001F
    FOP             L    00000027
    LOCVARSZ        L    00000010
    DI_SYNTAX       L    00000B94
    DI_EXIT         L    00000B9A
    DI_MESS         L    00000B9E
    LOOP            L    00000BC8
    LOOP2           L    00000BCE
    SKIP2           L    00000BFC
    NEWLINE         L    00000C02
```

```
g_cmd
    UD0                     E    0000B8BA
    UD1                     E    0000B8BE
    UD2                     E    0000B8C2
    UD3                     E    0000B8C6
    UD4                     E    0000B8CA
    UD5                     E    0000B8CE
    UD6                     E    0000B8D2
    UD7                     E    0000B8D6
    UA0                     E    0000B8DA
    UA1                     E    0000B8DE
    UA2                     E    0000B8E2
    UA3                     E    0000B8E6
    UA4                     E    0000B8EA
    UA5                     E    0000B8EE
    UA6                     E    0000B8F2
    UA7                     E    0000B8F6
    G_CMD                   E    00000C0C
    UPC                     E    0000B8B4
    USR                     E    0000B8B8
    TBP                     E    00000C9A
    BREAK                   E    00000C7E
    EOF                     L    0000001A
    CR                      L    0000000D
    LF                      L    0000000A
    TRAP15                  L    00004E4F
    GO                      L    00000C1C
    GO2                     L    00000C2E
    GT                      L    00000C44
    GT_SYNTAX               L    00000C5E
    GT_MESS                 L    00000C68
    SAVE                    L    0000B8B2
l_cmd
    L_CMD                   E    00000CC6
    CR                      L    0000000D
    LF                      L    0000000A
    CTRL_S                  L    00000013
    CTRL_Q                  L    00000011
    EOF                     L    0000001A
    BEL                     L    00000007
    LOAD1                   L    00000CCC
    S1S2                    L    00000CF8
    SKIP3                   L    00000D2C
    LOAD3                   L    00000D2E
    S0                      L    00000D48
    LOAD4                   L    00000D62
    SKIP01                  L    00000D6C
    S8S9                    L    00000D74
    DONE1                   L    00000D80
    DONE2                   L    00000D9C
    CHKERR                  L    00000DB6
    LD_EXIT                 L    00000DBC
    MESS1                   L    00000DC0
    MESS2                   L    00000DD4
    MESS3                   L    00000DE6
    MESS4                   L    00000DF3
m_cmd
    SIZE                    E    0000B8FA
    S_CMD                   E    00001070
    M_CMD                   E    00000DFE
    CR                      L    0000000D
    LF                      L    0000000A
    BEL                     L    00000007
    ESC                     L    0000001B
```

```
        MC                 L    00000E44
        MC3                L    00000E4C
        MC_SYNTAX          L    00000E54
        MC_EXIT            L    00000E5A
        MC_MESS            L    00000E5E
        MT                 L    00000E82
        MT2                L    00000E8A
        MT_SYNTAX          L    00000EAC
        MT_ERROR           L    00000EB4
        MT_EXIT            L    00000EBE
        MT_MESS            L    00000EC2
        MT_MESS2           L    00000ED9
        MT_MESS3           L    00000EE5
        MF                 L    00000F02
        MF_LOOP            L    00000F0C
        MF_SYNTAX          L    00000F14
        MF_EXIT            L    00000F1A
        MF_MESS            L    00000F1E
        MM                 L    00000F3A
        BACK               L    00000F3E
        BACK2              L    00000F56
        ENTER              L    00000F86
        AHEAD1             L    00000F8C
        AHEAD              L    00000F92
        DONE               L    00000F9E
        MM_SYNTAX          L    00000FA2
        MM_EXIT            L    00000FA8
        MM_MESS            L    00000FAC
        MD                 L    00000FC2
        LOOP2              L    00000FDC
        LOOP               L    00001000
        SKIP6              L    00001010
        SKIP3              L    0000101E
        SKIP5              L    00001022
        SKIP2              L    0000102A
        SKIP4              L    00001038
        MD_SYNTAX          L    0000104C
        MD_EXIT            L    00001052
        MD_MESS            L    00001056
        SKIP7              L    000010A2
        SZ_SYNTAX          L    000010A6
        SZ_EXIT            L    000010AC
        SZ_MESS            L    000010B0
        ASCII_BUF          L    0000B8FE
r_cmd
        R_CMD              E    000010E2
        RDS                E    000010E8
        MESSAGE            E    0000120A
        LOOP1              L    00001132
        SKIP0              L    0000114E
        SKIP2              L    0000115A
        SKIP3              L    00001176
        SKIP4              L    00001182
        SKIP5              L    0000118E
        SKIP6              L    0000119A
        SKIP7              L    000011A6
        LOOP               L    000011D8
        SKIP               L    000011F6
        DONE               L    000011F8
        STATUS_BUF         L    0000B90E
t_cmd
        T_CMD              E    0000126E
        TRE                E    00001328
```

```
        T_DELAY          E   0000B918
        CR               L   0000000D
        LF               L   0000000A
        TD               L   00001284
        TD_SYNTX         L   000012A6
        TD_MESS          L   000012B0
        TD_ZERO          L   000012C4
        ONE_SEC          L   00025800
        TD_ONE           L   000012C8
        TR               L   000012E4
        TR_SYNTX         L   0000130A
        TR_MESS          L   00001314
        TRE2             L   00001356
        SKIP             L   00001362
        AGAIN2           L   00001374
        EXIT             L   0000137E
        TRPROMPT         L   0000138A
period
        PERIOD           E   0000138E
        CR               L   0000000D
        SPACE            L   00000020
        SKIP             L   000013BC
        SKIP4            L   000013E0
        SKIP3            L   000013E6
        SKIP5            L   000013F6
        SKIP2            L   000013FE
        SKIP7            L   00001414
        SKIP6            L   0000141A
        SKIP8            L   0000143E
        SKIP9            L   00001444
        SKIP10           L   00001470
        SKIP11           L   00001480
        EXAMINE          L   00001486
        EXIT             L   0000148C
dcode68k
        (symbols deleted)
```

# MON68K.HEX

```
S00900006D6F6E36386BD3
S1130000000C000000004000000050600000050C0C
S11300100000051800000051E000005240000052A44
S1130020000005300000132800000536000053CE0
S1130030000005660000056600000542000054852
S11300400000056600000566000005660000056600
S11300500000056600000566000005660000566F0
S11300600000054E00004000000080060000800CE7
S113007000008012000080180000801E000004E8C8
S113008000000A5200000A7400000A9200000AA04C
S113009000000AF80000802400000802A0000080305C
S11300A0000080360000803C000080420000804850
S11300B00000804E0000805400000C7E00000C9A6A
S11300C0000005660000056600000566000005668
S11300D0000005660000056600000566000005667
S11300E0000005660000056600000566000005666
S11300F0000005660000056600000566000005665
S113010000000566000005660000056600000566 3F
S113011000000566000005660000056600000566 2F
S113012000000566000005660000056600000566 1F
S113013000000566000005660000056600000566 0F
S113014000000566000005660000056600000566 FF
S113015000000566000005660000056600000566 EF
S113016000000566000005660000056600000566 DF
S113017000000566000005660000056600000566 CF
S113018000000566000005660000056600000566 BF
S113019000000566000005660000056600000566 AF
S11301A000000566000005660000056600000566 9F
S11301B000000566000005660000056600000566 8F
S11301C000000566000005660000056600000566 7F
S11301D000000566000005660000056600000566 6F
S11301E000000566000005660000056600000566 5F
S11301F000000566000005660000056600000566 4F
S113020000000566000005660000056600000566 3E
S113021000000566000005660000056600000566 2E
S113022000000566000005660000056600000566 1E
S113023000000566000005660000056600000566 0E
S113024000000566000005660000056600000566 FE
S113025000000566000005660000056600000566 EE
S113026000000566000005660000056600000566 DE
S113027000000566000005660000056600000566 CE
S113028000000566000005660000056600000566 BE
S113029000000566000005660000056600000566 AE
S11302A000000566000005660000056600000566 9E
S11302B000000566000005660000056600000566 8E
S11302C000000566000005660000056600000566 7E
S11302D000000566000005660000056600000566 6E
S11302E000000566000005660000056600000566 5E
S11302F000000566000005660000056600000566 4E
S113030000000566000005660000056600000566 3D
S113031000000566000005660000056600000566 2D
S113032000000566000005660000056600000566 1D
S113033000000566000005660000056600000566 0D
S113034000000566000005660000056600000566 FD
S113035000000566000005660000056600000566 ED
S113036000000566000005660000056600000566 DD
S113037000000566000005660000056600000566 CD
S113038000000566000005660000056600000566 BD
S113039000000566000005660000056600000566 AD
```

```
S11303A00000056600000566000005660000005669D
S11303B00000056600000566000005660000005668D
S11303C00000056600000566000005660000005667D
S11303D00000056600000566000005660000005666D
S11303E00000056600000566000005660000005665D
S11303F00000056600000566000005660000005664D
S1130400027CF8FF007C07004EB80A3223FC00008F
S113041000020000B8FA23FC000000010000B91833
S1130420207C0000B8004E6033FC27000000B8B800
S113043023FC000080000000B8B4303C000E207C97
S11304400000B8BA429851C8FFFC43FA04964E42E1
S11304502E7C0000C00043FA04934E42227C00002C
S1130460B80072284E432E7C0000C0004EB808F835
S1130470227C0000B82810110C00002E6606103CE7
S1130480005A600A0C00003F6604103C00484A0011
S113049067BE6100055664B853000200001FE318EC
S11304A043FA00123031000022404ED143FA044591
S11304B04E42609C04AC04AC04AC0B7C04AC04ACB5
S11304C00C0C057004AC04AC04AC0CC60DFE04ACFE
S11304D004AC04AC04AC10E21070126E04AC04ACB6
S11304E004AC04AC8000138E48F97FFF0000B8BA56
S11304F023EF00020000B8B433D70000B8B84EB8F8
S1130500010E86000FF4C43FA02A5600443FA02AC11
S11305104E4243FA03BA604043FA02B1603443FAEC
S1130520002C2602E43FA02CB602843FA02D860224A
S113053043FA02E7601C43FA02F8601643FA030C1C
S11305406010 43FA0320600A43FA032A600443FA62
S113055003454E4243FA03704E42206F000261008D
S113056005CC6000FEEC43FA03434E426000FEE219
S113057043FA00084E426000FED80D0A2A2A2A2AAD
S11305802A204D4F4E36384B20434F4D4D414E445B
S11305902053554D4D415259202A2A2A2A2A0D0A00
S11305A03D3D3D3D3D3D3D3D3D3D3D3D3D3D3D3D77
S11305B03D3D3D3D3D3D3D3D3D3D3D3D3D3D3D3D67
S11305C03D3D0D0A4449202020202020646973617355
S11305D073656D626C6520696E737472756374699A
S11305E06F6E730D0A474F2020202020676F207400
S11305F06F20757365722070726F6772616D0D0D0A7A
S113060004754202020202020676F20746F2074656D6C
S1130610706F7261727920627265616B706F696E5E
S1130620740D0A4845202020202020686561C7020281D
S1130630646973706C61792074686973206D657383
S113064073616765290D0A4C47202020202020 6C6FB8
S1130650616420532D7265636F726473 20616E64EC
S113066020676F0D0A4C4F20202020 206C6F6164 9E
S113067020532D7265636F726473 0D0A4D432020FD
S113068020202020 6D656D6F727920636F70790D0A7B
S113069004D4420202020202020 6D656D6F72792064 7593
S1130 6A06D700D0A4D46202020202020 6D656D6F72 FF
S11306B0792066696C6C0D0A4D4D20202020 2020 6D38
S11306C0656D6F7279206D6F646966790D0A4D5449A
S11306D020202020206D656D6F727920746573744FD
S11306E00D0A5244202020202020726567697374465C6
S11306F0722064756D700D0A535A2020202020207 3D7
S1130700697A65206F66206461746120666F722067
S11307104D4420636F6D6D616E640D0A5444202056
S11307202020207472616365206465 6C61790D0A10
S1130730545220202020207472616365 20696E73 F6
S11307407472756374696F6E730D0A2E522058 2082 08B
S1130750202073657 42726567697374657220521 2
S113076020746F20616C75652 20580D0A3F20203 7
S11307702020202064697370 6C617920746869732 7
```

S1130780206D6573736167650D0A3D3D3D3D3D3D3DDB
S11307903D3D3D3D3D3D3D3D3D3D3D3D3D3D3D3D3D85
S11307A03D3D3D3D3D3D3D3D3D3D3D3D3D000D0A074B
S11307B0427573204572726F72000D0A07416464BA
S11307C072657373204572726F72000D0A07496C6B
S11307D06C6567616C20496E737472756374696FBC
S11307E06E000D0A075A65726F2044697669646564
S11307F0000D0A0743484B20496E7374727563748 5
S1130800696F6E000D0A07545241505620496E73A9
S1130810747275637469 6F6E000D0A07507269769D
S1130820696C6567652056696F6C6174696F6E00E9
S11308300D0A074C696E65203031303120456D75E5
S11308406C61746572205472617000000D0A074C696E6E06
S11308506520313131312 0456D756C6174652054 EA
S1130860726170000D0A07466F726D6174204572E3
S1130870726F72000D0A07556E696E697469616C56
S1130880697A656420496E74657272757074205655
S11308906563746F720D0A0753707572696F7573AF
S11308A020496E74657272757074000D0A07556E76
S11308B0696D706C656D656E74656420457863 65FB
S11308C07074696F6E000D0A5043203D20000D0ABC
S11308D04163636573732061646472657373203D5F
S11308E020000D0A4D4F4E36384B000D0A56342E5B
S10A08F0343E000D0A3F0035
S11308F8227C0000B800247C0000B828423900009B
S1130908B8311019B03C002067F860021019610072
S1130918007A14C00C00000D66044222605A0C00D0
S11309280020670260E64222247C0000B8321E3CA4
S11309380004088300004281101 90C00000D6606AB
S11309481E3C000160240C00002067140C00002CDD
S1130958670E08C30000610000228280E99960D80C
S11309680803000067D20883000052390000B83138
S10D0978E89924C1530766BE4E75CA
S11309820C00003A6504D03C00090200000F4E75C9
S11309926100005664040200 00DF4E750200000F7D
S11309A20C00000A65040 6000007060000304E75BC
S11309B202800000007F61186514000000200C0012
S11309C2006165060C0000676504023C00FE4E757A
S11309D202800000007F0C00003065060C00003A23
S11309E26504023C00FE4E7502800000007F0C008C
S11309F2006165060C00007B650A0C000041650677
S1130A020C00005B4E75023C00FE4E7540E73F0051
S1130A120240007F0C000020650A0C00007F40EFBA
S1130A2200026006026FFFFE0002301F46DF4E75B1
S1130A32207C0000C001117C00060000117C000F24
S1130A420000117C00BB0002117C000500044E75FD
S1130A522F083F07207C0000C0011E280002020765
S1130A62000167F6102800060200007F3E1F205F87
S1130A724E732F083F07207C0000C0011E2800028D
S1130A820207000467F6114000063E1F205F4E7302
S1130A922F00101967044E4160F8201F4E7348E777
S1130AA2E040424255414E400C00000467060C00EF
S1130AB2007F66184A4267EE43E9FFFF2F09227C52
S1130AC200000AF04E42225F534260DA4E41524223
S1130AD212C0B242660A103C000D4E112C06006BA
S1130AE20C00000D66C042114CDF02074E731B5B03
S1080AF2441B5B4B00F6
S1130AF82F083F00207C0000C001102800020200DB
S1130B0800011F400007301F205F4E732F00E818B4
S1130B186100FE844E41201F2F006100FE7A4E4181
S1130B28201F4E752F003F012008323C0004E19835
S1130B3861DA534166F8321F201F4E752F0943FAB4

S1130B4800084E42225F4E7520002F0943FA000820
S10C0B584E42225F4E750D0A00A5
S1130B624E406100FE1CE9183F004E406100FE1237
S10D0B72805F0280000000FF4E7552
S1130B7C28790000B8322E390000B8364A39000002
S1130B8CB83167046128600643FA00084E426000DD
S1130B9CF8B40D0A53594E5441583A204449206133
S1100BAC64647265737320636F756E74006A
S1130BBA48E7FFF6207C0000B842303C0007429820
S1130BCA51C8FFFC201C221C241C49ECFFF42A7C7B
S1130BDA0000B8626100107042390000B8AA227C91
S1130BEA00000C024E42224D4E424E4465045347C5
S1130BFA66D24CDF6FFF4E750D0A2D2D2D2D2D203B
S1040C0A00E5
S1130C0C207C0000B828102800010C000054672830
S1130C1C4A390000B831670A23F90000B8320000E1
S1130C2CB8B44CF97FFF0000B8BA2F390000B8B43F
S1130C3C3F390000B8B84E734A390000B831671216
S1130C4C20790000B83233D00000B8B230BC4E4F1B
S1130C5C60D043FA00084E426000F7EA0D0A53597B
S1130C6C4E5441583A2047542061646472657733E
S1040C7C0073
S1130C7E48F97FFF0000B8BA207C0000B8B420AF5A
S1130C8E0002559031570004600F7B848F97FFF11
S1130C9E0000B8BA207C0000B8B420AF0002559012
S1130CAE3157000420790000B83230B90000B8B2D0
S10B0CBE610004286000F78CBA
S1130CC643FA00F84E424E400C00005366F84E407C
S1130CD60C000030676C0C00003167160C00003203
S1130CE667100C000038670000860C000039677E28
S1130CF660D418006100FE66160014006100FE5EF2
S1130D065502D600E19824406100FE525302D600F3
S1130D16D08AB83C0032660EE19820406100FE3E5F
S1130D265302D600D08A24406100FE32D60014C095
S1130D36530266F46100FE26B1030C0300FF6670DD
S1130D46608443FA009C4E426100FE1216004883FA
S1130D5657436100FE086100FE04600A6100FDFE5F
S1130D666100FC2A4E4151CBFFF46000FF5A61003A
S1130D76FDEC16004883554342826100FDE0E18A9A
S1130D86140051CBFFF64A82670C43FA00614E42C7
S1130D9620426100FD924E400C00001A66F80C39A0
S1130DA600470000B829660E4A82670A2F084E7566
S1130DB643FA001C4E424EF804500D0A4C6F61640F
S1130DC620532D7265636F7264732E2E2E000D0AE6
S1130DD607436865636B73756D204572726F7200A5
S1130DE61320204D6F64756C653A20110020204550
S10A0DF66E7472793A2000CB
S1130DFE20790000B83222790000B8362479000038
S1130E0EB83A1E390000B83110390000B8290C0068
S1130E1E004367220C0000446700019A0C00004650
S1130E2E670000D20C00004D670001020C00005454
S1130E3E67426000F60E4A07670C43E9000114D8B6
S1130E4EB3C866FA600643FA00084E426000F5F431
S1130E5E0D0A53594E5441583A204D432073746130
S1130E6E727420656E642064657374696E6174694E
S1060E7E6F6E0090
S1130E824A07672643E900011C1046061086BC1077
S1130E92662046061086BC10661841E80001B3C8F5
S1130EA266E643FA00334E42601243FA00144E429D
S1130EB2600A43FA002F4E426100FC706000F59014
S1130EC20D0A53594E5441583A204D5420737461BB
S1130ED2727420656E64000D0A4D656D6F7279201F

```
S1130EE24F4B000D0A074D656D6F72792065727262
S1120EF26F72206174206164647265773732000F1
S1130F024A07670E43E900013C0A10C6B3C866FAF1
S1130F12600643FA00084E426000F5340D0A535944
S1130F224E5441583A204D462073746172742065C0
S1130F326E642062797465500A4A0767646100FC127A
S1130F426100FBE86100FBFC101812006100FBC4A5
S1130F526100FBF04E400C00002E67400C000020A4
S1130F62673A0C00000D671C0C00001B66224E4001
S1130F720C00005B66264E400C000041660C41E802
S1130F82FFFE60B81141FFFF60B20C00004267AC83
S1130F924E416100F9ECE909820060B84E416006F5
S1130FA243FA00084E426000FF700D0A53594E5432
S1120FB241583A204D4D20616464726573730099
S1130FC24A0767000086200080200000F02640220932
S1130FD2D27C00100241FFF0E8596100FB7420400A
S1130FE26100FB48287C0000B8FE343C00102A7CD7
S1130FF20000B8FA26156100FB4A6100FB46101B8B
S11310026100FB10530366066100FB38261561007C
S1131012F9FC650819BC002E20FF6004198020FF2A
S11310224E4464044E406028200B530266D0143CA4
S113103200106100FB0E103420FF4E41530266F68D
S11310425341670C200B6092600643FA00084E423B
S11310526000F3FC0D0A53594E5441583A204D4452
S110106220737461727420636F756E7400E6
S11310704A390000B831672E207C0000B832227C47
S113108000000B8FA20100280000000070C000001E4
S113109067100C000002670A0C0000046704103C8F
S11310A000022280600643FA00084E426000F3A268
S11310B00D0A53594E5441583A20535A206E202851
S11310C031203D20627974652C2032203D20776FD9
S11310D072642C2034203D206C6F6E67776F7264CD
S10510E02900E1
S11310E261044EF8045048E7F0F86100FA64267C83
S11310F20000B8B4247C0000120A143C0010224AF6
S11311024E4245EA0005205B6100FA20224A4E4223
S113111245EA0005101B6100F9FA101B6100F9F49D
S1131122103C003D4E41227C0000B90E103C0008E8
S113113212FC002E530066F84211227C0000B90E04
S1131142102BFFFEE318640412BC005443E90001AF
S1131152E518640412BC005343E90001E6180200D6
S11311620007000000301 2C0102BFFFFE9186404CE
S113117212BC005843E90001E318640412BC004E97
S113118243E90001E318640412BC005A43E9000174
S1131192E318640412BC005643E90001E318640432
S11311A212BC0043227C0000B90E4E42224A4E4237
S11311B245EA00054E686100F97223CF0000B8F6D3
S11311C2224A4E4245EA000520790000B8F6610041
S11311D2F95A6100F97C224A4E4245EA0005205B35
S11311E26100F9485302670E3202C23C00036604EE
S11311F26100F95E60E028790000B8B47E01610004
S1131202F9B84CDF1F0F4E752050433D0020535256
S11312123D002055533D002053533D002044303DB2
S1131222002044313D002044323D002044333D003F
S11312322044343D002044353D002044363D002006
S113124244373D002041303D002041313D002041E2
S1131252323D002041333D002041343D00204135E0
S10F12623D002041363D002041373D0096
S1131263E10390000B829B03C0052676AB03C004403
S113127E67044EF804504A390000B831671A203911
S1131283E0000B832C07C0007E508203B002A23C0CA
S1131293E0000B9184EF8045043FA00084E424EF8B6
```

S11312AE04500D0A53594E5441583A205444206464
S10812BE656C6179007C
S11312C4000000001000258000004B000000960009E
S11312D40012C00000258000004B000000960000AE
S11312E44A390000B831671E007980000000B8B89C
S11312F44CF97FFF0000B8BA2F390000B8B43F3965
S11313040000B8B84E7343FA00084E424EF8045035
S11313140D0A53594E5441583A20545220636F7560
S10613246E7400E0
S113132848F97FFF0000B8BA23EF00020000B8B400
S113133833D70000B8B86100FDA843FA00464E420E
S11313484A390000B83167122E390000B91853879A
S113135866FC53B90000B8326E12227C0000B80053
S11313684E430C39000D0000B800660A4CF97FFFA3
S11313780000B8BA4E7302797FFF0000B8B8600065
S1091388F0DE0D0A3A003C
S113138E6100F7C224390000B83208810000227CC3
S113139E0000B828267C0000B8B4287C0000120A8D
S11313AE102900030C00000D660408C1000010296A
S11313BE00020C0000536638102900010C00005383
S11313CE661608010000670A43EC000F204F600008
S11313DE00A82E42600000A808010000670A43EC32
S11313EE000A4E686000009228424E64600000902D
S11313FE0C00004366160801000067 0A43EC000067
S113140E206B00006072274200006072 0C000052D4
S113141E662408010000671843EC00054E42302B89
S113142E0004E1586100F6E0E1586100F6DA604E1E
S113143E37420004604842844285162900011 82967
S113144E00020284000000071A04E59CCAFC000591
S113145E0C030041660CD8BC00000020DABC00006E
S113146E002808010000670A43F450142073400654
S113147E60062782400660064E426100F6A26000B6
S105148EEFC2A7
S11314906100072E7C38CC54BC7C002067067C019C
S11314A0720060047CFF720F6100072A1CFC002C90
S11114B0548338143E3C01F461000544601C72
S11314C0610006FE54833E3C07EC610005321CFCBF
S10F14D0002C7C017200610006FC606CC2
S11314DC302C00021CFC00231CFC002461000BE0DB
S10714EC600008068A
S11314F06100048254831CFC00234280302C0002CF
S11315003214EC49C27C00036746B23C00016750C8
S11315105483202C000261000B401CC53014C07C95
S1131520003FB07C003C66223014C07C4000660062
S1131530 07F23214C27C00C0B27C0080670007E46A
S11315401CFC00531CFC0052603E610004B2603875
S11315502200E049670A2200EE415241660007C4B6
S107156048C060B269
S1071564600003B26A
S1131568616C1CC51CFC0023302C000248C06100BF
S10915780AE060000778A0
S10F1580610003F2610004786000007E4A
S109158C615860000078C4
S11315941CFC00233014C0BC0000000F61000AB618
S10715A4600000627D
S10915A8612C6000005CF0
S11315B03E3C07E4615C1CC53814EF5C61186000B4
S10515C00048DD
S11315C43E3C0FFD61481CC53814EF5C6114600097
S11315D400341CFC0041C83C0007883C00301CC497
S10B15E44E751CFC004460EE8E
S11115ECEF5C61F61CC5381461F0600000105D

```
S11315FCEF5C61D61CFC002C381461CE60000080BA
S10D160CEF5C61D660EE600003EAB3
S11316183E3C0FFF2004C07C01C0673AB07C01C087
S11316286710B07C00C0661E1AFC002E1AFC005716
S113163860081AFC002E1AFC004C61CE1CC5381434
S1111648EF5C618A603C081400006620600CB0
S11316580814000066163E3C0FFD6100031061AAE1
S11316681CC51814E20C6100FF766016610002FEC6
S11316781814E20C6100FF681CC538143E3C01FDD7
S109168861886000066A9F
S10D16903E3C07E46100FF7C60F0BB
S113169C2004C07C003FB07C003866081AFC002E85
S11316AC1AFC0053B07C003966081AFC002E1AFC94
S10716BC004C60D0AA
S11316C0610002B20804000366106100FF1A1CC521
S11316D01814E20C6100FF1060461CFC002D1CFC79
S11316E000286100FEF2203C282D2C296152181498
S10F16F0E20C6100FEE21CFC00296024F6
S11316FC610002761CFC00286100FED0203C282CE2
S113170C2B2961301814E20C6100FEC01CFC00296A
S10B171C1CFC002B600005D445
S10717246000021E3D
S11317281CFC00233014488048C0610009241CC5EF
S1131738EF5C6100FEAA60E01CC0E08866FA4E75A2
S1111748203C002C525361F0610002AC60CAD8
S1111758203C2C50535561E06100FE7460BAD1
S11317683E3C0FFD61000290203C0052532C61C89E
S105177860A665
S10F177C6100FE58203C5053552C60EED8
S11317883E3C0FFD61000270203C5243432C60DE56
S11317981AFC002E303C4C57080400066702E04847
S11317A81AC01814E20C082C00070001670E610027
S11317B8FE2E1CC53814611260000532610C1CC56C
S11317C81814E20C6100FE1860EE1CFC0024302C96
S11317D80002610008EE1CFC002838146100FDF0CA
S10917E81CFC00294E75F3
S10717F06000050488
S10D17F4610000EA6100020460F2E3
S113180038146100FDE21CC51CFC0024610000D2F8
S1051810602E44
S1131814610000CA1CFC00244A0467201AFC002E40
S11318241AFC0053488448C4D8A9FFFC54842004F7
S1131834E284650004EA6100088860B05483382CAB
S10F184400021AFC002E1AFC004C60DAB2
S1131850EF5C6100FD921CC53814610001A2609028
S113186054831CFC00234280302C00022200EA89AD
S10D1870660004B0610007E260DCCA
S113187C303C4C52080400086702E0481AC030148B
S113188CC07C00C0B07C00C06730610000DCEF5C41
S113189C0804000C6616C83C00076604883C000863
S11318AC883C00301CFC00231CC460046100FD2C2B
S11318BC1CC538146100FD2460981AFC002E1AFC17
S11318CC00570804000B6600044E3E3C01FC61000A
S11318DC012260E4700FC014E388323B00101AC17B
S11318ECE049B23C002067021AC14E7520542046D0
S11318FC4948534C43435343454E51454356535621
S10F190C4C50494D4547544C5447454C41
S11319183E3C0FFF610000E01CC53814E24CEA0CA1
S1131928E05CEB0CEA4C3E3C01FF1014B03C0001B7
S10F193866043E3C01FD610000BE602C12
S1131944612E1CFC0023EF5CC83C00076604883C41
S11319540008883C00301CC41CC538143014C07CF6
```

```
S113196400C067043E3C01FF6100009060000384F2
S113197434141AFC002EEC4AC47C000366061AFCD8
S113198400426016103C0057B43C0001670A103C46
S1131994004CB43C0002665E1AC04E756100FC44FF
S11319A40807000067504E756100FC280807000111
S11319B467444E751CFC00286100FC181CFC0029BB
S11319C40807000267304E751CFC00286100FC0403
S11319D41CFC00291CFC002B0807000367184E7527
S11319E41CFC002D1CFC00286100FBE81CFC0029E5
S10D19F40807000466E860000326FB
S11319FE2004E648C07C00076798B03C0001679E4F
S1131A0EB03C000267A4B03C000367B2B03C0004D3
S1131A1E67C4B03C00056760B03C000767700807F8
S1131A2E000667C832343000C27C070066BE30340C
S1131A3E3000488048C0610006121CFC002861007A
S1131A4EFB881CFC002C18343000E8046A06610084
S1131A5EFB7860046100FB821CFC002E38343000DD
S1131A6E103C00570804000B6704103C004C1CC0CB
S1131A7E1CFC002954834E75080700056756303444
S1131A8E300048C0610005C454836000FF1EC87C4A
S1131A9E0007661808070007673A3034300048C05C
S1131AAE1CFC00246100060854834E75B83C0001EA
S1131ABE661608070008671C1CFC0024203430003E
S1131ACE610005EC58834E75B83C0002662C08077D
S1131ADE000966046000023E3034300048C0D0A9CC
S1131AEEFFFC54801CFC0024610005C4203C2943E7
S1131AFE50286100FC3E54834E75B83C0003666466
S1131B0E0807000A67CE32343000C27C070066C470
S1131B1E10343001488048C0D0A9FFFC54801CFC0E
S1131B2E00246100058A203C2C4350286100FC04EB
S1131B3E38343000E95C0804000367066100FA8A51
S1131B4E60046100FA941CFC002E38343000303CE2
S1131B5E4C570804000B6702E0481CC01CFC00290B
S1131B6E54834E75B83C00046600FF6A0807000BE8
S1131B7E6700FF621CFC0023122DFFFFB23C004CD9
S1131B8E672430343000B23C004266102200E04933
S1131B9E670A2200EE4152416600FF3A48C06100D6
S1131BAE04AA54834E75203430006100049E588379
S1131BBE4E751AFC002E303C4C5708040006670282
S1091BCEE0481AC04E7548
S1131BD4342C000270207E2F538E7A30383C4144DA
S1131BE403026730B01666121D4400011D4500024D
S1131BF41D7C002D0003568E602E0C16002C67E805
S1131C04BE1667E41D4400011D4500021D7C002D21
S1131C14000360140C16002C670EB016670AB02E6D
S1131C2400016702568E1C875285D286BA3C00385E
S1131C3466AEB016670AB02E00016704568E1C8780
S10F1C441A3C0030E04C66981C804E7581
S1131C5048E7FFF04E51FFF048E91007FFF049E96B
S1131C60FFF0264D203C000000502C4B1CFC0020B3
S1131C70538066F82C4B2029FFFC61000472301459
S1131C804BFA00CA2C4DDDFC00000002B05D671A5F
S1131C90BBCE66F84BFA00B84DFA02BE3014C05DF4
S1131CA0B05D6708548DBBCE66F2607642861C1D1B
S1131CB0E58E42871E1D41FA02A04A4767084A186A
S1131CC06AFC538760F4701F4BF3000010180880FF
S1131CD0000766041AC060F41AC0760241FAF7B22B
S1131CE0D1C670274DF3000038141A3C002C3E3C3A
S1131CF001FD4ED054832C031CFC00202A4E700A94
S1131D004DF30000301C54A9FFFC610003BE5503D1
S1131D1066F22C4D2A4B2869FFFC4E594CDF0FFF0D
S1051D204E75FA
```

S1131D22701F4DF300004BFA0018101DB03C000464
S1091D3267041CC060F40C
S1131D3830146100038E760260B444432E57202089
S1091D48202024044AFBE4
S1131D4EFEC0E6C0FB38FEC0E4C0FB39FEC0E2C0F4
S1131D5EFB37FEC0E0C0FB36F018E018FB38F01875
S1131D6EE010FB39F018E008FB37F018E000FB3602
S1131D7EF0C0D0C06204F130D1008C35F000D00038
S1131D8E6204F1F8C1885F32F1F8C1485B32F1F8B0
S1131D9EC1405732F1F0C1008C31F1C0C1C04D3099
S1131DAEF1C0C0C04D2FF000C0007202F0C0B0C030
S1131DBE6206F138B1089B2EF100B1007205F000F5
S1131DCEB0006206F0C090C0622CF13091008C2DF0
S1131DDEF0009000622CF1F081008C2BF1C081C0D8
S1131DEE4D2AF1C080C04D29F00080007228F10008
S1131DFE7000A627FF006100E233FF006000E2419D
S1131E0EF0006000E126F0F850C8DC25F0C050C0A8
S1131E1ED924F1005100A523F1005000A522F1C0F0
S1131E2E41C04821F1C041804D20FFC04EC0831FE8
S1131E3EFFC04E80831EFFFF4E77D81DFFFF4E76E8
S1131E4ED81CFFFF4E75D81BFFFF4E73D81AFFFF29
S1131E5E4E721319FFFF4E71D818FFFF4E70D8172C
S1131E6EFFF84E68B23CFFF84E60BB3CFFF84E588C
S1131E7E4616FFF84E503615FFF04E404114FF80C3
S1131E8E4C800C0FFFC04AC03D13FF004A003C12A9
S1131E9EFFF848C03F11FFF848803F10FF8048808C
S1131EAE000FFFF848403F0EFFC04840800DFFC0B2
S1131EBE48003D0CFFC046C0B63BFF0046003C0B3D
S1131ECEFFC044C0BE3BFF0044003C0AFF0042007A
S1131EDE3C09FFC040C0AE3BFF0040003C08F00090
S1131EEE3000353BF0002000353CF0001000353A50
S1131EFEFF000C001806FF000A001805FF0006007C
S1131F0E1804FF0004001803FF0002001802FF006B
S1131F1E00001801F1380108C200FFC008C0F440E7
S1131F2EFFC00880F43FFFC00840F43EFFC0080025
S1131F3EF43DF1C001C0F040F1C00180F03FF1C0AA
S10D1F4E0140F03EF1C00100F03D37
S1131F584D4F5645D04FD2414EC45355C24144C447
S1131F68454FD2434DD04D4F56C54E4547D8434CA7
S1131F78D24E45C74E4FD44E4243C45045412ECC51
S1131F88535741502ED74D4F5645CD4558542ED70B
S1131F984558542ECC5453D45441532EC254524110
S1131FA8D04C494ECB554E4CCB52455345D44E4F4D
S1131FB8D053544FD05254C55254D354524150D68E
S1131FC85254D24A53D24A4DD043484B2ED74C454B
S1131FD8412ECC414444D1535542D1D344C2C24D7D
S1131FE84F5645512ECC4FD2444956552ED74449C5
S1131FF856532ED7534243C45355C2535542D8431C
S11320084D50CD4D554C552ED74D554C532ED7418B
S11320184243C44558C74253D24E554CCC4144441C
S1132028D841D34CD352CF524FD84D4F56452EC2D8
S11320384D4F56452ED74D4F56452ECC425453D46A
S1122048424348C742434CD2425345D44252C14B
S113205848E77B002E006A0844876B4E1CFC002D61
S113206842447C0A740122065381671A3602C6FC6C
S1132078000A4842C4FC000A4843D443484248433F
S11320883403538166E64280BE826D0652809E8286
S113209860F64A0066044A446708D03C00301CC015
S11320A81800538666BE4A4466041CFC00304CDFA4
S11320B800DE4E754840610A484060064840610A9F
S11320C848403200E058610230013400E8506102AF
S11320D83002C03C000F803C0030B03C00396F0235

S11320E85E401CC04E7548E7478041F90000B8427D
S11320F87EFF428622004A90670C92906B08B28752
S113210864042E012A0658885286BC7C000866E4BA
S11321184A876B1E4A4666084AB90000B8426712E5
S1132128200761981CFC002B1CFC0052DA3C003090
S1132138600A61881A3C00201CC51CC51CC54CDFFC
S107214801E24E75E9
S9030000FC

# Appendix F

# PAL Replacement Circuit

The use of a 16L8 for the address decoding in the SBC68K presents a problem for those without PAL programming capabilities. This appendix describes a substitute circuit that uses standard, inexpensive 7400-series ICs. Substituting the circuit described in this appendix is very straightforward. The monitor program, MON68K, and the examples given in this text will work on the modified SBC68K as is. No software changes are needed.

The replacement circuit is given in Figure F-1. Although it looks messy, an SBC68K built with this circuit will have only one more IC than the design in Chapter 8. However, some of the flexibility of the SBC68K is lost and the memory-space usage changes somewhat. These differences are explained in this appendix.

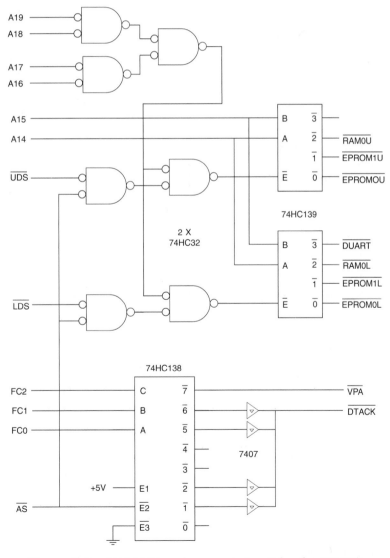

**Figure F-1.** PAL16L8 replacement circuit for the 68KMB.

Address decoding is performed using two 74HC32 quad OR ICs and one 74HC139 dual 2-line-to-4-line decoder. The chip select lines are active for the exact same addresses as the 16L8 PAL circuit given in Chapter 8. Note, however, that address line A20 is missing in Figure F-1. This means that the decoding is not as "full" as that using the 16L8. With reference to the memory map in Figure 8-10, the "expansion" space now extends only to address $0FFFFE (rather than to $1FFFFE), and the decoding is reflected in 512K word blocks through the 68000's 8M word address space.

The replacement circuit includes a slight change to the interrupt circuitry from Chapter 8 (Figure 8-8). The interrupt-generation portion of Figure 8-8 (the 74HC148) remains the same; however, the interrupt-acknowledge portion of Figure 8-8 (the two 74HC138s and the three 7407 buffers) should be deleted. Instead, a 74HC138 decoder and four 7407 buffers are used, as shown in Figure F-1. The new circuit generates $\overline{VPA}$ automatically for any interrupt-acknowledge (IACK) cycle. This means the SBC68K uses autovectoring only. The new circuit also generates $\overline{DTACK}$ automatically whenever the CPU performs a bus cycle. Recall that there are five types of bus cycles, as encoded on the 68000's function code lines. One is the IACK cycle and the other four are memory cycles in the supervisor data, supervisor program, user data, and user program spaces. $\overline{VPA}$ is now automatic for IACK cycles, and $\overline{DTACK}$ is now automatic for memory cycles. Although this arrangement is economical, it precludes implementing some advanced features, such as wait states or the use of $\overline{BERR}$ to terminate an illegal memory access.

One other small change must be made to implement the SBC68K using the circuit in Figure F-1. $\overline{DTACK}$ on the 68681 should be left open. Since $\overline{DTACK}$ is automatically generated from the circuit in Figure F-1, it is not necessary to connect the 68681's $\overline{DTACK}$ signal to the 68000. This means the 68681 will not implement "user" interrupt-acknowledge cycles, as it is capable of doing. Some flexibility is lost but it does not pose a major problem. The 68681 examples using interrupts in Chapter 9 use the level-2 autovector anyway, so the operation is exactly the same as before except the level-2 autovector is now forced through $\overline{VPA}$.

The four 7407 open collector buffers in Figure F-1 drive the 68000's $\overline{DTACK}$ input. A single pull-up resistor is required (not shown). Note that these buffers do not increase the chip count because two open-collector buffers were used in the generation of $\overline{RESET}$ and $\overline{HALT}$ (see Figure 8-7). The 7407 includes six buffers, so the four in Figure F-1 were available anyway. Since $\overline{VPA}$ has only one source now, an open-collector buffer is not used and a pull-up resistor is not required.

The ICs in the SBC68K using the circuit of Figure F-1 are summarized in Table F-1.

Table F-1.   ICs in the Modified SBC68K.

| Part Number | Description | Quantity |
|---|---|---|
| 68000 | CPU | 1 |
| 68681 | DUART | 1 |
| 2764A | EPROM | 2 |
| 6264 | RAM | 2 |
| MAX232 | RS232C transceiver | 1 |
| 74HC139 | decoder | 1 |
| 74HC138 | decoder | 1 |
| 74HC148 | encoder | 1 |
| 7407 | open collector buffer | 1 |
| 74HC32 | quad OR gate | 2 |
| 74HC14 | Schmitt trigger | 1 |
| | Total: | 14 |

# Appendix G

# 68000 Data Sheet*

**MOTOROLA**
■ **SEMICONDUCTOR** ■■■■■■■■■■■■■■■■
**TECHNICAL DATA**

## MC68000

*Technical Summary*
## 16-/32-Bit Microprocessor

This document contains both a summary of the MC68000 and a detailed set of parametrics. For detailed information on the MC68000, refer to M68000 UM/AD, *M68000 8-/16-/32-Bit Microprocessor User's Manual.* **3**

The MC68000 is the first implementation of the M68000 16-/32-bit microprocessor architecture. The MC68000 has a 16-bit data bus and 24-bit address bus; the full architecture provides for 32-bit address and data buses. It is completely code compatible with the MC68008 8-bit data bus implementation of the M68000 and is upward code compatible with the MC68010 virtual extensions and the MC68020 32-bit implementation of the architecture. Any user-mode programs using the MC68000 instruction set will run unchanged on the MC68008, MC68010, MC68020, MC68030, and MC68040 because the user programming model is identical for all processors and the instruction sets are proper subsets of the complete architecture.

The following resources are available to the MC68000 user:

- 17 32-Bit Data and Address Registers
- 16-Mbyte Direct Addressing Range
- 56 Powerful Instruction Types
- Operations on Five Main Data Types
- Memory-Mapped I/O
- 14 Addressing Modes

# INTRODUCTION

The MC68000 offers 16 32-bit registers and a 32-bit program counter (see Figure 1). The first eight registers (D0–D7) are used as data registers for byte (8-bit), word (16-bit), and long-word (32-bit) operations. The second set of seven registers (A0–A6) and the user stack pointer (USP) may be used as software stack pointers and base address registers. In addition, the registers can be used for word and long-word operations. All 16 registers may be used as index registers.

**3**

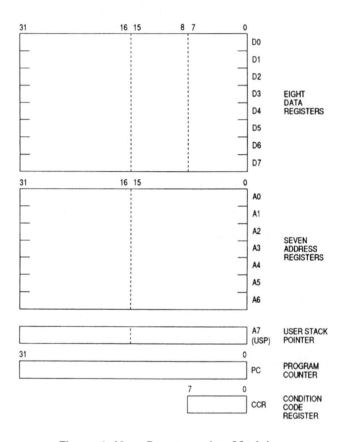

**Figure 1. User Programming Model**

In supervisor mode, the upper byte of the status register (SR) and the supervisor stack pointer (SSP) are also available to the programmer. These registers are shown in Figure 2.

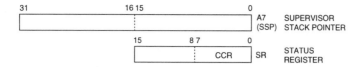

**Figure 2. Supervisor Programming Model Supplement**

The SR (see Figure 3) contains the interrupt mask (eight levels available) as well as the following condition codes: extend (X), negative (N), zero (Z), overflow (V), and carry (C). Additional status bits indicate that the processor is in a trace (T) mode and in a supervisor (S) or user state.

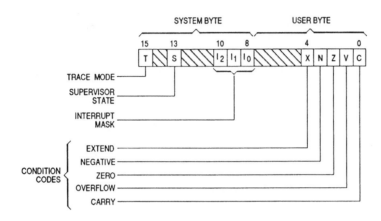

**Figure 3. Status Register**

# DATA TYPES AND ADDRESSING MODES

Five basic data types are supported:
  1. Bits
  2. BCD Digits (4 Bits)
  3. Bytes (8 Bits)
  4. Words (16 Bits)
  5. Long Words (32 Bits)
In addition, operations on other data types, such as memory addresses, status word data, etc., are provided in the instruction set.

The 14 addressing modes listed in Table 1 include six basic types:
1. Register Direct
2. Register Indirect
3. Absolute
4. Program Counter Relative
5. Immediate
6. Implied

Included in the register indirect addressing modes is the capability to perform postincrementing, predecrementing, offsetting, and indexing. The program counter relative mode can also be modified via indexing and offsetting.

**3**

### Table 1. Addressing Modes

| Addressing Modes | Syntax |
|---|---|
| Register Direct Addressing<br>  Data Register Direct<br>  Address Register Direct | <br>Dn<br>An |
| Absolute Data Addressing<br>  Absolute Short<br>  Absolute Long | <br>xxx.W<br>xxx.L |
| Program Counter Relative Addressing<br>  Relative with Offset<br>  Relative with Index Offset | <br>$d_{16}$(PC)<br>$d_8$(PC,Xn) |
| Register Indirect Addressing<br>  Register Indirect<br>  Postincrement Register Indirect<br>  Predecrement Register Indirect<br>  Register Indirect with Offset<br>  Indexed Register Indirect with Offset | <br>(An)<br>(An) +<br> − (An)<br>$d_{16}$(An)<br>$d_8$(An,Xn) |
| Immediate Data Addressing<br>  Immediate<br>  Quick Immediate | <br>#xxx<br>#1r#8 |
| Implied Addressing<br>  Implied Register | <br>SR/USP/SP/PC |

NOTES:
  Dn  = Data Register
  An  = Address Register
  Xn  = Address of Data Register Used as Index Register
  SR  = Status Register
  PC  = Program Counter
  SP  = Stack Pointer
 USP  = User Stack Pointer
  ( )  = Effective Address
  $d_8$  = 8-Bit Offset (Displacement)
  $D_{16}$  = 16-Bit Offset (Displacement)
 #xxx  = Immediate Data

# INSTRUCTION SET OVERVIEW

The MC68000 instruction set is listed in Table 2. Additional instructions that are variations or subsets of these instructions are listed in Table 3. Special emphasis is given to the instruction set's support of structured high-level languages to facilitate ease of programming. Each instruction, with few exceptions, operates on bytes, words, and long words, and most instructions can use any of the 14 addressing modes. Combining instruction types, data types, and addressing modes, over 1000 useful instructions are provided. These instructions include signed and unsigned, multiply and divide, quick arithmetic operations, BCD arithmetic, and expanded operations (through traps). For detailed information on the MC68000 instruction set refer to M68000 PM/AD, *M68000 Programmer's Reference Manual*.

**3**

## Table 2. Instruction Set Summary

| Mnemonic | Description | Mnemonic | Description |
|---|---|---|---|
| ABCD | Add Decimal with Extend | MOVE | Move |
| ADD | Add | MULS | Signed Multiply |
| AND | Logical AND | MULU | Unsigned Multiply |
| ASL | Arithmetic Shift Left | NBCD | Negate Decimal with Extend |
| ASR | Arithmetic Shift Right | NEG | Negate |
| Bcc | Branch Conditionally | NOP | No Operation |
| BCHG | Bit Test and Change | NOT | Ones Complement |
| BCLR | Bit Test and Clear | OR | Logical OR |
| BRA | Branch Always | PEA | Push Effective Address |
| BSET | Bit Test and Set | RESET | Reset External Devices |
| BSR | Branch to Subroutine | ROL | Rotate Left without Extend |
| BTST | Bit Test | ROR | Rotate Right without Extend |
| CHK | Check Register against Bounds | ROXL | Rotate Left with Extend |
| CLR | Clear Operand | ROXR | Rotate Right with Extend |
| CMP | Compare | RTE | Return from Exception |
| DBcc | Test Condition, Decrement and Branch | RTR | Return and Restore |
| DIVS | Signed Divide | RTS | Return from Subroutine |
| DIVU | Unsigned Divide | SBCD | Subtract Decimal with Extend |
| EOR | Exclusive OR | Scc | Set Conditional |
| EXG | Exchange Registers | STOP | Stop |
| EXT | Sign Extend | SUB | Subtract |
| JMP | Jump | SWAP | Swap Data Register Halves |
| JSR | Jump to Subroutine | TAS | Test and Set Operand |
| LEA | Load Effective Address | TRAP | Trap |
| LINK | Link Stack | TRAPV | Trap on Overflow |
| LSL | Logical Shift Left | TST | Test |
| LSR | Logical Shift Right | UNLK | Unlink |

## Table 3. Variations of Instruction Types

| Instruction Type | Variation | Description |
|---|---|---|
| ADD | ADD<br>ADDA<br>ADDQ<br>ADDI<br>ADDX | Add<br>Add Address<br>Add Quick<br>Add Immediate<br>Add with Extend |
| AND | AND<br>ANDI<br>ANDI to CCR<br>ANDI to SR | Logical AND<br>AND Immediate<br>AND Immediate to Condition Codes<br>AND Immediate to Status Register |
| CMP | CMP<br>CMPA<br>CMPM<br>CMPI | Compare<br>Compare Address<br>Compare Memory<br>Compare Immediate |
| EOR | EOR<br>EORI<br>EORI to CCR<br>EORI to SR | Exclusive OR<br>Exclusive OR Immediate<br>Exclusive OR Immediate to Condition Codes<br>Exclusive OR Immediate to Status Register |
| MOVE | MOVE<br>MOVEA<br>MOVEM<br>MOVEP<br>MOVEQ<br>MOVE from SR<br>MOVE to SR<br>MOVE to CCR<br>MOVE USP | Move<br>Move Address<br>Move Multiple Registers<br>Move Peripheral Data<br>Move Quick<br>Move from Status Register<br>Move to Status Register<br>Move to Condition Codes<br>Move User Stack Pointer |
| NEG | NEG<br>NEGX | Negate<br>Negate with Extend |
| OR | OR<br>ORI<br>ORI to CCR<br>ORI to SR | Logical OR<br>OR Immediate<br>OR Immediate to Condition Codes<br>OR Immediate to Status Register |
| SUB | SUB<br>SUBA<br>SUBI<br>SUBQ<br>SUBX | Subtract<br>Subtract Address<br>Subtract Immediate<br>Subtract Quick<br>Subtract with Extend |

**3**

# SIGNAL DESCRIPTION

The input and output signals (see Figure 4) are described in the following paragraphs.

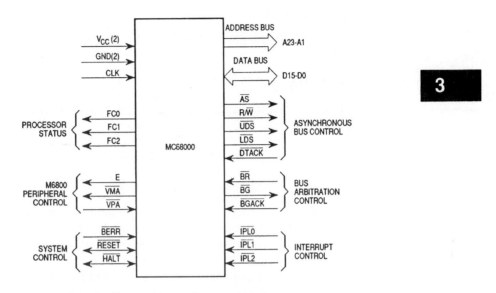

**Figure 4. Input and Output Signals**

## ADDRESS BUS (A1–A23)

This 23-bit, unidirectional, three-state bus is capable of addressing 16 Mbytes of data. It provides the address for bus operation during all cycles except interrupt cycles. During interrupt cycles, address lines A1, A2, and A3 provide information about what level interrupt is being serviced while address lines A4–A23 are set to a logic high.

## DATA BUS (D0–D15)

This 16-bit, bidirectional, three-state bus is the general-purpose data path that can transfer and accept data in either word or byte length. During an interrupt acknowledge cycle, the external device supplies the vector number on data lines D0–D7.

## ASYNCHRONOUS BUS CONTROL

Asynchronous data transfers are handled using the following control signals: address strobe, read/write, upper and lower data strobes, and data transfer acknowledge.

### Address Strobe ($\overline{AS}$)

This signal indicates a valid address on the address bus.

**3**

### Read/Write (R/$\overline{W}$)

This signal defines the data bus transfer as a read or write cycle. R/$\overline{W}$ also works in conjunction with the data strobes as explained in the following paragraph.

### Upper and Lower Data Strobe ($\overline{UDS}$, $\overline{LDS}$)

These signals control the flow of data on the data bus, as specified in Table 4. When R/$\overline{W}$ is high, the processor will read from the data bus as indicated. When R/$\overline{W}$ is low, the processor will write to the data bus as shown.

**Table 4. Data Strobe Control of Data Bus**

| $\overline{UDS}$ | $\overline{LDS}$ | R/$\overline{W}$ | D8–D15 | D0–D7 |
|---|---|---|---|---|
| 1 | 1 | — | No Valid Data | No Valid Data |
| 0 | 0 | 1 | Valid Data Bits 8–15 | Valid Data Bits 0–7 |
| 1 | 0 | 1 | No Valid Data | Valid Data Bits 0–7 |
| 0 | 1 | 1 | Valid Data Bits 8–15 | No Valid Data |
| 0 | 0 | 0 | Valid Data Bits 8–15 | Valid Data Bits 0–7 |
| 1 | 0 | 0 | Valid Data Bits 0–7* | Valid Data Bits 0–7 |
| 0 | 1 | 0 | Valid Data Bits 8–15 | Valid Data Bits 8–15* |

*These conditions are a result of current implementation and may not appear on future devices.

## Data Transfer Acknowledge (DTACK)

This input indicates that the data transfer is complete. When the processor recognizes DTACK during a read cycle, data is latched and the bus cycle is terminated. When DTACK is recognized during a write cycle, the bus cycle is terminated.

## BUS ARBITRATION CONTROL

Bus request, bus grant, and bus grant acknowledge form a bus arbitration circuit to determine which device will be the bus master.

3

## Bus Request (BR)

This input is wire-ORed with all other devices that could be bus masters. This input indicates to the processor that another device wishes to become the bus master.

## Bus Grant (BG)

This output indicates to all other potential bus master devices that the processor will release bus control at the end of the current bus cycle.

## Bus Grant Acknowledge (BGACK)

This input indicates that some other device has become the bus master. This signal should not be asserted until the following four conditions are met:

1. A bus grant has been received.
2. Address strobe is inactive, indicating that the microprocessor is not using the bus.
3. Data transfer acknowledge is inactive, indicating that neither memory nor peripherals are using the bus.
4. Bus grant acknowledge is inactive, indicating that no other device is claiming bus mastership.

## INTERRUPT CONTROL (IPL0, IPL1, IPL2)

These inputs indicate the encoded priority level of the device requesting an interrupt. Level 7 is the highest priority; level 0 indicates that no interrupts are requested. Level 7 cannot be masked. The least significant bit is given in IPL0, and the most significant bit is contained in $\overline{\text{IPL2}}$. These lines must remain stable until the processor signals interrupt acknowledge (FC0–FC2 are all high) to ensure that the interrupt is recognized.

## SYSTEM CONTROL

The three system control inputs are used to reset or halt the processor and to indicate to the processor that bus errors have occurred.

**3**

### Bus Error ($\overline{\text{BERR}}$)

This input informs the processor that there is a problem with the cycle currently being executed. Problems may be a result of:
1. Nonresponding devices
2. Interrupt vector number acquisition failure
3. Illegal access request as determined by a memory management unit
4. Other application-dependent errors

The bus error signal interacts with the halt signal to determine if the current bus cycle should be re-executed or if exception processing should be performed.

### Reset ($\overline{\text{RESET}}$)

This bidirectional signal resets (starts a system initialization sequence) the processor in response to an external $\overline{\text{RESET}}$ signal. An internally generated reset (result of a RESET instruction) causes all external devices to be reset, and the internal state of the processor is not affected. A total system reset (processor and external devices) is the result of external $\overline{\text{HALT}}$ and $\overline{\text{RESET}}$ signals applied simultaneously.

### Halt ($\overline{\text{HALT}}$)

When this bidirectional signal is driven by an external device, it causes the processor to stop at the completion of the current bus cycle. When the processor is halted using this input, all control signals are inactive, and all three-state lines are put in their high-impedance state.

When the processor stops executing instructions, such as in a double bus fault condition, the $\overline{\text{HALT}}$ line is driven by the processor to indicate to external devices that the processor has stopped.

## M6800 PERIPHERAL CONTROL

These control signals are used to interface synchronous M6800 peripheral devices with the asynchronous MC68000.

### Enable (E)

This signal is the standard enable signal common to all M6800-type peripheral devices. The period for this output is 10 MC68000 clock periods (six clocks low, four clocks high). Enable is generated by an internal ring counter which may come up in any state (i.e., at power-on, it is impossible to guarantee phase relationship of E to CLK). E is a free-running clock and runs regardless of the state of the bus on the MPU.

**3.**

### Valid Peripheral Address ($\overline{\text{VPA}}$)

This input indicates that the device or region addressed is an M6800 Family device and the data transfer should be synchronized with the enable (E) signal. This input also indicates that the processor should use automatic vectoring for an interrupt during an IACK cycle.

### Valid Memory Address ($\overline{\text{VMA}}$)

This output is used to indicate to M6800 peripheral devices that a valid address exists on the address bus and the processor is synchronized to E. This signal only responds to a valid peripheral address ($\overline{\text{VPA}}$) input, which indicates that the peripheral is an M6800 Family device.

## PROCESSOR STATUS (FC0, FC1, FC2)

These function code outputs indicate the state (user or supervisor) and the cycle type currently being executed (see Table 5). The information indicated by the function code outputs is valid whenever address strobe ($\overline{\text{AS}}$) is active.

**Table 5. Function Code Outputs**

| Function Code Output | | | Cycle Type |
|---|---|---|---|
| FC2 | FC1 | FC0 | |
| 0 | 0 | 0 | (Undefined, Reserved) |
| 0 | 0 | 1 | User Data |
| 0 | 1 | 0 | User Program |
| 0 | 1 | 1 | (Undefined, Reserved) |
| 1 | 0 | 0 | (Undefined, Reserved) |
| 1 | 0 | 1 | Supervisor Data |
| 1 | 1 | 0 | Supervisor Program |
| 1 | 1 | 1 | Interrupt Acknowledge |

## CLOCK (CLK)

The clock input is a TTL-compatible signal that is internally buffered for development of the internal clocks needed by the processor. The clock input should not be gated off at any time, and the clock signal must conform to minimum and maximum pulse-width times.

# DATA TRANSFER OPERATIONS

Transfer of data between devices involves the following signals:
1. Address bus A1–A23
2. Data bus D0–D15
3. Control signals

The address and data buses are separate parallel buses used to transfer data using an asynchronous bus structure. In all cycles, the bus master assumes responsibility for deskewing all signals it issues at both the start and end of a cycle. In addition, the bus master is responsible for deskewing the acknowledge and data signals from the slave device.

The following paragraphs explain the read, write, and read-modify-write cycles. The indivisible read-modify-write cycle is the method used by the MC68000 for interlocked multiprocessor communications.

## READ CYCLE

During a read cycle, the processor receives data from either memory or a peripheral device. The processor reads bytes of data in all cases. If the instruction specifies a word (or double word) operation, the processor reads both upper and lower bytes simultaneously by asserting both upper and lower data strobes. When the instruction specifies byte operation, the processor uses an internal A0 bit to determine which byte to read and then issues the data strobe required for that byte. For byte operations, when A0 equals zero, the upper data strobe is issued. When A0 equals one, the lower data strobe is issued. When the data is received, the processor correctly positions it internally.

## WRITE CYCLE

During a write cycle, the processor sends data to either the memory or a peripheral device. The processor writes bytes of data in all cases. If the instruction specifies a word operation, the processor writes both bytes. When the instruction specifies a byte operation, the processor uses an internal A0 bit to determine which byte to write and then issues the data strobe required for that byte. For byte operations, when A0 equals zero, the upper data strobe is issued. When A0 equals one, the lower data strobe is issued.

## READ-MODIFY-WRITE CYCLE

The read-modify-write cycle performs a read, modifies the data in the arithmetic logic unit, and writes the data back to the same address. In the MC68000, this cycle is indivisible in that the address strobe is asserted throughout the entire cycle. The test and set (TAS) instruction uses this cycle to provide meaningful communication between processors in a multiple processor environment. TAS is the only instruction that uses the read-modify-write cycles; thus, since TAS only operates on bytes, all read-modify-write cycles are byte operations.

# PROCESSING STATES

The MC68000 is always in one of three processing states: normal, exception, or halted.

## NORMAL PROCESSING

The normal processing state is that associated with instruction execution; the memory references are to fetch instructions and operands and to store results. A special case of normal state is the stopped state which the processor enters when a stop instruction is executed. In this state, no further references are made.

## EXCEPTION PROCESSING

The exception processing state is associated with interrupts, trap instructions, tracing, and other exception conditions. The exception may be internally generated by an instruction or by an unusual condition arising during the execution of an instruction. Externally, exception processing can be forced by an interrupt, a bus error, or a reset. Exception processing is designed to provide an efficient context switch so that the processor may handle unusual conditions.

## HALTED PROCESSING

The halted processing state is an indication of catastrophic hardware failure. For example, if, during the exception processing of a bus error, another bus error occurs, the processor assumes that the system is unusable and halts. Only an external reset can restart a halted processor. Note that a processor in the stopped state is not in the halted state, nor vice versa.

# INTERFACE WITH M6800 PERIPHERALS

Motorola's extensive line of M6800 peripherals are directly compatible with the MC68000. Some devices that are particularly useful are as follows:

MC6821    Peripheral Interface Adapter
MC6840    Programmable Timer Module
MC6845    CRT Controller
MC6850    Asynchronous Communications Interface Adapter
MC6854    Advanced Data Link Controller

To interface the synchronous M6800 peripherals with the asynchronous MC68000, the processor modifies its bus cycle to meet the M6800 cycle requirements whenever an M6800 device address is detected. This modification is possible since both processors use memory-mapped I/O.

# ELECTRICAL SPECIFICATIONS

## MAXIMUM RATINGS

| Rating | Symbol | Value | Unit |
|---|---|---|---|
| Supply Voltage | $V_{CC}$ | $-0.3$ to $+7.0$ | V |
| Input Voltage | $V_{in}$ | $-0.3$ to $+7.0$ | V |
| Operating Temperature Range<br>MC68000<br>MC68000C | $T_A$ | $T_L$ to $T_H$<br>0 to 70<br>$-40$ to 85 | °C |
| Storage Temperature | $T_{stg}$ | $-55$ to 150 | °C |

The device contains protection circuitry against damage due to high static voltages or electric fields; however, it is advised that normal precautions be taken to avoid application of voltages higher than maximum-rated voltages to this high-impedance circuit. Reliability of operation is enhanced if unused inputs are tied to an appropriate logic voltage level (e.g., either GND or $V_{CC}$).

## THERMAL CHARACTERISTICS

| Characteristic | Symbol | Value | Symbol | Value | Rating |
|---|---|---|---|---|---|
| Thermal Resistance (Still Air)<br>Ceramic, Type L/LC<br>Ceramic, Type R/RC<br>Plastic, Type P<br>Plastic, Type FN | $\theta_{JA}$ | <br>30<br>33<br>30<br>45* | $\theta_{JC}$ | <br>15*<br>15<br>15*<br>25* | °C/W |

*Estimated

## POWER CONSIDERATIONS

The average die-junction temperature, $T_J$, in °C can be obtained from:
$$T_J = T_A + (P_D \cdot \theta_{JA}) \qquad (1)$$
where:

$T_A$ = Ambient Temperature, °C
$\theta_{JA}$ = Package Thermal Resistance, Junction-to-Ambient, °C/W
$P_D$ = $P_{INT} + P_{I/O}$
$P_{INT}$ = $I_{CC} \times V_{CC}$, Watts — Chip Internal Power
$P_{I/O}$ = Power Dissipation on Input and Output Pins — User Determined
For most applications, $P_{I/O} < P_{INT}$ and can be neglected.

An appropriate relationship between $P_D$ and $T_J$ (if $P_{I/O}$ is neglected) is:
$$P_D = K \div (T_J + 273 \text{ °C}) \qquad (2)$$
Solving Equations (1) and (2) for K gives:
$$K = P_D \cdot (T_A + 273°C) + \theta_{JA} \cdot P_D^2 \qquad (3)$$
where K is a constant pertaining to the particular part. K can be determined from Equation (3) by measuring $P_D$ (at thermal equilibrium) for a known $T_A$. Using this value of K, the values of $P_D$ and $T_J$ can be obtained by solving Equations (1) and (2) iteratively for any value of $T_A$.

The curve shown in Figure 5 gives the graphic solution to the above equations for the specified power dissipation of 1.5 W over the ambient temperature range of −55 °C to 125 °C using a maximum $\theta_{JA}$ of 45 °C/W. Ambient temperature is that of the still air surrounding the device. Lower values of $\theta_{JA}$ cause the curve to shift downward slightly; for instance, for $\theta_{JA}$ of 40 °/W, the curve is just below 1.4 W at 25 °C.

The total thermal resistance of a package ($\theta_{JA}$) can be separated into two components, $\theta_{JC}$ and $\theta_{CA}$, representing the barrier to heat flow from the semiconductor junction to the package (case) surface ($\theta_{JC}$) and from the case to the outside ambient air ($\theta_{CA}$). These terms are related by the equation:

$$\theta_{JA} = \theta_{JC} + \theta_{CA} \tag{4}$$

$\theta_{JC}$ is device related and cannot be influenced by the user. However, $\theta_{CA}$ is user dependent and can be minimized by such thermal management techniques as heat sinks, ambient air cooling, and thermal convection. Thus, good thermal management on the part of the user can significantly reduce $\theta_{CA}$ so that $\theta_{JA}$ approximately equals $\theta_{JC}$. Substitution of $\theta_{JC}$ for $\theta_{JA}$ in Equation (1) results in a lower semiconductor junction temperature.

Table 6 summarizes maximum power dissipation and average junction temperature for the curve drawn in Figure 5, using the minimum and maximum values of ambient temperature for different packages and substituting $\theta_{JC}$ for $\theta_{JA}$ (assuming good thermal management). Table 7 provides the maximum power dissipation and average junction temperature assuming that no thermal management is applied (i.e., still air).

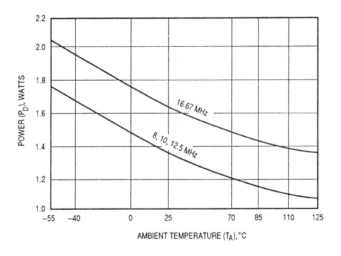

**Figure 5. Power Dissipation (P$_D$) vs Ambient Temperature (T$_A$)**

### Table 6. Power Dissipation and Junction Temperature
### vs Temperature ($\theta_{JC} = \theta_{JA}$)

| Package | $T_A$ Range | $\theta_{JC}$ (°C/W) | $P_D$ (W) @ $T_A$ Min. | $T_J$ (°C) @ $T_A$ Min. | $P_D$ (W) @ $T_A$ Max. | $T_J$ (°C) @ $T_A$ Max. |
|---|---|---|---|---|---|---|
| L/LC | 0°C to 70°C | 15 | 1.5 | 22.5 | 1.2 | 88 |
|  | −40°C to 85°C | 15 | 1.7 | −14.5 | 1.2 | 103 |
| P | 0°C to 70°C | 15 | 1.5 | 22.5 | 1.2 | 88 |
| R/RC | 0°C to 70°C | 15 | 1.5 | 22.5 | 1.2 | 88 |
|  | −40°C to 85°C | 15 | 1.7 | −14.5 | 1.2 | 103 |
| FN | 0°C to 70°C | 25 | 1.5 | 37.5 | 1.2 | 101 |

NOTE: Table does not include values for the MC68000 12F.

### Table 7. Power Dissipation and Junction Temperature
### vs Temperature ($\theta_{JA} \neq \theta_{JC}$)

| Package | $T_A$ Range | $\theta_{JA}$ (°C/W) | $P_D$ (W) @ $T_A$ Min. | $T_J$ (°C) @ $T_A$ Min. | $P_D$ (W) @ $T_A$ Max. | $T_J$ (°C) @ $T_A$ Max. |
|---|---|---|---|---|---|---|
| L/LC | 0°C to 70°C | 30 | 1.5 | 45 | 1.2 | 106 |
|  | −40°C to 85°C | 30 | 1.7 | 11 | 1.2 | 121 |
| P | 0°C to 70°C | 30 | 1.5 | 45 | 1.2 | 106 |
| R/RC | 0°C to 70°C | 33 | 1.5 | 49.5 | 1.2 | 109.6 |
|  | −40°C to 85°C | 33 | 1.7 | 16.1 | 1.2 | 124.6 |
| FN | 0°C to 70°C | 40 | 1.5 | 60 | 1.2 | 118 |

NOTE: Table does not include values for the MC68000 12F.

## AC ELECTRICAL SPECIFICATIONS DEFINITIONS

The AC specifications presented consist of output delays, input setup and hold times, and signal skew times. All signals are specified relative to an appropriate edge of the clock and possibly to one or more other signals.

The measurement of the AC specifications is defined by the waveforms shown in Figure 6. To test the parameters guaranteed by Motorola, inputs must be driven to the voltage levels specified in the figure. Outputs are specified with minimum and/or maximum limits, as appropriate, and are measured as shown. Inputs are specified with minimum setup and hold times, and are measured as shown. Finally, the measurement for signal-to-signal specifications is also shown.

**3**

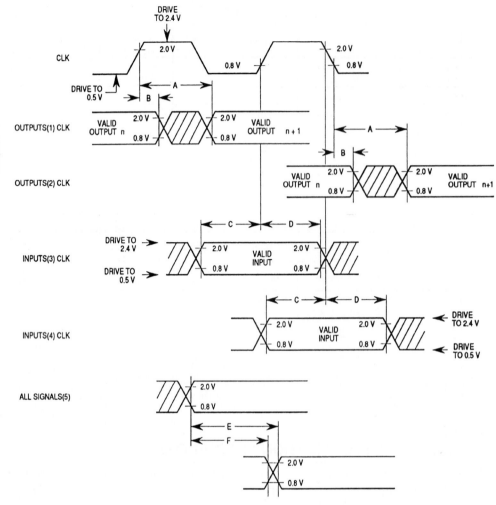

NOTES:
1. This output timing is applicable to all parameters specified relative to the rising edge of the clock.
2. This output timing is applicable to all parameters specified relative to the falling edge of the clock.
3. This input timing is applicable to all parameters specified relative to the rising edge of the clock.
4. This input timing is applicable to all parameters specified relative to the falling edge of the clock.
5. This timing is applicable to all parameters specified relative to the assertion/negation of another signal.

LEGEND:
A. Maximum output delay specification.
B. Minimum output hold time.
C. Minimum input setup time specification.
D. Minimum input hold time specification.
E. Signal valid to signal valid specification (maximum or minimum).
F. Signal valid to signal invalid specification (maximum or minimum).

**Figure 6. Drive Levels and Test Points for AC Specifications**

## DC ELECTRICAL SPECIFICATIONS (V$_{CC}$ = 5.0 Vdc ± 5%; GND = 0 Vdc; T$_A$ = T$_L$ to T$_H$)

| Characteristic | | Symbol | Min | Max | Unit |
|---|---|---|---|---|---|
| Input High Voltage | | V$_{IH}$ | 2.0 | V$_{CC}$ | V |
| Input Low Voltage | | V$_{IL}$ | GND − 0.3 | 0.8 | V |
| Input Leakage Current | BERR, BGACK, BR, DTACK, CLK, IPL0–IPL2, VPA | I$_{IN}$ | — | 2.5 | μA |
| (a 5.25 V | HALT, RESET | | — | 20 | |
| Three-State (Off State) Input Current | AS, A1–A23, D0–D15, FC0–FC2, | I$_{TSI}$ | — | 20 | μA |
| (a 2.4 V/0.4 V | LDS, R/W, UDS, VMA | | | | |
| Output High Voltage (I$_{OH}$ = −400 μA) | E* | V$_{OH}$ | V$_{CC}$ − 0.75 | — | V |
| (I$_{OH}$ = −400 μA) | E, AS, A1–A23, BG, D0–D15, FC0–FC2, LDS, R/W, UDS, VMA | | 2.4 | 2.4 | |
| Output Low Voltage | | V$_{OL}$ | | | V |
| (I$_{OL}$ = 1.6 mA) | HALT | | — | 0.5 | |
| (I$_{OL}$ = 3.2 mA) | A1–A23, BG, FC0–FC2 | | — | 0.5 | |
| (I$_{OL}$ = 5.0 mA) | RESET | | — | 0.5 | |
| (I$_{OL}$ = 5.3 mA) | E, AS, D0–D15, LDS, R/W, UDS, VMA | | — | 0.5 | |
| Power Dissipation | | P$_D$*** | — | — | W |
| Capacitance (V$_{in}$ = 0 V, T$_A$ = 25°C, Frequency = 1 MHz)** | | C$_{in}$ | — | 20.0 | pF |
| Load Capacitance | HALT | C$_L$ | — | 70 | pF |
| | All Others | | — | 130 | |

*With external pullup resistor of 1.1 KΩ.
**Capacitance is periodically sampled rather than 100% tested.
***During normal operation instantaneous V$_{CC}$ current requirements may be as high as 1.5 A.

## AC ELECTRICAL SPECIFICATIONS — CLOCK INPUT (see Figure 7)

| Num. | Characteristic | Symbol | 8 MHz* | | 10 MHz* | | 12.5 MHz* | | 16.67 MHz '12F' | | Unit |
|---|---|---|---|---|---|---|---|---|---|---|---|
| | | | Min | Max | Min | Max | Min | Max | Min | Max | |
| | Frequency of Operation | f | 4.0 | 8.0 | 4.0 | 10.0 | 4.0 | 12.5 | 8.0 | 16.7 | MHz |
| 1 | Cycle Time | t$_{cyc}$ | 125 | 250 | 100 | 250 | 80 | 250 | 60 | 125 | ns |
| 2,3 | Clock Pulse Width (Measured from 1.5 V to 1.5 V for 12F) | t$_{CL}$ | 55 | 125 | 45 | 125 | 35 | 125 | 27 | 62.5 | ns |
| | | t$_{CH}$ | 55 | 125 | 45 | 125 | 35 | 125 | 27 | 62.5 | |
| 4,5 | Clock Rise and Fall Times | t$_{Cr}$ | — | 10 | — | 10 | — | 5 | — | 5 | ns |
| | | t$_{Cf}$ | — | 10 | — | 10 | — | 5 | — | 5 | |

*These specifications represent an improvement over previously published specifications for the 8-, 10-, and 12.5-MHz MC68000 and are valid only for product bearing date codes of 8827 and later.

3

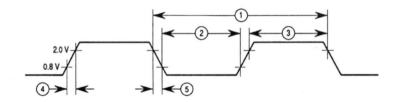

NOTE:  Timing measurements are referenced to and from a low voltage of 0.8 V and a high
voltage of 2.0 V, unless otherwise noted.  The voltage swing through this range
should start outside and pass through the range such that the rise or fall will be linear
between 0.8 V and 2.0 V.

**Figure 7. Clock Input Timing Diagram**

# AC ELECTRICAL SPECIFICATIONS — READ AND WRITE CYCLES

($V_{CC} = 5.0$ Vdc $\pm$ 5%; GND $= 0$ Vdc; $T_A = T_L$ to $T_H$; see Figures 8 and 9)

| Num. | Characteristic | Symbol | 8 MHz* | | 10 MHz* | | 12.5 MHz* | | 16.67 MHz '12F' | | Unit |
|------|----------------|--------|-----|-----|-----|-----|-----|-----|-----|-----|------|
| | | | Min | Max | Min | Max | Min | Max | Min | Max | |
| 6 | Clock Low to Address Valid | tCLAV | — | 62 | — | 50 | — | 50 | — | 50 | ns |
| 6A | Clock High to FC Valid | tCHFCV | — | 62 | — | 50 | — | 45 | — | 45 | ns |
| 7 | Clock High to Address, Data Bus High Impedance (Maximum) | tCHADZ | — | 80 | — | 70 | — | 60 | — | 50 | ns |
| 8 | Clock High to Address, FC Invalid (Minimum) | tCHAFI | 0 | — | 0 | — | 0 | — | 0 | — | ns |
| 9[1] | Clock High to AS, DS Asserted | tCHSL | 3 | 60 | 3 | 50 | 3 | 40 | 3 | 40 | ns |
| 11[2] | Address Valid to AS, DS Asserted (Read)/AS Asserted (Write) | tAVSL | 30 | — | 20 | — | 15 | — | 15 | — | ns |
| 11A[2] | FC Valid to AS, DS Asserted (Read)/AS Asserted (Write) | tFCVSL | 90 | — | 70 | — | 60 | — | 30 | — | ns |
| 12[1] | Clock Low to AS, DS Negated | tCLSH | — | 62 | — | 50 | — | 40 | — | 40 | ns |
| 13[2] | AS, DS Negated to Address, FC Invalid | tSHAFI | 40 | — | 30 | — | 20 | — | 10 | — | ns |
| 14[2] | AS (and DS Read) Width Asserted | tSL | 270 | — | 195 | — | 160 | — | 120 | — | ns |
| 14A | DS Width Asserted (Write) | tDSL | 140 | — | 95 | — | 80 | — | 60 | — | ns |
| 15[2] | AS, DS Width Negated | tSH | 150 | — | 105 | — | 65 | — | 60 | — | ns |
| 16 | Clock High to Control Bus High Impedance | tCHCZ | — | 80 | — | 70 | — | 60 | — | 50 | ns |
| 17[2] | AS, DS Negated to R/W Invalid | tSHRH | 40 | — | 30 | — | 20 | — | 10 | — | ns |
| 18[1] | Clock High to R/W High (Read) | tCHRH | 0 | 55 | 0 | 45 | 0 | 40 | 0 | 40 | ns |
| 20[1] | Clock High to R/W Low (Write) | tCHRL | 0 | 55 | 0 | 45 | 0 | 40 | 0 | 40 | ns |
| 20A[2,6] | AS Asserted to R/W Valid (Write) | tASRV | — | 10 | — | 10 | — | 10 | — | 10 | ns |
| 21[2] | Address Valid to R/W Low (Write) | tAVRL | 20 | — | 0 | — | 0 | — | 0 | — | ns |
| 21A[2] | FC Valid to R/W Low (Write) | tFCVRL | 60 | — | 50 | — | 30 | — | 20 | — | ns |
| 22[2] | R/W Low to DS Asserted (Write) | tRLSL | 80 | — | 50 | — | 30 | — | 20 | — | ns |
| 23 | Clock Low to Data-Out Valid (Write) | tCLDO | — | 62 | — | 50 | — | 50 | — | 50 | ns |
| 25[2] | AS, DS Negated to Data-Out Invalid (Write) | tSHDOI | 40 | — | 30 | — | 20 | — | 15 | — | ns |
| 26[2] | Data-Out Valid to DS Asserted (Write) | tDOSL | 40 | — | 30 | — | 20 | — | 15 | — | ns |
| 27[5] | Data-In Valid to Clock Low (Setup Time on Read) | tDICL | 10 | — | 10 | — | 10 | — | 7 | — | ns |
| 28[2] | AS, DS Negated to DTACK Negated (Asynchronous Hold) | tSHDAH | 0 | 240 | 0 | 190 | 0 | 150 | 0 | 110 | ns |
| 29 | AS, DS Negated to Data-In Invalid (Hold Time on Read) | tSHDII | 0 | — | 0 | — | 0 | — | 0 | — | ns |
| 29A | AS, DS Negated to Data-In High Impedance | tSHDZ | — | 187 | — | 150 | — | 120 | — | 90 | ns |
| 30 | AS, DS Negated to BERR Negated | tSHBEH | 0 | — | 0 | — | 0 | — | 0 | — | ns |
| 31[2,5] | DTACK Asserted to Data-In Valid (Setup Time) | tDALDI | — | 90 | — | 65 | — | 50 | — | 40 | ns |
| 32 | HALT and RESET Input Transition Time | tRHr,f | 0 | 200 | 0 | 200 | 0 | 200 | 0 | 150 | ns |
| 33 | Clock High to BG Asserted | tCHGL | — | 62 | — | 50 | — | 40 | — | 40 | ns |
| 34 | Clock High to BG Negated | tCHGH | — | 62 | — | 50 | — | 40 | — | 40 | ns |
| 35 | BR Asserted to BG Asserted | tBRLGL | 1.5 | 3.5 | 1.5 | 3.5 | 1.5 | 3.5 | 1.5 | 3.5 | Clks |
| 36[7] | BR Negated to BG Negated | tBRHGH | 1.5 | 3.5 | 1.5 | 3.5 | 1.5 | 3.5 | 1.5 | 3.5 | Clks |
| 37 | BGACK Asserted to BG Negated | tGALGH | 1.5 | 3.5 | 1.5 | 3.5 | 1.5 | 3.5 | 1.5 | 3.5 | Clks |
| 37A[8] | BGACK Asserted to BR Negated | tGALBRH | 20 | 1.5 Clks | 20 | 1.5 Clks | 20 | 1.5 Clks | 10 | 1.5 Clks | ns |

## AC ELECTRICAL SPECIFICATIONS — READ AND WRITE CYCLES
(Continued)

| Num. | Characteristic | Symbol | 8 MHz* Min | 8 MHz* Max | 10 MHz* Min | 10 MHz* Max | 12.5 MHz* Min | 12.5 MHz* Max | 16.67 MHz '12F' Min | 16.67 MHz '12F' Max | Unit |
|---|---|---|---|---|---|---|---|---|---|---|---|
| 38 | BG Asserted to Control, Address, Data Bus High Impedance (AS Negated) | tGLZ | — | 80 | — | 70 | — | 60 | — | 50 | ns |
| 39 | BG Width Negated | tGH | 1.5 | — | 1.5 | — | 1.5 | — | 1.5 | — | Clks |
| 40 | Clock Low to VMA Asserted | tCLVML | — | 70 | — | 70 | — | 70 | — | 50 | ns |
| 41 | Clock Low to E Transition | tCLET | — | 55 | — | 45 | — | 35 | — | 35 | ns |
| 42 | E Output Rise and Fall Time | tEr,f | — | 15 | — | 15 | — | 15 | — | 15 | ns |
| 43 | VMA Asserted to E High | tVMLEH | 200 | — | 150 | — | 90 | — | 80 | — | ns |
| 44 | AS, DS Negated to VPA Negated | tSHVPH | 0 | 120 | 0 | 90 | 0 | 70 | 0 | 50 | ns |
| 45 | E Low to Control, Address Bus Invalid (Address Hold Time) | tELCAI | 30 | — | 10 | — | 10 | — | 10 | — | ns |
| 46 | BGACK Width Low | tGAL | 1.5 | — | 1.5 | — | 1.5 | — | 1.5 | — | Clks |
| 47[5] | Asynchronous Input Setup Time | tASI | 10 | — | 10 | — | 10 | — | 10 | — | ns |
| 48[2,3] | BERR Asserted to DTACK Asserted | tBELDAL | 20 | — | 20 | — | 20 | — | 10 | — | ns |
| 49[9] | AS, DS, Negated to E Low | tSHEL | −70 | 70 | −55 | 55 | −45 | 45 | −35 | 35 | ns |
| 50 | E Width High | tEH | 450 | — | 350 | — | 280 | — | 220 | — | ns |
| 51 | E Width Low | tEL | 700 | — | 550 | — | 440 | — | 340 | — | ns |
| 53 | Data-Out Hold from Clock High | tCHDOI | 0 | — | 0 | — | 0 | — | 0 | — | ns |
| 54 | E Low to Data-Out Invalid | tELDOI | 30 | — | 20 | — | 15 | — | 10 | — | ns |
| 55 | R/W Asserted to Data Bus Impedance Change | tRLDBD | 30 | — | 20 | — | 10 | — | 0 | — | ns |
| 56[4] | HALT/RESET Pulse Width | tHRPW | 10 | — | 10 | — | 10 | — | 10 | — | Clks |
| 57 | BGACK Negated to AS, DS, R/W Driven | tGASD | 1.5 | — | 1.5 | — | 1.5 | — | 1.5 | — | Clks |
| 57A | BGACK Negated to FC, VMA Driven | tGAFD | 1 | — | 1 | — | 1 | — | 1 | — | Clks |
| 58[7] | BR Negated to AS, DS, R/W Driven | tRHSD | 1.5 | — | 1.5 | — | 1.5 | — | 1.5 | — | Clks |
| 58A[7] | BR Negated to FC, VMA Driven | tRHFD | 1 | — | 1 | — | 1 | — | 1 | — | Clks |

*These specifications represent improvement over previously published specifications for the 8-, 10-, and 12.5-MHz MC68000 and are valid only for product bearing date codes of 8827 and later.

NOTES:
1. For a loading capacitance of less than or equal to 50 pF, subtract 5 ns from the value given in the maximum columns.
2. Actual value depends on clock period.
3. If #47 is satisfied for both DTACK and BERR, #48 may be ignored. In the absence of DTACK, BERR is an asynchronous input using the asynchronous input setup time (#47).
4. For power-up, the MC68000 must be held in the reset state for 100 ms to allow stabilization of on-chip circuitry. After the system is powered up, #56 refers to the minimum pulse width required to reset the processor.
5. If the asynchronous input setup time (#47) requirement is satisfied for DTACK, the DTACK-asserted to data setup time (#31) requirement can be ignored. The data must only satisfy the data-in to clock low setup time (#27) for the following clock cycle.
6. When AS and R/W are equally loaded (±20%), subtract 5 ns from the values given in these columns.
7. The processor will negate BG and begin driving the bus again if external arbitration logic negates BR before asserting BGACK.
8. The minimum value must be met to guarantee proper operation. If the maximum value is exceeded, BG may be re-asserted.
9. The falling edge of S6 triggers both the negation of the strobes (AS and xDS) and the falling edge of E. Either of these events can occur first, depending upon the loading on each signal. Specification #49 indicates the absolute maximum skew that will occur between the rising edge of the strobes and the falling edge of E.

3

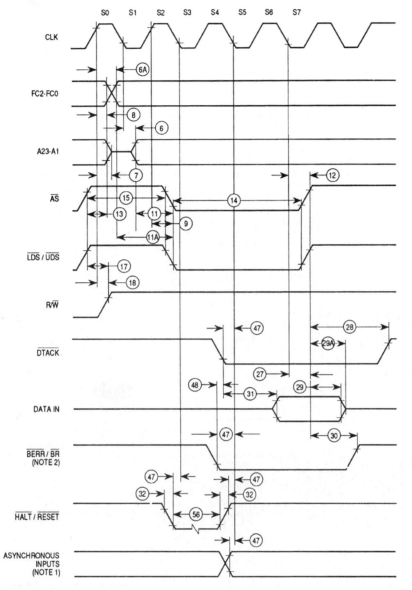

CLK

FC2-FC0

A23-A1

$\overline{AS}$

$\overline{LDS}$ / $\overline{UDS}$

R/$\overline{W}$

$\overline{DTACK}$

DATA IN

$\overline{BERR}$ / $\overline{BR}$
(NOTE 2)

$\overline{HALT}$ / $\overline{RESET}$

ASYNCHRONOUS
INPUTS
(NOTE 1)

NOTES:
1. Setup time for the asynchronous inputs $\overline{IPL2}$-$\overline{IPL0}$ and $\overline{VPA}$ (#47) guarantees their recognition at the next falling edge of the clock.
2. $\overline{BR}$ need fall at this time only to ensure being recognized at the end of the bus cycle.
3. Timing measurements are referenced to and from a low voltage of 0.8 V and a high voltage of 2.0 V, unless otherwise noted. The voltage swing through this range should start outside and pass through the range such that the rise or fall is linear between 0.8 V and 2.0 V.

## Figure 8. Read Cycle Timing Diagram

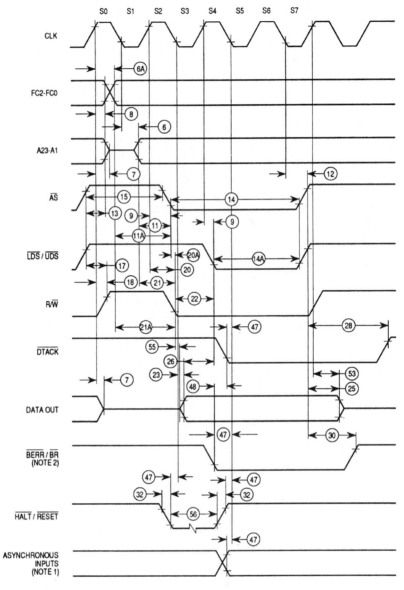

NOTES:
1. Timing measurements are referenced to and from a low voltage of 0.8 V and a high voltage of 2.0 V, unless otherwise noted. The voltage swing through this range should start outside and pass through the range such that the rise or fall is linear between 0.8 V and 2.0 V.
2. Because of loading variations, R/$\overline{\text{W}}$ may be valid after $\overline{\text{AS}}$ even though both are initiated by the rising edge of S2 (specification #20A).

**Figure 9. Write Cycle Timing Diagram**

## AC ELECTRICAL SPECIFICATIONS — PERIPHERAL CYCLES TO M6800

($V_{CC} = 5.0$ Vdc $\pm 5\%$; GND $= 0$ Vdc; $T_A = T_L$ to $T_H$; see Figures 10 and 11)

| Num. | Characteristic | Symbol | 8 MHz* | | 10 MHz* | | 12.5 MHz* | | 16.67 MHz '12F' | | Unit |
|---|---|---|---|---|---|---|---|---|---|---|---|
| | | | Min | Max | Min | Max | Min | Max | Min | Max | |
| 12[1] | Clock Low to $\overline{AS}$, $\overline{DS}$ Negated | $t_{CLSH}$ | — | 62 | — | 50 | — | 40 | — | 40 | ns |
| 18[1] | Clock High to R/$\overline{W}$ High (Read) | $t_{CHRH}$ | 0 | 55 | 0 | 45 | 0 | 40 | 0 | 40 | ns |
| 20[1] | Clock High to R/$\overline{W}$ Low (Write) | $t_{CHRL}$ | 0 | 55 | 0 | 45 | 0 | 40 | 0 | 40 | ns |
| 23 | Clock Low to Data-Out Valid (Write) | $t_{CLDO}$ | — | 62 | — | 50 | — | 50 | — | 50 | ns |
| 27 | Data-In Valid to Clock Low (Setup Time of Read) | $t_{DICL}$ | 10 | — | 10 | — | 10 | — | 7 | — | ns |
| 29 | $\overline{AS}$, $\overline{DS}$ Negated to Data-In Invalid (Hold Time on Read) | $t_{SHDII}$ | 0 | — | 0 | — | 0 | — | 0 | — | ns |
| 40 | Clock Low to $\overline{VMA}$ Asserted | $t_{CLVML}$ | — | 70 | — | 70 | — | 70 | — | 50 | ns |
| 41 | Clock Low to E Transition | $t_{CLET}$ | — | 55 | — | 45 | — | 35 | — | 35 | ns |
| 42 | E Output Rise and Fall Time | $t_{Er,f}$ | — | 15 | — | 15 | — | 15 | — | 15 | ns |
| 43 | $\overline{VMA}$ Asserted to E High | $t_{VMLEH}$ | 200 | — | 150 | — | 90 | — | 80 | — | ns |
| 44 | $\overline{AS}$, $\overline{DS}$ Negated to $\overline{VPA}$ Negated | $t_{SHVPH}$ | 0 | 120 | 0 | 90 | 0 | 70 | 0 | 50 | ns |
| 45 | E Low to Control, Address Bus Invalid (Address Hold Time) | $t_{ELCAI}$ | 30 | — | 10 | — | 10 | — | 10 | — | ns |
| 47 | Asynchronous Input Setup Time | $t_{ASI}$ | 10 | — | 10 | — | 10 | — | 10 | — | ns |
| 49[2] | $\overline{AS}$, $\overline{DS}$, Negated to E Low | $t_{SHEL}$ | -70 | 70 | -55 | 55 | -45 | 45 | -35 | 35 | ns |
| 50 | E Width High | $t_{EH}$ | 450 | — | 350 | — | 280 | — | 220 | — | ns |
| 51 | E Width Low | $t_{EL}$ | 700 | — | 550 | — | 440 | — | 340 | — | ns |
| 54 | E Low to Data-Out Invalid | $t_{ELDOI}$ | 30 | — | 20 | — | 15 | — | 10 | — | ns |

*These specifications represent an improvement over previously published specifications for the 8-, 10-, and 12.5-MHz MC68000 and are valid only for product bearing date codes of 8827 and later.

NOTES:
1. For a loading capacitance of less than or equal to 50 pF, subtract 5 ns from the value given in the maximum columns.
2. The falling edge of S6 trigger both the negation of the strobes ($\overline{AS}$ and x$\overline{DS}$) and the falling edge of E. Either of these events can occur first, depending upon the loading on each signal. Specification #49 indicates the absolute maximum skew that will occur between the rising edge of the strobes and the falling edge of E.

**3**

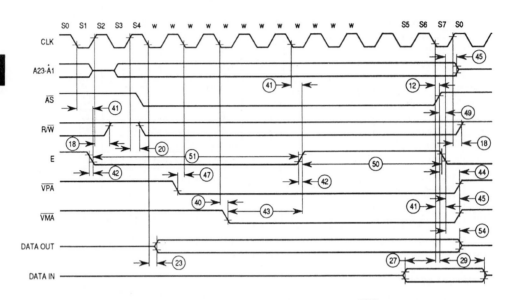

NOTE: This timing diagram is included for those who wish to design their own circuit to generate $\overline{VMA}$. It shows the best case possibly attainable.

**Figure 10. MC68000 to MC6800 Timing Diagram (Best Case)**

**M68000 FAMILY REFERENCE MANUAL**                    MOTOROLA

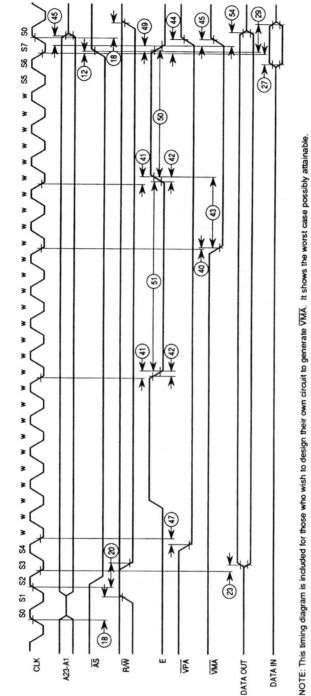

Figure 11. MC68000 to MC6800 Timing Diagram (Worst Case)

NOTE: This timing diagram is included for those who wish to design their own circuit to generate VMA. It shows the worst case possibly attainable.

## AC ELECTRICAL SPECIFICATIONS — BUS ARBITRATION

($V_{CC}$ = 5.0 Vdc ± 5%; GND = 0 Vdc; $T_A$ = $T_L$ to $T_H$; see Figures 12–15)

| Num. | Characteristic | Symbol | 8 MHz* | | 10 MHz* | | 12.5 MHz* | | 16.67 MHz '12F' | | Unit |
|------|---------------|--------|-----|-----|-----|-----|-----|-----|-----|-----|------|
| | | | Min | Max | Min | Max | Min | Max | Min | Max | |
| 7 | Clock High to Address, Data Bus High Impedance (Maximum) | $t_{CHADZ}$ | — | 80 | — | 70 | — | 60 | — | 50 | ns |
| 16 | Clock High to Control Bus High Impedance | $t_{CHCZ}$ | — | 80 | — | 70 | — | 60 | — | 50 | ns |
| 33 | Clock High to $\overline{BG}$ Asserted | $t_{CHGL}$ | — | 62 | — | 50 | — | 40 | — | 40 | ns |
| 34 | Clock High to $\overline{BG}$ Negated | $t_{CHGH}$ | — | 62 | — | 50 | — | 40 | — | 40 | ns |
| 35 | $\overline{BR}$ Asserted to $\overline{BG}$ Asserted | $t_{BRLGL}$ | 1.5 | 3.5 | 1.5 | 3.5 | 1.5 | 3.5 | 1.5 | 3.5 | Clks |
| 36[1] | $\overline{BR}$ Negated to $\overline{BG}$ Negated | $t_{BRHGH}$ | 1.5 | 3.5 | 1.5 | 3.5 | 1.5 | 3.5 | 1.5 | 3.5 | Clks |
| 37 | $\overline{BGACK}$ Asserted to $\overline{BG}$ Negated | $t_{GALGH}$ | 1.5 | 3.5 | 1.5 | 3.5 | 1.5 | 3.5 | 1.5 | 3.5 | Clks |
| 37A[2] | $\overline{BGACK}$ Asserted to $\overline{BR}$ Negated | $t_{GALBRH}$ | 20 | 1.5 Clks | 20 | 1.5 Clks | 20 | 1.5 Clks | 10 | 1.5 Clks | ns |
| 38 | $\overline{BG}$ Asserted to Control, Address, Data Bus High Impedance ($\overline{AS}$ Negated) | $t_{GLZ}$ | — | 80 | — | 70 | — | 60 | — | 50 | ns |
| 39 | $\overline{BG}$ Width Negated | $t_{GH}$ | 1.5 | — | 1.5 | — | 1.5 | — | 1.5 | — | Clks |
| 46 | $\overline{BGACK}$ Width Low | $t_{GAL}$ | 1.5 | — | 1.5 | — | 1.5 | — | 1.5 | — | Clks |
| 47 | Asynchronous Input Setup Time | $t_{ASI}$ | 10 | — | 10 | — | 10 | — | 10 | — | ns |
| 57 | $\overline{BGACK}$ Negated to $\overline{AS}$, $\overline{DS}$, R/$\overline{W}$ Driven | $t_{GASD}$ | 1.5 | — | 1.5 | — | 1.5 | — | 1.5 | — | Clks |
| 57A | $\overline{BGACK}$ Negated to FC, $\overline{VMA}$ Driven | $t_{GAFD}$ | 1 | — | 1 | — | 1 | — | 1 | — | Clks |
| 58[1] | $\overline{BR}$ Negated to $\overline{AS}$, $\overline{DS}$, R/$\overline{W}$ Driven | $t_{RHSD}$ | 1.5 | — | 1.5 | — | 1.5 | — | 1.5 | — | Clks |
| 58A[1] | $\overline{BR}$ Negated to FC, $\overline{VMA}$ Driven | $t_{RHFD}$ | 1 | — | 1 | — | 1 | — | 1 | — | Clks |

*These specifications represent an improvement over previously published specifications for the 8-, 10-, and 12.5-MHz MC68000 and are valid only for product bearing date codes of 8827 and later.

NOTES:
1. The processor will negate $\overline{BG}$ and begin driving the bus again if external arbitration logic negates $\overline{BR}$ before asserting $\overline{BGACK}$.
2. The minimum value must be met to guarantee proper operation. If the maximum value is exceeded, $\overline{BG}$ may be re-asserted.

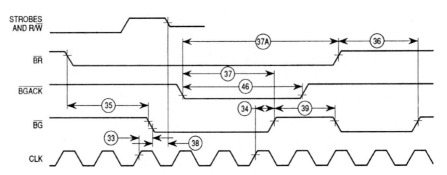

NOTE: Setup time to the clock (#47) for the asynchronous inputs $\overline{BERR}$, $\overline{BGACK}$, $\overline{BR}$, $\overline{DTACK}$, IPL2–IPL0, and $\overline{VPA}$ guarantees their recognition at the next falling edge of the clock.

### Figure 12. Bus Arbitration Timing Diagram

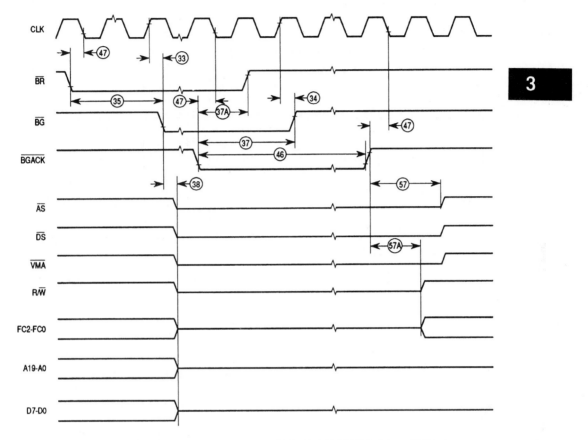

NOTE: Waveform measurements for all inputs and outputs are specified at: logic high 2.0 V, logic low = 0.8 V.

**Figure 13. Bus Arbitration Timing — Idle Bus Case**

**3**

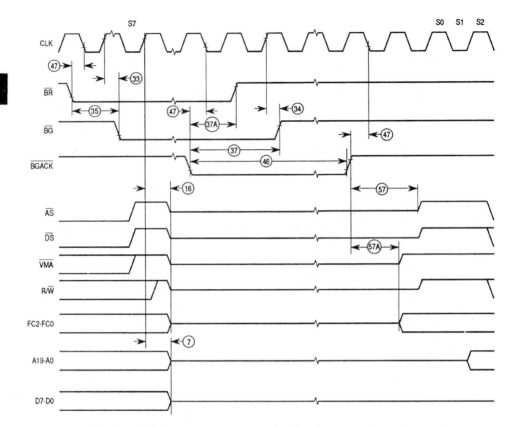

NOTE: Waveform measurements for all inputs and outputs are specified at: logic high 2.0 V, logic low = 0.8 V.

**Figure 14. Bus Arbitration Timing — Active Bus Case**

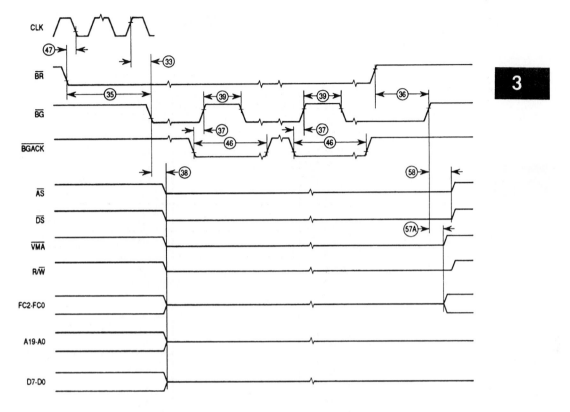

NOTE: Waveform measurements for all inputs and outputs are specified at: logic high 2.0 V, logic low = 0.8 V.

**Figure 15. Bus Arbitration Timing — Multiple Bus Request**

# PIN ASSIGNMENTS

## 64-LEAD DUAL-IN-LINE PACKAGE

**3**

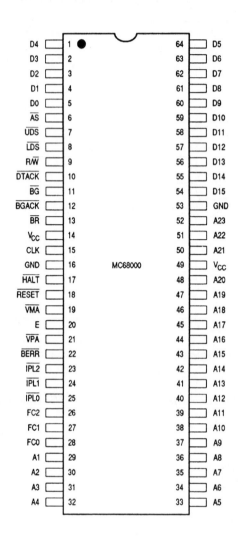

## 68-LEAD PIN GRID ARRAY

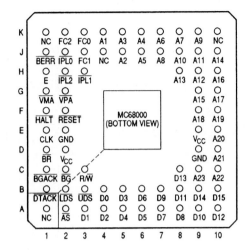

## 68-LEAD PLASTIC LEADED CHIP CARRIER

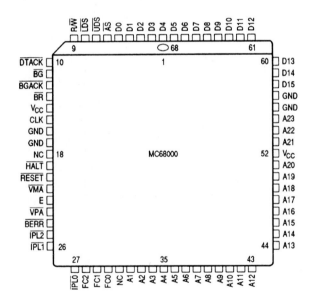

# Appendix H

# 68681 Data Sheet*

**MOTOROLA**
■■■ **SEMICONDUCTOR**
**TECHNICAL DATA**

## MC68681

*Advance Information*

## Dual Asynchronous
## Receiver/Transmitter

The MC68681 dual universal asynchronous receiver/transmitter (DUART) is part of the M68000 Family of peripherals and directly interfaces to the MC68000 processor via an asynchronous bus structure. The MC68681 consists of eight major sections: internal control logic, timing logic, interrupt control logic, a bidirectional 8-bit data bus buffer, two independent communication channels (A and B), a 6-bit parallel input port, and an 8-bit parallel output port (see Figure 1).

7

The following features are included on the MC68681:

- M68000 Bus Compatible

- Two, Independent, Full-Duplex Asynchronous Receiver/Transmitter Channels

- Maximum Data Transfer
  - 1X — 1 Mbps
  - 16X — 125 kbps

- Quadruple-Buffered Receiver Data Registers

- Double-Buffered Transmitter Data Registers

- Independently Programmable Baud Rate for Each Receiver and Transmitter Selectable from:
  - 18 Fixed Rates: 50 to 38.4k Baud
  - One User-Defined Rate Derived from a Programmable Timer/Counter
  - External 1X Clock or 16X Clock

- Programmable Data Format
  - Five to Eight Data Bits plus Parity
  - Odd, Even, No Parity, or Force Parity
  - One, One and One-Half, or Two Stop Bits Programmable in One-Sixteenth-Bit Increments

- Programmable Channel Modes
  - Normal (Full Duplex)
  - Automatic Echo
  - Local Loopback
  - Remote Loopback

- Automatic Wakeup Mode for Multidrop Applications

- Multifunction 6-Bit Input Port
  - Can Serve as Clock or Control Inputs
  - Change-of-State Detection on Four Inputs

- Multifunction 8-Bit Output Port
  - Individual Bit Set/Reset Capability
  - Outputs Can Be Programmed To Be Status/Interrupt Signals

- Multifunction 16-Bit Programmable Counter/Timer

- Versatile Interrupt System
  - Single Interrupt Output with Eight Maskable Interrupting Conditions
  - Interrupt Vector Output on Interrupt Acknowledge
  - Output Port Can Be Configured To Provide a Total of up to Six Separate Wire-ORable Interrupt Outputs

**FEATURES (Continued)**

- Parity, Framing, and Overrun Error Detection
- False-Start Bit Detection
- Line-Break Detection and Generation
- Detects Break Originating in the Middle of a Character
- Start/End Break Interrupt/Status
- On-Chip Crystal Oscillator
- TTL Compatible
- Single +5-V Power Supply

# INTERNAL CONTROL LOGIC

The internal control logic receives operation commands from the central processing unit (CPU) and generates appropriate signals to the internal sections to control device operation. It allows the registers within the DUART to be accessed and various commands to be performed by decoding the four register select lines (RS1–RS4). In addition to the four register select lines, there are three inputs to the internal control logic from the CPU: read/write (R/$\overline{W}$), which allows read and write transfers between the CPU and DUART via the data bus buffer; chip select ($\overline{CS}$), which is the DUART chip select; and reset ($\overline{RESET}$), which is used to initialize or reset the DUART. The data transfer acknowledge ($\overline{DTACK}$) signal, asserted during read, write, or interrupt acknowledge is an output from the internal control logic. $\overline{DTACK}$ indicates to the CPU that data has been latched on a CPU write cycle or that valid data is present on the data bus during a CPU read cycle or interrupt acknowledge ($\overline{IACK}$) cycle.

**7**

# TIMING LOGIC

The timing logic consists of a crystal oscillator, a baud rate generator, a programmable 16-bit counter/timer, and four clock selectors. The crystal oscillator operates directly from a 3.6864-MHz crystal connected across X1/CLK and X2 or from an external clock of the appropriate frequency connected to X1/CLK. The clock serves as the basic timing reference for the baud rate generator, the counter/timer, and other internal circuits. A clock signal within the limits given in **ELECTRICAL SPECIFICATIONS** must always be supplied to the DUART.

The baud rate generator operates from the oscillator or external clock input and is capable of generating 18 commonly used data communication baud rates ranging from 50 to 38.4k by producing internal clock outputs at 16 times

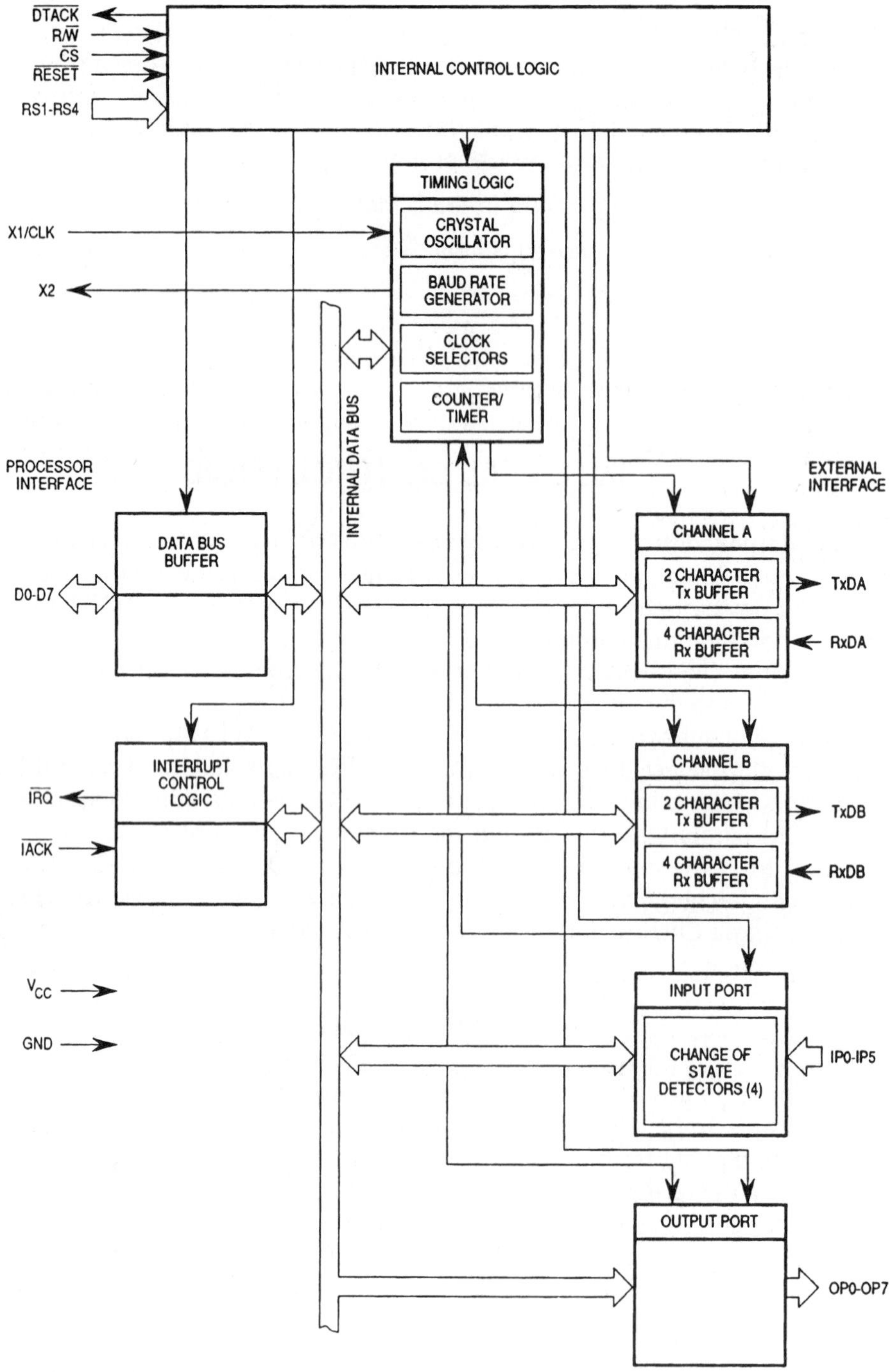

**Figure 1. Block Diagram**

the actual baud rate. The counter/timer can be used in the timer mode to produce a 16X clock for any other baud rate by counting down the crystal clock or external clock. Other baud rates may also be derived by connecting 16X or 1X clocks to certain input port pins that have alternate functions as receiver or transmitter clock inputs. The four clock selectors allow each receiver and transmitter to independently select any of these baud rates.

The 16-bit counter/timer included within the DUART and timing logic can be programmed to use one of several timing sources as input. The output of the counter/timer, which is available to the internal clock selectors, can also be programmed to be a parallel output at OP3. In the timer mode, the counter/timer acts as a programmable divider and can be used to generate a square-wave output at OP3. In the counter mode, the contents of the counter/timer can be read by the CPU, and it can be stopped and started under program control. The counter counts down the number of pulses stored in the concatenation of the counter/timer upper register and counter/timer lower register and produces an interrupt. This system-oriented feature may be used to keep track of timeouts when implementing various application protocols.

## INTERRUPT CONTROL LOGIC

The following registers are associated with the interrupt control logic: interrupt mask register (IMR), interrupt status register (ISR), auxiliary control register (ACR), and interrupt vector register (IVR).

An active-low interrupt request ($\overline{IRQ}$) can be used to notify the processor that any of eight internal events has occurred. The IMR can be programmed to select only certain conditions that cause $\overline{IRQ}$ to be asserted; the ISR can be read by the CPU to determine all currently active interrupting conditions. When an active-low $\overline{IACK}$ from the processor is assserted while the DUART has an interrupt pending, the DUART will place the contents of the IVR (i.e., the interrupt vector) on the data bus and assert $\overline{DTACK}$.

In addition, the DUART offers the ability to program the parallel outputs OP3–OP7 to provide discrete interrupt outputs for the transmitters, the receivers, and the counter/timer.

7

# DATA BUS BUFFER

The data bus buffer, which provides the interface between the external and internal data buses, is controlled by the internal control logic to allow read and write data transfer operations to occur between the controlling CPU and DUART via the eight parallel data lines (D0–D7).

# COMMUNICATION CHANNELS A AND B

Each communication channel comprises a full-duplex universal asynchronous receiver/transmitter (UART). The operating frequency for each receiver and each transmitter can be independently selected from the baud rate generator, the counter/timer, or an external clock.

The transmitter accepts parallel data from the CPU, converts it to a serial bit stream, inserts the appropriate start, stop, and optional parity bits, and outputs a composite serial stream of data on the TxD output pin. The receiver accepts serial data on the RxD pin, converts this serial input to parallel format, checks for a start bit, stop bit, parity bit (if any), or break condition, and transfers an assembled character to the CPU during read operations.

# INPUT PORT

The inputs to this unlatched 6-bit port (IP0–IP5) can be read by the CPU during a read operation. High or low inputs to the input port result in the CPU reading a logic one or logic zero, respectively; that is, there is no inversion of the logic level. Since the input port is a 6-bit port, performing a read operation will result in D7 being read as a logic one and D6 reflecting the logic level of $\overline{\text{IACK}}$. Besides functioning as general-purpose inputs, the inputs to this port can be individually assigned specific auxiliary functions serving the communication channels.

Four change-of-state detectors, also provided within the input port, are associated with inputs IP0, IP1, IP2, and IP3. A high-to-low or low-to-high transition of these inputs lasting longer than 25 to 30 µs (best-to-worst times) will set the corresponding bit in the input port change register (IPCR). The bits are cleared when the register is read by the CPU. Also, the DUART can be programmed so any particular change of state can generate an interrupt to the CPU. The DUART internally recognizes a level change on an input pin after it has sampled the new level on the pin for two successive pulses of the sampling clock. The sampling clock is 38.4 kHz and is derived from one of the baud rate generator taps. The resulting sampling period is slightly more than 25 µs (assuming a clock input of 3.6864 MHz). Subsequently, if the level change occurs on or just before a sampling pulse, it will be recognized internally after 25 μs. However, if the level change occurs just after a sampling pulse, it will be sampled the first time after 25 μs. Thus, in this case, the level change will not be recognized internally until 50 μs after the level change occurred on the pin.

# OUTPUT PORT

This 8-bit multipurpose output port can be used as a general-purpose output port. All bits of the output port register (OPR) can be individually set and reset. A bit is set by performing a write operation at the appropriate address with the accompanying data specifying the bits to be set (one equals set and zero equals no change). Similarly, a bit is reset by performing a write operation at another address with the accompanying data specifying the bits to be reset (one equals reset and zero equals no change).

The OPR stores data that is to be output at the output port pins. Unlike the input port, if a particular bit of the OPR is set to a logic one or logic zero, the output pin will be at a low or high level, respectively. Thus, a *logic inversion* occurs internal to the DUART with respect to this register. The outputs are complements of the data contained in the OPR.

Besides functioning as general-purpose outputs, the outputs can be individually assigned specific auxiliary functions serving the communication channels. The assignment is accomplished by appropriately programming the channel A and B mode registers (MR1A, MR1B, MR2A, and MR2B) and the output port configuration register (OPCR).

**7**

# SIGNAL DESCRIPTION

The following paragraphs contain a brief description of the input and output signals.

### NOTE

The terms **assertion** and **negation** will be used extensively to avoid confusion when dealing with a mixture of active-low and active-high signals. The term assert or assertion is used to indicate that a signal is active or true, independent of whether that level is represented by a high or low voltage. The term negate or negation is used to indicate that a signal is inactive or false.

## V<sub>CC</sub> AND GND

Power is supplied to the DUART using these two signals. V<sub>CC</sub> is power (+5 V) and GND is the ground connection.

## CRYSTAL INPUT OR EXTERNAL CLOCK (X1/CLK)

This input is one of two connections to a crystal or a connection to an external clock. A crystal or a clock within the specified limits must be supplied at all times. If a crystal is used, a capacitor of approximately 10 to 15 pF should be connected from this pin to GND.

## CRYSTAL OUTPUT (X2)

This output is an additional connection to a crystal. If an external TTL-level clock is used, this pin should be tied to GND. If a crystal is used, a capacitor of approximately 0 to 5 pF should be connected from this pin to GND.

## RESET ($\overline{\text{RESET}}$)

The DUART can be reset by asserting the $\overline{\text{RESET}}$ signal or by programming the appropriate command register. A hardware reset, assertion of $\overline{\text{RESET}}$, clears status registers A and B (SRA and SRB), the IMR, the ISR, the OPR, and the OPCR. $\overline{\text{RESET}}$ initializes the IVR to $0F, places parallel outputs OP0–OP3 in the high state, places the counter/timer in timer mode, and places channels A and B in the inactive state with the channel A transmitter serial data output (TxDA) and channel B transmitter serial data output (TxDB) in the mark (high) state.

Software resets are not as encompassing and are achieved by appropriately programming the channel A and/or B command register. Reset commands can be programmed through the command register to reset the receiver, transmitter, error status, or break-change interrupts for each channel.

## CHIP SELECT ($\overline{\text{CS}}$)

This active-low input signal, when low, enables data transfers between the CPU and DUART on D0–D7. These data transfers are controlled by R/$\overline{\text{W}}$ and the register select inputs (RS1–RS4). When $\overline{\text{CS}}$ is high, D0–D7 are placed in the high-impedance state.

## READ/WRITE (R/W̄)

When high, this input indicates a read cycle, and when low, it indicates a write cycle. A cycle is initiated by assertion of C̄S̄.

## DATA TRANSFER ACKNOWLEDGE (D̄T̄ĀC̄K̄)

This three-state, active-low, open-drain output is asserted in read, write, or interrupt acknowledge cycles to indicate the proper transfer of data between the CPU and DUART.

## REGISTER SELECT BUS (RS1–RS4)

The register select bus lines during read/write operations select the DUART internal registers, ports, or commands.

## DATA BUS (D0–D7)

These bidirectional three-state data lines are used to transfer commands, data, and status between the CPU and DUART. D0 is the least significant bit.

## INTERRUPT REQUEST (ĪR̄Q̄)

This active-low open-drain output signals the CPU that one or more of the eight maskable interrupting conditions are true.

**7**

## INTERRUPT ACKNOWLEDGE (ĪĀC̄K̄)

This active-low input indicates an interrupt acknowledge cycle. If an interrupt is pending (ĪR̄Q̄ asserted) and this pin is asserted, the DUART responds by placing the interrupt vector on the data bus and then asserting D̄T̄ĀC̄K̄. If there is no interrupt pending (ĪR̄Q̄ negated), the DUART ignores the status of this pin.

## CHANNEL A TRANSMITTER SERIAL DATA OUTPUT (TxDA)

This signal is the transmitter serial data output for channel A. This output is held high (mark condition) when the transmitter is disabled, idle, or operating in the local loopback mode. (Mark is high and space is low.) Data is shifted out of TxDA on the falling edge of the programmed clock source, with the least significant bit transmitted first.

## CHANNEL A RECEIVER SERIAL DATA INPUT (RxDA)

This signal is the receiver serial data input for channel A. Data on RxDA is sampled on the rising edge of the programmed clock source, with the least significant bit received first.

## CHANNEL B TRANSMITTER SERIAL DATA OUTPUT (TxDB)

This signal is the transmitter serial data output for channel B. The output is held high (mark condition) when the transmitter is disabled, idle, or operating in the local loopback mode. Data is shifted out of TxDB on the falling edge of the programmed clock source, with the least significant bit transmitted first.

## CHANNEL B RECEIVER SERIAL DATA INPUT (RxDB)

This signal is the receiver serial data input for channel B. Data on RxDB is sampled on the rising edge of the programmed clock source, with the least significant bit received first.

## PARALLEL INPUTS (IP0–IP5)

Each parallel signal can be used as a general-purpose input. However, each input has an alternate function(s), which is described in the following paragraphs.

IP0   This signal can be used as the channel A clear-to-send active-low input ($\overline{\text{CTSA}}$). A change-of-state detector is also associated with this input.

IP1   This signal can be used as the channel B clear-to-send active-low input ($\overline{\text{CTSB}}$). A change-of-state detector is also associated with this input.

IP2   This signal can be used as the channel B receiver external clock input (RxCB) or as the counter/timer external clock input. When this input is used as the external clock by the receiver, the received data is sampled on the rising edge of the clock. A change-of-state detector is also associated with this input.

IP3   This signal can be used as the channel A transmitter external clock input (TxCA). When this input is used as the external clock by the transmitter, the transmitted data is clocked on the falling edge of the clock. A change-of-state detector is also associated with this input.

IP4   This signal can be used as the channel A receiver external clock input (RxCA). When this input is used as the external clock by the receiver, the received data is sampled on the rising edge of the clock.

IP5 This signal can be used as the channel B transmitter external clock input (TxCB). When this input is used as the external clock by the transmitter, the transmitted data is clocked on the falling edge of the clock.

## PARALLEL OUTPUTS (OP0–OP7)

Each parallel signal can be used as a general-purpose output. However, each output has an alternate function(s), which is described in the following paragraphs.

OP0 This signal can be used as the channel A active-low request-to-send output ($\overline{RTSA}$). When used for this function, it is automatically negated and reasserted by either the receiver or transmitter.

OP1 This signal can be used as the channel B active-low request-to-send output ($\overline{RTSB}$). When used for this function, it is negated and reasserted automatically by either the receiver or transmitter.

OP2 This signal can be used as the channel A transmitter 1X clock or 16X clock output or as the channel A receiver 1X clock output.

OP3 This signal can be used as the open-drain active-low counter-ready output, the open-drain timer output, the channel B transmitter 1X clock output, or the channel B receiver 1X clock output.

OP4 This signal can be used as the channel A open-drain active-low receiver-ready or buffer-full interrupt outputs ($\overline{RxRDYA}/\overline{FFULLA}$) by appropriately programming bit 6 of MR1A.

OP5 This signal can be used as the channel B open-drain active-low receiver-ready or buffer-full interrupt outputs ($\overline{RxRDYB}/\overline{FFULLB}$) by appropriately programming bit 6 of MR1B.

OP6 This signal can be used as the channel A open-drain active-low transmitter-ready interrupt output ($\overline{TxRDYA}$) by appropriately programming bit 6 of the OPCR.

OP7 This signal can be used as the channel B open-drain active-low transmitter-ready interrupt output ($\overline{TxRDYB}$) by appropriately programming bit 7 of the OPCR.

## SIGNAL SUMMARY

Table 1 provides a summary of all MC68681 signals.

### Table 1. Signal Summary

| Signal Name | Mnemonic | Pin No. | Input/Output | Active State |
|---|---|---|---|---|
| Power Supply (+5 V) | $V_{CC}$ | 40 | Input | High |
| Ground | GND | 20 | Input | Low |
| Crystal Input or External Clock | X1/CLK | 32 | Input | — |
| Crystal Output | X2 | 33 | Output | — |
| Reset | $\overline{RESET}$ | 34 | Input | Low |
| Chip Select | $\overline{CS}$ | 35 | Input | Low |
| Read/Write | $R/\overline{W}$ | 8 | Input | High/Low |
| Data Transfer Acknowledge | $\overline{DTACK}$ | 9 | Output* | Low |
| Register Select Bus Bit 4 | RS4 | 6 | Input | — |
| Register Select Bus Bit 3 | RS3 | 5 | Input | — |
| Register Select Bus Bit 2 | RS2 | 3 | Input | — |
| Register Select Bus Bit 1 | RS1 | 1 | Input | — |
| Bidirectional Data Bus Bit 7 | D7 | 19 | Input/Output | — |
| Bidirectional Data Bus Bit 6 | D6 | 22 | Input/Output | — |
| Bidirectional Data Bus Bit 5 | D5 | 18 | Input/Output | — |
| Bidirectional Data Bus Bit 4 | D4 | 23 | Input/Output | — |
| Bidirectional Data Bus Bit 3 | D3 | 17 | Input/Output | — |
| Bidirectional Data Bus Bit 2 | D2 | 24 | Input/Output | — |
| Bidirectional Data Bus Bit 1 | D1 | 16 | Input/Output | — |
| Bidirectional Data Bus Bit 0 (Least Significant Bit) | D0 | 25 | Input/Output | — |
| Interrupt Request | $\overline{IRQ}$ | 21 | Output* | Low |
| Interrupt Acknowledge | $\overline{IACK}$ | 37 | Input | Low |
| Channel A Transmitter Serial Data | TxDA | 30 | Output | — |
| Channel A Receiver Serial Data | RxDA | 31 | Input | — |
| Channel B Transmitter Serial Data | TxDB | 11 | Output | — |
| Channel B Receiver Serial Data | RxDB | 10 | Input | — |
| Parallel Input 5 | IP5 | 38 | Input | — |
| Parallel Input 4 | IP4 | 39 | Input | — |
| Parallel Input 3 | IP3 | 2 | Input | — |
| Parallel Input 2 | IP2 | 36 | Input | — |
| Parallel Input 1 | IP1 | 4 | Input | — |
| Parallel Input 0 | IP0 | 7 | Input | — |

7

Table 1. Signal Summary (Continued)

| Signal Name | Mnemonic | Pin No. | Input/Output | Active State |
|---|---|---|---|---|
| Parallel Output 7 | OP7 | 15 | Output** | — |
| Parallel Output 6 | OP6 | 26 | Output** | — |
| Parallel Output 5 | OP5 | 14 | Output** | — |
| Parallel Output 4 | OP4 | 27 | Output** | — |
| Parallel Output 3 | OP3 | 13 | Output** | — |
| Parallel Output 2 | OP2 | 28 | Output | — |
| Parallel Output 1 | OP1 | 12 | Output | — |
| Parallel Output 0 | OP0 | 29 | Output | — |

*Requires a pullup resistor.
**May require a pullup resistor, depending upon its programmed function.

7

# PROGRAMMING AND REGISTER DESCRIPTION

The operation of the DUART is programmed by writing control words into the appropriate registers. Operational feedback is provided by the status registers, which can be read by the CPU. The DUART register address and address-triggered commands are described in Table 2.

**Table 2. Register Addressing and Address-Triggered Commands**

| RS4 | RS3 | RS2 | RS1 | Read (R/$\overline{W}$ = 1) | Write (R/$\overline{W}$ = 0) |
|---|---|---|---|---|---|
| 0 | 0 | 0 | 0 | Mode Register A (MR1A, MR2A) | Mode Register A (MR1A, MR2A) |
| 0 | 0 | 0 | 1 | Status Register A (SRA) | Clock Select Register A (CSRA) |
| 0 | 0 | 1 | 0 | Do Not Access* | Command Register A (CRA) |
| 0 | 0 | 1 | 1 | Receiver Buffer A (RBA) | Transmitter Buffer A (TBA) |
| 0 | 1 | 0 | 0 | Input Port Change Register (IPCR) | Auxiliary Control Register (ACR) |
| 0 | 1 | 0 | 1 | Interrupt Status Register (ISR) | Interrupt Mask Register (IMR) |
| 0 | 1 | 1 | 0 | Counter Mode: Current MSB of Counter (CUR) | Counter/Timer Upper Register (CTUR) |
| 0 | 1 | 1 | 1 | Counter Mode: Current LSB of Counter (CLR) | Counter/Timer Lower Register (CTLR) |
| 1 | 0 | 0 | 0 | Mode Register B (MR1B, MR2B) | Mode Register B (MR1B, MR2B) |
| 1 | 0 | 0 | 1 | Status Register B (SRB) | Clock Select Register B (CSRB) |
| 1 | 0 | 1 | 0 | Do Not Access* | Command Register B (CRB) |
| 1 | 0 | 1 | 1 | Receiver Buffer B (RBB) | Transmitter Buffer B (TBB) |
| 1 | 1 | 0 | 0 | Interrupt Vector Register (IVR) | Interrupt Vector Register (IVR) |
| 1 | 1 | 0 | 1 | Input Port (Unlatched) | Output Port Configuration Register (OPCR) |
| 1 | 1 | 1 | 0 | Start Counter Command** | Output Port Register (OPR) Bit Set Command** |
| 1 | 1 | 1 | 1 | Stop Counter Command** | Output Port Register (OPR) Bit Reset Command** |

*This address location is used for factory testing of the DUART and should not be read. Reading this location will result in undesired effects and possible incorrect transmission or reception of characters. Register contents may also be changed.
**Address-triggered commands.

Figure 2 illustrates a block diagram of the DUART from a programming standpoint and details the register configuration for each block. The locations marked "do not access" should never be read during normal operation. They are used by the factory for testing purposes.

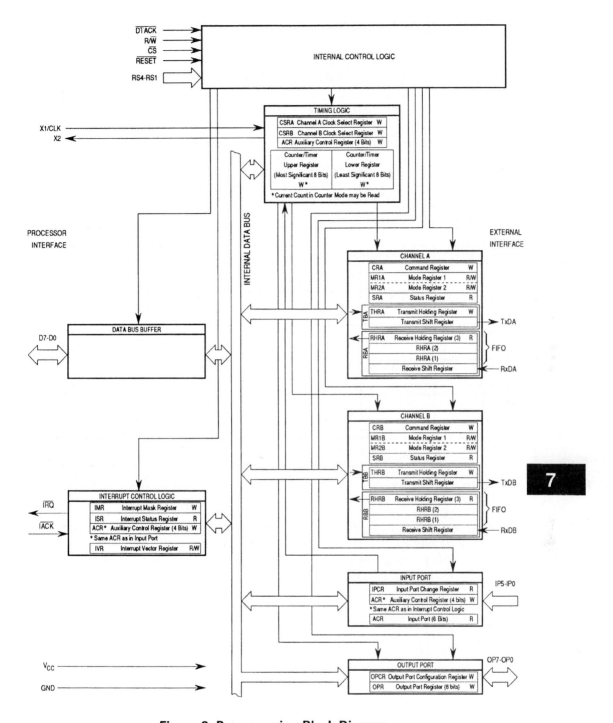

**Figure 2. Programming Block Diagram**

Tables 3 and 4 list the various input port pin functions and output port pin functions, respectively.

## Table 3. Programming of Input Port Functions

| Function | Input Port Pin | | | | | |
|---|---|---|---|---|---|---|
| | IP5 | IP4 | IP3 | IP2 | IP1 | IP0 |
| General Purpose | Default | Default | Default | Default | Default | Default |
| Change-of-State Detector | | | Default | Default | Default | Default |
| External Counter 1X Clock Input | | | | ACR[6:4] = 000 | | |
| External Timer 16X Clock Input | | | | ACR[6:4] = 100 | | |
| External Timer 1X Clock Input | | | | ACR[6:4] = 101 | | |
| RxCA 16X | | CSRA[7:4] = 1110 | | | | |
| RxCA 1X | | CSRA[7:4] = 1111 | | | | |
| TxCA 16X | | | CSRA[3:0] = 1110 | | | |
| TxCA 1X | | | CSRA[3:0] = 1111 | | | |
| RxCB 16X | | | | CSRB[7:4] = 1110 | | |
| RxCB 1X | | | | CSRB[7:4] = 1111 | | |
| TxCB 16X | CSRB[3:0] = 1110 | | | | | |
| TxCB 1X | CSRB[3:0] = 1111 | | | | | |
| TxCTSA | | | | | | MR2A[4] = 1 |
| TxCTSB | | | | | MR2B[4] = 1 | |

*In these modes, because IP2 is used for the counter/timer clock input, it is not available for use as the channel B receiver clock input.

NOTE: Default refers to the function the input port pins perform when not used in one of the other modes. Only those functions which show the register programming are available for use.

**7**

## Table 4. Programming of Output Port Functions

| Function | Output Port Pin | | | | | | | |
|---|---|---|---|---|---|---|---|---|
| | OP7 | OP6 | OP5 | OP4 | OP3 | OP2 | OP1 | OP0 |
| General Purpose | OPCR[7]=0 | OPCR[6]=0 | OPCR[5]=0 | OPCR[4]=0 | OPCR[3:2]=00 | OPCR[1:0]=00 | MR1B[7]=0 MR2B[5]=0 | MR1A[7]=0 MR2A[5]=0 |
| $\overline{\text{CTRDY}}$ | | | | | OPCR[3:2]=01, ACR[6]=0* | | | |
| Timer Output | | | | | OPCR[3:2]=01, ACR[6]=1* | | | |
| TxCB 1X | | | | | OPCR[3:2]=10 | | | |
| RxCB 1X | | | | | OPCR[3:2]=11 | | | |
| TxCA 16X | | | | | | OPCR[1:0]=01 | | |
| TxCA 1X | | | | | | OPCR[1:0]=10 | | |
| RxCA 1X | | | | | | OPCR[1:0]=11 | | |
| $\overline{\text{TxRDYA}}$ | | OPCR[6]=1* | | | | | | |
| $\overline{\text{TxRDYB}}$ | OPCR[7]=1* | | | | | | | |
| $\overline{\text{RxRDYA}}$ | | | | OPCR[4]=1, MR1A[6]=0* | | | | |
| $\overline{\text{RxRDYB}}$ | | | OPCR[5]=1, MR1B[6]=0* | | | | | |
| $\overline{\text{FFULLA}}$ | | | | OPCR[4]=1, MR1A[6]=1 | | | | |
| $\overline{\text{FFULLB}}$ | | | OPCR[5]=1, MR1B[6]=1* | | | | | |
| $\overline{\text{RxRTSA}}$ | | | | | | | | MR1A[7]=1 |
| $\overline{\text{TxRTSA}}$ | | | | | | | | MR2A[5]=1 |
| $\overline{\text{RxRTSB}}$ | | | | | | | MR1B[7]=1 | |
| $\overline{\text{TxRTSB}}$ | | | | | | | MR2B[5]=1 | |

NOTE: Only those functions showing the register programming are available for use.
*Pin requires a pullup resistor if used for this function.

7

Table 5 lists the various clock sources that may be selected for the counter and timer. More detailed information is provided in Table 6.

**Table 5. Selection of Clock Sources for the Counter and Timer Modes**

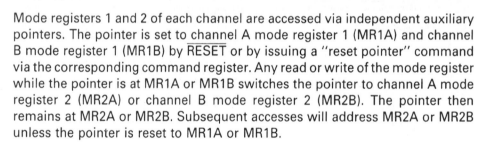

| Counter Mode Clock Sources (ACR[6]=0) | ACR[5:4] = | Timer Mode Clock Sources (ACR[6]=1) | ACR[5:4] = |
|---|---|---|---|
| External Input via Input Port Pin 2 (IP2) | 00 | External Input via Input Port Pin 2 (IP2) | 00 |
| Channel A 1X Transmitter Clock TxCA | 01 | External Input Divide by 16 via Input Port Pin 2 (IP2) | 01 |
| Channel B 1X Transmitter Clock TxCB | 10 | Crystal Oscillator via X1/CLK and X2 | 10 |
| Crystal Oscillator Divide by 16 via X1/Clk and X2 | 11 | Crystal Oscillator Divide by 16 via X1/CLK and X2 | 11 |
| External Input Divide by 16 via X1/CLK Input Pin | 11 | External Input via X1/CLK Input Pin | 10 |
| | | External Input Divide by 16 via X1/CLK Input Pin | 11 |

NOTE: Only those functions showing the register programming are available for use.

Care should be exercised if register contents are changed during receiver/transmitter operation since certain changes may cause undesired results. For example, changing the number of bits per character while the transmitter is active may cause the transmission of an incorrect character. The contents of the mode registers, the clock select register (CSR), the OPCR, and bit 7 of the ACR should only be changed after the receiver(s) and transmitter(s) have been issued software Rx and Tx reset commands. Similarly, certain changes to ACR bits 6–4 should only be made while the counter/timer is not used (i.e., stopped if in counter mode; output and/or interrupt masked in timer mode).

Mode registers 1 and 2 of each channel are accessed via independent auxiliary pointers. The pointer is set to channel A mode register 1 (MR1A) and channel B mode register 1 (MR1B) by RESET or by issuing a "reset pointer" command via the corresponding command register. Any read or write of the mode register while the pointer is at MR1A or MR1B switches the pointer to channel A mode register 2 (MR2A) or channel B mode register 2 (MR2B). The pointer then remains at MR2A or MR2B. Subsequent accesses will address MR2A or MR2B unless the pointer is reset to MR1A or MR1B.

Mode, command, clock select, and status registers are duplicated for each channel to provide independent operation and control. Refer to Table 6 for descriptions of the registers.

## Table 6. Register Bit Formats

CHANNEL A MODE REGISTER 1 (MR1A) AND CHANNEL B MODE REGISTER 1 (MR1B)

| Rx RTS Control | Rx IRQ Select | Error Mode | Parity Mode | | Parity Type | Bits-per-Character | |
|---|---|---|---|---|---|---|---|
| Bit 7 | Bit 6 | Bit 5 | Bit 4 | Bit 3 | Bit 2 | Bit 1 | Bit 0 |
| | | | | | With Parity 0 = Even 1 = Odd | | |
| 0 = Disabled 1 = Enabled | 0 = RxRDY 1 = FFULL | 0 = Char 1 = Block | 0 0 = With Parity 0 1 = Force Parity 1 0 = No Parity 1 1 = Multidrop Mode* | | Force Parity 0 = Low 1 = High | 0 0 = 5 0 1 = 6 1 0 = 7 1 1 = 8 | |
| | | | | | Multidrop Mode 0 = Data 1 = Address | | |

*The parity bit is used as the address/data bit in multidrop mode.

CHANNEL A MODE REGISTER 2 (MR2A) AND CHANNEL B MODE REGISTER 2 (MR2B)

| Channel Mode | | Tx RTS Control | CTS Enable Transmitter | Stop Bit Length | | | |
|---|---|---|---|---|---|---|---|
| Bit 7 | Bit 6 | Bit 5 | Bit 4 | Bit 3 | Bit 2 | Bit 1 | Bit 0 |
| | | | | | | 6-8 Bits/ Character | 5-Bits/ Character |
| 0 0 = Normal 0 1 = Automatic Echo 1 0 = Local Loopback 1 1 = Remote Loopback | | 0 = Disabled 1 = Enabled | 0 = Disabled 1 = Enabled | (0) 0 0 0 0 = (1) 0 0 0 1 = (2) 0 0 1 0 = (3) 0 0 1 1 = (4) 0 1 0 0 = (5) 0 1 0 1 = (6) 0 1 1 0 = (7) 0 1 1 1 = (8) 1 0 0 0 = (9) 1 0 0 1 = (A) 1 0 1 0 = (B) 1 0 1 1 = (C) 1 1 0 0 = (D) 1 1 0 1 = (E) 1 1 1 0 = (F) 1 1 1 1 = | | 0.563 0.625 0.688 0.750 0.813 0.875 0.938 1.000 1.563 1.625 1.688 1.750 1.813 1.875 1.938 2.000 | 1.063 1.125 1.188 1.250 1.313 1.375 1.438 1.500 1.563 1.625 1.688 1.750 1.813 1.875 1.938 2.000 |

NOTE:
If an external 1X clock is used for the transmitter, MR2 bit 3 = 0 selects one stop bit and MR2 bit 3 = 1 selects two stop bits to be transmitted.

7

## Table 6. Register Bit Formats (Continued)

CLOCK-SELECT REGISTER A (CSRA)

| Receiver-Clock Select | | | | Transmitter-Clock Select | | | |
|---|---|---|---|---|---|---|---|
| Bit 7 | Bit 6 | Bit 5 | Bit 4 | Bit 3 | Bit 2 | Bit 1 | Bit 0 |
| | Baud Rate | | | | Baud Rate | | |
| | | Set 1 ACR Bit 7 = 0 | Set 2 ACR Bit 7 = 1 | | | Set 1 ACR Bit 7 = 0 | Set 2 ACR Bit 7 = 1 |
| 0 0 0 0 | | 50 | 75 | 0 0 0 0 | | 50 | 75 |
| 0 0 0 1 | | 110 | 110 | 0 0 0 1 | | 110 | 110 |
| 0 0 1 0 | | 134.5 | 134.5 | 0 0 1 0 | | 134.5 | 134.5 |
| 0 0 1 1 | | 200 | 150 | 0 0 1 1 | | 200 | 150 |
| 0 1 0 0 | | 300 | 300 | 0 1 0 0 | | 300 | 300 |
| 0 1 0 1 | | 600 | 600 | 0 1 0 1 | | 600 | 600 |
| 0 1 1 0 | | 1200 | 1200 | 0 1 1 0 | | 1200 | 1200 |
| 0 1 1 1 | | 1050 | 2000 | 0 1 1 1 | | 1050 | 2000 |
| 1 0 0 0 | | 2400 | 2400 | 1 0 0 0 | | 2400 | 2400 |
| 1 0 0 1 | | 4800 | 4800 | 1 0 0 1 | | 4800 | 4800 |
| 1 0 1 0 | | 7200 | 1800 | 1 0 1 0 | | 7200 | 1800 |
| 1 0 1 1 | | 9600 | 9600 | 1 0 1 1 | | 9600 | 9600 |
| 1 1 0 0 | | 38.4k | 19.2k | 1 1 0 0 | | 38.4k | 19.2k |
| 1 1 0 1 | | Timer | Timer | 1 1 0 1 | | Timer | Timer |
| 1 1 1 0 | | IP4-16X | IP4-16X | 1 1 1 0 | | IP3-16X | IP3-16X |
| 1 1 1 1 | | IP4-1X | IP4-1X | 1 1 1 1 | | IP3-1X | IP3-1X |

NOTE: Receiver clock is always a 16X clock except when CSRA bits 7–4 equal 1111.

NOTE: Transmitter clock is always a 16X clock except when CSRA bits 3–0 equal 1111.

CLOCK-SELECT REGISTER B (CSRB)

| Receiver-Clock Select | | | | Transmitter-Clock Select | | | |
|---|---|---|---|---|---|---|---|
| Bit 7 | Bit 6 | Bit 5 | Bit 4 | Bit 3 | Bit 2 | Bit 1 | Bit 0 |
| | Baud Rate | | | | Baud Rate | | |
| | | Set 1 ACR Bit 7 = 0 | Set 2 ACR Bit 7 = 1 | | | Set 1 ACR Bit 7 = 0 | Set 2 ACR Bit 7 = 1 |
| 0 0 0 0 | | 50 | 75 | 0 0 0 0 | | 50 | 75 |
| 0 0 0 1 | | 110 | 110 | 0 0 0 1 | | 110 | 110 |
| 0 0 1 0 | | 134.5 | 134.5 | 0 0 1 0 | | 134.5 | 134.5 |
| 0 0 1 1 | | 200 | 150 | 0 0 1 1 | | 200 | 150 |
| 0 1 0 0 | | 300 | 300 | 0 1 0 0 | | 300 | 300 |
| 0 1 0 1 | | 600 | 600 | 0 1 0 1 | | 600 | 600 |
| 0 1 1 0 | | 1200 | 1200 | 0 1 1 0 | | 1200 | 1200 |
| 0 1 1 1 | | 1050 | 2000 | 0 1 1 1 | | 1050 | 2000 |
| 1 0 0 0 | | 2400 | 2400 | 1 0 0 0 | | 2400 | 2400 |
| 1 0 0 1 | | 4800 | 4800 | 1 0 0 1 | | 4800 | 4800 |
| 1 0 1 0 | | 7200 | 1800 | 1 0 1 0 | | 7200 | 1800 |
| 1 0 1 1 | | 9600 | 9600 | 1 0 1 1 | | 9600 | 9600 |
| 1 1 0 0 | | 38.4k | 19.2k | 1 1 0 0 | | 38.4k | 19.2k |
| 1 1 0 1 | | Timer | Timer | 1 1 0 1 | | Timer | Timer |
| 1 1 1 0 | | IP2-16X | IP2-16X | 1 1 1 0 | | IP5-16X | IP5-16X |
| 1 1 1 1 | | IP2-1X | IP2-1X | 1 1 1 1 | | IP5-1X | IP5-1X |

NOTE: Receiver clock is always a 16X clock except when CSRB bits 7–4 equal 1111.

NOTE: Transmitter clock is always a 16X clock except when CSRB bits 3–0 equal 1111.

## Table 6. Register Bit Formats (Continued)

CHANNEL A COMMAND REGISTER (CRA) AND CHANNEL B COMMAND REGISTER (CRB)

| Not Used* | Miscellaneous Commands | | | Transmitter Commands | | Receiver Commands | |
|---|---|---|---|---|---|---|---|
| Bit 7 | Bit 6 | Bit 5 | Bit 4 | Bit 3 | Bit 2 | Bit 1 | Bit 0 |
| X | 0 0 0 No Command | | | 0 0 No Action, Stays in Present Mode | | 0 0 No Action, Stays in Present Mode | |
| | 0 0 1 Reset MR Pointer to MR1 | | | | | | |
| | 0 1 0 Reset Receiver | | | 0 1 Transmitter Enabled | | 0 1 Receiver Enabled | |
| | 0 1 1 Reset Transmitter | | | 1 0 Transmitter Disabled | | 1 0 Receiver Disabled | |
| | 1 0 0 Reset Error Status | | | 1 1 Don't Use, Indeterminate | | 1 1 Don't Use, Indeterminate | |
| | 1 0 1 Reset Channel's Break-Change Interrupt | | | | | | |
| | 1 1 0 Start Break | | | | | | |
| | 1 1 1 Stop Break | | | | | | |

*Bit 7 is not used and may be set to either zero or one.

CHANNEL A STATUS REGISTER (SRA) AND CHANNEL B STATUS REGISTER (SRB)

| Received Break | Framing Error | Parity Error | Overrun Error | TxEMT | TxRDY | FFULL | RxRDY |
|---|---|---|---|---|---|---|---|
| Bit 7* | Bit 6* | Bit 5* | Bit 4 | Bit 3 | Bit 2 | Bit 1 | Bit 0 |
| 0 = No | 0 = No | 0 = No | 0 = No | 0 = No | 0 = No | 0 = No | 0 = No |
| 1 = Yes | 1 = Yes | 1 = Yes | 1 = Yes | 1 = Yes | 1 = Yes | 1 = Yes | 1 = Yes |

*These status bits are appended to the corresponding data character in the receive FIFO and are valid only when RxRDY is set. A read of the status register provides these bits (7–5) from the top of the FIFO together with bits 4–0. These bits are cleared by a reset error status command. In character mode, they are discarded when the corresponding data character is read from the FIFO.

OUTPUT PORT CONFIGURATION REGISTER (OPCR)

| OP7 | OP6 | OP5 | OP4 | OP3 | | OP2 | |
|---|---|---|---|---|---|---|---|
| Bit 7 | Bit 6 | Bit 5 | Bit 4 | Bit 3 | Bit 2 | Bit 1 | Bit 0 |
| 0 = OPR Bit 7 | 0 = OPR Bit 6 | 0 = OPR Bit 5 | 0 = OPR Bit 4 | 0 0 = OPR Bit 3 | | 0 0 = OPR Bit 2 | |
| 1 = TxRDYB | 1 = TxRDYA | 1 = RxRDYB / FFULLB | 1 = RxRDYA/ FFULLA | 0 1 = C/T Output * | | 0 1 = TxCA (16X) | |
| | | | | 1 0 = TxCB (1X) | | 1 0 = TXCA (1X) | |
| | | | | 1 1 = RxCB (1X) | | 1 1 = RxCA (1X) | |

*If OP3 is to be used for the timer output, the counter/timer should be programmed for timer mode (ACR[6] = 1), the counter/timer preload registers (CTUR and CTLR) initialized, and the start counter command issued before setting OPCR[3:2] = 01.

NOTE: OP1 and OP0 can be used as transmitter and receiver RTS control lines by appropriately programming the mode registers (MR1[7] for RxRTS and MR2[5] forTxRTS). OP1 is used for the channel B RTS control line and OP0 for the channel A RTS control line. When OP1 and OP0 are not used for RTS control, they may be used as general-purpose outputs.

OUTPUT PORT REGISTER (OPR)

| OPR7 | OPR6 | OPR5 | OPR4 | OPR3 | OPR2 | OPR1 | OPR0 |
|---|---|---|---|---|---|---|---|
| Bit 7 | Bit 6 | Bit 5 | Bit 4 | Bit 3 | Bit 2 | Bit 1 | Bit 0 |

7

## Table 6. Register Bit Formats (Continued)

AUXILIARY CONTROL REGISTER (ACR)

| BRG SET Select* | Counter/Timer Mode and Source** | | | Delta*** IP3 IRQ | Delta*** IP2 IRQ | Delta*** IP1 IRQ | Delta*** IP0 IRQ |
|---|---|---|---|---|---|---|---|
| Bit 7 | Bit 6 | Bit 5 | Bit 4 | Bit 3 | Bit 2 | Bit 1 | Bit 0 |
| 0 = Set 1 1 = Set 2 | Mode 0 0 0 Counter 0 0 1 Counter 0 1 0 Counter 0 1 1 Counter 1 0 0 Timer 1 0 1 Timer 1 1 0 Timer 1 1 1 Timer | Clock Source External (IP2)**** TxCA – 1X Clock of Channel A Transmitter TxCB – 1X Clock of Channel B Transmitter Crystal or External Clock (X1/CLK) Divided by 16 External (IP2)**** External (IP2) Divided by 16**** Crystal or External Clock (X1/CLK) Crystal or External Clock (X1/CLK) Divided by 16 | | 0 = Disabled 1 = Enabled | 0 = Disabled 1 = Enabled | 0 = Disabled 1 = Enabled | 0 = Disabled 1 = Enabled |

 * Should only be changed after both channels have been reset and are disabled.
 ** Should only be altered while the counter/timer is not in use (i.e., stopped if in counter mode, output and/or interrupt masked if in timer mode).
 *** Delta is equivalent to change-of-state.
 **** In these modes, because IP2 is used for the counter/timer clock input, it is not available for use as the channel B receiver-clock input.

INPUT PORT CHANGE REGISTER (IPCR)

| Delta* Detected IP3 | Delta* Detected IP2 | Delta* Detected IP1 | Delta* Detected IP0 | Level IP3 | Level IP2 | Level IP1 | Level IP0 |
|---|---|---|---|---|---|---|---|
| Bit 7 | Bit 6 | Bit 5 | Bit 4 | Bit 3 | Bit 2 | Bit 1 | Bit 0 |
| 0 = No 1 = Yes | 0 = No 1 = Yes | 0 = No 1 = Yes | 0 = No 1 = Yes | 0 = Low 1 = High | 0 = Low 1 = High | 0 = Low 1 = High | 0 = Low 1 = High |

 * Delta is equivalent to change-of-state.

INTERRUPT STATUS REGISTER (ISR)

| Input Port Change | Delta Break B | RxRDYB/ FFULLB | TxRDYB | Counter/ Timer Ready | Delta Break A | RxRDYA/ FFULLA | TxRDYA |
|---|---|---|---|---|---|---|---|
| Bit 7 | Bit 6 | Bit 5 | Bit 4 | Bit 3 | Bit 2 | Bit 1 | Bit 0 |
| 0 = No 1 = Yes | 0 = No 1 = Yes | 0 = No 1 = Yes | 0 = No 1 = Yes | 0 = No 1 = Yes | 0 = No 1 = Yes | 0 = No 1 = Yes | 0 = No 1 = Yes |

INTERRUPT MASK REGISTER (IMR)

| Input Port Change IRQ | Delta Break B IRQ | RxRDYB/ FFULLB IRQ | TxRDYB IRQ | Counter/ Timer Ready IRQ | Delta Break A IRQ | RxRDYA/ FFULLA IRQ | TxRDYA IRQ |
|---|---|---|---|---|---|---|---|
| Bit 7 | Bit 6 | Bit 5 | Bit 4 | Bit 3 | Bit 2 | Bit 1 | Bit 0 |
| 0 = Masked 1 = Pass | 0 = Masked 1 = Pass | 0 = Masked 1 = Pass | 0 = Masked 1 = Pass | 0 = Masked 1 = Pass | 0 = Masked 1 = Pass | 0 = Masked 1 = Pass | 0 = Masked 1 = Pass |

## Table 6. Register Bit Formats (Concluded)

COUNTER/TIMER UPPER REGISTER (CTUR)

| C/T[15] | C/T[14] | C/T[13] | C/T[12] | C/T[11] | C/T[10] | C/T[9] | C/T[8] |
|---|---|---|---|---|---|---|---|
| Bit 7 | Bit 6 | Bit 5 | Bit 4 | Bit 3 | Bit 2 | Bit 1 | Bit 0 |

COUNTER/TIMER LOWER REGISTER (CTLR)

| C/T[7] | C/T[6] | C/T[5] | C/T[4] | C/T[3] | C/T[2] | C/T[1] | C/T[0] |
|---|---|---|---|---|---|---|---|
| Bit 7 | Bit 6 | Bit 5 | Bit 4 | Bit 3 | Bit 2 | Bit 1 | Bit 0 |

INTERRUPT VECTOR REGISTER (IVR)

| IVR[7] | IVR[6] | IVR[5] | IVR[4] | IVR[3] | IVR[2] | IVR[1] | IVR[0] |
|---|---|---|---|---|---|---|---|
| Bit 7 | Bit 6 | Bit 5 | Bit 4 | Bit 3 | Bit 2 | Bit 1 | Bit 0 |

INPUT PORT

| * | ** | IP5 | IP4 | IP3 | IP2 | IP1 | IP0 |
|---|---|---|---|---|---|---|---|
| Bit 7 | Bit 6 | Bit 5 | Bit 4 | Bit 3 | Bit 2 | Bit 1 | Bit 0 |

*Bit 7 has no external pin. Upon reading the input port, bit 7 will always be read as a one.
**Bit 6 has no external pin. Upon reading the input port, bit 6 will reflect the current logic level of $\overline{IACK}$.

OUTPUT PORT

| OP7 | OP6 | OP5 | OP4 | OP3 | OP2 | OP1 | OP0 |
|---|---|---|---|---|---|---|---|
| Bit 7 | Bit 6 | Bit 5 | Bit 4 | Bit 3 | Bit 2 | Bit 1 | Bit 0 |
| $\overline{OPR[7]}$ | $\overline{OPR[6]}$ | $\overline{OPR[5]}$ | $\overline{OPR[4]}$ | $\overline{OPR[3]}$ | $\overline{OPR[2]}$ | $\overline{OPR[1]}$ | $\overline{OPR[0]}$ |

# ELECTRICAL SPECIFICATIONS

## MAXIMUM RATINGS

| Rating | Symbol | Value | Unit |
|---|---|---|---|
| Supply Voltage | $V_{CC}$ | −0.5 to +6.0 | V |
| Input Voltage | $V_{in}$ | −0.5 to +6.0 | V |
| Operating Temperature Range | $T_A$ | 0 to +70 | °C |
| Storage Temperature | $T_{stg}$ | −65 to +150 | °C |

This device contains circuitry to protect the inputs against damage due to high static voltages or electric fields; however, it is advised that normal precautions be taken to avoid application of any voltage higher than maximum-rated voltages to this high-impedance circuit. Reliability of operation is enhanced if unused inputs are tied to an appropriate logic voltage level (e.g., either GND or $V_{CC}$).

## THERMAL CHARACTERISTICS

| Characteristic | Value | | Rating |
|---|---|---|---|
| | $\theta_{JA}$ | $\theta_{JC}$ | |
| Thermal Resistance (Still Air) | | | °C/W |
| Ceramic, Type L | 50 | 25* | |
| Plastic, Type P | | | |
| Cu Lead Frame | 50 | 25* | |
| A42 Lead Frame | 100 | 50* | |
| PLCC, Type FN | TBD | TBD | |

*Estimated

**7**

## POWER CONSIDERATIONS

The average chip-junction temperature, $T_J$, in °C can be obtained from:

$$T_J = T_A + (P_D \cdot \theta_{JA}) \qquad (1)$$

where:

$T_A$ = Ambient Temperature, °C
$\theta_{JA}$ = Package Thermal Resistance, Junction-to-Ambient, °C/W
$P_D$ = $P_{INT} + P_{I/O}$
$P_{INT}$ = $I_{CC} \times V_{CC}$, Watts – Chip Internal Power
$P_{I/O}$ = Power Dissipation on Input and Output Pins – User Determined

For most applications $P_{I/O} < P_{INT}$ and can be neglected.

The following is an approximate relationship between $P_D$ and $T_J$ (if $P_{I/O}$ is neglected):

$$P_D = K \div (T_J + 273°C) \qquad (2)$$

Solving equations (1) and (2) for K gives:

$$K = P_D \cdot (T_A + 273°C) + \theta_{JA} \cdot P_D^2 \qquad (3)$$

where K is a constant pertaining to the particular part. K can be determined from equation (3) by measuring $P_D$ (at equilibrium) for a known $T_A$. Using this value of K, the values of $P_D$ and $T_J$ can be obtained by solving equations (1) and (2) iteratively for any value of $T_A$.

The total thermal resistance of a package ($\theta_{JA}$) can be separated into two components, $\theta_{JA}$ and $\theta_{CA}$, representing the barrier to heat flow from the semiconductor junction to the package (case) surface ($\theta_{JC}$) and from the case to the outside ambient ($\theta_{CA}$). These terms are related by the equation:

$$\theta_{JA} = \theta_{JC} + \theta_{CA} \qquad (4)$$

$\theta_{JC}$ is device related and cannot be influenced by the user. However, $\theta_{CA}$ is user dependent and can be minimized by such thermal management techniques as heat sinks, ambient air cooling and thermal convection. Thus, good thermal management on the part of the user can significantly reduce $\theta_{CA}$ so that $\theta_{JA}$ aproximately equals $\theta_{JC}$. Substitution of $\theta_{JC}$ for $\theta_{JA}$ in equation (1) will result in a lower semiconductor junction temperature.

Values for thermal resistance presented in this document, unless estimated, were derived using the procedure described in Motorola Reliability Report 7843, "Thermal Resistance Measurement Method for MC68XX Microcomponent Devices," and are provided for design purposes only. Thermal measurements are complex and dependent on procedure and setup. User-derived values for thermal resistance may differ.

## DC ELECTRICAL CHARACTERISTICS ($T_A = 0°C$ to $70°C$; $V_{CC} = 5.0$ V ± 5%)

| Characteristic | Symbol | Min | Typ | Max | Unit |
|---|---|---|---|---|---|
| Input High Voltage, Except X1/CLK | $V_{IH}$ | 2.0 | — | — | V |
| Input High Voltage, X1/CLK | $V_{IH}$ | 4.0 | — | — | V |
| Input Low Voltage | $V_{IL}$ | — | — | 0.8 | V |
| Output High Voltage, Except Open-Collector Outputs ($I_{OH} = -400$ μA) | $V_{OH}$ | 2.4 | — | — | V |
| Output Low Voltage ($I_{OL} = 2.4$ mA) | $V_{OL}$ | — | — | 0.4 | V |
| Input Leakage Current ($V_{in} = 0$ to $V_{CC}$) | $I_{IL}$ | −10 | — | 10 | μA |
| Data Bus Hi-Z Leakage Current ($V_{out} = 0$ to $V_{CC}$) | $I_{LL}$ | −10 | — | 10 | μA |
| Open-Collector Output Leakage Current ($V_{out} = 0$ to $V_{CC}$) | $I_{OC}$ | −10 | — | 10 | μA |
| Power Supply Current | $I_{CC}$ | — | — | 150 | mA |
| Capacitance ($V_{in} = 5$ V, $T_A = 25°C$, f = 1 MHz) | $C_{in}$ | — | — | 15 | pF |
| Load Capacitance<br>  Interrupt Outputs<br>  All Other Outputs | $C_L$ | — | — | <br>50<br>150 | pF |
| X1/CLK Low Input Current<br>  $V_{in} = 0$, X2 Grounded<br>  $V_{in} = 0$, X2 Floated | $I_{X1L}$ | <br>−4.0<br>−3.0 | <br>−2.0<br>−1.5 | <br>0<br>0 | mA |
| X1/CLK High Input Current<br>  $V_{in} = V_{CC}$, X2 Grounded<br>  $V_{in} = V_{CC}$, X2 Floated | $I_{X1H}$ | <br>−1.0<br>0 | <br>0.2<br>3.5 | <br>1.0<br>10.0 | mA |
| X2 Low Input Current<br>  $V_{in} = 0$, X1/CLK Floated | $I_{X2L}$ | −100 | −30 | 0 | μA |
| X2 High Input Current<br>  $V_{in} = V_{CC}$, X1/CLK Floated | $I_{X2H}$ | 0 | 30 | 100 | μA |

## AC ELECTRICAL CHARACTERISTICS ($T_A = 0°C$ to $70°C$; $V_{CC} = 5.0$ V ± 5%)

**7**

| Characteristic | Symbol | Min | Max | Unit |
|---|---|---|---|---|
| X1/CLK Frequency (see Note 2) | $f_{CLK}$ | 2.0 | 4.0 | MHz |
| Counter/Timer Clock Frequency | $f_{CTC}$ | 0 | 4.0 | MHz |
| Receiver Clock Frequency (RxC)<br>  16X Clock<br>  1X Clock | $f_{Rx}$ | <br>0<br>0 | <br>2.0<br>1.0 | MHz |
| Transmitter Clock Frequency (TxC)<br>  16X Clock<br>  1X Clock | $f_{Tx}$ | <br>0<br>0 | <br>2.0<br>1.0 | MHz |

NOTES:
1. All voltage measurements are referenced to GND. For testing, all input signals except X1/CLK swing between 0.4 V and 2.4 V with a maximum transition time of 20 ns. For X1/CLK, this swing is between 0.4 V and 4.4 V. All time measurements are referenced at input and output voltages of 0.8 V and 2.0 V, as appropriate. Test conditions for outputs $C_L = 150$ pF, $R_L = 750$ Ω to $V_{CC}$.
2. To use the standard baud rates selected by the clock select register given in Table 6, the X1/CLK frequency should be set to 3.6864 MHz or a 3.6864-MHz crystal should be connected across pins X1/CLK and X2.

## AC ELECTRICAL CHARACTERISTICS—$\overline{\text{RESET}}$ TIMING (see Figure 3)

| Characteristic | Symbol | Min | Max | Unit |
|---|---|---|---|---|
| $\overline{\text{RESET}}$ Pulse Width | $t_{RES}$ | 1.0 | — | µs |

NOTE: All voltage measurements are referenced to GND. For testing, all input signals swing between 0.4 V and 2.4 V with a maximum transition time of 20 ns. All time measurements are referenced at input and output voltages of 0.8 V and 2.0 V, as appropriate. Test conditions for noninterrupt outputs: $C_L = 150$ pF, $R_L = 750$ $\Omega$ to $V_{CC}$. Test conditions for interrupt outputs: $C_L = 50$ pF, $R_L = 27$ k$\Omega$ to $V_{CC}$.

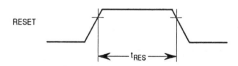

**Figure 3. $\overline{\text{RESET}}$ Timing**

## AC ELECTRICAL CHARACTERISTICS — READ CYCLE BUS TIMING
(see Figure 4)

| Characteristic | Symbol | Min | Max | Unit |
|---|---|---|---|---|
| $\overline{\text{CS}}$ Setup Time to X1/CLK High (see Note 2) | $t_{CSC}$ | 90 | — | ns |
| RS1–RS4 Setup Time to $\overline{\text{CS}}$ Asserted | $t_{RSS}$ | 10 | — | ns |
| R/$\overline{\text{W}}$ Setup Time to $\overline{\text{CS}}$ Asserted | $t_{RWS}$ | 0 | — | ns |
| $\overline{\text{CS}}$ Pulse Width Asserted (see Note 3) | $t_{CSWL}$ | 205 | — | ns |
| Data Valid from $\overline{\text{CS}}$ Asserted | $t_{DD}$ | — | 175 | ns |
| $\overline{\text{DTACK}}$ Asserted from X1/CLK High | $t_{DCR}$ | — | 125 | ns |
| $\overline{\text{CS}}$ Negated from $\overline{\text{DTACK}}$ Asserted (see Note 3) | $t_{CSD}$ | 20 | — | ns |
| RS1–RS4 Hold Time from $\overline{\text{CS}}$ Negated | $t_{RSH}$ | 0 | — | ns |
| R/$\overline{\text{W}}$ Hold Time from $\overline{\text{CS}}$ Negated | $t_{RWH}$ | 0 | — | ns |
| Data Hold Time from $\overline{\text{CS}}$ Negated | $t_{DH}$ | 0 | — | ns |
| Data Bus Floating from $\overline{\text{CS}}$ Negated | $t_{DF}$ | — | 100 | ns |
| $\overline{\text{DTACK}}$ Negated from $\overline{\text{CS}}$ Negated | $t_{DAH}$ | — | 100 | ns |
| $\overline{\text{DTACK}}$ Hi-Z from $\overline{\text{CS}}$ Negated | $t_{DAT}$ | — | 125 | ns |
| $\overline{\text{CS}}$ Pulse Width Negated | $t_{CSWH}$ | 90 | — | ns |

NOTES:
1. All voltage measurements are referenced to GND. For testing, all input signals except X1/CLK swing between 0.4 V and 2.4 V with a maximum transition time of 20 ns. For X1/CLK, this swing is between 0.4 V and 4.4 V. All time measurements are referenced at input and output voltages of 0.8 V and 2.0 V, as appropriate. Test conditions for noninterrupt outputs: $C_L = 150$ pF, $R_L = 750$ $\Omega$ to $V_{CC}$. Test conditions for interrupt outputs: $C_L = 50$ pF, $R_L = 27$ k$\Omega$ to $V_{CC}$.
2. This specification is made only to ensure $\overline{\text{DTACK}}$ is asserted with respect to the rising edge of X1/CLK as shown in Figure 4, not to guarantee operation of the part. If the setup time is violated, $\overline{\text{DTACK}}$ may be asserted as shown or may be asserted one clock cycle later.
3. The $t_{CSD}$ specification is made only to ensure that $\overline{\text{DTACK}}$ will be asserted. If $\overline{\text{CS}}$ is negated before $\overline{\text{DTACK}}$ is asserted, $\overline{\text{DTACK}}$ may not be asserted.

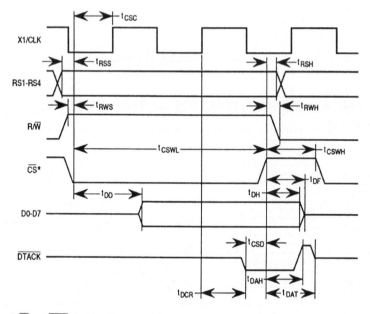

* $\overline{CS}$ and $\overline{IACK}$ should not be asserted simultaneously.

**Figure 4. Read Cycle Bus Timing**

## AC ELECTRICAL CHARACTERISTICS — WRITE CYCLE BUS TIMING
(see Figure 5)

| Characteristic | Symbol | Min | Max | Unit |
|---|---|---|---|---|
| $\overline{CS}$ Setup Time to X1/CLK High (see Note 2) | $t_{CSC}$ | 90 | — | ns |
| RS1–RS4 Setup Time to $\overline{CS}$ Asserted | $t_{RSS}$ | 10 | — | ns |
| R/$\overline{W}$ Setup Time to $\overline{CS}$ Asserted | $t_{RWS}$ | 0 | — | ns |
| $\overline{CS}$ Pulse Width Asserted (see Notes 3 and 4) | $t_{CSWL}$ | 205 | — | ns |
| Data Setup Time to X1/CLK High (see Note 4) | $t_{DS}$ | 100 | — | ns |
| Data Setup Time to $\overline{CS}$ Negated (see Note 4) | $t_{DSCS}$ | 100 | — | ns |
| $\overline{DTACK}$ Asserted from X1/CLK High | $t_{DCW}$ | — | 125 | ns |
| $\overline{CS}$ Negated from $\overline{DTACK}$ Asserted (see Note 3) | $t_{CSD}$ | 20 | — | ns |
| RS1–RS4 Hold Time from $\overline{CS}$ Negated | $t_{RSH}$ | 0 | — | ns |
| R/$\overline{W}$ Hold Time from $\overline{CS}$ Negated | $t_{RWH}$ | 0 | — | ns |
| Data Hold Time from $\overline{CS}$ Negated | $t_{DH}$ | 0 | — | ns |
| $\overline{DTACK}$ Negated from $\overline{CS}$ Negated | $t_{DAH}$ | — | 100 | ns |
| $\overline{DTACK}$ Hi-Z from $\overline{CS}$ Negated | $t_{DAT}$ | — | 125 | ns |
| $\overline{CS}$ Pulse Width Negated (see Note 5) | $t_{CSWH}$ | 90 | — | ns |

NOTES:
1. All voltage measurements are referenced to GND. For testing, all input signals except X1/CLK swing between 0.4 V and 2.4 V with a maximum transition time of 20 ns. For X1/CLK, this swing is between 0.4 V and 4.4 V. All time measurements are referenced at input and output voltages of 0.8 V and 2.0 V, as appropriate. Test conditions for noninterrupt outputs: $C_L = 150$ pF, $R_L = 750\ \Omega$ to $V_{CC}$. Test conditions for interrupt outputs: $C_L = 50$ pF, $R_L = 27$ k$\Omega$ to $V_{CC}$.
2. This specification is made only to ensure $\overline{DTACK}$ is asserted with respect to the rising edge of X1/CLK as shown in Figure 4, not to guarantee operation of the part. If the setup time is violated, $\overline{DTACK}$ may be asserted as shown or maybe asserted one clock cycle later.
3. The $t_{CSD}$ specification is made only to ensure that $\overline{DTACK}$ will be asserted. If $\overline{CS}$ is negated before $\overline{DTACK}$ is asserted, $\overline{DTACK}$ may not be asserted.
4. During write cycles, data is latched on either the asserting edge of $\overline{DTACK}$ or the negating edge of $\overline{CS}$, whichever occurs first. If $\overline{CS}$ is negated within one clock cycle after $\overline{CS}$ has been recognized (i.e., first rising edge of X1/CLK where $\overline{CS}$ is asserted), then $\overline{DTACK}$ may not be generated. In this case, data will be latched on the negating edge of $\overline{CS}$. Thus, $t_{DS}$ can be ignored, but $t_{DSCS}$ must be observed.
5. Consecutive write operations to the same command register (CRA or CRB) require at least three transitions of X1/CLK between write cycles. Typically, a processor is incapable of accessing the same command register a second time prior to three transitions on the X1/CLK pin.

7

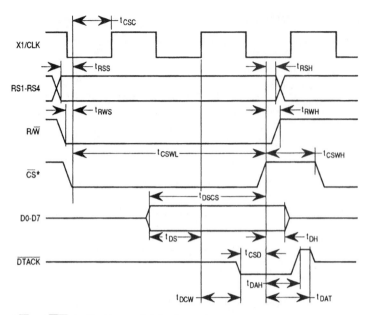

\* $\overline{CS}$ and $\overline{IACK}$ should not be asserted simultaneously.

**Figure 5. Write Cycle Bus Timing**

## AC ELECTRICAL CHARACTERISTICS — INTERRUPT CYCLE
### BUS TIMING\* (see Figure 6)

| Characteristic | Symbol | Min | Max | Unit |
|---|---|---|---|---|
| $\overline{IACK}$ Setup Time to X1/CLK High (see Note 2) | $t_{CSC}$ | 90 | — | ns |
| $\overline{IACK}$ Pulse Width Asserted (see Note 3) | $t_{IAWL}$ | 205 | — | ns |
| Data Valid from $\overline{IACK}$ Asserted | $t_{DD}$ | — | 175 | ns |
| $\overline{DTACK}$ Asserted from X1/CLK High | $t_{DCR}$ | — | 125 | ns |
| $\overline{IACK}$ Negated from $\overline{DTACK}$ Asserted (see Note 3) | $t_{CSD}$ | 0 | — | ns |
| Data Hold Time from $\overline{IACK}$ Negated | $t_{DH}$ | 0 | — | ns |
| Data Bus Floating from $\overline{IACK}$ Negated | $t_{DF}$ | — | 100 | ns |
| $\overline{DTACK}$ Negated from $\overline{IACK}$ Negated | $t_{DAH}$ | — | 100 | ns |
| $\overline{DTACK}$ Hi-Z from $\overline{IACK}$ Negated | $t_{DAT}$ | — | 125 | ns |

\*During interrupt acknowledge cycles, the status of R/$\overline{W}$ is ignored.

NOTES:
1. All voltage measurements are referenced to GND. For testing, all input signals except X1/CLK swing between 0.4 V and 2.4 V with a maximum transition time of 20 ns. For X1/CLK, this swing is between 0.4 V and 4.4 V. All time measurements are referenced at input and output voltages of 0.8 V and 2.0 V, as appropriate. Test conditions for noninterrupt outputs: $C_L = 150$ pF, $R_L = 750$ $\Omega$ to $V_{CC}$. Test conditions for interrupt outputs: $C_L = 50$ pF, $R_L = 27$ k$\Omega$ to $V_{CC}$.
2. This specification is made only to ensure $\overline{DTACK}$ is asserted with respect to the rising edge of X1/CLK as shown in Figure 4, not to guarantee operation of the part. If the setup time is violated, $\overline{DTACK}$ may be asserted as shown or may be asserted one clock cycle later.
3. The $t_{CSD}$ specification is made only to ensure that $\overline{DTACK}$ will be asserted. If $\overline{CS}$ is negated before $\overline{DTACK}$ is asserted, $\overline{DTACK}$ may not be asserted.

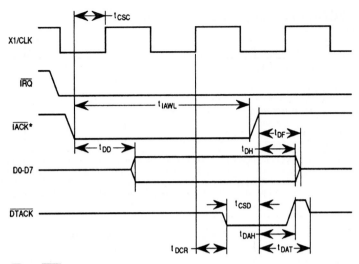

\* $\overline{CS}$ and $\overline{IACK}$ should not be asserted simultaneously.

**Figure 6. Interrupt Cycle Bus Timing**

## AC ELECTRICAL CHARACTERISTICS — PORT TIMING (see Figure 7)

| Characteristic | Symbol | Min | Max | Unit |
|---|---|---|---|---|
| Port Input Setup Time to $\overline{CS}$ Asserted | $t_{PS}$ | 0 | — | ns |
| Port Input Hold Time from $\overline{CS}$ Negated | $t_{PH}$ | 0 | — | ns |
| Port Output Valid from $\overline{CS}$ Negated | $t_{PD}$ | — | 400 | ns |

NOTE: All voltage measurements are referenced to GND. For testing, all signals except X1/CLK swing between 0.4 V and 2.4 V with a maximum transition time of 20 ns. For X1/CLK, this swing is between 0.4 V and 4.4 V. All time measurements are referenced at input and output voltages of 0.8 V and 2.0 V, as appropriate. Test conditions for noninterrupt outputs: $C_L = 150$ pF, $R_L = 750$ $\Omega$ to $V_{CC}$. Test conditions for interrupt outputs: $C_L = 50$ pF, $R_L = 27$ k$\Omega$ to $V_{CC}$.

7

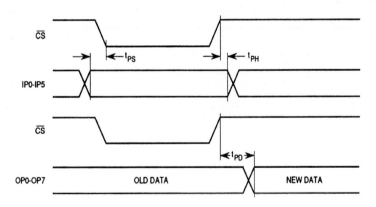

**Figure 7. Port Timing**

## AC ELECTRICAL CHARACTERISTICS—INTERRUPT RESET TIMING
(see Figure 8)

| Characteristic | Symbol | Min | Max | Unit |
|---|---|---|---|---|
| $\overline{\text{IRQ}}$ Negated or OP3–OP7 High from $\overline{\text{CS}}$ Negated When Used as Interrupts from: | $t_{IR}$ | | | ns |
|     Read RB (RxRDY/FFULL Interrupt) | | — | 300 | |
|     Write TB (TxRDY Interrupt) | | — | 300 | |
|     Reset Command (Delta Break Interrupt) | | — | 300 | |
|     Stop C/T Command (Counter Interrupt) | | — | 300 | |
|     Read IPCR (Input Port Change Interrupt) | | — | 300 | |
|     Write IMR (Clear of Interrupt Mask Bit) | | — | 300 | |

NOTE: All voltage measurements are referenced to GND. For testing, all input signals except X1/CLK swing between 0.4 V and 2.4 V with a maximum transition time of 20 ns. For X1/CLK, this swing is between 0.4 and 4.4 V. All time measurements are referenced at input and output voltages of 0.8 V and 2.0 V, as appropriate. Test conditions for noninterrupt outputs: $C_L = 150$ pF, $R_L = 750$ Ω to $V_{CC}$. Test conditions for interrupt outputs: $C_L = 50$ pF, $R_L = 27$ kΩ to $V_{CC}$.

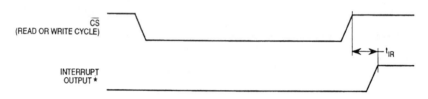

\* $\overline{\text{IRQ}}$ or OP3–OP7 when used as interrupt outputs.

**Figure 8. Interrupt Reset Timing**

## AC ELECTRICAL CHARACTERISTICS — CLOCK TIMING (see Figure 9)

| Characteristic | Symbol | Min | Max | Unit |
|---|---|---|---|---|
| X1/CLK High or Low Time | $t_{CLK}$ | 100 | — | ns |
| Counter/Timer Clock High or Low Time | $t_{CTC}$ | 100 | — | ns |
| Receive Clock (RxC) High or Low Time | $t_{Rx}$ | 220 | — | ns |
| Transmit Clock (TxC) High or Low Time | $t_{Tx}$ | 220 | — | ns |
| Clock Rise Time | $t_r$ | — | 20 | ns |
| Clock Fall Time | $t_f$ | — | 20 | ns |

NOTE: All voltage measurements are referenced to GND. For testing, all signals except X1/CLK swing between 0.4 V and 2.4 V with a maximum transition time of 20 ns. For X1/CLK, this swing is between 0.4 V and 4.4 V. All time measurements are referenced at input and output voltages of 0.8 V and 2.0 V, as appropriate. Test conditions for noninterrupt outputs: $C_L = 150$ pF, $R_L = 750$ Ω to $V_{CC}$. Test conditions for interrupt outputs: $C_L = 50$ pF, $R_L = 27$ kΩ to $V_{CC}$.

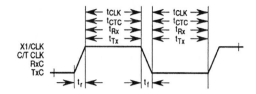

**Figure 9. Clock Timing**

## AC ELECTRICAL CHARACTERISTICS — TRANSMITTER TIMING
(see Figure 10)

| Characteristic | Symbol | Min | Max | Unit |
|---|---|---|---|---|
| TxD Output Valid from TxC Low | $t_{TxD}$ | — | 350 | ns |
| TxC Low to TxD Output Valid | $t_{TCS}$ | — | 150 | ns |

NOTE: All voltage measurements are referenced to GND. For testing, all signals except X1/CLK swing between 0.4 V and 2.4 V with a maximum transition time of 20 ns. For X1/CLK, this swing is between 0.4 V and 4.4 V. All time measurements are referenced at input and output voltages of 0.8 V and 2.0 V, as appropriate. Test conditions for noninterrupt outputs: $C_L = 150$ pF, $R_L = 750$ $\Omega$ to $V_{CC}$. Test conditions for interrupt outputs: $C_L = 50$ pF, $R_L = 27$ k$\Omega$ to $V_{CC}$.

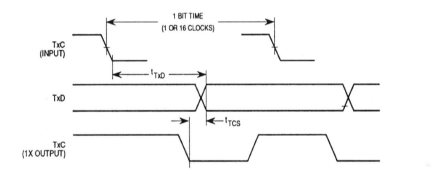

**Figure 10. Transmitter Timing**

7

## AC ELECTRICAL CHARACTERISTICS — RECEIVER TIMING (see Figure 11)

| Characteristics | Symbol | Min | Max | Unit |
|---|---|---|---|---|
| RxD Data Setup Time to RxC High | $t_{RxS}$ | 240 | — | ns |
| RxD Data Hold Time from RxC High | $t_{RxH}$ | 200 | — | ns |

NOTE: All voltage measurements are referenced to GND. For testing, all signals except X1/CLK swing between 0.4 V and 2.4 V with a maximum transition time of 20 ns. For X1/CLK, this swing is between 0.4 V and 4.4 V. All time measurements are referenced at input and output voltages of 0.8 V and 2.0 V, as appropriate. Test conditions for noninterrupt outputs: $C_L = 150$ pF, $R_L = 750 \ \Omega$ to $V_{CC}$. Test conditions for interrupt outputs: $C_L = 50$ pF, $R_L = 27$ k$\Omega$ to $V_{CC}$.

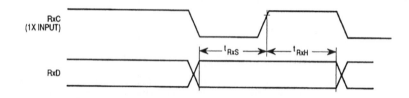

**Figure 11. Receiver Timing**

7

# PIN ASSIGNMENTS

## 40-LEAD DUAL-IN-LINE PACKAGE

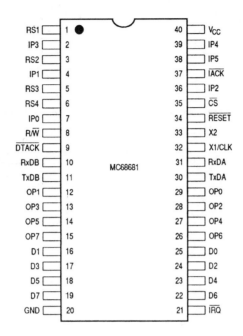

## 44-LEAD PLASTIC LEADED CHIP CARRIER

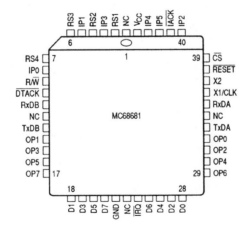

7

# Appendix I

# 6821 Data Sheet*

 MOTOROLA

## MC6821

## MOS
### (N-CHANNEL, SILICON-GATE, DEPLETION LOAD)

## PERIPHERAL INTERFACE ADAPTER

---

## PERIPHERAL INTERFACE ADAPTER (PIA)

The MC6821 Peripheral Interface Adapter provides the universal means of interfacing peripheral equipment to the M6800 family of microprocessors. This device is capable of interfacing the MPU to peripherals through two 8-bit bidirectional peripheral data buses and four control lines. No external logic is required for interfacing to most peripheral devices.

The functional configuration of the PIA is programmed by the MPU during system initialization. Each of the peripheral data lines can be programmed to act as an input or output, and each of the four control/interrupt lines may be programmed for one of several control modes. This allows a high degree of flexibility in the overall operation of the interface.

- 8-Bit Bidirectional Data Bus for Communication with the MPU
- Two Bidirectional 8-Bit Buses for Interface to Peripherals
- Two Programmable Control Registers
- Two Programmable Data Direction Registers
- Four Individually-Controlled Interrupt Input Lines; Two Usable as Peripheral Control Outputs
- Handshake Control Logic for Input and Output Peripheral Operation
- High-Impedance Three-State and Direct Transistor Drive Peripheral Lines
- Program Controlled Interrupt and Interrupt Disable Capability
- CMOS Drive Capability on Side A Peripheral Lines
- Two TTL Drive Capability on All A and B Side Buffers
- TTL-Compatible
- Static Operation

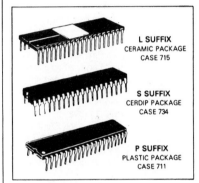

**L SUFFIX**
CERAMIC PACKAGE
CASE 715

**S SUFFIX**
CERDIP PACKAGE
CASE 734

**P SUFFIX**
PLASTIC PACKAGE
CASE 711

3

---

### ORDERING INFORMATION

| Package Type | Frequency (MHz) | Temperature | Order Number |
|---|---|---|---|
| Ceramic L Suffix | 1.0 | 0°C to 70°C | MC6821L |
| | 1.0 | −40°C to 85°C | MC6821CL |
| | 1.5 | 0°C to 70°C | MC68A21L |
| | 1.5 | −40°C to 85°C | MC68A21CL |
| | 2.0 | 0°C to 70°C | MC68B21L |
| Cerdip S Suffix | 1.0 | 0°C to 70°C | MC6821S |
| | 1.0 | −40°C to 85°C | MC6821CS |
| | 1.5 | 0°C to 70°C | MC68A21S |
| | 1.5 | −40°C to 85°C | MC68A21CS |
| | 2.0 | 0°C to 70°C | MC68B21S |
| Plastic P Suffix | 1.0 | 0°C to 70°C | MC6821P |
| | 1.0 | −40°C to 85°C | MC6821CP |
| | 1.5 | 0°C to 70°C | MC68A21P |
| | 1.5 | −40°C to 85°C | MC68A21CP |
| | 2.0 | 0°C to 70°C | MC68B21P |

### PIN ASSIGNMENT

| | | | |
|---|---|---|---|
| $V_{SS}$ | 1 | 40 | CA1 |
| PA0 | 2 | 39 | CA2 |
| PA1 | 3 | 38 | $\overline{IRQA}$ |
| PA2 | 4 | 37 | $\overline{IRQB}$ |
| PA3 | 5 | 36 | RS0 |
| PA4 | 6 | 35 | RS1 |
| PA5 | 7 | 34 | $\overline{RESET}$ |
| PA6 | 8 | 33 | D0 |
| PA7 | 9 | 32 | D1 |
| PB0 | 10 | 31 | D2 |
| PB1 | 11 | 30 | D3 |
| PB2 | 12 | 29 | D4 |
| PB3 | 13 | 28 | D5 |
| PB4 | 14 | 27 | D6 |
| PB5 | 15 | 26 | D7 |
| PB6 | 16 | 25 | E |
| PB7 | 17 | 24 | CS1 |
| CB1 | 18 | 23 | $\overline{CS2}$ |
| CB2 | 19 | 22 | CS0 |
| $V_{CC}$ | 20 | 21 | $R/\overline{W}$ |

---

*Reprinted with permission of Motorola.

## MC6821

**MAXIMUM RATINGS**

| Characteristics | Symbol | Value | Unit |
|---|---|---|---|
| Supply Voltage | $V_{CC}$ | −0.3 to +7.0 | V |
| Input Voltage | $V_{in}$ | −0.3 to +7.0 | V |
| Operating Temperature Range<br>MC6821, MC68A21, MC68B21<br>MC6821C, MC68A21C | $T_A$ | $T_L$ to $T_H$<br>0 to 70<br>−40 to +85 | °C |
| Storage Temperature Range | $T_{stg}$ | −55 to +150 | °C |

**THERMAL CHARACTERISTICS**

| Characteristic | Symbol | Value | Unit |
|---|---|---|---|
| Thermal Resistance<br>Ceramic<br>Plastic<br>Cerdip | $\theta_{JA}$ | 50<br>100<br>60 | °C/W |

This device contains circuitry to protect the inputs against damage due to high static voltages or electric fields; however, it is advised that normal precautions be taken to avoid applications of any voltage higher than maximum rated voltages to this high-impedance circuit. For proper operation it is recommended that $V_{in}$ and $V_{out}$ be constrained to the range GND $\leq (V_{in}$ or $V_{out}) \leq V_{CC}$.

Unused inputs must always be tied to an appropriate logic voltage level (e.g., either GND or $V_{CC}$).

**3**

### POWER CONSIDERATIONS

The average chip-junction temperature, $T_J$, in °C can be obtained from:

$$T_J = T_A + (P_D \bullet \theta_{JA}) \tag{1}$$

Where:

$T_A \equiv$ Ambient Temperature, °C

$\theta_{JA} \equiv$ Package Thermal Resistance, Junction-to-Ambient, °C/W

$P_D \equiv P_{INT} + P_{PORT}$

$P_{INT} \equiv I_{CC} \times V_{CC}$, Watts — Chip Internal Power

$P_{PORT} \equiv$ Port Power Dissipation, Watts — User Determined

For most applications $P_{PORT} \blacktriangleleft P_{INT}$ and can be neglected. $P_{PORT}$ may become significant if the device is configured to drive Darlington bases or sink LED loads.

An approximate relationship between $P_D$ and $T_J$ (if $P_{PORT}$ is neglected) is:

$$P_D = K \div (T_J + 273°C) \tag{2}$$

Solving equations 1 and 2 for K gives:

$$K = P_D \bullet (T_A + 273°C) + \theta_{JA} \bullet P_D^2 \tag{3}$$

Where K is a constant pertaining to the particular part. K can be determined from equation 3 by measuring $P_D$ (at equilibrium) for a known $T_A$. Using this value of K the values of $P_D$ and $T_J$ can be obtained by solving equations (1) and (2) iteratively for any value of $T_A$.

**DC ELECTRICAL CHARACTERISTICS** ($V_{CC} = 5.0$ Vdc $\pm 5\%$, $V_{SS} = 0$, $T_A = T_L$ to $T_H$ unless otherwise noted).

| Characteristic | Symbol | Min | Typ | Max | Unit |
|---|---|---|---|---|---|
| **BUS CONTROL INPUTS (R/$\overline{W}$, Enable, $\overline{RESET}$, RS0, RS1, CS0, CS1, CS2)** | | | | | |
| Input High Voltage | $V_{IH}$ | $V_{SS} + 2.0$ | — | $V_{CC}$ | V |
| Input Low Voltage | $V_{IL}$ | $V_{SS} - 0.3$ | — | $V_{SS} + 0.8$ | V |
| Input Leakage Current ($V_{in} = 0$ to 5.25 V) | $I_{in}$ | — | 1.0 | 2.5 | μA |
| Capacitance ($V_{in} = 0$, $T_A = 25°C$, f = 1.0 MHz) | $C_{in}$ | — | — | 7.5 | pF |
| **INTERRUPT OUTPUTS ($\overline{IRQA}$, $\overline{IRQB}$)** | | | | | |
| Output Low Voltage ($I_{Load} = 1.6$ mA) | $V_{OL}$ | — | — | $V_{SS} + 0.4$ | V |
| Hi-Z Output Leakage Current | $I_{OZ}$ | — | 1.0 | 10 | μA |
| Capacitance ($V_{in} = 0$, $T_A = 25°C$, f = 1.0 MHz) | $C_{out}$ | — | — | 5.0 | pF |
| **DATA BUS (D0-D7)** | | | | | |
| Input High Voltage | $V_{IH}$ | $V_{SS} + 2.0$ | — | $V_{CC}$ | V |
| Input Low Voltage | $V_{IL}$ | $V_{SS} - 0.3$ | — | $V_{SS} + 0.8$ | V |
| Hi-Z Input Leakage Current ($V_{in} = 0.4$ to 2.4 V) | $I_{IZ}$ | — | 2.0 | 10 | μA |
| Output High Voltage ($I_{Load} = -205$ μA) | $V_{OH}$ | $V_{SS} + 2.4$ | — | — | V |
| Output Low Voltage ($I_{Load} = 1.6$ mA) | $V_{OL}$ | — | — | $V_{SS} + 0.4$ | V |
| Capacitance ($V_{in} = 0$, $T_A = 25°C$, f = 1.0 MHz) | $C_{in}$ | — | — | 12.5 | pF |

## MC6821

### DC ELECTRICAL CHARACTERISTICS (Continued)

| Characteristic | | Symbol | Min | Typ | Max | Unit |
|---|---|---|---|---|---|---|
| **PERIPHERAL BUS (PA0-PA7, PB0-PB7, CA1, CA2, CB1, CB2)** | | | | | | |
| Input Leakage Current (V$_{in}$ = 0 to 5.25 V) | R/$\overline{W}$, $\overline{RESET}$, RS0, RS1, CS0, CS1, $\overline{CS2}$, CA1, CB1, Enable | I$_{in}$ | – | 1.0 | 2.5 | μA |
| Hi-Z Input Leakage Current (V$_{in}$ = 0.4 to 2.4 V) | PB0-PB7, CB2 | I$_{IZ}$ | – | 2.0 | 10 | μA |
| Input High Current (V$_{IH}$ = 2.4 V) | PA0-PA7, CA2 | I$_{IH}$ | – 200 | – 400 | – | μA |
| Darlington Drive Current (V$_O$ = 1.5 V) | PB0-PB7, CB2 | I$_{OH}$ | – 1.0 | – | – 10 | mA |
| Input Low Current (V$_{IL}$ = 0.4 V) | PA0-PA7, CA2 | I$_{IL}$ | – | – 1.3 | – 2.4 | mA |
| Output High Voltage (I$_{Load}$ = – 200 μA) (I$_{Load}$ = – 10 μA) | PA0-PA7, PB0-PB7, CA2, CB2 PA0-PA7, CA2 | V$_{OH}$ | V$_{SS}$ + 2.4 V$_{CC}$ – 1.0 | – – | – – | V |
| Output Low Voltage (I$_{Load}$ = 3.2 mA) | | V$_{OL}$ | – | – | V$_{SS}$ + 0.4 | V |
| Capacitance (V$_{in}$ = 0, T$_A$ = 25°C, f = 1.0 MHz) | | C$_{in}$ | – | – | 10 | pF |
| **POWER REQUIREMENTS** | | | | | | |
| Internal Power Dissipation (Measured at T$_L$ = 0°C) | | P$_{INT}$ | – | – | 550 | mW |

**3**

### BUS TIMING CHARACTERISTICS (See Notes 1 and 2)

| Ident. Number | Characteristic | Symbol | MC6821 Min | MC6821 Max | MC68A21 Min | MC68A21 Max | MC68B21 Min | MC68B21 Max | Unit |
|---|---|---|---|---|---|---|---|---|---|
| 1 | Cycle Time | t$_{cyc}$ | 1.0 | 10 | 0.67 | 10 | 0.5 | 10 | μs |
| 2 | Pulse Width, E Low | PW$_{EL}$ | 430 | – | 280 | – | 210 | – | ns |
| 3 | Pulse Width, E High | PW$_{EH}$ | 450 | – | 280 | – | 220 | – | ns |
| 4 | Clock Rise and Fall Time | t$_r$, t$_f$ | – | 25 | – | 25 | – | 20 | ns |
| 9 | Address Hold Time | t$_{AH}$ | 10 | – | 10 | – | 10 | – | ns |
| 13 | Address Setup Time Before E | t$_{AS}$ | 80 | – | 60 | – | 40 | – | ns |
| 14 | Chip Select Setup Time Before E | t$_{CS}$ | 80 | – | 60 | – | 40 | – | ns |
| 15 | Chip Select Hold Time | t$_{CH}$ | 10 | – | 10 | – | 10 | – | ns |
| 18 | Read Data Hold Time | t$_{DHR}$ | 20 | 50* | 20 | 50* | 20 | 50* | ns |
| 21 | Write Data Hold Time | t$_{DHW}$ | 10 | – | 10 | – | 10 | – | ns |
| 30 | Output Data Delay Time | t$_{DDR}$ | – | 290 | – | 180 | – | 150 | ns |
| 31 | Input Data Setup Time | t$_{DSW}$ | 165 | – | 80 | – | 60 | – | ns |

*The data bus output buffers are no longer sourcing or sinking current by t$_{DHR}$max (High Impedance).

**FIGURE 1 — BUS TIMING**

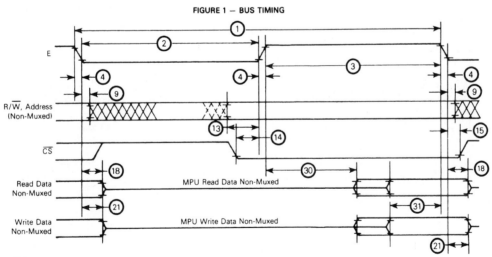

Notes:
1. Voltage levels shown are V$_L$ ≤ 0.4 V, V$_H$ ≥ 2.4 V, unless otherwise specified.
2. Measurement points shown are 0.8 V and 2.0 V, unless otherwise specified.

## MC6821

**PERIPHERAL TIMING CHARACTERISTICS** ($V_{CC}$ = 5.0 V ± 5%, $V_{SS}$ = 0 V, $T_A = T_L$ to $T_H$ unless otherwise specified)

| Characteristic | Symbol | MC6821 Min | MC6821 Max | MC68A21 Min | MC68A21 Max | MC68B21 Min | MC68B21 Max | Unit | Reference Fig. No. |
|---|---|---|---|---|---|---|---|---|---|
| Data Setup Time | $t_{PDS}$ | 200 | — | 135 | — | 100 | — | ns | 6 |
| Data Hold Time | $t_{PDH}$ | 0 | — | 0 | — | 0 | — | ns | 6 |
| Delay Time, Enable Negative Transition to CA2 Negative Transition | $t_{CA2}$ | — | 1.0 | — | 0.670 | — | 0.500 | µs | 3, 7, 8 |
| Delay Time, Enable Negative Transition to CA2 Positive Transition | $T_{RS1}$ | — | 1.0 | — | 0.670 | — | 0.500 | µs | 3, 7 |
| Rise and Fall Times for CA1 and CA2 Input Signals | $t_r, t_f$ | — | 1.0 | — | 1.0 | — | 1.0 | µs | 8 |
| Delay Time from CA1 Active Transition to CA2 Positive Transition | $t_{RS2}$ | — | 2.0 | — | 1.35 | — | 1.0 | µs | 3, 8 |
| Delay Time, Enable Negative Transition to Data Valid | $t_{PDW}$ | — | 1.0 | — | 0.670 | — | 0.5 | µs | 3, 9, 10 |
| Delay Time, Enable Negative Transition to CMOS Data Valid PA0-PA7, CA2 | $t_{CMOS}$ | — | 2.0 | — | 1.35 | — | 1.0 | µs | 4, 9 |
| Delay Time, Enable Positive Transition to CB2 Negative Transition | $t_{CB2}$ | — | 1.0 | — | 0.670 | — | 0.5 | µs | 3, 11, 12 |
| Delay Time, Data Valid to CB2 Negative Transition | $t_{DC}$ | 20 | — | 20 | — | 20 | — | ns | 3, 10 |
| Delay Time, Enable Positive Transition to CB2 Positive Transition | $t_{RS1}$ | — | 1.0 | — | 0.670 | — | 0.5 | µs | 3, 11 |
| Control Output Pulse Width, CA2/CB2 | $PW_{CT}$ | 500 | — | 375 | — | 250 | — | ns | 3, 11 |
| Rise and Fall Time for CB1 and CB2 Input Signals | $t_r, t_f$ | — | 1.0 | — | 1.0 | — | 1.0 | µ | 12 |
| Delay Time, CB1 Active Transition to CB2 Positive Transition | $t_{RS2}$ | — | 2.0 | — | 1.35 | — | 1.0 | µs | 3, 12 |
| Interrupt Release Time, $\overline{IRQA}$ and $\overline{IRQB}$ | $t_{IR}$ | — | 1.60 | — | 1.10 | — | 0.85 | µs | 5, 14 |
| Interrupt Response Time | $t_{RS3}$ | — | 1.0 | — | 1.0 | — | 1.0 | µs | 5, 13 |
| Interrupt Input Pulse Time | $PW_I$ | 500 | — | 500 | — | 500 | — | ns | 13 |
| $\overline{RESET}$ Low Time* | $t_{RL}$ | 1.0 | — | 0.66 | — | 0.5 | — | µs | 15 |

*The $\overline{RESET}$ line must be high a minimum of 1.0 µs before addressing the PIA.

FIGURE 2 — BUS TIMING TEST LOADS

(D0-D7)    5.0 V

$R_L$ = 2.4 kΩ

Test Point

MMD6150 or Equiv.

C 130 pF    R 11.7 kΩ

MMD7000 or Equiv.

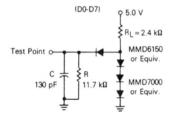

FIGURE 3 — TTL EQUIVALENT TEST LOAD

(PA0–PA7, PB0–PB7, CA2, CB2)

5.0 V

$R_L$ = 1.25 kΩ

Test Point    $I_I$

$V_I$

MMD6150 or Equiv.

C    R

MMD7000 or Equiv.

C = 30 pF, R = 12 k

FIGURE 4 — CMOS EQUIVALENT TEST LOAD

(PA0-PA7, CA2)

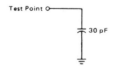

Test Point

30 pF

FIGURE 5 — NMOS EQUIVALENT TEST LOAD

($\overline{IRQ}$ Only)
5.0 V

1.5 kΩ

Test Point

100 pF

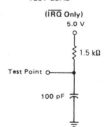

## MC6821

FIGURE 6 — PERIPHERAL DATA SETUP AND HOLD TIMES
(Read Mode)

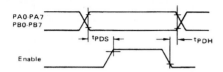

FIGURE 7 — CA2 DELAY TIME
(Read Mode; CRA-5 = CRA3 = 1, CRA-4 = 0)

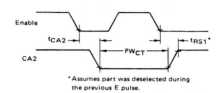

*Assumes part was deselected during
the previous E pulse.

FIGURE 8 — CA2 DELAY TIME
(Read Mode; CRA-5 = 1, CRA-3 = CRA-4 = 0)

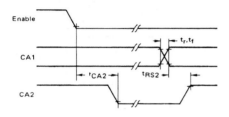

FIGURE 9 — PERIPHERAL CMOS DATA DELAY TIMES
(Write Mode; CRA-5 = CRA-3 = 1, CRA-4 = 0)

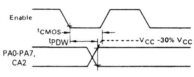

FIGURE 10 — PERIPHERAL DATA AND CB2 DELAY TIMES
(Write Mode; CRB-5 = CRB-3 = 1, CRB-4 = 0)

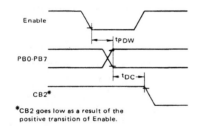

*CB2 goes low as a result of the
positive transition of Enable.

FIGURE 11 — CB2 DELAY TIME
(Write Mode; CRB-5 = CRB-3 = 1, CRB-4 = 0)

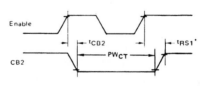

*Assumes part was deselected during the
previous E pulse.

FIGURE 12 — CB2 DELAY TIME
(Write Mode; CRB-5 = 1, CRB-3 = CRB-4 = 0)

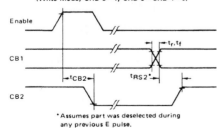

*Assumes part was deselected during
any previous E pulse.

FIGURE 13 — INTERRUPT PULSE WIDTH AND $\overline{IRQ}$ RESPONSE

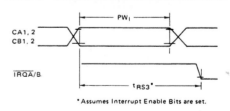

*Assumes Interrupt Enable Bits are set.

Note: Timing measurements are referenced to and from a low voltage of 0.8 volts and a high voltage of 2.0 volts, unless otherwise noted.

## MC6821

FIGURE 14 — $\overline{\text{IRQ}}$ RELEASE TIME

FIGURE 15 — $\overline{\text{RESET}}$ LOW TIME

*The $\overline{\text{RESET}}$ line must be a $V_{IH}$ for a minimum of 1.0 μs before addressing the PIA.

Note: Timing measurements are referenced to and from a low voltage of 0.8 volts and a high voltage of 2.0 volts, unless otherwise n

FIGURE 16 — EXPANDED BLOCK DIAGRAM

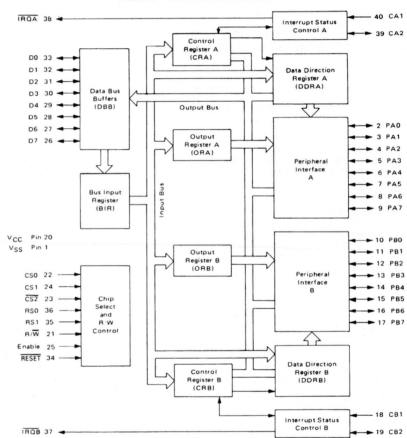

**3**

# MC6821

## PIA INTERFACE SIGNALS FOR MPU

The PIA interfaces to the M6800 bus with an 8-bit bidirectional data bus, three chip select lines, two register select lines, two interrupt request lines, a read/write line, an enable line and a reset line. To ensure proper operation with the MC6800, MC6802, or MC6808 microprocessors, VMA should be used as an active part of the address decoding.

**Bidirectional Data (D0-D7)** — The bidirectional data lines (D0-D7) allow the transfer of data between the MPU and the PIA. The data bus output drivers are three-state devices that remain in the high-impedance (off) state except when the MPU performs a PIA read operation. The read/write line is in the read (high) state when the PIA is selected for a read operation.

**Enable (E)** — The enable pulse, E, is the only timing signal that is supplied to the PIA. Timing of all other signals is referenced to the leading and trailing edges of the E pulse.

**Read/Write (R/$\overline{W}$)** — This signal is generated by the MPU to control the direction of data transfers on the data bus. A low state on the PIA read/write line enables the input buffers and data is transferred from the MPU to the PIA on the E signal if the device has been selected. A high on the read/write line sets up the PIA for a transfer of data to the bus. The PIA output buffers are enabled when the proper address and the enable pulse E are present.

**$\overline{RESET}$** — The active low $\overline{RESET}$ line is used to reset all register bits in the PIA to a logical zero (low). This line can be used as a power-on reset and as a master reset during system operation.

**Chip Selects (CS0, CS1, and $\overline{CS2}$)** — These three input signals are used to select the PIA. CS0 and CS1 must be high and $\overline{CS2}$ must be low for selection of the device. Data transfers are then performed under the control of the enable and read/write signals. The chip select lines must be stable for the duration of the E pulse. The device is deselected when any of the chip selects are in the inactive state.

**Register Selects (RS0 and RS1)** — The two register select lines are used to select the various registers inside the PIA. These two lines are used in conjunction with internal Control Registers to select a particular register that is to be written or read.

The register and chip select lines should be stable for the duration of the E pulse while in the read or write cycle.

**Interrupt Request ($\overline{IRQA}$ and $\overline{IRQB}$)** — The active low Interrupt Request lines ($\overline{IRQA}$ and $\overline{IRQB}$) act to interrupt the MPU either directly or through interrupt priority circuitry. These lines are "open drain" (no load device on the chip). This permits all interrupt request lines to be tied together in a wire-OR configuration.

Each Interrupt Request line has two internal interrupt flag bits that can cause the Interrupt Request line to go low. Each flag bit is associated with a particular peripheral interrupt line. Also, four interrupt enable bits are provided in the PIA which may be used to inhibit a particular interrupt from a peripheral device.

Servicing an interrupt by the MPU may be accomplished by a software routine that, on a prioritized basis, sequentially reads and tests the two control registers in each PIA for interrupt flag bits that are set.

The interrupt flags are cleared (zeroed) as a result of an MPU Read Peripheral Data Operation of the corresponding data register. After being cleared, the interrupt flag bit cannot be enabled to be set until the PIA is deselected during an E pulse. The E pulse is used to condition the interrupt control lines (CA1, CA2, CB1, CB2). When these lines are used as interrupt inputs, at least one E pulse must occur from the inactive edge to the active edge of the interrupt input signal to condition the edge sense network. If the interrupt flag has been enabled and the edge sense circuit has been properly conditioned, the interrupt flag will be set on the next active transition of the interrupt input pin.

## PIA PERIPHERAL INTERFACE LINES

The PIA provides two 8-bit bidirectional data buses and four interrupt/control lines for interfacing to peripheral devices.

**Section A Peripheral Data (PA0-PA7)** — Each of the peripheral data lines can be programmed to act as an input or output. This is accomplished by setting a "1" in the corresponding Data Direction Register bit for those lines which are to be outputs. A "0" in a bit of the Data Direction Register causes the corresponding peripheral data line to act as an input. During an MPU Read Peripheral Data Operation, the data on peripheral lines programmed to act as inputs appears directly on the corresponding MPU Data Bus lines. In the input mode, the internal pullup resistor on these lines represents a maximum of 1.5 standard TTL loads.

The data in Output Register A will appear on the data lines that are programmed to be outputs. A logical "1" written into the register will cause a "high" on the corresponding data line while a "0" results in a "low." Data in Output Register A may be read by an MPU "Read Peripheral Data A" operation when the corresponding lines are programmed as outputs. This data will be read properly if the voltage on the peripheral data lines is greater than 2.0 volts for a logic "1" output and less than 0.8 volt for a logic "0" output. Loading the output lines such that the voltage on these lines does not reach full voltage causes the data transferred into the MPU on a Read operation to differ from that contained in the respective bit of Output Register A.

**Section B Peripheral Data (PB0-PB7)** — The peripheral data lines in the B Section of the PIA can be programmed to act as either inputs or outputs in a similar manner to PA0-PA7. They have three-state capability, allowing them to enter a high-impedance state when the peripheral data line is used as an input. In addition, data on the peripheral data lines

## MC6821

PB0-PB7 will be read properly from those lines programmed as outputs even if the voltages are below 2.0 volts for a "high" or above 0.8 V for a "low". As outputs, these lines are compatible with standard TTL and may also be used as a source of at least 1 milliampere at 1.5 volts to directly drive the base of a transistor switch.

**Interrupt Input (CA1 and CB1)** — Peripheral input lines CA1 and CB1 are input only lines that set the interrupt flags of the control registers. The active transition for these signals is also programmed by the two control registers.

**Peripheral Control (CA2)** — The peripheral control line CA2 can be programmed to act as an interrupt input or as a peripheral control output. As an output, this line is compatible with standard TTL; as an input the internal pullup resistor on this line represents 1.5 standard TTL loads. The function of this signal line is programmed with Control Register A.

**Peripheral Control (CB2)** — Peripheral Control line CB2 may also be programmed to act as an interrupt input or peripheral control output. As an input, this line has high input impedance and is compatible with standard TTL. As an output it is compatible with standard TTL and may also be used as a source of up to 1 milliampere at 1.5 volts to directly drive the base of a transistor switch. This line is programmed by Control Register B.

## INTERNAL CONTROLS

### INITIALIZATION

A RESET has the effect of zeroing all PIA registers. This will set PA0-PA7, PB0-PB7, CA2 and CB2 as inputs, and all interrupts disabled. The PIA must be configured during the restart program which follows the reset.

There are six locations within the PIA accessible to the MPU data bus: two Peripheral Registers, two Data Direction Registers, and two Control Registers. Selection of these locations is controlled by the RS0 and RS1 inputs together with bit 2 in the Control Register, as shown in Table 1.

Details of possible configurations of the Data Direction and Control Register are as follows:

**TABLE 1 — INTERNAL ADDRESSING**

| RS1 | RS0 | Control Register Bit CRA-2 | Control Register Bit CRB-2 | Location Selected |
|-----|-----|------|------|------------------|
| 0 | 0 | 1 | X | Peripheral Register A |
| 0 | 0 | 0 | X | Data Direction Register A |
| 0 | 1 | X | X | Control Register A |
| 1 | 0 | X | 1 | Peripheral Register B |
| 1 | 0 | X | 0 | Data Direction Register B |
| 1 | 1 | X | X | Control Register B |

X = Don't Care

### PORT A-B HARDWARE CHARACTERISTICS

As shown in Figure 17, the MC6821 has a pair of I/O ports whose characteristics differ greatly. The A side is designed to drive CMOS logic to normal 30% to 70% levels, and incorporates an internal pullup device that remains connected even in the input mode. Because of this, the A side requires more drive current in the input mode than Port B. In contrast, the B side uses a normal three-state NMOS buffer which cannot pullup to CMOS levels without external resistors. The B side can drive extra loads such as Darlingtons without problem. When the PIA comes out of reset, the A port represents inputs with pullup resistors, whereas the B side (input mode also) will float high or low, depending upon the load connected to it.

Notice the differences between a Port A and Port B read operation when in the output mode. When reading Port A, the actual pin is read, whereas the B side read comes from an output latch, ahead of the actual pin.

### CONTROL REGISTERS (CRA and CRB)

The two Control Registers (CRA and CRB) allow the MPU to control the operation of the four peripheral control lines CA1, CA2, CB1, and CB2. In addition they allow the MPU to enable the interrupt lines and monitor the status of the interrupt flags. Bits 0 through 5 of the two registers may be written or read by the MPU when the proper chip select and register select signals are applied. Bits 6 and 7 of the two registers are read only and are modified by external interrupts occurring on control lines CA1, CA2, CB1, or CB2. The format of the control words is shown in Figure 18.

### DATA DIRECTION ACCESS CONTROL BIT (CRA-2 and CRB-2)

Bit 2, in each Control Register (CRA and CRB), determines selection of either a Peripheral Output Register or the corresponding Data Direction E Register when the proper register select signals are applied to RS0 and RS1. A "1" in bit 2 allows access of the Peripheral Interface Register, while a "0" causes the Data Direction Register to be addressed.

**Interrupt Flags (CRA-6, CRA-7, CRB-6, and CRB-7)** — The four interrupt flag bits are set by active transitions of signals on the four Interrupt and Peripheral Control lines when those lines are programmed to be inputs. These bits cannot be set directly from the MPU Data Bus and are reset indirectly by a Read Peripheral Data Operation on the appropriate section.

**Control of CA2 and CB2 Peripheral Control Lines (CRA-3, CRA-4, CRA-5, CRB-3, CRB-4, and CRB-5)** — Bits 3, 4, and 5 of the two control registers are used to control the CA2 and CB2 Peripheral Control lines. These bits determine if the control lines will be an interrupt input or an output control signal. If bit CRA-5 (CRB-5) is low, CA2 (CB2) is an interrupt input line similar to CA1 (CB1). When CRA-5 (CRB-5) is high, CA2 (CB2) becomes an output signal that may be used to control peripheral data transfers. When in the output mode, CA2 and CB2 have slightly different loading characteristics.

# MC6821

**Control of CA1 and CB1 Interrupt Input Lines (CRA-0, CRB-0, CRA-1, and CRB-1)** — The two lowest-order bits of the control registers are used to control the interrupt input lines CA1 and CB1. Bits CRA-0 and CRB-0 are used to enable the MPU interrupt signals $\overline{IRQA}$ and $\overline{IRQB}$, respectively. Bits CRA-1 and CRB-1 determine the active transition of the interrupt input signals CA1 and CB1.

FIGURE 17 — PORT A AND PORT B EQUIVALENT CIRCUITS

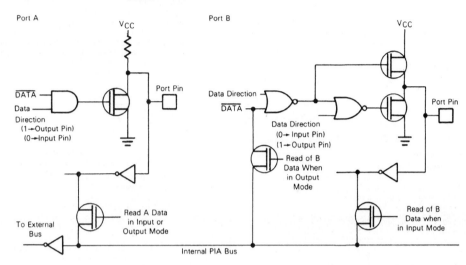

ORDERING INFORMATION

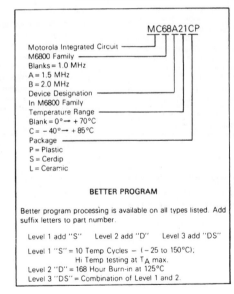

MC68A21CP

Motorola Integrated Circuit ——
M6800 Family ——
Blanks = 1.0 MHz
A = 1.5 MHz
B = 2.0 MHz
Device Designation ——
In M6800 Family
Temperature Range ——
Blank = 0° → +70°C
C = −40° → +85°C
Package ——
P = Plastic
S = Cerdip
L = Ceramic

### BETTER PROGRAM

Better program processing is available on all types listed. Add suffix letters to part number.

Level 1 add "S"     Level 2 add "D"     Level 3 add "DS"

Level 1 "S" = 10 Temp Cycles − (−25 to 150°C);
            Hi Temp testing at $T_A$ max.
Level 2 "D" = 168 Hour Burn-in at 125°C
Level 3 "DS" = Combination of Level 1 and 2.

## MC6821

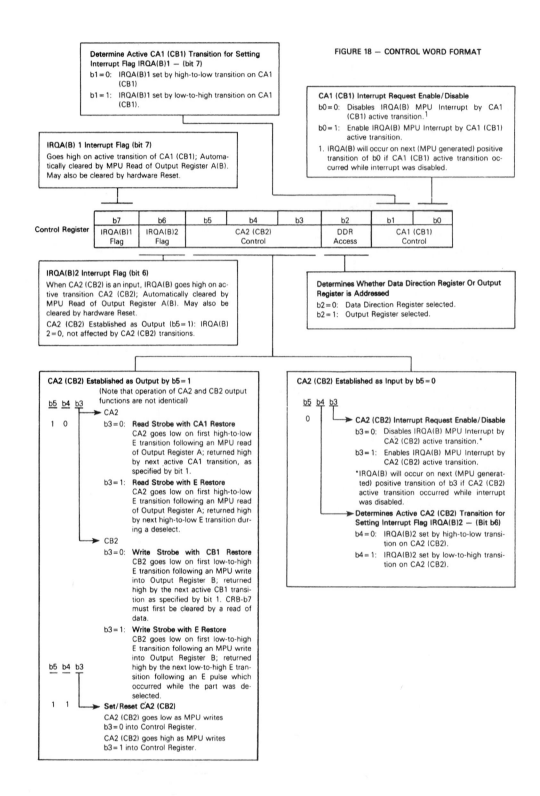

**FIGURE 18 — CONTROL WORD FORMAT**

**Determine Active CA1 (CB1) Transition for Setting Interrupt Flag IRQA(B)1 — (bit 7)**

b1=0:  IRQA(B)1 set by high-to-low transition on CA1 (CB1)

b1=1:  IRQA(B)1 set by low-to-high transition on CA1 (CB1).

**CA1 (CB1) Interrupt Request Enable/Disable**

b0=0:  Disables IRQA(B) MPU Interrupt by CA1 (CB1) active transition.[1]

b0=1:  Enable IRQA(B) MPU Interrupt by CA1 (CB1) active transition.

1. IRQA(B) will occur on next (MPU generated) positive transition of b0 if CA1 (CB1) active transition occurred while interrupt was disabled.

**IRQA(B) 1 Interrupt Flag (bit 7)**

Goes high on active transition of CA1 (CB1); Automatically cleared by MPU Read of Output Register A(B). May also be cleared by hardware Reset.

**Control Register**

| b7 | b6 | b5 | b4 | b3 | b2 | b1 | b0 |
|----|----|----|----|----|----|----|----|
| IRQA(B)1 Flag | IRQA(B)2 Flag | CA2 (CB2) Control | | | DDR Access | CA1 (CB1) Control | |

**IRQA(B)2 Interrupt Flag (bit 6)**

When CA2 (CB2) is an input, IRQA(B) goes high on active transition CA2 (CB2); Automatically cleared by MPU Read of Output Register A(B). May also be cleared by hardware Reset.

CA2 (CB2) Established as Output (b5=1): IRQA(B) 2=0, not affected by CA2 (CB2) transitions.

**Determines Whether Data Direction Register Or Output Register is Addressed**

b2=0:  Data Direction Register selected.

b2=1:  Output Register selected.

**CA2 (CB2) Established as Output by b5=1**

(Note that operation of CA2 and CB2 output functions are not identical)

| b5 | b4 | b3 | |
|----|----|----|--|
| | | | → CA2 |
| 1 | 0 | | |

b3=0:  **Read Strobe with CA1 Restore**
CA2 goes low on first high-to-low E transition following an MPU read of Output Register A; returned high by next active CA1 transition, as specified by bit 1.

b3=1:  **Read Strobe with E Restore**
CA2 goes low on first high-to-low E transition following an MPU read of Output Register A; returned high by next high-to-low E transition during a deselect.

→ CB2

b3=0:  **Write Strobe with CB1 Restore**
CB2 goes low on first low-to-high E transition following an MPU write into Output Register B; returned high by the next active CB1 transition as specified by bit 1. CRB-b7 must first be cleared by a read of data.

b3=1:  **Write Strobe with E Restore**
CB2 goes low on first low-to-high E transition following an MPU write into Output Register B; returned high by the next low-to-high E transition following an E pulse which occurred while the part was deselected.

| b5 | b4 | b3 | |
|----|----|----|--|
| 1 | 1 | | → Set/Reset CA2 (CB2) |

CA2 (CB2) goes low as MPU writes b3=0 into Control Register.

CA2 (CB2) goes high as MPU writes b3=1 into Control Register.

**CA2 (CB2) Established as Input by b5=0**

| b5 | b4 | b3 | |
|----|----|----|--|
| 0 | | | → CA2 (CB2) Interrupt Request Enable/Disable |

b3=0:  Disables IRQA(B) MPU Interrupt by CA2 (CB2) active transition.*

b3=1:  Enables IRQA(B) MPU Interrupt by CA2 (CB2) active transition.

*IRQA(B) will occur on next (MPU generated) positive transition of b3 if CA2 (CB2) active transition occurred while interrupt was disabled.

→ **Determines Active CA2 (CB2) Transition for Setting Interrupt Flag IRQA(B)2 — (Bit b6)**

b4=0:  IRQA(B)2 set by high-to-low transition on CA2 (CB2).

b4=1:  IRQA(B)2 set by low-to-high transition on CA2 (CB2).

**3**

# Solutions to Odd-Numbered Problems

## CHAPTER 0

1. $10110_2 = -10_{10}$
   $0010010011_2$ (BCD) $= 93_{10}$
   $10101.0101_2 = 21.3125_{10}$
   $1\ 1110\ 1101\ 1011_2 = 1EDB_{16}$
   $1111011011011_2 = 17333_8$
   $FEA_{16} = 1111\ 1110\ 1010_2$
   $C57_{16} = 3,159_{10}$
   $110000_2$ (ASCII) $=$ '0'
   $-21_{10} = 11101011_2$
   $19.125_{10} = 10011.001_2$

3. 0 to 127

5. **Representation  Value**

   sign-magnitude    -38
   2s complement     -26
   unsigned          102

7. $1111100101_2$

9. $1111100001_2 = 993_{10}$

11. 16

13. 330 Ω

    Notes:
    1. $R = V/I = 3.3/10 = 0.33\ k\Omega = 330\ \Omega$
    2. $V_{LED} = 1.7$ volts (see Example 0-9)

15.

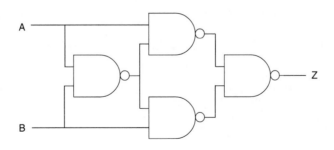

17.

19.

21. (a) B
    (b) A•(B+D)
    (c) C•(A+B)

23. (a) 262,144
    (b) 15

# CHAPTER 1

1. Decimal:        4095
   Binary:         111111111111
   Octal:          7777
   Hexadecimal:    FFF

3. 256

5. C3FF$_{16}$

7. 22

9. (a) 3100
   (b) 86 bytes
   (c) 3155$_{16}$

# CHAPTER 2

1. (a) 10
   (b) X, N, Z, V, and C

3. $00001000

5. D7 = $FFFFFF00
   CCR = $15 (X = 1, N = 0, Z = 1, V = 0, C = 1)

7. $2FF2 (The branch does not take place.)

9. 256

11. The absolute address $FFFFF is *odd*. A word variable cannot be moved to an odd address.

13. Cannot use immediate mode addressing when destination uses PC-relative addressing.

15. $00002001

17. $0000FFFC

19. $000E

21. $00000001

23. (a) $000E
    (b) 16 bits
    (c) because the branch is forward

25. i  What is wrong with the instruction MOV.B #1,D5?
       (mnemonic misspelled)
    ii  What is wrong with the instruction BRA $10F5?
       (cannot branch to an odd address)
    iii  What is wrong with the instruction MULU #5,$1000?
       (destination operand must be in a data register)
    iv  What is wrong with the instruction ORI D4,D5
       (ORI requires immediate operand)
    v  What is wrong with the instruction NEG #1,A4
       (NEG is a single-operand instruction)

27. (a) $060000
    (b) $00400000

29. MOVE.L $1000,D7 moves data from *memory location* $1000 to D7; whereas,
    MOVE.L#$1000,D7 move the *immediate data constant* $1000 to D7.

31. MOVE        D0,$1234            no condition
    MOVE        D0,(A0)             A0 = $001234
    MOVE        D0,8(A7)            A7 = $00122E
    MOVE        D0,0(A4,D5.W)       D5 + A4 = $001234
    MOVE        D0,-(A6)            A6 = $001236
    MOVE        D0,(A0)+            A0 = $001234
    MOVE        D0,-16(A5)          A5 = $001244

---

# CHAPTER 3

1. i.  The SUB instruction is available in two forms

       SUB <ea>,Dn
       SUB Dn,<ea>

    whereas CMP is only available in the form

       CMP <ea>,Dn

    ii. The CMP instruction does not affect the X bit in the CCR whereas the SUB instruction does.

3. i.  65,536        $(2^{16} = 65,536)$
   ii.  57,344       $(65,536 - 2 \times 2^{12} = 57,344)$
   iii  8,192        $(2 \times 2^{12} = 8,192)$

5. MOVE.L        (A6)+,D0            3 μs
   MOVEM.W       (A7)+,A3/A6         5 μs
   BTST.B        #3,25(A0)           4 μs
   CLR.W         100(A2,D3)          4.5 μs

7. High

9.

```
2  0000A000 7000         MOVE.L   #0,D0  ;NOTE: converted to quick
3  0000A002 7000         MOVEQ.L  #0,D0
4  0000A004 C1FC0000     MULS     #0,D0
5  0000A008 C0FC0000     MULU     #0,D0
6  0000A00C 02800000     ANDI.L   #0,D0
   0000A010 0000
7  0000A012 4280         CLR.L    D0
8  0000A014 9080         SUB.L    D0,D0
```

11. MOVEA.L   #$009020,A0
    MOVEM.L   D0-D7,-(A0)

13. D0 = $0000FF55, D1 = $AAAA5555

15. Only the addressing modes differ. With JMP, the destination address can be specified using any of the *control* addressing modes (see Appendix B). With BRA the destination address is specified using PC-relative addressing.

17. EXT.W   D7
    EXT.L   D7

# CHAPTER 4

1. Answers are shown below in the comments to the right of each instruction.

```
 1  00001000                 ORG     $1000
 2  00001000 303CFFFF        MOVE    #-1,D0
 3  00001004 103C00FF        MOVE.B   #-1,D0
 4  00001008 303C000A        MOVE    #5.SHL.1,D0
 5  0000100C 103C0001        MOVE.B  #5/3,D0
 6  00001010 303C0002        MOVE #5.MOD.3,D0
 7  00001014 303C0000        MOVE    #5.AND.$A,D0
 8  00001018 303C000F        MOVE    #5.OR.$A,D0
 9  0000101C 103C00FF        MOVE.B  #5.EQ.%101,D0
10  00001020 7041           MOVE.L  #.HIGH.'AB',D0
11  00001022 103C0000        MOVE.B  #'A'.GT.'B',D0
```

3. Answers are shown below in boldface type.

```
12  00000019           COUNT   EQU 25
13  00002000           ORG     $002000
14  00002000 48656C6C  START   DC.B 'Hello'
    00002004 6F
15  00002005           FINISH  EQU *
16  00002006 0005      LENGTH  DC.W FINISH-START
17  00002008 E7                DC.B -COUNT
18  00002009 FF                DC.B COUNT.LT.100
19  0000200A           END
```

5. EQU directives make programs easier to read and easier to change.

7. (a) $001F2A
   (b) $001F00, $001FCF
   (c) $004800, $004827
   (d) $001F5E

# CHAPTER 5

1.

```
 1                   ***************************************************
 2                   *  SUB.SRC                                       *
 3                   ***************************************************
 4  00008000                   ORG     $8000
 5  00008000 207C0000 SUB      MOVE.L  #FIRST,A0
    00008004 9000
 6  00008006 3018             MOVE.W  (A0)+,D0
 7  00008008 3218             MOVE.W  (A0)+,D1
 8  0000800A 9240             SUB.W   D0,D1
 9  0000800C 3081             MOVE.W  D1,(A0)
10  0000800E 4E4E             TRAP    #14
11
12  00009000                   ORG     $9000
13  00009000 FFFF    FIRST    DC.W    -1
14  00009002 0019    SECOND   DC.W    25
15  00009004 0000    RESULT   DC.W    0
16  00009006                   END
```

3.

```
 1                   ***************************************************
 2                   *  COMBINE.SRC                                    *
 3                   ***************************************************
 4  00008000                   ORG     $8000        ;program at $8000
 5  00008000 207C0000 COMBINE  MOVEA.L #BYTES,A0
    00008004 9000
 6  00008006 303C0003         MOVE.W  #3,D0
 7  0000800A 1E18    LOOP     MOVE.B  (A0)+,D7
 8  0000800C 323C0003         MOVE.W  #3,D1
 9  00008010 E91F             ROL.B   #4,D7
10  00008012 E317    LOOP2    ROXL.B  #1,D7
11  00008014 E356             ROXL.W  #1,D6
12  00008016 51C9FFFA         DBRA    D1,LOOP2
13  0000801A 51C8FFEE         DBRA    D0,LOOP
14  0000801E 3086             MOVE.W  D6,(A0)
15  00008020 4E4E             TRAP    #14
16
17  00009000         ORG     $9000                  ;data at $9000
18  00009000 4F3A522C BYTES   DC.B    $4F,$3A,$52,$2C
19  00009004 0000    RESULT   DC.W    0              ;result
20  00009006         END
```

5.

```
 8  00008000 207C0000 ADD3     MOVEA.L #NUMBERS,A0 ;n1 = 12 (2)
    00008004 9000
 9  00008006 323C0003         MOVE.W  #COUNT,D1   ;n2 = 8  (2)
10  0000800A 4240             CLR.W   D0          ;n3 = 4  (2)
11  0000800C D058    LOOP     ADD.W   (A0)+,D0    ;n4 = 8  (1)
12  0000800E 5341             SUBQ    #1,D1       ;n5 = 8  (1)
13  00008010 66FA             BNE     LOOP        ;n6 = 10 (1)  (branch taken)
                                                  ;n7 = 8  (1)  (branch not taken)
14  00008012 3080             MOVE.W  D0,(A0)     ;n8 = 8  (2)
15  00008014 4E4E             TRAP    #14         ;n9 = 34 (4/3)
```

(a)  $t_{EXE} = 14.2\ \mu s$

Notes:

$$
\begin{aligned}
n &= n1 + n2 + n3 + COUNT(n4 + n5 + n6) - (n6 - n7) + n8 + n9 \\
&= 12 + 8 + 4 + 3(8 + 8 + 10) - 2 + 8 + 34 \\
&= 64 + 3(26) \\
&= 142\ \text{cycles}
\end{aligned}
$$

$t_C = 0.1\ \mu s$

(b)  $t_{EXE} = 188 \times 0.0625 = 11.75\ \mu s$

Notes:

bump up all *n*s by 2 × number of memory cycles in parentheses, so

$$
\begin{aligned}
n &= 16 + 12 + 8 + COUNT(10 + 10 + 12) - 2 + 12 + 48 \\
&= 92 + 3(32) \\
&= 188\ \text{cycles}
\end{aligned}
$$

$t_C = 1/16 = 0.0625\ \mu s$

(c)  $t_{EXE} = t_C \times (64 + COUNT \times 26)$

(d)  $t_{EXE} = 1/8 \times (64 + 1{,}000 \times 26) = 3.258\ \text{ms}$

7.

```
 1            **********************************************************
 2            *  FIND2.SRC                                             *
 3            **********************************************************
 4 00008000                 ORG      $8000
 5 00008000 207C0000 FIND2  MOVEA.L  #LENGTH,A0
   00008004 9002
 6 00008006 3018            MOVE.W   (A0)+,D0
 7 00008008 600A            BRA.S    AHEAD
 8 0000800A 4241            CLR.W    D1
 9 0000800C B258     LOOP   CMP.W    (A0)+,D1
10 0000800E 6204            BHI.S    AHEAD
11 00008010 3228FFFE        MOVE.W   -2(A0),D1
12 00008014 51C8FFF6 AHEAD  DBRA     D0,LOOP
13 00008018 33C10000        MOVE.W   D1,>RESULT
   0000801C 9000
14 0000801E 4E4E            TRAP     #14
15
16 00009000                 ORG      $9000
17 00009000 0000     RESULT DC.W     0
18 00009002 0005     LENGTH DC.W     5
19 00009004 0002F000 LIST   DC.W     2,$F000,5,999,55
   00009008 000503E7
   0000900C 0037
20 0000900E                 END
```

9.

```
 1            **********************************************************
 2            *  COUNT.SRC                                             *
 3            **********************************************************
 4 00008000                 ORG      $8000
 5 00008000 207C0000 COUNT  MOVEA.L  #KEY,A0
   00008004 9001
 6 00008006 1E18            MOVE.B   (A0)+,D7      ;get key
 7 00008008 4200            CLR.B    D0
 8 0000800A 1C18     LOOP   MOVE.B   (A0)+,D6
 9 0000800C 6708            BEQ.S    EXIT
10 0000800E BE06            CMP.B    D6,D7
11 00008010 66F8            BNE.S    LOOP
```

```
12 00008012 5200              ADDQ.B  #1,D0
13 00008014 60F4              BRA.S   LOOP
14 00008016 13C00000  EXIT    MOVE.B  D0,>RESULT
   0000801A 9000
15 0000801C 4E4E              TRAP    #14
16
17 00009000              ORG     $9000
18 00009000 00       RESULT   DC.B    0
19 00009001 5A       KEY      DC.B    'Z'
20 00009002 5343495A STRING   DC.B    'SCIZZOR',0
   00009006 5A4F5200
21 0000900A              END
```

**11.**

```
 1                      ************************************************
 2                      * STRLEN.SRC                                   *
 3                      ************************************************
 4 00008000                    ORG     $8000
 5 00008000 207C0000           MOVEA.L #STRING,A0
   00008004 9000
 6 00008006 6102               BSR.S   STRLEN
 7 00008008 4E4E               TRAP    #14
 8 0000800A 4240     STRLEN    CLR.W   D0
 9 0000800C 4A18     AGAIN     TST.B   (A0)+
10 0000800E 6704               BEQ.S   EXIT
11 00008010 5240               ADDQ.W  #1,D0
12 00008012 60F8               BRA     AGAIN
13 00008014 4E75     EXIT      RTS
14
15
16 00009000                    ORG     $9000
17 00009000 686F7720 STRING    DC.B    'how big is it?',0
   00009004 62696720
   00009008 69732069
   0000900C 743F00
18 0000900F                    END
```

**13.**

```
 1                      ************************************************
 2                      * UNPACK.SRC                                   *
 3                      ************************************************
 4 00008000                    ORG     $8000
 5 00008000 207C0000  UNPACK   MOVEA.L #NUMBER,A0
   00008004 9000
 6 00008006 323C0003           MOVE.W  #3,D1
 7 0000800A 3018               MOVE.W  (A0)+,D0
 8 0000800C E958     LOOP      ROL.W   #4,D0
 9 0000800E 1400               MOVE.B  D0,D2
10 00008010 C43C000F           AND.B   #$F,D2
11 00008014 843C0030           OR.B    #$30,D2
12 00008018 10C2               MOVE.B  D2,(A0)+
13 0000801A 51C9FFF0           DBRA    D1,LOOP
14 0000801E 4E4E               TRAP    #14
15
16 00009000                    ORG     $9000
17 00009000 6789     NUMBER    DC.W    $6789
18 00009002 00000000 RESULT    DC.B    0,0,0,0
19
20 00009006                    END
```

## CHAPTER 6

1. EOR     #$2000,SR     ;S = 0
3. MOVE    #$0700,SR    ;S = 0, mask = 7
5. A privilege violation exception occurs. The PC and SR are saved on the system stack and a longword address is read from location $000020 and put into the PC. The exception routine begins execution from this address.
7. $000094

9.

```
11 0000800A 2F07      SQUARE  MOVE.L  D7,-(SP)         ;save D7
12 0000800C 4287              CLR.L   D7               ;use D7 for status
13 0000800E 41BC0009          CHK     #9,D0            ;9 = max. size of D0
14 00008012 4A87              TST.L   D7               ;index too large?
15 00008014 6604              BNE.S   EXIT             ;yes: exit, D0 as is
16 00008016 103B0006          MOVE.B  TABLE(PC,D0),D0  ;no: compute square
17 0000801A 2E1F      EXIT    MOVE.L  (SP)+,D7         ;restore D7
18 0000801C 4E75              RTS                      ;return
19 0000801E 00010409  TABLE   DC.B    0,1,4,9,16,25,36,49,64,81
   00008022 10192431
   00008026 4051
20 00008028              END     ENTER
```

11. (a)

| Memory Address | Memory Contents | Register | Register Contents |
|---|---|---|---|
| 000094 | 0005F | PC | 5F1F00 |
| 000096 | 1F00 | SSP | 00BFEA |
| | | SR | 2503 |

(b)

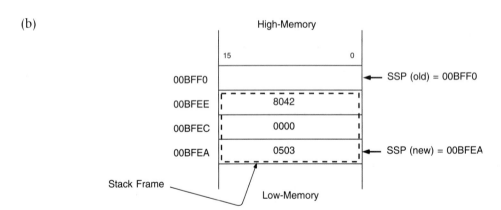

Stack Frame / Low-Memory

13.

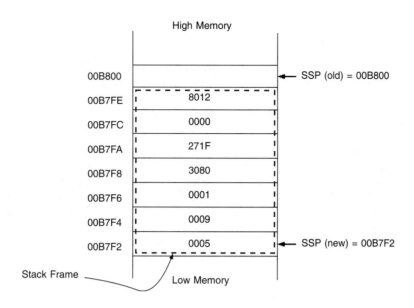

15.  $17\ k\Omega$

Notes:
$Vcap = Vcc—Vcc(e^{-t/RC})$
$(Vcap—Vcc)/\text{-}Vcc = e^{-t/RC}$
$\ln([Vcc—Vcap]/Vcc) = \ln(e^{-t/RC})$
$\ln(0.52) = -0.25/(R \times 0.000022)$
$R = 17378\ \text{ohms} \approx 17\ k\Omega$

---

# CHAPTER 7

1.  (a)  Best case = 1,333 ns
        Worst case = 4,333 ns

Notes:
CPU clock frequency = 6 MHz, $t_C = 1/6 = 167$ ns
Best case:      $n = 8$ cycles, $t = n \times t_C = 8 \times 167 = 1,333$ ns
Worst case:    $n = 26$ cycles, $t = n \times t_C = 26 \times 167 = 4,333$ ns

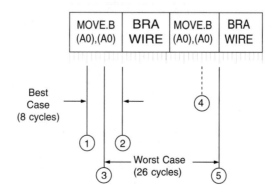

(b)  Best case = 833 ns
   Worst case = 2,583 ns

Notes:

CPU clock frequency = 12 MHz, $t_C = 1/12 = 83.3$ ns

Best case:     $n = 10$ cycles, $t = n \times t_C = 83.3 \times 833$ ns

Worst case:   $n = 31$ cycles, $t = n \times t_c = 83.3 \times 2,583$ ns

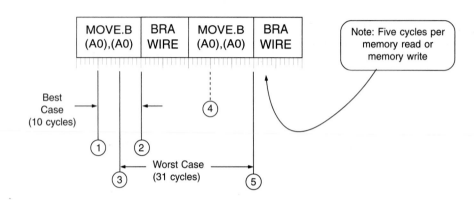

3.

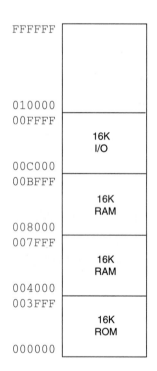

5.

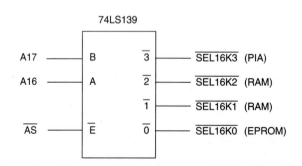

7. (a) $000F40
   (b) $00F900

9.

```
1 00001000                    ORG     $1000
2 00001000 007C0700           ORI     #$0700,SR
3 00001004 027CFBFF           ANDI    #$FBFF,SR
```

Notes:

The 1st instruction sets all three interrupt mask bits and leaves the other SR bits alone. The 2nd instruction puts $011_2$ in the interrupt mask bits (leaving the other SR bits alone). Setting the mask bits in the first instruction is a better approach than clearing them. This prevents pending low-level interrupts from inadvertently interrupting the CPU.

11.

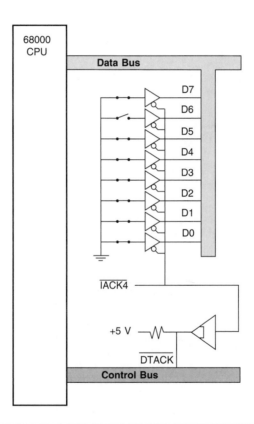

# CHAPTER 8

1. The system will hang because $\overline{\text{DTACK}}$ is not asserted to terminate the cycle.
3. The equation for dtack should be simplified to dtack = !as

# CHAPTER 9

Note:

Solutions to questions 3, 5, 9, 11, and 21 are not included here. These questions are found in the lab manual accompanying the 68KMB single-board computer.

1.

```
1          ********************************************************
2          * INIT681A.SRC                                        *
3          ********************************************************
```

```
 4 0000C001              DUART    EQU     $C001    ;68681 base address
 5 00000010              MR1B     EQU     8*2      ;mode register 1B
 6 00000010              MR2B     EQU     8*2      ;mode register 2B
 7 00000012              CSRB     EQU     9*2      ;clock select register B
 8 00000014              CRB      EQU     10*2     ;command register B
 9 000000BB              B9600    EQU     $BB      ;9600 baud initialize value
10
11 00008000                       ORG     $8000
12 00008000 207C0000 CH9_1A MOVEA.L #DUART,A0         ;A0 points to DUART
   00008004 C001
13 00008006 117C0013           MOVE.B  #$13,MR1B(A0)   ;8 data, no parity
   0000800A 0010
14 0000800C 117C0008           MOVE.B  #$08,MR2B(A0)   ;1.563 stop bits
   00008010 0010
15 00008012 117C00BB           MOVE.B  #B9600,CSRB(A0) ;set baud rate
   00008016 0012
16 00008018 117C0005           MOVE.B  #$05,CRB(A0)    ;Tx/Rx enabled
   0000801C 0014
17 0000801E                    END     INIT681A
```

7.

```
 1              ***********************************************************
 2              * STAR6.SRC                                              *
 3              ***********************************************************
 4 0000C001              DUART    EQU     $00C001  ;68681 base address
 5 00000008              ACR      EQU     4*2      ;auxiliary control register
 6 0000000C              CTUR     EQU     6*2      ;counter/timer upper register
 7 0000000E              CTLR     EQU     7*2      ;counter/timer lower register
 8 0000000A              IMR      EQU     5*2      ;interrupt mask register
 9 00000018              IVR      EQU     12*2     ;interrupt vector register
10 0000001E              STOP     EQU     15*2     ;timer stop command address
11 0000001A              I2VECTOR EQU     26       ;I2 autovector number
12
13 00008000                       ORG     $8000    ;MON68K jump table
14 00008000 4EF90000 CH9_6B JMP     >INIT    ;user program at $8000
   00008004 8024
15 00008006 4EF90000           JMP     >L2ISR   ;INT2 entry at $8006
   0000800A 8052
16 0000800C 4EF90000           JMP     >L3ISR   ;ERROR
   00008010 805E
17 00008012 4EF90000           JMP     >L4ISR   ;ERROR
   00008016 8064
18 00008018 4EF90000           JMP     >L5ISR   ;ERROR
   0000801C 806A
19 0000801E 4EF90000           JMP     >L6ISR   ;ERROR
   00008022 8070
20 00008024 207C0000 INIT    MOVEA.L #DUART,A0 ;A0 -> 68681 DUART
   00008028 C001
21 0000802A 117C0008           MOVE.B  #$08,IMR(A0)
   0000802E 000A
22 00008030 117C001A           MOVE.B  #I2VECTOR,IVR(A0)
   00008034 0018
23 00008036 117C00FF           MOVE.B  #$FF,CTUR(A0)
   0000803A 000C
24 0000803C 117C00FF           MOVE.B  #$FF,CTLR(A0)
   00008040 000E
25 00008042 117C0070           MOVE.B  #$70,ACR(A0)
   00008046 0008
26 00008048 007C0700           ORI.W   #$0700,SR    ;mask all interrupts
27 0000804C 027CF9FF           ANDI.W  #$F9FF,SR    ;mask level 1 only
```

```
28 00008050 60FE            BRA      *          ;sit on this awhile
29
30                          **********************************************************
31                          * L2ISR—Level 2 Interrupt Service Routine              *
32                          *                                                      *
33                          *   —read 68681 STOP_COUNTER_COMMAND register          *
34                          *    to clear the timer interrupt flag                 *
35                          *   —send an asterisk to the serial port               *
36                          **********************************************************
37 00008052 4A28001E L2ISR  TST.B    STOP(A0)   ;stop command, clear interrupt
38 00008056 103C002A        MOVE.B   #'*',D0    ;send an asterisk
39 0000805A 4E41            TRAP     #1         ; upon each interrupt
40 0000805C 4E73            RTE
41
42                          **********************************************************
43 0000805E 103C0033 L3ISR  MOVE.B   #'3',D0
44 00008062 6010            BRA.S    AHEAD
45 00008064 103C0034 L4ISR  MOVE.B   #'4',D0
46 00008068 600A            BRA.S    AHEAD
47 0000806A 103C0035 L5ISR  MOVE.B   #'5',D0
48 0000806E 6004            BRA.S    AHEAD
49 00008070 103C0036 L6ISR  MOVE.B   #'6',D0
50 00008074 227C0000 AHEAD  MOVEA.L  #MESSAGE,A1
   00008078 8080
51 0000807A 4E42            TRAP     #2
52 0000807C 4E41            TRAP     #1
53 0000807E 4E73            RTE
54 00008080 0D0A4552 MESSAGE DC.B    $0D,$0A,'ERROR: Unimplemented '
   00008084 524F523A
   00008088 20556E69
   0000808C 6D706C65
   00008090 6D656E74
   00008094 656420
55 00008097 696E7465        DC.B     'interrupt on level ',0
   0000809B 72727570
   0000809F 74206F6E
   000080A3 206C6576
   000080A7 656C2000
56 000080AB                 END      STAR6
```

Note:

To test the problem above, use a test probe with one end connected to ground. To generate a level-3 spurious interrupt, simply touch pin 13 on the 74LS148. To test level-4, level-5, and level-6 spurious interrupts, two steps must be followed: First, touch pin 1, 2, or 3 of the 74LS148, then touch pin 5 of the 7407. The latter step is required to terminate the IACK cycle by pulsing $\overline{VPA}$ low.

13.

```
 1                          ***********************************************************
 2                          * LS165A.SRC—Input expansion using 74LS165s            *
 3                          ***********************************************************
 4 0000C001         DUART    EQU     $00C001           ;68681 base address
 5 0000001A         IPR      EQU     13*2              ;input port register
 6 0000001C         OPR_SET  EQU     14*2              ;set bit command register
 7 0000001E         OPR_CLR  EQU     15*2              ;clear bit command register
 8 0000000D         CR       EQU     $0D               ;ASCII carriage return code
 9 0000000A         LF       EQU     $0A               ;ASCII line feed code
10 00000002         CHIPS    EQU     2                 ;number of 165s
11 00000002         CLOCK    EQU     $02               ;bit 1 on output port
12 00000001         LOAD     EQU     $01               ;bit 0 on output port
```

```
13 00032000              ONE_SEC  EQU      204800               ;count for 1-second delay
14
15 00008000              ORG      $8000
16 00008000 207C0000 CH7_8A  MOVEA.L  #DUART,A0               ;A0 points to 68681
   00008004 C001
17 00008006 117C0003         MOVE.B   #3,OPR_CLR(A0)          ;set interface lines
   0000800A 001E
18 0000800C 227C0000         MOVEA.L  #BANNER,A1              ;send banner message
   00008010 80AC
19 00008012 4E42             TRAP     #2                     ; using OUTSTR trap
20
21                   ***********************************************************
22                   * The main loop reads the 74LS165 inputs, outputs the   *
23                   * ASCII hexadecimal code to the console, delays 1/5      *
24                   * second, and repeats.                                   *
25                   ***********************************************************
26 00008014 6112     LOOP     BSR.S    RD165               ;read 74ls165 data
27 00008016 6158              BSR.S    REPORT              ;report result
28 00008018 2E3C0000         MOVE.L   #ONE_SEC/5,D7       ;delay 1/5 second
   0000801C A000
29 0000801E 6102              BSR.S    DELAY
30 00008020 60F2              BRA      LOOP
31 00008022 5387     DELAY    SUBQ.L   #1,D7
32 00008024 66FC              BNE      DELAY
33 00008026 4E75              RTS
34
35                   ***********************************************************
36                   * RD165—Read inputs from multiple 74LS165s               *
37                   *                                                       *
38                   * The interface between the 74LS165s and the 68681       *
39                   * uses the following lines:                              *
40                   *                                                       *
41                   *      74LS165  68681                                    *
42                   *      ====================                             *
43                   *      IP0      DATA IN                                  *
44                   *      OP1      CLOCK                                    *
45                   *      OP0      SHIFT/-LOAD                              *
46                   *                                                       *
47                   *      ENTER:  no conditions                            *
48                   *   EXIT:   data in RAM at $A000 & $A001                 *
49                   *           all registers intact                        *
50                   *   USES:   no subroutines                              *
51                   ***********************************************************
52 00008028 48E7F0C0 RD165    MOVEM.L  D0-D3/A0-A1,-(SP)   ;save register on stack
53 0000802C 207C0000         MOVEA.L  #DUART,A0           ;A0 points to 68681
   00008030 C001
54                   * a single pulse on LOAD latches data into the 74LS165s
55 00008032 117C0001         MOVE.B   #LOAD,OPR_SET(A0)   ;pulse for 1 us
   00008036 001C
56 00008038 117C0001         MOVE.B   #LOAD,OPR_CLR(A0)   ;-----_____-----
   0000803C 001E
57 0000803E 163C0002         MOVE.B   #CHIPS,D3           ;number of LS165s
58 00008042 227C0000         MOVEA.L  #LINES+CHIPS,A1     ;just past buffer
   00008046 A002
59                   * multiple pulses on CLOCK shift data out the 74LS165s
60 00008048 103C0008 BACK2    MOVE.B   #8,D0               ;8 lines per LS165
61 0000804C 1228001A BACK     MOVE.B   IPR(A0),D1          ;read LS165
62 00008050 E211              ROXR.B   #1,D1               ;put bit in C bit
63 00008052 E212              ROXR.B   #1,D2               ;data byte in D2
64 00008054 117C0002         MOVE.B   #CLOCK,OPR_SET(A0)  ;pulse for 1 us
   00008058 001C
```

```
65 0000805A 117C0002        MOVE.B    #CLOCK,OPR_CLR(A0) ;-----_____-----
   0000805E 001E
66 00008060 5300            SUBQ.B    #1,D0             ;last bit read?
67 00008062 66E8            BNE       BACK              ;no:  get next bit
68 00008064 1302            MOVE.B    D2,-(A1)          ;yes: store byte
69 00008066 5303            SUBQ.B    #1,D3             ;last LS165 read?
70 00008068 66DE            BNE       BACK2             ;no:  read next
71 0000806A 4CDF030F        MOVEM.L   (SP)+,D0-D3/A0-A1 ;yes: restore &
72 0000806E 4E75            RTS                         ;       return
73
74                          ****************************************************
75                          * Report results on console (debugging aid)       *
76                          *                                                  *
77                          * Reports in binary as xxxxxxxx xxxxxxx (x = 0 or 1) *
78                          ****************************************************
79 00008070 48E7F040 REPORT MOVEM.L   D0-D3/A1,-(SP)    ;save register on stack
80 00008074 103C000D        MOVE.B    #CR,D0            ;send CR using
81 00008078 4E41            TRAP      #1                ; OUTCHR trap
82 0000807A 227C0000        MOVEA.L   #LINES,A1         ;A1 points to data
   0000807E A000
83 00008080 323C0001        MOVE.W    #CHIPS-1,D1       ;D1 counts LS165s
84 00008084 1419     REPORT2 MOVE.B   (A1)+,D2          ;get data
85 00008086 363C0007        MOVE.W    #7,D3             ;D3 counts bits
86 0000808A E312     REPORT3 ROXL.B   #1,D2             ;rotate bits into
87 0000808C E310            ROXL.B    #1,D0             ;   D0 and trans-
88 0000808E 02000001        ANDI.B    #$01,D0           ;   form into
89 00008092 00000030        ORI.B     #$30,D0           ;   ASCII 0 or 1
90 00008096 4E41            TRAP      #1                ;send character
91 00008098 51CBFFF0        DBRA      D3,REPORT         ;repeat 8 times
92 0000809C 103C0020        MOVE.B    #$20,D0           ;put SPACE between
93 000080A0 4E41            TRAP      #1                ;   bytes
94 000080A2 51C9FFE0        DBRA      D1,REPORT2        ;no:  send another
95 000080A6 4CDF020F        MOVEM.L   (SP)+,D0-D3/A1    ;yes: restore &
96 000080AA 4E75            RTS                         ;       return
97
98 000080AC 0D0A2A2A BANNER  DC.B    CR,LF,'*** TEST 74LS165s (modified) ***',CR,LF,0
   000080B0 2A205445
   000080B4 53542037
   000080B8 344C5331
   000080BC 36357320
   000080C0 286D6F64
   000080C4 69666965
   000080C8 6429202A
   000080CC 2A2A0D0A
   000080D0 00
99
100 0000A000                ORG       $A000             ;data segment
101 0000A000        LINES    DS.B      CHIPS            ;1 byte per LS165
102 0000A002                END       LS165A
```

15.

$$\text{Ans: } f = \frac{f_c \times \text{STEP}}{2560 \times \text{COUNT} + 11264} \text{ Hz}$$

17.     Ans:   61 μs if a key was hit

12 μs if a key was not hit

19. ATOH     EQU   $0982      ;MON68K, V4.4

ISDIGIT   EQU   $09D2

# Bibliography

## 68000 TEXT BOOKS

Antonakos, J. L. 1993. *The 68000 Microprocessor: Hardware and Software Principles and Applications.* 2nd. ed. New York: Macmillan Publishing Company.

Barry, A. 1992. *68000 Assembly Language Programming and Interfacing.* Englewood Cliffs, NJ: Regents/Prentice Hall.

Brey, B. B. 1991. *The Motorola Microprocessor Family: 68000, 68008, 68010. 68020, 68030, and 68040: Programming and Interfacing with Applications.* New York: Harcourt Brace Javanovich College Publisher.

Clements, A. 1992. *The Principles of Computer Hardware.* 2nd. ed. Oxford, UK: Oxford University Press.

Ford, W., and W. Topp. 1992. *Assembly Language and Systems Programming for the M68000 Family.* Lexington, MA: D. C. Heath and Company.

Hall, D. V., and A. L. Rood. 1992. *Microprocessors and Interfacing: Programming and Hardware: 68000 Version.* Columbus, OH: Macmillan/McGraw-Hill.

Leventhal, L. A., D. Hawkins, G. Kane, and W. D. Cramer. *68000 Assembly Language Programming.* Berkeley, CA: Osborne/McGraw-Hill.

Liu, Y.-L. 1991. *The M68000 Microprocessor Family: Fundamentals of Assembly Language Programming and Interface Design.* Englewood Cliffs, NJ: Prentice Hall.

Livadas, P. E., and C. Ward. 1993. *Computer Organization and the M68000.* Englewood Cliffs, NJ: Prentice Hall.

Miller, M. A. 1992. *The 68000 Microprocessor Family: Architecture, Programming, and Applications.* 2nd ed. New York: Macmillan Publishing Company.

Scanlon, L. J. 1982. *The 68000: Principles and Programming.* Indianapolos, IN: Howard W. Sams & Co., Inc.

Subarao, W. V. 1991. *16/32-Bit Microprocessors: 68000/68010/68020: Software, Hardware, and Design Applications.* New York: Macmillan Publishing Company.

Triebel, W. A., and Singh, A. 1986. *The 68000 Microprocessor: Architecture, Software, and Interfacing Techniques.* Englewood Cliffs, NJ: Prentice Hall.

## MOTOROLA REFERENCE BOOKS

*M68000 Family Reference* (M68000FR/AD). 1990. Phoenix, AZ: Motorola Inc.

*MC68000, MC80008, MC68010, MC68020 8-/16-/32-Bit Microprocessor User's Manual.* 8th. ed. (M68000UM/AD). 1989. Phoenix, AZ: Motorola Inc.

*M68000 Programmer's Reference Manual* (M68000PM/AD). 1989. Phoenix, AZ: Motorola Inc.

*MC68020, MC68EC020 Microprocessors User's Manual* (M68020UM/AD). 1992. Phoenix, AZ: Motorola Inc.

*MC68030 Enhanced 32-Bit Microprocessor User's Manual* (MC68030UM/AD). 1990. Phoenix, AZ: Motorola Inc.

*MC68040, MC68EC040, MC68LC040 Microprocessors User's Manual* (M68040UM/AD). 1992. Phoenix, AZ: Motorola Inc.

*MC68306 Integrated EC000 Processor User's Manual* (MC68306UM/AD). 1993. Phoenix, AZ: Motorola Inc.

# Index